ENERGY BALANCES OF OECD COUNTRIES

2004 - 2005

BILANS ÉNERGÉTIQUES DES PAYS DE L'OCDE

2007 Edition

INTERNATIONAL ENERGY AGENCY

The International Energy Agency (IEA) is an autonomous body which was established in November 1974 within the framework of the Organisation for Economic Co-operation and Development (OECD) to implement an international energy programme.

It carries out a comprehensive programme of energy co-operation among twenty-six of the OECD thirty member countries. The basic aims of the IEA are:

- To maintain and improve systems for coping with oil supply disruptions.
- To promote rational energy policies in a global context through co-operative relations with non-member countries, industry and international organisations.
- To operate a permanent information system on the international oil market.
- To improve the world's energy supply and demand structure by developing alternative energy sources and increasing the efficiency of energy use.
- To assist in the integration of environmental and energy policies.

The IEA member countries are: Australia, Austria, Belgium, Canada, Czech Republic, Denmark, Finland, France, Germany, Greece, Hungary, Ireland, Italy, Japan, Republic of Korea, Luxembourg, Netherlands, New Zealand, Norway, Portugal, Spain, Sweden, Switzerland, Turkey, United Kingdom and United States. The Slovak Republic and Poland are likely to become member countries in 2007/2008. The European Commission also participates in the work of the IEA.

ORGANISATION FOR ECONOMIC CO-OPERATION AND DEVELOPMENT

The OECD is a unique forum where the governments of thirty democracies work together to address the economic, social and environmental challenges of globalisation. The OECD is also at the forefront of efforts to understand and to help governments respond to new developments and concerns, such as corporate governance, the information economy and the challenges of an ageing population. The Organisation provides a setting where governments can compare policy experiences, seek answers to common problems, identify good practice and work to co-ordinate domestic and international policies.

The OECD member countries are: Australia, Austria, Belgium, Canada, Czech Republic, Denmark, Finland, France, Germany, Greece, Hungary, Iceland, Ireland, Italy, Japan, Republic of Korea, Luxembourg, Mexico, Netherlands, New Zealand, Norway, Poland, Portugal, Slovak Republic, Spain, Sweden, Switzerland, Turkey, United Kingdom and United States.
The European Commission takes part in the work of the OECD.

© OECD/IEA, 2007

International Energy Agency (IEA),
Head of Communication and Information Office,
9 rue de la Fédération, 75739 Paris Cedex 15, France.

Warning: please note that this publication is subject to specific restrictions that limit its use and distribution. The terms and conditions are available online at ***http://www.iea.org/Textbase/about/copyright.asp***

AGENCE INTERNATIONALE DE L'ÉNERGIE

L'Agence Internationale de l'Énergie (AIE) est un organe autonome institué en novembre 1974 dans le cadre de l'Organisation de coopération et de développement économiques (OCDE) afin de mettre en œuvre un programme international de l'énergie.

Elle applique un programme général de coopération dans le domaine de l'énergie entre vingt-six des trente pays membres de l'OCDE. Les objectifs fondamentaux de l'AIE sont les suivants :

- Tenir à jour et améliorer des systèmes permettant de faire face à des perturbations des approvisionnements pétroliers.
- Œuvrer en faveur de politiques énergétiques rationnelles dans un contexte mondial grâce à des relations de coopération avec les pays non membres, l'industrie et les organisations internationales.
- Gérer un système d'information continue sur le marché international du pétrole.
- Améliorer la structure de l'offre et de la demande mondiales d'énergie en favorisant la mise en valeur de sources d'énergie de substitution et une utilisation plus rationnelle de l'énergie.
- Contribuer à l'intégration des politiques d'énergie et d'environnement.

Les pays membres de l'AIE sont : Allemagne, Australie, Autriche, Belgique, Canada, Danemark, Espagne, États-Unis, Finlande, France, Grèce, Hongrie, Irlande, Italie, Japon, Luxembourg, Norvège, Nouvelle-Zélande, Pays-Bas, Portugal, République de Corée, République Tchèque, Royaume-Uni, Suède, Suisse et Turquie. Il est envisagé que la Pologne et la République Slovaque deviennent membres en 2007/2008. La Commission Européenne participe également aux travaux de l'AIE.

ORGANISATION DE COOPÉRATION ET DE DÉVELOPPEMENT ÉCONOMIQUES

L'OCDE est un forum unique en son genre où les gouvernements de trente démocraties œuvrent ensemble pour relever les défis économiques, sociaux et environnementaux que pose la mondialisation. L'OCDE est aussi à l'avant-garde des efforts entrepris pour comprendre les évolutions du monde actuel et les préoccupations qu'elles font naître. Elle aide les gouvernements à faire face à des situations nouvelles en examinant des thèmes tels que le gouvernement d'entreprise, l'économie de l'information et les défis posés par le vieillissement de la population. L'Organisation offre aux gouvernements un cadre leur permettant de comparer leurs expériences en matière de politiques, de chercher des réponses à des problèmes communs, d'identifier les bonnes pratiques et de travailler à la coordination des politiques nationales et internationales.

Les pays membres de l'OCDE sont : Allemagne, Australie, Autriche, Belgique, Canada, Danemark, Espagne, États-Unis, Finlande, France, Grèce, Hongrie, Irlande, Islande, Italie, Japon, Luxembourg, Mexique, Norvège, Nouvelle Zélande, Pays-Bas, Pologne, Portugal, République de Corée, République slovaque, République tchèque, Royaume-Uni, Suède, Suisse et Turquie. La Commission européenne participe aux travaux de l'OCDE.

© OCDE/AIE, 2007

Agence Internationale de l'Énergie (AIE),
Direction du Service de la communication et de l'information,
9 rue de la Fédération, 75739 Paris Cedex 15, France.

Attention, la diffusion de cette publication est soumise à des conditions qui en limitent l'usage et la communication et dont les termes sont disponibles sur le site :
http://www.iea.org/Textbase/about/copyright.asp

TABLE OF CONTENTS

TABLE DES MATIERES

ABBREVIATIONS

Btu:	British thermal unit
GWh:	gigawatt hour
kcal:	kilocalorie
kg:	kilogramme
kJ:	kilojoule
Mt:	million tonnes
m^3:	cubic metre
t:	metric ton = tonne = 1000 kg
TJ:	terajoule
toe:	tonne of oil equivalent = 10^7 kcal
CHP:	combined heat and power
GCV:	gross calorific value
GDP:	gross domestic product
HHV:	higher heating value = GCV
LHV:	lower heating value = NCV
NCV:	net calorific value
PPP:	purchasing power parity
TPES:	total primary energy supply
IEA:	International Energy Agency
IPCC:	Intergovernmental Panel on Climate Change
ISIC:	International Standard Industrial Classification
OECD:	Organisation for Economic Co-Operation and Development
OLADE:	Organización Latinoamericana de Energía
UN:	United Nations
UNIPEDE:	International Union of Producers and Distributors of Electrical Energy
c	confidential
e	estimated
..	not available
-	nil
x	not applicable

ABREVIATIONS

Btu :	British thermal unit
GWh :	gigawattheure
kcal :	kilocalorie
kg :	kilogramme
kJ :	kilojoule
Mt :	million de tonnes
m^3 :	mètre cube
t :	tonne métrique = 1000 kg
tep :	tonne d'équivalent pétrole = 10^7 kcal
TJ :	térajoule
ATEP :	approvisionnements totaux en énergie primaire
PCI :	pouvoir calorifique inférieur
PCS :	pouvoir calorifique supérieur
PIB :	produit intérieur brut
PPA :	parité de pouvoir d'achat
AIE :	Agence internationale de l'énergie
CITI :	Classification internationale type par industrie
GIEC :	Groupe d'experts intergouvernemental sur l'évolution du climat
OCDE :	Organisation de coopération et de développement économiques
OLADE :	Organización Latinoamericana de Energía
ONU :	Organisation des nations unies
UNIPEDE :	Union Internationale des Producteurs et Distributeurs d'Energie Electrique
c	confidentiel
e	estimation
..	non disponible
-	néant
x	sans objet

INTRODUCTION

An analysis of energy problems requires a comprehensive presentation of basic statistics in original units such as tonnes of coal and kilowatt hours of electricity. This type of presentation is published in *Energy Statistics of OECD Countries,* the sister volume to this publication. The usefulness of such basic data can be considerably improved by expressing them in a common unit suitable for uses such as estimation of total energy supply, forecasting and the study of substitution and conservation. The energy balance is a presentation of the basic supply and demand data for all fuels in a manner which shows the main fuels together but separately distinguished and expressed in a common energy unit. Both of these characteristics will allow the easy comparison of the contribution each fuel makes to the economy and their interrelationships through the conversion of one fuel into another. *Energy Balances of OECD Countries* provides standardised energy balance sheets expressed in a common unit for each OECD country, as well as for the following regions: OECD Total, OECD North America, OECD Pacific, OECD Europe and IEA.

Due to market liberalisation, some data have become confidential. As a result, the IEA has introduced a data qualifier "c" to indicate where these confidential data are.

Energy data on OECD countries are collected from Member countries by the team in the Energy Statistics Division (ESD) of the IEA Secretariat, headed by Mr. Jean-Yves Garnier. Coal, renewables and electricity statistics are the responsibility of Mr. Michel Francoeur with the help of Mr. Paul Tepes, Ms. Jung-Ah Kang and Mr. Steve Gervais. Oil and natural gas statistics are the responsibility of Ms. Mieke Reece with the help of Ms. Cintia Gavay and Mr. Armel le Jeune. Ms. Karen Tréanton, with the help of Mr. Nikos Roukounakis, has overall production and editorial responsibility. Secretarial support was supplied by Ms. Sharon Burghgraeve and Ms. Susan Stolarow.

Data from 1960 to 2005 are available on CD-ROM suitable for use on IBM-compatible personal computers.

In addition, a data service is available on the internet. It includes unlimited access through an annual subscription as well as the possibility to obtain data on a pay-per-view basis. Details are available at http://www.iea.org.

Enquiries about data or methodology should be addressed to Ms. Karen Tréanton:

Telephone: (+33-1) 40-57-66-33,
Fax: (+33-1) 40-57-66-49,
E-mail: karen.treanton@iea.org.

INTRODUCTION

L'analyse des questions énergétiques suppose une présentation détaillée de statistiques de base exprimées dans leurs différentes unités d'origine : tonnes de charbon et kilowattheures d'électricité, par exemple. Ces informations sont présentées dans les *Statistiques de l'énergie des pays de l'OCDE*, recueil publié parallèlement au présent document. On peut accroître considérablement l'utilité de ces données de base en adoptant, pour les exprimer, une unité commune qui permette de les exploiter, par exemple, pour estimer les approvisionnements totaux en énergie, établir des prévisions, ou étudier les possibilités de substitution ou d'économies d'énergie. Le bilan énergétique présente les données de base concernant l'offre et la demande pour toutes les formes d'énergie, selon une méthode permettant de les présenter groupées par grandes catégories, mais aussi de les indiquer séparément selon une unité commune d'énergie. Ces deux caractéristiques permettent une comparaison aisée de la contribution des différentes formes d'énergie à l'économie et faciliteront l'étude de leurs relations réciproques grâce à l'utilisation de coefficients de conversion. Ce recueil des *Bilans énergétiques des pays de l'OCDE* présente des bilans énergétiques normalisés exprimés dans une unité commune pour tous les pays de l'OCDE ainsi que pour les régions suivantes : OCDE Total, OCDE Amérique du Nord, OCDE Pacifique, OCDE Europe et AIE.

Du fait de la libéralisation du marché, certaines données sont devenues confidentielles. En conséquence, l'AIE a été amenée à introduire dans ses tableaux le code "c" pour indiquer la place de ces données confidentielles.

Les données énergétiques sur les pays de l'OCDE sont collectées auprès des pays membres par la Division des Statistiques Energétiques (ESD) du Secrétariat de l'AIE, dirigée par M. Jean-Yves Garnier. M. Michel Francoeur, assisté par M. Paul Tepes, Mlle Jung-Ah Kang et M. Steve Gervais, est responsable des statistiques du charbon, des énergies renouvelables et de l'électricité. Mme Mieke Reece, assistée par Mlle Cintia Gavay et M. Armel le Jeune, est responsable des statistiques du pétrole et du gaz naturel. Mme Karen Tréanton, assistée par M. Nikos Roukounakis, est responsable de la publication. Mme Sharon Michel et Mme Susan Stolarow ont assuré le secrétariat d'édition.

Les données relatives aux années 1960 à 2005 sont disponibles sur CD-ROM exploitables sur ordinateurs personnels compatibles IBM.

En outre, un service de données est disponible sur internet. Ce service comprend une souscription annuelle pour un accès illimité ou bien la possibilité de payer uniquement pour des données sélectionnées. Pour plus de détails, veuillez consulter http://www.iea.org.

Les demandes de renseignements sur les données ou la méthodologie doivent être adressées à Mme Karen Tréanton:

Téléphone : (+33-1) 40-57-66-33,
Fax : (+33-1) 40-57-66-49,
E-mail : karen.treanton@iea.org

MULTILINGUAL GLOSSARIES

See multilingual glossary at the end of the publication.
Voir le glossaire en plusieurs langues à la fin du présent recueil.
Deutsches GLOSSAR auf der letzten Umschlagseite.
Riferirsi al glossario poliglotta alla fine del libro.
巻 末 の 日 本 語 用 語 集 を 参 照
Véase el glosario plurilingüe al final del libro.
Смотрите многоязычный словарь в конце книги.

OECD ENERGY TRENDS

In 2005, 18% of the world population lived in the OECD, while 78% of the world GDP was created in its 30 member countries.

Total primary energy (TPES) needed to supply the OECD in 2005 represented about 48% of the world TPES, while the total energy production of the OECD accounted for 33% of the global energy production.

Table 1. OECD in the World, 2005

	Population (millions)	GDP*	TPES (Mtoe)	Production (Mtoe)
OECD	1 172	28 394	5 548	3 834
World**	6 430	36 258	11 471	11 450
OECD Share**	18%	78%	48%	33%

* (billion US$, 2000 prices and exchange rates)

** preliminary figures

With 4.7 toe per capita (compared to a world average of 1.8 toe per capita), the OECD is the main energy consuming region in terms of TPES/population. Several factors explain this high consumption: e.g. an electrification rate of almost 100%, a high rate of cars per household, large industry and service sectors, high heating degree-days and a high GDP per capita.

In contrast, with 0.20 toe per thousand US$[1] (compared to a world average of approximately 0.32 toe per thousand US$), the OECD is the least energy consuming region in terms of TPES/GDP. Several factors also explain the lower consumption: high GDP compared to other regions, high efficiency in the transformation sector (especially power plants), high efficiency in final consumption (efficient cars, insulation of houses) and delocalisation of high energy-consuming industries.

1. 2000 prices and exchange rates.

In 2005, the OECD produced 3 834 Mtoe of primary energy while its total primary energy supply reached 5 548 Mtoe. As a consequence, 31% of the energy consumed by the OECD had to be imported from non-OECD countries.

The share of imports, the breakdown of the imports by fuel, the indigenous production of energy and many other key components of the energy situation in the OECD varied over time, especially after the first oil crisis in 1973.

The following paragraphs highlight the main changes since 1971 as well as giving a snapshot of the situation in 2005.

Production

OECD primary energy production decreased slightly by 0.7% to 3 834 Mtoe in 2005. This represents a 63.6% increase compared to the 1971 production of 2 343 Mtoe, i.e. an annual average growth of 1.5% over the 34-year period.

However, the increase was not uniform over the period, with a much stronger growth in the first half of the period (2.2% per year) compared to the second half (0.7% per year).

After the first oil shock in 1973 and the establishment of the International Energy Agency, a special effort was made by most of the OECD countries to reduce their dependence on imported oil by various policies, including the development of alternative sources of energy, and for some of them, by exploiting their oil reserves.

Within 15 years, the launch of large nuclear programmes in several countries and the exploitation of new open-sky mines in North America led to a dramatic increase of nuclear and coal production. In 1971, nuclear represented 27 Mtoe whereas in 1988 it accounted for 418 Mtoe. Similarly coal went up from 812 Mtoe in 1971 to 1 053 Mtoe in 1988. These increases, combined with the increase in indigenous oil production (especially in the Gulf of Mexico and the United Kingdom) from 685 to 968 Mtoe, explain the relatively high growth in energy production observed in the first half of the 34-year period.

During the second half of the period (from 1988 to 2005), the situation was significantly different with almost no increase in oil production (except in Norway) and a decrease in coal production due to the closing of high-cost deep mines in Europe and Asia. On the other hand, nuclear continued to rise at a steady rate, going from 418 Mtoe in 1988 to 611 Mtoe in 2005. In addition, the discovery and exploitation of large gas fields in North America led to a major increase in gas production from 682 Mtoe in 1988 to 912 Mtoe in 2005.

When analysing changes in the OECD energy situation, it is also interesting to break the 34-year period into two periods of different length (1971-1990, 1990-2005), since 1990 is the reference year for the Kyoto Protocol. The comparative annual growth for each of the main fuels (except for gas) shows similar trends, i.e. a much higher growth in the first part of the period (see Figure 1).

Figure 1. Average Annual Growth Rates in OECD Primary Energy Production

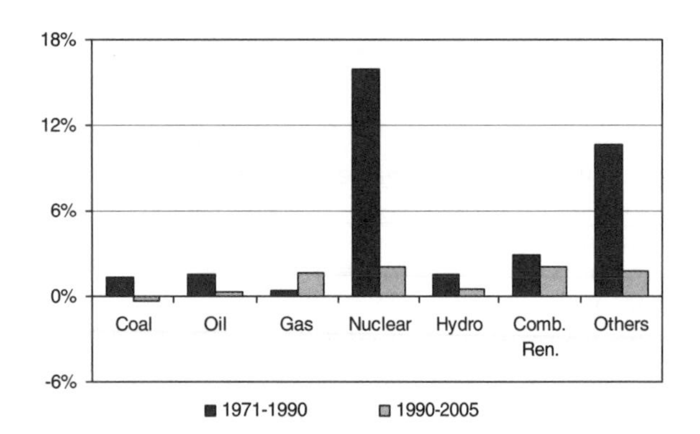

As a consequence of the contrasting evolution of the various fuels over the period, the shares of the main fuels in total production changed significantly between 1971 and 2005 (see Figure 2).

Figure 2. Fuel Shares in OECD Production

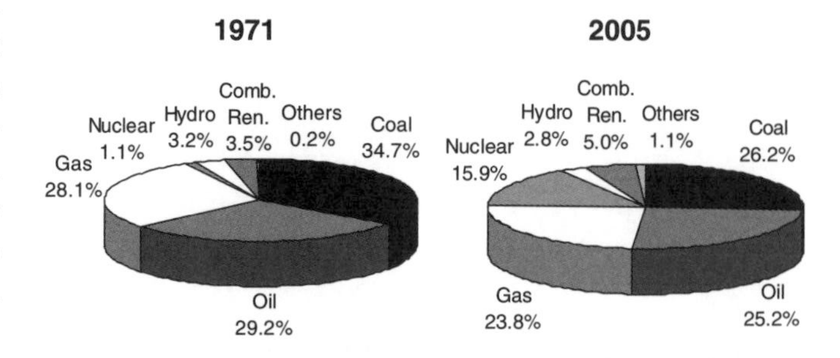

In 2005, the share of fossil fuels in total OECD production accounted for 75.2%; coal, oil and gas each represented roughly one quarter of TPES. Nuclear accounted for 15.9%, a large increase from 1.1% in 1971.

Energy from renewables and wastes represented 8.9% in 2005; with combustible renewables and waste contributing for more than a half, hydro for about a third and geothermal energy accounting for most of the rest.

As regards the other forms of renewable energy, their production started to grow steadily in recent years, although their shares remain limited. For example, solar and wind energy, experienced high annual growth since 1990, but their combined production accounted for only 0.3% of primary energy production in 2005.

Trade

In 1971, 98.3% of the 1 153 Mtoe of total net imports of energy for OECD were related to oil; net imports represented half of the OECD energy production. The policies taken by OECD member countries in order to reduce their dependence on imported oil had twofold consequences for the period 1971-1985:

- a decrease in net imports of oil from 1 465 Mtoe in 1977 to 796 Mtoe in 1985
- a decrease in the share of oil imports in total net imports (from 98.3% in 1971 to 88.0% in 1985).

The fall of oil prices in the mid 1980s had an impact on the historical trend of OECD energy trade. Net imports of oil in the OECD started to increase again in 1986, since then growing on average by 2.8% per year. In 2005, net imports reached a new 25-year high at 1 393 Mtoe.

On the other hand, volatility of oil prices, increasing performance of gas-fired power plants, fuel switching for heating purposes and the growing interest in the use of gas for its lower CO_2 emissions led to an increase of net imports of gas, which reached new highs in 2005, with 292 Mtoe. This reduced the share of oil in total energy imports, which fell to 76.8% in 2005.

Figure 3. Net Imports of Primary Energy by Fuel for the OECD

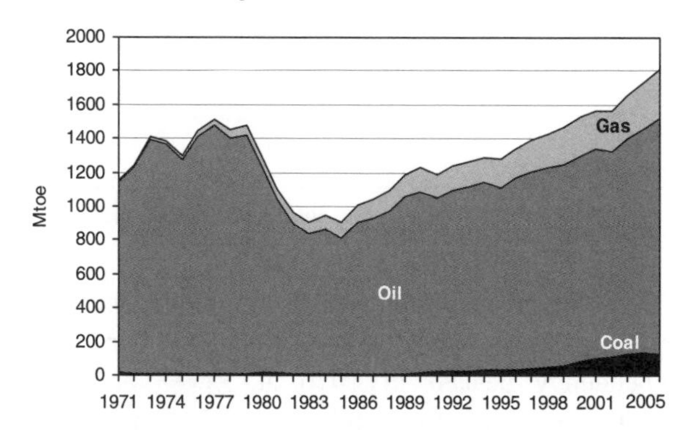

France, Germany, the Netherlands and the United States figured amongst the main importers of oil produced in other OECD countries. The proximity to the producing areas of the OECD played an important role: European countries mainly imported crude from Norway and the United Kingdom while the United States imported crude from Mexico and Canada.

Excluding intra-OECD trade, the principal trading routes differed for the three OECD regions: crude oil from Central Africa (Nigeria, Angola) and South America (Venezuela) was mainly imported by North America, which also imported about a fourth of the total exports from the Middle East. Crude oil in OECD Europe was supplied by Russia, North Africa and the Middle East, while the OECD Pacific region was essentially dependant on supplies from the Middle East (nearly half of Middle Eastern exports of crude) and Indonesia.

Inter-OECD trade in petroleum products is largely developed: Europe, in particular the Netherlands, the United Kingdom, Italy, France and Belgium all exported a significant amount of petroleum products towards other European OECD countries. Similarly, Korea played a key role exporting petroleum products to Japan and China.

Gas trade implies higher infrastructure costs than for oil; therefore gas trade remains more regional than global. In OECD North America most of the trade occurs between Canada and the United States. In OECD Europe - which accounts for more than two thirds of the total OECD imports of gas - Russia and Algeria are the main two suppliers; Russian gas is piped through Ukraine, and Algerian gas piped through the Mediterranean and imported by LNG carriers. Nigeria is also starting to export to the European market, but the LNG chain limits the volume of gas imported. Imports of gas to the OECD Pacific area accounted for nearly all the remaining third of total OECD net gas imports. Korea and Japan are the only gas importers in the OECD Pacific area. Nearly a third of their imports were supplied by the Middle East, while most of the remaining fraction was provided by exports from ASEAN gas producers (Indonesia, Malaysia and Brunei).

Total Primary Energy Supply

Despite the policies taken after the first oil supply shock to reduce the dependency on oil, oil remains the main component of TPES in the OECD. However, its share has decreased from 51.0% in 1971 to 40.5% in 2005 (see Figure 4).

Figure 4. Fuel Shares in TPES for the OECD*

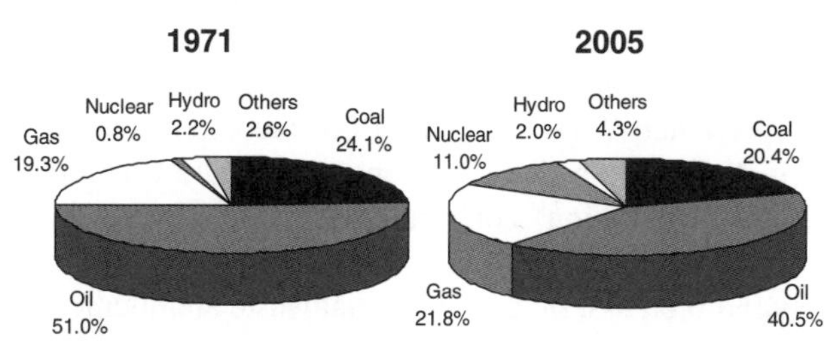

* Includes electricity trade.

Although efforts have been made to reduce the use of oil in sectors where it can be substituted by other fuels, e.g. electricity production, the growing demand in "captive" sectors such as transport explains why the share of oil remains the highest amongst all energy sources.

The share of fossil fuels in total primary energy supply decreased from 94.4% in 1971 to 82.7% in 2005.

Coal share in total TPES was 24.1% in 1971 and decreased to 20.4% in 2005. In the last decade, coal was partly replaced by gas, notably for electricity generation. Gas was the only fossil fuel with increasing shares in the last 34 years (from 19.3% in 1971 to 21.8% in 2005) and became the second fuel in the OECD starting in 1999.

The share of nuclear energy in OECD TPES grew from 0.8% in 1971 to 11.0% in 2005. The development of nuclear energy was particularly intense between 1971 and 1990, with an average growth of 16.0% per year. Since then, the development of nuclear energy has slowed, with a growth of 1.8% per year.

Figure 5. Share of Fossil Fuels and Nuclear in OECD TPES

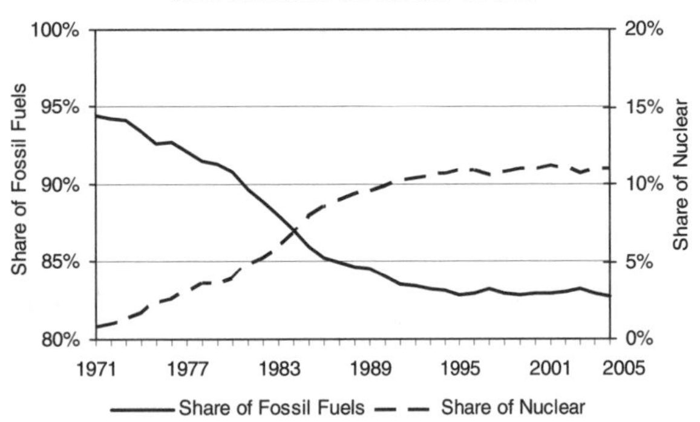

Although hydro energy increased from 75 Mtoe in 1971 to 109 Mtoe in 2005, the share of hydro in TPES fell slightly from 2.2% to 2.0% over the period.

The impact of other alternative energy sources grew from 2.6% in 1971 to 4.3% in 2005. Within this category, solid biomass (including wood, wood wastes and other solid wastes) was the largest contributor and represented 2.6% of total TPES. Geothermal energy (including both direct use and energy used for electricity generation) contributed 0.5% to TPES. Small amounts also came from solar, wind, tide/wave/ocean, liquid biomass, biogas, industrial waste and municipal waste.

Figure 6. OECD TPES by Fuel

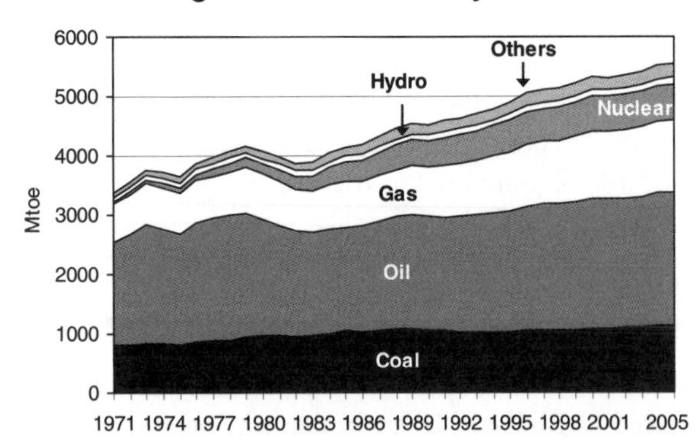

TPES rose from 3 391 Mtoe in 1971 to 5 548 Mtoe in 2005, at an annual average rate of growth of 1.5% per year. This growth was about half that of the growth in GDP observed for the OECD over the same period.

As a consequence, energy intensity (TPES/GDP) fell from 0.31 toe per thousand US$ in 1971 to 0.20 toe per thousand US$ in 2005.

Figure 7. TPES/GDP in the OECD

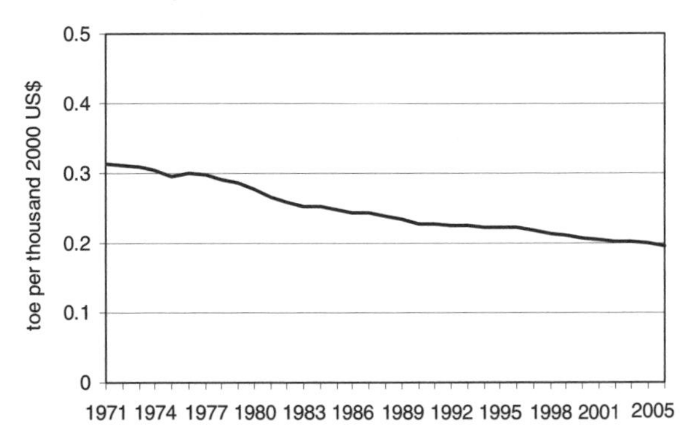

Energy dependency, defined as the complement to 1 of the production/TPES ratio, was 30.9% in 1971. Dependency peaked in 1976 at 35.4% and then rapidly decreased to 21.6% in 1985. Since 1986, energy dependency has steadily increased, once again reaching 30.9%.

The level of dependency is strongly influenced by the evolution of OECD oil production and imports. The fraction of TPES not supplied by OECD production touched its maximum in the mid-1970s, when the increase in oil production in the OECD had not yet started. Energy dependency declined sharply after 1979, when a consistent part of the oil imports started to be replaced by domestic production.

In the following years the trend of energy dependency was mainly influenced by the variations of OECD oil production (and imports), but it was smoothed by the increasing weight of other energy sources. As a result, energy dependency has grown slowly between 1986 and 2005 and is back to 1971 levels.

Figure 8. Energy Dependency in the OECD

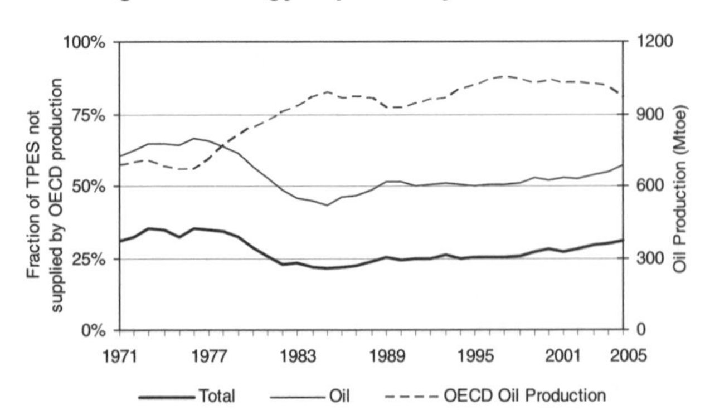

Electricity Generation

Electricity generation increased by more than 3.0% per year since 1971, twice as fast as TPES but at a rate comparable to the growth in GDP. Total generation, including the part from CHP, amounted to 10 393 TWh in 2005.

Figure 9. GDP, TPES and Electricity Output in the OECD

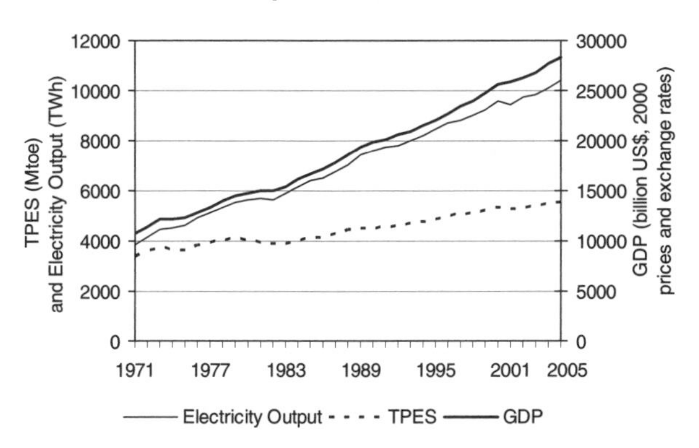

Over the last 34 years, generation has decreased only two times: the first time in 1982 and again in 2001, when mild weather conditions in the United States and a slow-down in the economy caused a drop of 1.4%. For the first time in 2004, OECD electricity generation went above the level of 10 000 TWh.

The fuels used for electricity production changed significantly over time and, as for TPES, the trend in the fuel mix was affected by oil prices and the energy policy of OECD member countries. Power generation is the sector where the efforts to reduce dependency on oil found their best ground.

Figure 10. Electricity Generation by Fuel in the OECD

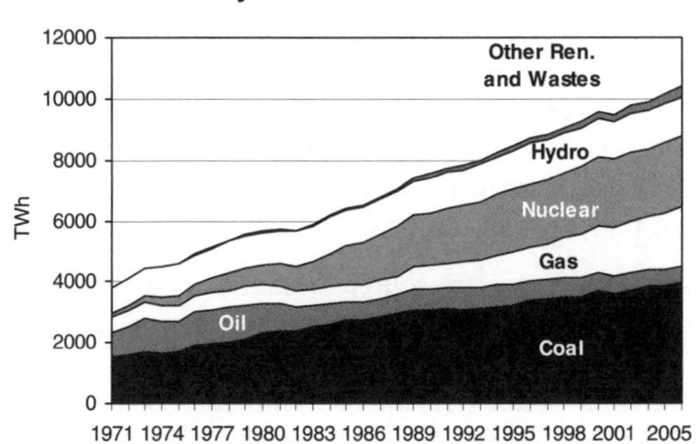

Oil accounted for more than 21.5% of the electricity production in 1971, but its share was reduced to 5.2% in 2005. Most of the decline occurred in the late 1970s and in the early 1980s.

The share of coal remained more or less stable over the period at around 39%. On average, electricity from coal increased by 2.9% per year after 1971, but its growth was weaker after 1988 (1.7% per year, on average), especially because of the increasing use of gas in power generation.

Gas accounted for 13.0% of OECD electricity production in 1971. The share of gas in electricity decreased until the late 1980s and reached its minimum in 1988, when gas-fired power plants contributed only 8.5% of the total electricity output. Technological improvements (highly efficient gas turbines and combined cycle plants), low CO_2 emissions and relatively low prices reversed the trend and allowed gas to gain in importance during the 1990s. Outputs from gas-fired power plants reached 18.8% in 2005.

The share of hydro decreased dramatically from 22.9% in 1971 to 12.2% in 2005, despite an increase in absolute value, since most of the possible sites for large hydro production had already been equipped in 1971.

Figure 11. Fuel Shares in OECD Electricity Output

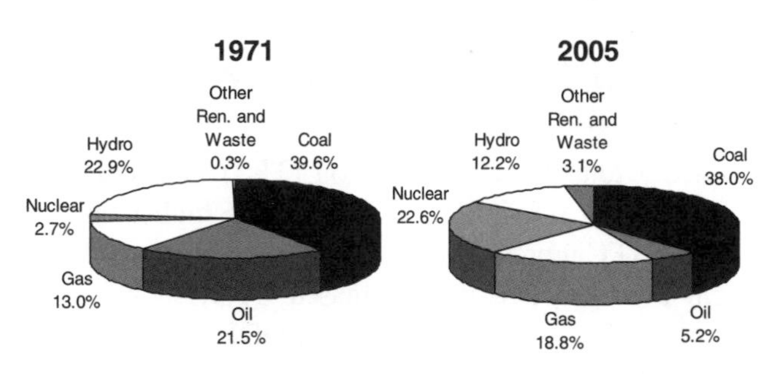

The development of nuclear energy has been extremely important in electricity generation. Nuclear power represented nearly a quarter of the total electricity output in 2005, while its share was less than 3% in 1971.

Other energy sources gave a limited contribution to electricity generation in 2005. Combustible renewables and waste represented 1.8% of total output. Although wind electricity grew by 24% per year between 1990 and 2005, it did not exceed 0.9% of the total output generated in OECD countries. However, for the first time in 2001, wind accounted for more electricity generation than geothermal.

The overall efficiency of electricity generation improved over time, but less than might have been expected as new power stations were built. The increase was due to technical improvements, especially in combined cycles. However, the primary energy from nuclear (obtained from traditional cycles with an efficiency close to 33%) and the weight of nuclear in total electricity production offset the gain in the overall efficiency of power plants.

Table 2. Electricity Consumption in the OECD

Electricity (TWh)	1971	Share of TFC	2005	Share of TFC
Total Final Consumption	3 227		8 952	
Industry Sector	1 597	49.5%	3 096	34.6%
Commercial/Public Services and Residential	1 519	47.1%	5 500	61.4%

The fraction of TPES consumed for electricity and heat generation increased significantly between 1971 and 2005. The reasons behind such an increase can be found in the transition of OECD economies from industry to services (which are more electricity-intensive than industry), in the growing use of electric-intensive technologies and in the growing share of electricity consumption (with respect to other energies) in the industrial, commercial/public services and residential sectors.

Total Final Consumption

OECD total final consumption (TFC) of energy accounted for 3 853 Mtoe in 2005, 0.6% higher than in 2004. TFC represented more than two-thirds of TPES. On average, TFC has increased by 1.2% per year since 1971, less than half of the GDP growth of the OECD.

Trends were not homogeneous amongst energy sources. End-use of coal tended to decrease in all sectors, while oil consumption was heavily affected by the high oil prices in the mid 1970s and early 1980s and declined in all non-captive sectors. Gas increased by 1.3% per year from 1971 to 2005 while electricity almost doubled its share in TFC from 1971 to 2005.

Despite all the efforts made to reduce the oil dependency of OECD countries, the transport sector has always been a captive sector for oil, which accounted for 96.7% of transport consumption in 2005 as compared to 95.1% in 1971.

Moreover, the weight of transport in TFC increased during the last 34 years due to the rising number of vehicles, the tendency to use larger engines and the high use of road transport in trading goods. In 2005, transport was about one third of the total final consumption, while it only accounted for a fourth in 1971.

Figure 12. TFC by Fuel and by Sector in the OECD

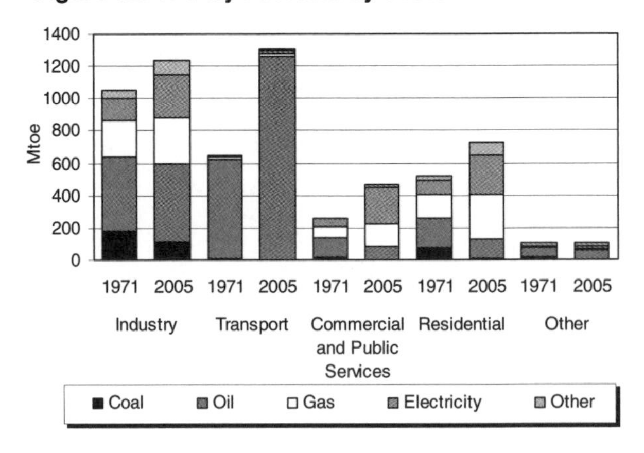

Industry, residential and services sectors also increased, but with lower rates of growth and always accompanied by the substitution of oil and coal by gas or electricity.

The share of coal in industry dropped from 17.6% in 1971 to 8.8% in 2005; it went down from 14.7% to 1.6% in residential. The oil share in commercial/public services represented 46.0% of consumption in 1971 and fell to 16.9% in 2005. Similarly, the oil share declined from 35.4% to 16.5% in residential.

Driven by the development of electricity-intensive technologies (electronics, robotics, etc.), total final consumption of electricity grew by 3.0% per year between 1971 and 2005. The greatest increases concerned commercial/public services (4.4%) and the residential sector (3.4%). Electricity accounted for 20.0% of TFC in 2005, while it contributed for only 10.7% of TFC in 1971.

The growth of gas was more moderate, with an increase of 1.3% per year, and mainly concerned the residential, commercial and public services sectors, with an average increase of 2.2% during the 34-year period. Use of gas in agriculture increased by 12.1% per year and road increased by 7.8% per year, however, both sectors started from very low bases.

Use of other energy sources (mainly combustible renewables) was limited to certain industrial activities (paper, pulp, wood and wood products) and to the residential sector. Its share in total final consumption was 3.6% in 2005.

PART I

METHODOLOGY

PARTIE I

METHODOLOGIE

1. EXPLANATORY NOTES

Unit

The IEA energy balance methodology is based on the calorific content of the energy commodities and a common unit of account. The unit of account adopted by the IEA is the tonne of oil equivalent (toe) which is *defined* as 10^7 kilocalories (41.868 gigajoules). This quantity of energy is, within a few per cent, equal to the net heat content of 1 tonne of crude oil. Throughout this publication 1 tonne means 1 metric ton or 1000 kg.

Conversion (from original units to toe)

The change from using the original units to tonnes of oil equivalent implies choosing coefficients of equivalence between different forms and sources of energy. This problem can be approached in many different ways. For example, one could adopt a single equivalence for each major primary energy source in all countries, e.g. 29 307 kJ/kg (7 000 kcal/kg) for hard coal, 41 868 kJ/kg (10 000 kcal/kg) for oil, etc. The main objection to this method is that it results in distortions since there is a wide spread in calorific values between types of coal and individual coal products, and between calorific values of these fuels in different countries. The Secretariat has therefore adopted specific factors supplied by the national administrations for the main categories of each quality of coal and for each flow or use (i.e. production, imports, exports, electricity generation, coke ovens, blast furnaces and industry). For crude oil, specific factors have been used for production, imports and exports based on consultations with experts from the national administrations, while petroleum products have a single set of conversion factors for all countries. Gas data in *Energy Statistics of OECD Countries* are presented in terajoules on **a gross calorific basis**. Data on combustible renewables & waste are presented in terajoules on **a net calorific basis**. See Section 2, Units and Conversions.

The balances are expressed in terms of "net" calorific value. The difference between the "net" and the "gross" calorific value for each fuel is the latent heat of vaporisation of the water produced during combustion of the fuel. For coal and oil, net calorific value is about 5% less than gross, for most forms of natural and manufactured gas the difference is 9-10%, while for electricity and heat there is no difference as the concept has no meaning in this case. The use of net calorific value is consistent with the practice of the Statistical Offices of the European Communities and the United Nations.

Electricity data are converted from original units of gigawatt hours to million tonnes of oil equivalent using the relationship: 1 terawatt hour = 0.086 Mtoe.

Primary Energy Conventions

When constructing an energy balance, it is necessary to adopt conventions for primary energy from several sources, such as nuclear, geothermal, solar, hydro, wind, etc. The two types of assumptions that have to be made are described below.

Choice of the primary energy form

For each of these sources, there is a need to define the form of primary energy to be considered; for instance, in the case of hydro energy, a choice must be made between the kinetic energy of falling water and the electricity produced. For nuclear energy, the choice is between the energy content of the nuclear fuel, the heat generated in the reactors and the electricity produced. For photovoltaic electricity, the choice is between the solar radiation received and the electricity produced.

The principle adopted by the IEA is that the primary energy form should be the first energy form downstream in the production process for which multiple energy uses are practical. The application of this principle leads to the choice of the following primary energy forms:

- **Heat** for nuclear, geothermal and solar thermal;
- **Electricity** for hydro, wind, tide/wave/ocean and solar photovoltaic.

Calculation of the primary energy equivalent

There are essentially two methods that can be used to calculate the primary energy equivalent of the above energy sources: the partial substitution method and the physical energy content method.

The partial substitution method: In this method, the primary energy equivalent of the above sources of electricity generation represents the amount of energy that would be necessary to generate an identical amount of electricity in conventional thermal power plants. The primary energy equivalent is calculated using an average generating efficiency of these plants. This method has several shortcomings, including the difficulty of choosing an appropriate generating efficiency and the fact that the partial substitution method is not relevant for countries with a high share of hydro electricity. For these reasons, the IEA, as most of the international organisations, has now stopped using this method and adopted the physical energy content method.

The physical energy content method: This method uses the physical energy content of the primary energy source as the primary energy equivalent. As a consequence, there is an obvious link between the principles adopted in defining the primary energy forms of energy sources and the primary energy equivalent of these sources.

For instance, in the case of nuclear electricity production, as heat is the primary energy form selected by the IEA, the primary energy equivalent is the quantity of heat generated in the reactors. However, as the amount of heat produced is not always known, the IEA estimates the primary energy equivalent from the electricity generation by assuming an efficiency of 33%, which is the average of nuclear power plants in Europe.

In the case of hydro and solar PV, as electricity is the primary energy form selected, the primary energy equivalent is the physical energy content of the electricity generated in the plant, which amounts to assuming an efficiency of 100%. A more detailed presentation of the assumptions used by the IEA in establishing its energy balances is given in Section 2.

For geothermal, if no country-specific information is available, the primary energy equivalent is calculated as follows:

- 10% for geothermal electricity;
- 50% for geothermal heat.

Since these two types of energy balances differ significantly in the treatment of electricity from solar, hydro, wind, etc., the share of renewables in total energy supply will appear to be very different depending on the method used. As a result, when looking at the percentages of various energy sources in total supply, it is important to understand the underlying conventions that were used to calculate the primary energy balances.

Indicators

Energy Production: total primary energy production, expressed in Mtoe.

Net Imports: imports minus exports for total energy, expressed in Mtoe.

Total Primary Energy Supply: expressed in Mtoe.

Net Oil Imports: imports minus exports of oil, expressed in Mtoe.

Oil Supply: primary supply of oil, expressed in Mtoe.

Electricity Consumption: domestic consumption, i.e. gross production + imports - exports - distribution losses, expressed in TWh.

Population: the main source of these series for 1970 to 2005 is *National Accounts of OECD Countries, Volume 1*, 2007. Data for 1960 to 1969 have been estimated using the growth rates from the population series published in the *OECD Economic Outlook No 76*. For the **Czech Republic**, **Hungary** and **Poland** (1960 to 1969) and **Mexico** (1960 to 1962), the data are estimated using the growth rates from the population series from the World Bank published in the *World Development Indicators CD-ROM*. For the **Slovak Republic**, population data for 1960 to 1989 are from the Demographic Research Centre, Infostat, Slovak Republic.

GDP: the main source of these series for 1970 to 2005 is *National Accounts of OECD Countries, Volume 1*, 2007. GDP data for 1960 to 1969 have been estimated using the growth rates from the series in the *OECD Economic Outlook No 76* and data previously published by the OECD. Data prior to 1990 for the **Czech Republic** and **Poland**, prior to 1991 for **Hungary**, and prior to 1992 for the **Slovak Republic** are IEA Secretariat estimates based on GDP growth rates from the World Bank.

Greece made very large and extensive revisions to its national accounts in the autumn of 2006 for the years 2000 to 2005 that resulted in an increase of 25.7% to GDP in the year 2000, but did not greatly affect growth rates. The revisions stem from the introduction of improved methods and the availability of more up-to-date source data. Data for years prior to 2000 have been derived by linking the previously published estimates to the revised data.

The GDP data have been compiled for individual countries at market prices in local currency and annual rates. These data have been scaled up/down to the price levels of 2000 and then converted to US dollars using the yearly average 2000 exchange rates or purchasing power parities (PPPs).

Purchasing power parities are the rates of currency conversion that equalise the purchasing power of different currencies. A given sum of money, when converted into different currencies at the PPP rates, buys the same basket of goods and services in all countries. In other words, PPPs are the rates of currency conversion which eliminate the differences in price levels between different countries. The PPPs selected to convert the GDP from national currencies to US dollars were aggregated using the Geary-Khamis (GK) method and rebased on the United States. For a more detailed description of the methodology please see *Purchasing Power Parities and Real Expenditures, GK Results, Volume II, 1990*, OECD 1993.

Industrial Production Index: the main source of these series is the OECD publication *Indicators of Industrial Activity*, 2007. Industrial production refers to the goods produced by establishments engaged in mining (including oil extraction), manufacturing, and production of electricity, gas and water. These are categories C, D and E of ISIC[1] Rev. 3.

1. International Standard Industrial Classification of All Economic Activities, Series M, No. 4 / Rev. 3, United Nations, New York, 1990.

Layout

The energy balances are presented in tabular format: columns for the various sources of energy and rows for the different origins and uses.

Columns

Across the top of the table from left to right, there are eleven columns with the following headings:

Column 1: *Coal* includes all coal, both primary (including hard coal and lignite/brown coal) and derived fuels (including patent fuel, coke oven coke, gas coke, BKB, coke oven gas, blast furnace gas and oxygen steel furnace gas). Peat is also included in this category.

Column 2: *Crude oil* comprises crude oil, natural gas liquids, refinery feedstocks, and additives as well as other hydrocarbons (including emulsified oils, synthetic crude oil, mineral oils extracted from bituminous minerals such as oil shale, bituminous sand, etc., and oils from coal liquefaction).

Column 3: *Petroleum products* comprise refinery gas, ethane, LPG, aviation gasoline, motor gasoline, jet fuels, kerosene, gas/diesel oil, heavy fuel oil, naphtha, white spirit, lubricants, bitumen, paraffin waxes, petroleum coke and other petroleum products.

Column 4: *Gas* includes natural gas (excluding natural gas liquids) and gas works gas. The latter appears as a positive figure in the "gas works" row but is not part of production.

Column 5: *Nuclear* shows the primary heat equivalent of the electricity produced by a nuclear power plant with an average thermal efficiency of 33%.

Column 6: *Hydro* shows the energy content of the electricity produced in hydro power plants. Hydro output *excludes* output from pumped storage plants.

Column 7: *Geothermal, solar, etc.;* production of geothermal, solar, wind and tide/wave/ocean energy and the use of these energy forms for electricity and heat generation. Unless the actual efficiency of the geothermal process is known, the quantity of geothermal energy entering electricity generation is inferred from the electricity production at geothermal plants assuming an average thermal efficiency of 10%. For solar, wind and tide/wave/ocean energy, the quantities entering electricity generation are equal to the electrical energy generated. Other uses shown in this column relate to geothermal and solar thermal heat.

Column 8: *Combustible renewables & waste* comprises solid biomass, liquid biomass, biogas, industrial waste and municipal waste. Biomass is defined as any plant matter used directly as fuel or converted into fuels (e.g. charcoal) or electricity and/or heat. Included here are wood, vegetal waste (including wood waste and crops used for energy production), ethanol, animal materials/wastes and sulphite lyes (also known as "black liquor" is an alkaline spent liquor from the digesters in the production of sulphate or soda pulp during the manufacture of paper where the energy content is derived from the lignin removed from the wood pulp and which in its concentrated form is usually 65-70% solid). Municipal waste comprises wastes produced by the residential, commercial and public service sectors that are collected by local authorities for disposal in a central location for the production of heat and/or power. Hospital waste is included in this category.

Data under this heading are often based on incomplete information. Thus the data give only a broad impression of developments, and are not strictly comparable between countries. In some cases complete categories of vegetal fuel are omitted due to lack of information. Please refer to individual country data when consulting regional aggregates.

Column 9: *Electricity* shows final consumption and trade in electricity, which is accounted at the same heat value as electricity in final consumption (i.e. 1 GWh = 0.000086 Mtoe).

Column 10: *Heat* shows the disposition of heat produced for sale. The large majority of the heat included in this column results from the combustion of fuels although some small amounts are produced from electrically powered heat pumps and boilers. Any heat extracted from ambient air by heat pumps is shown as production.

Column 11: *Total* = the total of Columns 1 to 10.

Rows

The categories on the left hand side of the table have the following functions:

Row 1: *Production* is the production of primary energy, i.e. hard coal, lignite/brown coal, peat, crude oil, NGLs, natural gas, combustible renewables and waste, nuclear, hydro, geothermal, solar and the heat from heat pumps that is extracted from the ambient environment. Production is calculated after removal of impurities (e.g. sulphur from natural gas). Calculation of production of hydro, geothermal, etc. and nuclear electricity is explained in Section 2, Units and Conversions.

Row 2/3: *Imports* and *exports* comprise amounts having crossed the national territorial boundaries of the country, whether or not customs clearance has taken place.

For coal: Imports and exports comprise the amount of fuels obtained from or supplied to other countries, whether or not there is an economic or customs union between the relevant countries. Coal in transit should not be included.

For oil and gas: Quantities of crude oil and oil products imported or exported under processing agreements (i.e. refining on account) are included. Quantities of oil in transit are excluded. Crude oil, NGL and natural gas are reported as coming from the country of origin; refinery feedstocks and oil products are reported as coming from the country of last consignment. Re-exports of oil imported for processing within bonded areas are shown as exports of product from the processing country to the final destination.

For electricity: Amounts are considered as imported or exported when they have crossed the national territorial boundaries of the country. If electricity is "wheeled" or transited through a country, the amount is shown as both an import and an export.

Row 4: *International marine bunkers* covers those quantities delivered to ships of all flags that are engaged in international navigation. The international navigation may take place at sea, on inland lakes and waterways, and in coastal waters. Consumption by ships engaged in domestic navigation is excluded. The domestic/international split is determined on the basis of port of departure and port of arrival, and not by the flag or nationality of the ship. Consumption by fishing vessels and by military forces is also excluded. See *domestic navigation* (Row 40), *fishing* (Row 46) and *non-specified "other sectors"* (Row 47).

Row 5: *Stock changes* reflects the difference between opening stock levels on the first day of the year and closing levels on the last day of the year of stocks on national territory held by producers, importers, energy transformation industries and large consumers. A stock build is shown as a negative number, and a stock draw as a positive number.

Row 6: *Total primary energy supply (TPES)* is made up of *production* (Row 1) + *imports* (Row 2) - *exports* (Row 3) - *international marine bunkers* (Row 4) ± *stock changes* (Row 5).

Row 7: *Transfers* include interproduct transfers, products transferred and recycled products (e.g. used lubricants which are reprocessed).

Row 8: *Statistical differences* includes the sum of the unexplained statistical differences for individual fuels, as they appear in the basic energy statistics. It also includes the statistical differences that arise because of the variety of conversion factors in the coal and oil columns. See introduction to *Energy Statistics of OECD Countries* for further details.

Row 9: *Electricity plants* refers to plants which are designed to produce electricity only. If one or more units of the plant is a CHP unit (and the inputs and outputs can not be distinguished on a unit basis) then the whole plant is designated as a CHP plant. Both main activity producer (formerly known as public)[2] and autoproducer[3] plants are included here. Columns 1 through 8 show the use of primary and secondary fuels for the production of electricity as negative entries. Heat from chemical processes used for electricity generation will appear in Column 10. Gross electricity produced (including power stations' own consumption) appears as a positive quantity in the electricity column. Transformation losses appear in the total column as a negative number.

Row 10: *Combined heat and power plants (CHP)*, refers to plants which are designed to produce both heat and electricity, sometimes referred as co-generation power stations. If possible, fuel inputs and electricity/heat outputs are on a unit basis rather than on a plant basis. However, if data are not available on a unit basis, the convention for defining a CHP plant noted above is adopted. Both main activity producer (formerly known as public) and autoproducer plants are included here. *Note that for autoproducer's CHP plants, all fuel inputs to electricity production are taken into account, while only the part of fuel inputs to heat* ***sold*** *is shown. Fuel inputs for the production of heat consumed within the autoproducer's establishment are* ***not*** *included here but are included with figures for the final consumption of fuels in the appropriate consuming sector.*

Columns 1 through 8 show the use of primary and secondary fuels for the production of electricity and heat as negative entries. Total gross electricity produced appears as a positive quantity in the electricity column and heat produced appears as a positive number in the heat column. Transformation losses appear in the total column as a negative number.

Row 11: *Heat plants* refers to plants (including heat pumps and electric boilers) designed to produce heat only, which is sold to a third party under the provisions of a contract. Both main activity producer (formerly known as public) and autoproducer plants are included here. Heat pumps that are operated within the residential sector where the heat is not sold are not considered a transformation process and are not included here – the electricity consumption appears as residential use.

Columns 1 through 8 show the use of primary and secondary fuels in a heating system that transmits and distributes heat from one or more energy source to, among others, residential, industrial, and commercial consumers, for space heating, cooking, hot water and industrial processes.

Row 12: *Gas works* is treated similarly to electricity generation, with the quantity produced appearing as a positive figure in the gas column, inputs as negative entries in the coal, petroleum products and gas columns, and conversion losses appearing in the total column.

Row 13: *Petroleum refineries* shows the use of primary energy for the manufacture of finished petroleum products and the corresponding output. Thus, the total reflects transformation losses. In certain cases the data in the total column are positive numbers. This can be due either to problems in the primary refinery balance, or to the fact that the IEA uses standardised net calorific values for petroleum products.

Row 14: *Coal transformation* contains losses in transformation of coal from primary to secondary fuels and from secondary to tertiary fuels (hard coal to coke, coke to blast furnace gas, lignite to BKB, etc.). It is often difficult to correctly account for all inputs and outputs in energy transformation industries, and to

2. Main activity producer (formerly known as public supply undertakings) generate electricity and/or heat for sale to third parties, *as their primary activity*. They may be privately or publicly owned. Note that the sale need not take place through the public grid.

3. Autoproducer undertakings generate electricity and/or heat, wholly or partly for their own use as an activity which supports their primary activity. They may be privately or publicly owned.

separate energy that is transformed from energy that is combusted. As a result, in certain cases the data in the total column are positive numbers, indicating a problem in the underlying energy data.

***Row 15:** Liquefaction plants* includes diverse liquefaction processes, such as coal liquefaction plants and gas-to-liquid plants.

***Row 16:** Other transformation* covers non-specified transformation not shown elsewhere, such as the transformation of solid biomass into charcoal and the blending of other gases with natural gas. It also includes backflows from the petrochemical sector. Backflows from oil products that are used for non-energy purposes (i.e. white spirit and lubricants) are not included here, but in non-energy use.

***Row 17:** Own use* contains the primary and secondary energy consumed by transformation industries for heating, pumping, traction and lighting purposes [ISIC[4] Divisions 10-12, 23 and 40]. These quantities are shown as negative figures. Included here are, for example, own use of energy in coal mines, own consumption in power plants (which includes net electricity consumed for pumped storage) and energy used for oil and gas extraction.

***Row 18:** Distribution and transmission losses* includes losses in gas distribution, electricity transmission and coal transport.

***Row 19:** Total final consumption* (TFC) is the sum of consumption by the different end-use sectors. Backflows from the petrochemical industry are not included in final consumption (see Row 16, *other transformation* and Row 50, *of which petrochemical feedstocks*).

***Rows 20-33:** Industry sector* consumption is specified in the following sub-sectors (energy used for transport by industry is not included here but is reported under transport):

Iron and steel industry [ISIC Group 271 and Class 2731];

Chemical and petrochemical industry [ISIC Division 24] excluding petrochemical feedstocks. *Prior to last year, the petrochemical feedstocks were included in energy use in the industry sector: starting with last year they have been included with non-energy use*;

Non-ferrous metals basic industries [ISIC Group 272 and Class 2732];

Non-metallic minerals such as glass, ceramic, cement, etc. [ISIC Division 26];

Transport equipment [ISIC Divisions 34 and 35];

Machinery comprises fabricated metal products, machinery and equipment other than transport equipment [ISIC Divisions 28 to 32];

Mining (excluding fuels) and quarrying [ISIC Divisions 13 and 14];

Food and tobacco [ISIC Divisions 15 and 16];

Paper, pulp and printing [ISIC Divisions 21 and 22];

Wood and wood products (other than pulp and paper) [ISIC Division 20];

Construction [ISIC Division 45];

Textile and leather [ISIC Divisions 17 to 19];

Non-specified (any manufacturing industry not included above) [ISIC Divisions 25, 33, 36 and 37].

Note: Most countries have difficulties supplying an industrial breakdown for all fuels. In these cases, the *non-specified* industry row has been used. Regional aggregates of industrial consumption should therefore be used with caution.

***Rows 34-41:** Transport sector* includes all fuels used for transport except international marine bunkers [ISIC Divisions 60 to 62]. It includes transport in the industry sector and covers *international aviation*, *domestic aviation*, *road*, *rail*, *pipeline transport*, *domestic navigation* and *non-specified transport*. Domestic aviation includes deliveries of aviation fuels to aircraft for domestic aviation – commercial, private, agriculture, etc. It includes use for purpose other than flying, e.g. bench testing of engines, but not airline use of fuel for road transport. The domestic/international split should be determined on the basis of departure and landing locations and not by the nationality of the airline. Note that this may include journeys of considerable length between two airports in a country (e.g. San Francisco to Honolulu). For many countries, the split between international aviation and domestic aviation incorrectly allocates fuel use for both domestic and international departures of domestically owned carriers to domestic air. Fuel used for ocean, coastal and inland fishing (included under *fishing*) and military consumption (included in *other sectors non-specified*) are excluded from the transport sector.

4. International Standard Industrial Classification of All Economic Activities, Series M, No. 4 / Rev. 3, United Nations, New York, 1990.

Rows 42-47: *Other sectors* covers *residential, commercial and public services* [ISIC Divisions 41, 50-52, 55, 63-67, 70-75, 80, 85, 90-93, 95 and 99], *agriculture/ forestry* [ISIC Divisions 01 and 02], *fishing* [ISIC Division 05] and *non-specified consumption. Non-specified* includes military fuel use for all mobile and stationary consumption (e.g. ships, aircraft, road and energy used in living quarters) regardless of whether the fuel delivered is for the military of that country or for the military of another country. In many cases administrations find it impossible to distinguish energy consumption in *commercial and public services* from *residential* consumption. Some cannot distinguish consumption in *agriculture* from that in *residential.* In these cases, the residential sector will also include consumption in agriculture and/or commercial/ public services. The *other sectors* total is, therefore, more accurate than its components.

Rows 48-52: *Non-energy use* covers use of *other petroleum products* such as white spirit, paraffin waxes, lubricants, bitumen and other products. It also includes the non-energy use of coal (excluding peat). These products are shown separately in final consumption under the heading *non-energy use.* It is assumed that the use of these products is exclusively non-energy use. An exception to this treatment is petroleum coke, which is included as non-energy use only when there is evidence of such use; otherwise it is included as energy use in *industry* or in *other sectors.*

of which: petrochemical feedstocks. The petrochemical industry includes cracking and reforming processes for the purpose of producing ethylene, propylene, butylene, synthesis gas, aromatics, butadene and other hydrocarbon-based raw materials in processes such as steam cracking, aromatics plants and steam reforming [part of ISIC Group 241]. *Prior to last year, the petrochemical feedstocks were included in energy use in the industry sector: starting last year they have been included with non-energy use.*

Rows 53-55: *Electricity generated* shows the total number of TWh generated by thermal power plants separated into electricity plants and CHP plants, as well as production by nuclear and hydro (excluding pumped storage production), geothermal, etc. (see, however, the notes on Rows 9 and 10). Electricity produced by heat from chemical processes is shown in the *heat* column.

Rows 56-58: *Heat generated* shows the total amount of PJ generated by power plants separated into CHP plants and heat plants. Heat produced by electric boilers is shown in the *electricity* column. Heat produced by heat pumps, heat from chemical processes and heat from non-specified combustible fuels is shown in the *heat* column.

2. UNITS AND CONVERSIONS

General Conversion Factors for Energy

To:	TJ	Gcal	Mtoe	MBtu	GWh
From:	multiply by:				
TJ	1	238.8	2.388×10^{-5}	947.8	0.2778
Gcal	4.1868×10^{-3}	1	10^{-7}	3.968	1.163×10^{-3}
Mtoe	4.1868×10^{4}	10^{7}	1	3.968×10^{7}	11630
MBtu	1.0551×10^{-3}	0.252	2.52×10^{-8}	1	2.931×10^{-4}
GWh	3.6	860	8.6×10^{-5}	3412	1

Conversion Factors for Mass

To:	kg	T	Lt	st	lb
From:	multiply by:				
kilogramme (kg)	1	0.001	9.84×10^{-4}	1.102×10^{-3}	2.2046
tonne (t)	1000	1	0.984	1.1023	2204.6
long ton (lt)	1016	1.016	1	1.120	2240.0
short ton (st)	907.2	0.9072	0.893	1	2000.0
pound (lb)	0.454	4.54×10^{-4}	4.46×10^{-4}	5.0×10^{-4}	1

Conversion Factors for Volume

To:	gal U.S.	gal U.K.	bbl	ft^3	l	m^3
From:	multiply by:					
U.S. gallon (gal)	1	0.8327	0.02381	0.1337	3.785	0.0038
U.K. gallon (gal)	1.201	1	0.02859	0.1605	4.546	0.0045
Barrel (bbl)	42.0	34.97	1	5.615	159.0	0.159
Cubic foot (ft^3)	7.48	6.229	0.1781	1	28.3	0.0283
Litre (l)	0.2642	0.220	0.0063	0.0353	1	0.001
Cubic metre (m^3)	264.2	220.0	6.289	35.3147	1000.0	1

Decimal Prefixes

10^{1}	deca (da)	10^{-1}	deci (d)
10^{2}	hecto (h)	10^{-2}	centi (c)
10^{3}	kilo (k)	10^{-3}	milli (m)
10^{6}	mega (M)	10^{-6}	micro (µ)
10^{9}	giga (G)	10^{-9}	nano (n)
10^{12}	tera (T)	10^{-12}	pico (p)
10^{15}	peta (P)	10^{-15}	femto (f)
10^{18}	exa (E)	10^{-18}	atto (a)

Gas

Energy Statistics of OECD Countries expresses the following gases in terajoules, using their gross calorific value.

1 terajoule = 0.00002388 Mtoe.

To calculate the net heat content of a gas from its gross heat content, multiply the gross heat content by the appropriate following factor.

Gas	Gross to Net Ratio
Natural gas	0.9
Gas works gas	0.9
Coke oven gas	0.9
Blast furnace gas	1.0
Oxygen Steel Furnace Gas	1.0

Electricity

Figures for electricity production, trade, and final consumption are calculated using the energy content of the electricity (i.e. at a rate of 1 TWh = 0.086 Mtoe). Hydro-electricity production (excluding pumped storage) and electricity produced by other non-thermal means (wind, tide/wave/ocean, photovoltaic, etc.) are accounted for similarly using 1 TWh = 0.086 Mtoe. However, the primary energy equivalent of nuclear electricity is calculated from the gross generation by assuming a 33% conversion efficiency, i.e. 1 TWh = (0.086 ÷ 0.33) Mtoe. In the case of electricity produced from geothermal heat, if the actual geothermal efficiency is not known, then the primary equivalent is calculated assuming an efficiency of 10%, so 1 TWh = (0.086 ÷ 0.1) Mtoe.

Crude Oil

Country-specific net calorific values (NCV) for production, imports and exports by country are used to calculate the balances. The average value is used to convert all the other flows to heat values. Country-specific net calorific values for 2004 and 2005 are given in Part II.

Petroleum Products

The following conversion factors are used for all countries and all years (toe per tonne):

Product	Toe per Tonne
Refinery gas	1.150
Ethane	1.130
LPG	1.130
Naphtha	1.075
Aviation Gasoline	1.070
Motor Gasoline	1.070
Jet Gasoline	1.070
Jet Kerosene	1.065
Other Kerosene	1.045
Gas/Diesel Oil	1.035
Heavy Fuel Oil	0.960
Petroleum Coke	0.740
Other Products	0.960

Coal

Coal has separate net calorific values for production, imports, exports, inputs to main activity producer power plants and coal used in coke ovens, blast furnaces and industry. All other flows are converted using an average net calorific value. Country-specific net calorific values for 2004 and 2005 are given in Part II.

Combustible Renewables and Waste

The heat content of primary solid biomass, biogas, municipal waste and industrial waste, expressed in terajoules on a net calorific value basis, is presented in *Energy Statistics of OECD Countries.* The Secretariat does not receive information on volumes and other characteristics of these fuels.

1 terajoule = 0.00002388 Mtoe.

Data for charcoal are converted from tonnes using the average net calorific values given in Part II.

Data for liquid biomass are converted from tonnes using 0.65 toe per tonne unless country-specific information has been provided.

Heat

Information on heat is supplied in terajoules and 1 terajoule = 0.00002388 Mtoe.

For geothermal heat, the actual heat inputs should be counted in the transformation sector. If no information is available, then an efficiency of 50% is assumed.

Examples

The following examples indicate how to calculate the net calorific content (in Mtoe) of the quantities expressed in original units in *Energy Statistics of OECD Countries, 2004-2005.*

From Original Units	To Mtoe (NCV)
Coking coal production (Poland) for 2005 in thousand tonnes	multiply by 0.0007070
Natural gas in terajoules (gross)	multiply by 0.00002149
Motor gasoline in thousand tonnes	multiply by 0.0010700
Heat in terajoules (net)	multiply by 0.00002388

3. COUNTRY NOTES

General Notes

The notes given below refer to data for the years 1960 to 2005 and cover the summary tables at the back of the book, as well as the information on CD-ROM and the on-line data service. In general, more detailed notes are available for data starting in 1990.

Prior to 1974, most fuel inputs and electricity and heat outputs for autoproducers are included in main activity producers. The figures for the quantities of fuels used for the generation of electricity and heat and the corresponding outputs in CHP and heat plants should be used with caution. Despite estimates introduced by the Secretariat, inputs and outputs are not always consistent. Please refer to notes below under *Electricity and Heat*.

In 1996, the Secretariat extensively revised data on coal and coke use in blast furnaces, and in the iron and steel industry (for those countries with blast furnaces), based on data provided to the OECD Steel Committee and other sources. The quantities of fuels transformed into blast furnace gas have been estimated by the Secretariat based on its blast furnace model.

Moreover, in 1996 and 1997, the Secretariat extensively revised data on combustible renewables and waste (i.e. solid biomass, biogas, liquid biomass, industrial waste and municipal waste) based on data from Eurostat (for the EU-15 Member countries) and on other national sources for other OECD Member countries. As consumption data for combustible renewables and waste from Eurostat are generally available from 1989, there may be breaks in series between 1988 and 1989 for some EU Member countries.

In December 1999, the Energy Statistics Working Group, made up of the IEA, the United Nations, the United Nations Economic Commission for Europe, Eurostat and their respective Member Governments, decided to develop a separate annual questionnaire on renewables and wastes in the hope that this would improve the quality of reporting by national administrations. As a result of this new questionnaire, it is possible that there will be breaks in renewables and waste time series between 1997 and 1998 until national statistical offices are able to revise their series. In order to improve the quality of renewables and waste statistics and to ensure data compatibility, the IEA initiated a project in 2002 with the objective to compare and harmonise historical IEA data with those of national administrations and/or Eurostat, where applicable. As a result, the renewables and waste time series of many countries were revised back to the year 1990.

Australia

All data refer to the fiscal year, July 2004 to June 2005 for 2005. For the 2002 data, the Australian Administration started to use a new survey methodology which caused shifts in the structure of industry consumption. The Australian Administration is planning to revise the historical series.

Coal: Data on blast furnace gas for electricity production by autoproducers begins in 1986. Consumption in wood and wood products is included in paper, pulp and print from 2001 onwards. The drop in BKB production in 2004 was due to a fire in the main production plant.

Combustible Renewables and Waste: For combustible renewables and waste, a different industry consumption breakdown is available from 1996 and leads to breaks in series. Biogas production at sewage treatment works is unavailable. Inputs of solid biomass to autoproducer CHP are estimated by the Secretariat until 1999.

Oil: Negative refinery losses are caused by differences in treatment of transfers between refineries. Imports of heavy fuel oil have been estimated by the Australian Administration. The drop in the production of crude oil in 1999 is due to a gas explosion at the Longford plant.

Gas: Prior to 1991, natural gas data include ethane. Data for 1999 and 2000 are estimated by the Australian Administration. Starting from 2002, indigenous production includes colliery gas.

Electricity and Heat: Inputs and outputs from autoproducer CHP plants are not available prior to 1986. The breakdown of electricity production by fuel at autoproducer CHP plants has been estimated by the Secretariat from 1992 to 2001. The production of electricity from wind is available from 1994 and solar electricity from 1999. Prior to 1995, electricity production from biogas is included in natural gas. In 2002, the Australian Administration started to use a new survey methodology and reclassified the types of plants between main activity producers and autoproducers.

Oil and gas inputs to autoproducer CHP are included in industry consumption prior to 2002.

Austria

Historical revisions by the Austrian Administration have resulted in some breaks in series between 1989 and 1990.

Coal: The amount of gas works gas is negligible and it is mostly consumed by households. There is no production of brown coal in 2005 due to the closure of the last mine in the second quarter of 2004.

Combustible Renewables and Waste: Data for 1986 to 1989 for combustible renewables and waste are Secretariat estimates based on information published by OSTAT in *Energieversongung Österreichs Endgültige Energiebilanz*. Due to a change in the survey methodology, the heat produced in small plants (capacity inferior to 1 MW) is not reported starting in 2002.

Gas: The break in the time series for autoproducer electricity and CHP plants between 1995 and 1996 is due to the availability of more detailed data from 1996 onwards. Differences due to measurement are included with distribution losses prior to 2000 and with statistical difference starting in 2000.

Electricity and Heat: Starting in 1990, small amounts of electricity used in heat pumps have been included in the residential sector. There are breaks in series between 1995 and 1996 and between 1998 and 1999 due to new methods of survey.

For heat, own use is included in distribution losses. Consumption in the iron and steel industry includes consumption in coke ovens. Consumption in commercial/public services includes electric energy in the field of electricity supply, district heating and water supply prior to 1990.

Belgium

Coal: Production of other bituminous coal ceased on 31 August 1992. Production includes the recuperation of coal from coal dumps. The use of coke oven gas in the chemical and petrochemical sector ceased in 1996. The decrease of bituminous coal and coke oven coke in the iron and steel sector in 2002 is due to the closure of several plants.

Combustible Renewables and Waste: In 2003, combustion of municipal waste for electricity and heat generation purposes increased significantly. However, as a large portion of the heat produced is not used (sold) it has led to a significant drop in plant efficiencies between 2002 and 2003.

Oil: The decrease in heavy fuel oil industry consumption since 1993 is due to the introduction of an excise tax as well as increased use of natural gas. In 2002, patent fuel plants used residual fuel oil to increase the calorific value of patent fuel.

Gas: The large decrease in non-specified industry in 2003 is due to improvements in data collection. New legislation for data collection has led to breaks in series for industry and own use between 2004 and 2005.

Electricity and Heat: For 1998 and 1999, electricity production at CHP plants with annual heat output below 0.5 TJ is reported with electricity only plants. From 2000, autoproducer electricity plants have been reclassified as autoproducer CHP plants. Also from 2000, electricity production at CHP plants is reported with CHP plants; the heat output is used for internal industrial processes and is not sold to third parties.

Breaks in series exist between 1991 and 1992 for heat consumption in chemical and non-specified industry.

Canada

Revisions received by the Canadian Administration and incorporated into the 2002 edition have resulted in breaks in series between 1989 and 1990.

Coal: Due to a Canadian confidentiality law, starting in 2002, some of the disaggregation of primary coal has been estimated by the IEA Secretariat.

Combustible Renewables and Waste: The IEA Secretariat has estimated the data for municipal waste, industrial waste and biogas from 1990 to 2005 and liquid biomass (ethanol) from 1998 to 2004 based on information supplied by Natural Resources Canada.

Oil: From 1988 onwards, data for several industrial sub-sectors are no longer available. Transfers for naphtha and *other petroleum products* include purchases of feedstock and other additives from non-reporting companies. Ethane is mainly used as a petrochemical feedstock. Prior to 1990, hydrogen used for the upgrading of synthetic crude oil production was included in natural gas supply; from 1990, a different methodology was adopted by the Canadian Administration. Canada imported orimulsion from Venezuela from 1994 to 2000.

Gas: Starting in 1992, consumption of natural gas in main activity producer CHP plants includes use in three new co-generation facilities in the province of Ontario. The data reported in the non-specified element of the transformation sector represent quantities of natural gas used for the upgrading of refined oil products. In 2000, the increase in main activity producer electricity data is due to new generation plants in Alberta and Ontario, while the increase in autoproducer electricity is due to the addition of independent power production.

Electricity and Heat: Heat production includes heat produced by nuclear power stations for distribution to other consumers. The breakdown of electricity and heat generation between natural gas and oil products in main activity producer CHP plants has been estimated by the Canadian Administration starting in 1990. This may cause breaks in the time series between 1989 and 1990. The inputs of combustible renewables and waste to autoproducer electricity plants, as well as the final energy consumption in the pulp and paper sector from 1981 to 2004, were revised by the IEA Secretariat.

Czech Republic

Data are available starting in 1971.

Coal: End-use consumption data were submitted by the Czech Administration starting with 1996 data. Due to economic restructuring in the end-use consumption sectors in the late 1990s (big state enterprises subdividing and/or privatising and the utilisation of new technologies by businesses), there might be breaks in time series in these sectors. Prior to 1993, consumption was estimated by the Secretariat. Data for 1990 to 1995 were estimated based on the Czech publication *Energy Economy Year Book.* In 1995, town gas production ceased. Beginning in 1996, the Czech Administration reported gas works gas in autoproducer CHP. In 1997, coke oven gas consumption in chemical and petrochemical stopped. Also in 1997, other bituminous coal started being extracted at a deeper level, which increased the calorific value of this coal. Revisions by the Czech Administration have resulted in some breaks in series between 2001 and 2002. Production from other sources of other bituminous coal in 2004 are coal slurries.

Combustible Renewables and Waste: Data for combustible renewables are not available prior to 1991. The restructuring of the Czech electricity market leads to breaks in the time series in all sectors between 1998 and 1999. Data for liquid biomass are available starting in 1992 and for municipal waste starting in 1999. New survey systems cause breaks in final consumption in 1999 and in 2002. Breaks in both supply and consumption of combustible renewables and waste occur again in 2003. The exports of biodiesel increased in 2005 driven by high prices for the commodity.

Oil: Data prior to 1994 are estimated by the Secretariat. The Czech Administration submitted an Oil Questionnaire to the IEA for the first time with 1994 data. Breaks in series between 1998 and 1999 for the final consumption of gas/diesel oil are due to a new data management system implemented by the Czech Administration.

Gas: Data from 1993 onwards have been officially submitted by the Czech Statistical Office. The breaks in series between 1993 and 1994 are due to a change in the energy balance methodology between former

Czechoslovakia and the Czech Republic. Prior to 1994, data in the transport sector are for former Czechoslovakia. Natural gas inputs into gas works ceased in 1996.

Electricity and Heat: Electricity statistics from 1971 to 1989 have been estimated by the Secretariat except for final consumption and trade which were submitted by the Czech Administration. Data on heat production, and the corresponding fuel inputs, have been estimated from 1980 to 1989 based on consumption in the residential and commercial/public services sectors. Prior to that, inputs are included in industry. Data from 1990 onwards have been officially submitted by the Czech Administration. This may lead to breaks in series between 1989 and 1990. Prior to 1990, electricity production in main activity producer CHP and autoproducer CHP plants is included in main activity producer electricity plants. Heat production prior to 1990 excludes heat sold by industry. The breakdown of heat production between main activity producer CHP and heat plants is not available prior to 1990. Accordingly, all heat production is reported in main activity producer heat plants. Data on biogas and wastes in main activity producer CHP and autoproducer heat plants start in 1993. In 1999 and 2000, various big enterprises have been divided, sold and merged. This causes breaks in the time series of all types of plants. The new reporting methodology used by the Czech Administration for combustible renewables and wastes causes some breaks in time series between 2002 and 2003. In the 2006 edition, major revisions were made to the time series by the Czech Administration from 1990 onwards.

Denmark

In the 2004 edition, major revisions were made by the Danish Administration for the 1990 to 2001 data, which may cause breaks in time series between 1989 and 1990.

Oil: Information on waste oil recycling and end-use consumption begins in 1989 and is reported in *other petroleum products*. Prior to 1990, Greenland and the Danish Faroes are included in the oil data. Also prior to 1990, gas/diesel oil consumption and heavy fuel oil consumption for fishing are included in domestic navigation, while after this date they are reported in the agriculture sector. Consumption data are based on a detailed survey sent to companies in Denmark every other year. For non-survey years, the consumption figures are estimated by the Danish Energy Agency. Due to better survey methods, inputs to electricity and heat generation have been reclassified, causing a break in series between 1993 and 1994. The marked increase in inputs of heavy fuel oil to CHP production in 1994 is due to increased electricity exports to Norway. Industry sector detail for 1994 and 1995 is based on a new survey. Orimulsion imports (used for electricity generation) began in 1995 and ceased in 2003. The oil inputs used in industrial sectors for producing surplus heat, which is delivered to district heating networks, are allocated to these industrial sectors.

Electricity and Heat: From 1984 onwards, small amounts of heat have been imported from Germany. Heat produced for sale by heat pumps starts in 1994. Prior to 1994 the electricity and heat production are estimated based on fuel inputs.

Finland

A new survey system and a reclassification of the data lead to breaks in the time series between 1999 and 2000 for most products and sectors. The new survey system is more detailed and has better product coverage, especially in electricity, CHP and heat production, as well as in industry.

Coal: The first coking plant started operation in 1987, hence imports of coking coal and production of coke oven coke and coke oven gas started in that year. The increase of other bituminous coal inputs into main activity producer electricity plants from 1993 to 1994 was due to coal replacing imported electricity and hydro power. Production of gas works gas ceased in April 1994.

Combustible Renewables and Waste: There is a break in series between 1991 and 1992 for the municipal waste data. Data for biogas and industrial waste are available from 1996. Prior to 2004, industrial waste also included other energy forms such as hydrogen, heat from chemical processes, natural gas and blast furnace gas.

Oil: In 1995, there is a break in series for petroleum products trade due to the aligning of the National Board of Customs trade data collection system with the European Union's Intrastat system. Due to a new calculation model, there is a break in heavy fuel oil consumption in *other sectors* between 1998 and 1999.

Gas: Prior to 1989, natural gas consumption in the residential and agricultural sectors has been estimated by the Finnish Administration. Due to a new system of data collection, the breakdown between residential and commercial/public services is available since 1995.

Electricity and Heat: Prior to 1992, outputs from the use of combustible renewables and waste to generate electricity and/or heat are included in coal. Electricity and heat production from biogas are available from 1996. Heat output from autoproducer CHP plants is available starting in 1996 and from autoproducer heat plants starting in 2000. Heat from chemical processes used for electricity production is available from 2004. The amount of heat reported under other sources is steam from hydrogen in industrial processes. The decrease in electricity production in 2005 is mainly due to lower production from coal and peat generation which was offset by increased electricity imports from Sweden.

Consumption of heat in residential includes consumption in agriculture and commercial/public services. A breakdown of heat consumption by industry sub-sector is not available.

France

Coal: For 1989 to 1998, the Secretariat has estimated industry consumption based on *Consommations d'Energie dans l'Industrie*, SESSI.

Combustible Renewables and Waste: Plants using municipal waste were reclassified as autoproducer CHP plants from 1995, which leads to a break in time series. The breakdown of the final energy consumption of biogas was estimated by the French Administration from 1970 to 2003.

Oil: Additives and oxygenates data are available from 1991. From 1998, imported petroleum products needing further refinery processing are no longer reported as refinery feedstock imports but as oil product imports and products transferred. The consumption of kerosene type jet fuel includes military use as of 1998. Starting in 2000, data for non-ferrous metals are included in non-specified industry for petroleum coke. Ethylene produced in Lacq is not included in NGL from 2002 onwards.

Gas: From 1990 to 1998, statistical difference includes gas consumption that is not broken down by sector. From 1999 onwards, a new methodology was used for preparing the natural gas balances which leads to breaks in series between 1999 and 2000. There is a break in series for commercial/public services and residential in 2001. Gas for pipelines is included in distribution losses.

Electricity and Heat: Data on heat sold to third parties are not available prior to 1989. Electricity production from wind is available from 1993. From 1995, due to a change in the economic activity classification, data have been reported in non-specified *other sectors*. A new method of survey and a reclassification between main activity producer electricity plants and autoproducer electricity plants may cause breaks in the series for other bituminous coal between 1998 and 1999. For 2001 to 2004, there are further classification problems for inputs and output of electricity from oil. The French Administration is working to reconcile their data collection methods for the inputs and the outputs for electricity generation. Due to a new survey, in the 2007 edition the French Administration has revised the data back to 2000 and included heat produced from fossil fuels. Unfortunately it is not possible to separate out the amount of heat not sold in autoproducer CHP plants so these amounts have been included. However, no double counting occurs since the corresponding inputs have not been included in final consumption.

Non-specified *other sectors* consumption includes exports to Monaco prior to 1992.

Germany

German data include the new federal states of Germany from 1970 onwards.

Coal: Due to reclassification of several sectors by the German Administration, breaks in series may occur between 1990 and 1992; this particularly affects BKB, lignite and coke oven coke. BKB inputs to gas works plants stopped in 1997. Breaks in series may occur between 1998 and 1999 for coke oven gas and blast furnace gas.

Combustible Renewables and Waste: The German Administration started reporting near the surface geothermal energy in 1995, which leads to a break in time series with 1994, where only deep geothermal energy is reported. A new survey for renewables causes breaks in the time series between 1998 and 1999. The German Administration submitted an incomplete annual questionnaire on renewables and waste for the years 2001 and 2002. As a consequence, the Secretariat estimated the missing data based on statistics published by the Federal Environment Ministry and data submitted in the Electricity and Heat Questionnaire. Where estimation was impossible due to lack of information, the data from the previous year were used. A new reporting system leads to break in series between 2002 and 2003. The German Administration is undertaking the reconciliation of historical data. There is a large drop in the series reported for industrial waste between 2004 and 2005 because new information redistributed amounts previously reported as industrial waste into municipal waste, solid biomass and biogas.

Oil: Beginning with 1994, final consumption by individual sector has been improved due to new survey methods instituted by the Mineralölwirtschaftsverband. In 1995, a break in gas/diesel oil consumption occurs as a result of an alignment with the Classification of the Economic Activities in the European Community (NACE). Breaks in series in consumption data between 2002 and 2004 are due to structural changes in energy statistics following the newly introduced Energy Statistics Law.

Gas: Prior to 1995, inputs of natural gas for main activity producer heat are included with main activity producer CHP. Also prior to 1995, end-use consumption data are based on *Arbeitsgemeinschaft Energiebilanzen*. From 1995 onwards, the industry sector breakdown is based on the new 1995 NACE classification. This leads to a number of breaks in series between 1994 and 1995. In 2003, there is a break in series for electricity and CHP plants (both autoproducers and main activity producers). With the exception of inputs to electricity/heat generation, most of the consumption has been estimated for 2003 to 2005 by the National Administration.

Electricity and Heat: Data should be used with caution since numerous breaks in series occur between 1998 and 2005. In some instances, electricity generation from nuclear, hydro, solar and wind in autoproducer electricity plants is confidential or not available and therefore is included in main activity producer electricity plants. For 2002 and 2003, the German Administration did not submit the breakdown of electricity and heat production from combustible fuels. The data were estimated as follows: renewables and waste were taken from the Renewables and Waste Questionnaire and the other combustible fuels were estimated pro rata based on 2001 estimates. Electricity production in electricity plants includes production from CHP plants until 2003, except for electricity production from natural gas and from combustible renewables and waste in 2003. All heat production has been included in main activity producer CHP plants until 2003, except for heat production from BKB/peat briquettes, from natural gas since 2001 and from combustible renewables and waste in 2003. Due to the implementation of the Energy Statistics Act, collection concerning heat produced in heat plants and district heating plants was more efficient and more complete. This leads to breaks in series between 2002 and 2003 and between 2004 and 2005. Detailed data by fuel is not available for total heat production. The non-allocated part is reported as "other sources".

The German Federal Statistics Office reclassified some industrial branches which may cause a break in series in final consumption sub-sectors of industry between 1994 and 1995. Own use of electricity is not available for small industrial plants in 2000, which may cause a break in the time series. The breakdown of heat consumption is not available for the period 2002 to 2005. The data were estimated as follows: the transformation and distribution losses were estimated based on previous years, the heat produced by autoproducers was included in non-specified industry, and the remaining consumption included in non-specified *other sectors*.

Greece

Coal: Production of gas works gas ceased in 1997. Lignite is used in main activity producer CHP plants since 1997.

Combustible Renewables and Waste: Wood consumption in commercial/public services is included in residential. Data for biogas are available from 1990 and data for industrial waste from 1992. New information on solid biomass is available from 1996 and leads to breaks between 1995 and 1996.

Oil: Data on feedstocks for cracking in refineries are available from 1986. From 1993, a better allocation of oil used in specific industrial sectors is available. Due to changes in reporting methods, more detailed end-use information has become available starting in 1996. Crude oil production stopped in November 1998 and started again in December 1999.

Gas: Natural gas produced in Greece has an average gross calorific value of around 53 188 kJ/m^3, due to a high content of C_2/C_4 hydrocarbons. In 1997, a new pipeline between Russia and Greece became operational. In 1998, consumption in the residential sector is included with commercial/public services.

Electricity and Heat: A break in series exists between 1991 and 1992 for electricity consumption in the transport sector. Data on combustible renewables and waste are available from 1992. Production or consumption of distributed heat (heat sold) that is produced from lignite is available from 1997.

Hungary

Data are available starting in 1965.

Coal: Due to sale of an autoproducer power plant, breaks in series occur for coke oven gas and blast furnace gas between 1997 and 1998.

Combustible Renewables and Waste: Data for biogas are available from 2000.

Oil: The Hungarian Administration submitted questionnaires to the IEA for the first time with 1993 data. Data for additives and aviation gasoline are available starting from 1998.

Gas: Due to a new methodology, some breaks in series exist between 1996 and 1997. From 1997, two autoproducer heat plants have been reclassified to main activity producer heat plants. Prior to 2004, iron and steel consumption includes transformation of natural gas in blast furnaces.

Electricity and Heat: The revision of heat production data to conform to IEA reporting methodologies may result in a mismatch of fuel inputs with electricity and heat outputs by plant type, which could cause high efficiencies. There is a break in the time series in 1990 due to a reclassification of autoproducer heat plants using solid biomass. Electricity and heat production from solid biomass autoproducer CHP plants is available from 1995. Geothermal heat production from main activity producer heat plants is also available from 1995. For natural gas, there are breaks in series between 1996 and 1997 for main activity producer and autoproducer plants. The Hungarian Administration reclassified some of their plants for 1996 and 2000 which may lead to breaks in the time series.

Geothermal direct use is available from 1990. Direct use of solar thermal heat is available from 2001.

Iceland

Coal: Final consumption increased in 2000 due to a new iron and steel plant coming on-line.

Combustible Renewables and Waste: The use of municipal waste to produce heat is available from 1993.

Electricity and Heat: Electricity production from geothermal sources in main activity producer CHP plants is available from 1992. Heat production from municipal waste is available from 1993. In 1998, 60 MW of generating capacity was installed in the geothermal CHP plant at Nesjavellir. Since the plant was inoperable for four months, production of geothermal heat decreased compared to 1997. The extra electricity capacity caused electricity production from geothermal to almost double over the same period. In 2002, the increase of heat produced by geothermal was due to the installation of a third unit at the Nesjavellir CHP power plant.

Own use of electricity refers mainly to the use of electricity by the geothermal industry to pump geothermal water from underground sources. From 1991, electricity consumption in transport refers to the pumping of hot water from the geothermal station "Nesjavellir" to Reykjavik. The consumption of electricity and heat in the NATO base at Keflavik airport is reported in *other sectors.* The increase of electricity consumption in the construction sector from 2003 to 2005 is due to the drilling of tunnels for the Kárahnjúkar power plant.

Ireland

Coal: The production of gas works gas ceased in 1987 due to fuel switching to natural gas. Other bituminous coal inputs to main activity producer electricity plants increased from 1986 due to three new generating units at Moneypoint coming on-line. A reclassification causes a break in the series for own use of peat from 1989 to 1990.

Combustible Renewables and Waste: Data on solid biomass and biogas are available from 1990.

Oil: Consumption in commercial/public services includes quantities used by state-owned agricultural companies. Consumption data collected for 1993 are based on a detailed survey. Data for historical years back to 1990 were revised by the National Administration based on the results of this survey. Owing to these revisions, breaks in series exist between 1989 and 1990 in the detailed consumption data for LPG, kerosene, gas/diesel oil and heavy fuel oil.

Gas: The large increase in imports since 1996 is due to the depletion of the Kinsale gas field and the availability of a new pipeline system to the United Kingdom. The decrease in natural gas consumption in the iron and steel industry from 2001 onwards, is due to the shutdown of Ireland's main steel plant. Consumption in the chemical industry fell in 2003, due to the shutdown of a fertilizer plant. The high consumption in food, beverages and tobacco in 2003 is due to a new methodology.

Electricity and Heat: Electricity production from wind begins in 1992.

Direct use of geothermal and solar thermal heat is available from 1989 and 1990 respectively.

The decrease of electricity consumption in the iron and steel industry from 2001 onwards, is due to the fact that the main steel plant in Ireland has ceased production. The increase of electricity consumption in the rail sector from 2004 onwards is due to the Irish new light rail transit system in Dublin.

Italy

Coal: From 1986 onwards, figures from lignite are given using the same methodology as in the *Bilancio Energetico Nazionale*. In 1991, all industrial activities were reclassified on the basis of ISTAT/NACE 91. This has implied some transfers of activities which may result in some anomalies between 1991 and earlier years. Due to a change in the survey system, breaks in series may occur between 1997 and 1998 for final consumption.

Oil: Inputs to electricity and heat generation have been estimated by the Secretariat for the years 1984 to 1997 based on submissions of the Electricity and Heat Questionnaire. All other data for the years 1992 to 1997 and the detailed consumption breakdown for other years have been estimated by the Secretariat based on *Bilancio Energetico Nazionale*. Due to new surveys, breaks appear in the consumption series between 1998 and 1999. For gas/diesel oil, non-specified use is included in the commercial/public service sector.

Gas: The production of gas works gas from natural gas ceased in 1996.

Electricity and Heat: Electricity production from orimulsion is confidential and has been included with residual fuel oil. From 2000 onwards, the Italian Administration defines electricity production from autoproducers as including generation from producers consuming more than 70% of their own production. However for the 2000 to 2002 period, all electricity production from autoproducers is reported with main activity producers. The production of electricity reported in the category *other fuel sources* refers to electricity produced from the regasification of LNG or heat recovered from industrial processes. From 2000 onwards, electricity generation from synthetic gas produced in the oil tar gasification process is included under generation from oil products. Heat production is reported starting in 2004.

Japan

For the fourth consecutive year, the IEA has received revisions from the Japanese Administration. The first set of revisions received in 2004 increased the 1990 supply by 5% for coal, 2% for natural gas and 0.7% for oil compared to the previous data. This led to an increase of 2.5% in 1990 CO_2 emissions calculated using the Reference Approach while the Sectoral Approach remained fairly constant. For the 2006 edition, the IEA has received revisions to the coal and oil data which have a significant impact on both the energy data and the CO_2 emissions. The most significant revisions occurred for coke oven coke, naphtha, blast furnace gas and petroleum coke. These revisions affected consumption rather than supply in the years concerned. As a result, the sectoral approach CO_2 emissions increased for all the years, however at different rates. For example, the sectoral approach CO_2 emissions for 1990 were 4.6% higher than those calculated for the 2005 edition while the 2003 emissions were 1.1% higher than those of the previous edition. Due to the impact these successive revisions have had on the final energy balance as well as on CO_2 emissions, the IEA is in close contact with the Japanese Administration to better understand the reasons behind these changes. These changes are mainly due to the Government of Japan's efforts to improve the input-output balances in the production of oil products and coal products in response to inquiries from the UNFCCC Secretariat. To cope with this issue, the Japanese Administration established a working group in March 2004. The working group completed its work in April 2006. Many of its conclusions were already incorporated prior to this year, but some further revisions to the time series (especially in industry and *other sectors*) were submitted this year.

Starting in 1990, data are reported on a fiscal year basis (April 2005 to March 2006 for 2005).

Coal: From 1998, inputs of coke oven gas, blast furnace gas and oxygen steel furnace gas into autoproducer electricity plants include the amount used to produce electricity with TRT technology (Top pressure Recovery Turbines) which was previously included in the industry sector.

Combustible Renewables and Waste: Inputs to charcoal production have been estimated assuming an efficiency of 40%.

Oil: Orimulsion imports for electricity generation begin in 1991.

Electricity and Heat: Data for the entire time series refer to fiscal year. Electricity production in autoproducer CHP plants is included in autoproducer electricity plants. Electricity and heat produced in main activity producer CHP plants are not included in the data series. Data on heat produced for sale by autoproducer heat plants are not available. Heat production from geothermal and solar thermal sources in Japan is not reported by the Japanese Administration. Production of electricity from wind began in 1993. Prior to 1998, the electricity produced using TRT technology (Top pressure Recovery Turbines) was included with electricity generated from wood, wood waste and other solid waste. Now it is included with electricity generated from coal gases.

Korea

Data are available starting in 1971. Data for 2002 have been reported on a different basis, causing breaks in series between 2001 and 2002, especially for inputs and outputs to electricity generation and consumption in the iron and steel industry. The Korean Administration is planning to revise the historical series as time and resources permit.

Coal: Data for coal and coal products from 1971 to 2000 are based on information provided by the Korean Administration, as well as information from the *Yearbook of Energy Statistics 2001*, the *Yearbook of Coal Statistics 2000* (both from the Ministry of Commerce, Industry and Energy), and *Statistics of Electric Power in Korea 2000* (from the Korea Electric Power Corporation). Data on sub-bituminous coal were estimated by the Secretariat based on statistics of the exporting countries.

Combustible Renewables and Waste: The Korean Administration is undertaking a study to improve its energy statistics reporting from 2003 onwards. As part of this effort, the time series of industrial waste, municipal waste, primary solid biomass and biogas were revised back to 1990.

Oil: Inputs of residual fuel oil and naphtha to autoproducer electricity and autoproducer CHP are included with end-use consumption.

Gas: Consumption for machinery is included with transportation equipment.

Electricity and Heat: Electricity statistics from 1971 to 1993 have been estimated by the Secretariat based on the Korean National Statistics. Data from 1994 have been submitted by the Korean Administration. This leads to breaks in series between 1993 and 1994. Before 1994, electricity production from main activity producer CHP plants is included with main activity producer electricity only plants. Heat data are available starting in 1991. For these years, the breakdown of heat output by type of fuel has been estimated by the Secretariat. In 2001, the Korean Administration started to report heat statistics for some heat plants which were not reported before. This can lead to breaks in series between 2000 and 2001 and between 2001 and 2002. Electricity and heat production by autoproducers using natural gas and liquid fuels were reported for the first time in 2002.

Luxembourg

Coal: Steel production from blast furnaces ceased at the end of 1997. As a consequence, Luxembourg no longer uses coke oven coke and blast furnace gas.

Combustible Renewables and Waste: Data on solid biomass are available from 1992.

Gas: Residential sector consumption includes consumption in commercial and agriculture. The large increase of gas consumption in the transformation sector from 2002 onwards is due to a new 350-MW combined cycle power plant.

Electricity and Heat: Most of the hydro production shown for Luxembourg is from the Vianden pumped storage plant and is exported directly to Germany. Electricity and heat production from natural gas for autoproducer CHP plants are available starting in 1995. Electricity and heat production from biogas are available from 1999. Data for solar thermal are available starting in 1999. The increase in electricity production in 2002 is due to a new natural gas combined cycle power plant.

The iron and steel industry has stopped production of electricity at the end of 1997.

Mexico

Data are available starting in 1971 and are partly estimated based on the publication *Balance Nacional - Energía*. The Mexican Administration submitted data directly by questionnaire for the first time with 1992 data. As a result, some breaks in series may occur between 1991 and 1992.

Coal: Data for coke oven gas and blast furnace gas are reported for the first time in 1999.

Combustible Renewables and Waste: Data on biogas are available from 1998.

Oil: Inputs of oil for autoproducer electricity and heat generation have been included in industry. Because of a change in the processing of the data, breaks in series occur between 1998 and 1999.

Gas: Natural gas reported in the IEA publications may be different from what is reported in the Mexican energy publications, as IEA includes only dry gas and excludes natural gas liquids. Distribution losses have been included in own use. Beginning with 1993, data have been submitted by the "Secretaria de Energia".

Electricity and Heat: Electricity production from wind is available from 1994. Electricity output from solar photovoltaic and combustible renewables and waste are available from 1998. Starting in 1998, the CRE (Comisión Reguladora de Energia) has published new data for electricity generation by autoproducers. This may lead to breaks in the time series between 1997 and 1998. Prior to 1998, data reported in non-specified petroleum products for autoproducers include all types of combustible fuels. New autoproducer electricity plants fuelled with coal gases were put on-line in 1999. In the 2006 edition, the time series for electricity production from natural gas plants have been revised by the Mexican Administration from 1990 onwards.

Data for direct use of solar thermal are available from 1998.

Some own use of electricity is included in the industry sector where it was generated (e.g. the chemical industry, as well as in industry non-specified).

Netherlands

In the national statistical system of the Netherlands, use of fuel in manufacturing industries for CHP production is considered to be consumption in the transformation sector. However, in IEA statistics, this own use for heat production (autoproduced heat) is reported under the relevant industry sector, based on estimates provided by the Central Bureau of Statistics.

Coal: Paper, pulp and print includes furniture.

Combustible Renewables and Waste: In the 2007 edition, data on some solid biomass were reclassified into liquid biofuels back to 2002 by the Dutch Administration. Charcoal production was available from 1990.

Oil: Refinery gas includes chemical gas and is included in chemical industry consumption. Refinery gas inputs to main activity producer CHP plants begin in 1995.

Gas: From 2003 onwards, an improved method to allocate unsold steam from autoproducer CHP has been used; data are therefore not comparable with the earlier years. All heat plants were converted to CHP plants in 1990. Consumption in the commercial/public services sector includes consumption from *other sectors* starting in 1988.

Electricity and Heat: Electricity from *other sources* includes power from chemical waste gases and heat bought from other industries. Electricity production from solar photovoltaic is available from 1992. The decrease of electricity produced from nuclear in 1997 is due to the closure for five months of one nuclear power plant. Heat produced from combustible renewables is available from 1990. A new main activity producer CHP plant fuelled by refinery gas started up in 1999 and there was a fuel reclassification in 2000. In the 2007 edition, the Dutch Administration implemented a reporting methodology which causes some breaks between 2004 and 2005. Prior to 2005, all electricity and heat produced from coal, oil and natural gas are included in CHP plants.

Commercial/public services sector electricity consumption includes small users. The large increase in electricity trade in 1999 is due to the liberalisation of the Dutch electricity market. The new reporting methodology starting in 2005 causes breaks in the heat consumption series.

New Zealand

Coal: Peat, although produced in New Zealand, is not used as a fuel. It is used for agricultural purposes only. In final consumption, non-ferrous metals is included with iron and steel; wood and wood products is included with pulp, paper and print; mining and quarrying is included in agriculture, and construction is included with commercial/public services. Sub-bituminous coal inputs into blast furnaces refers to coal that is merged with iron sand to form the inputs for the multi-hearth-furnace (Glenbrook Steel Site).

Combustible Renewables and Waste: Data reported are for the fiscal year. In 1999, a re-classification of autoproducer plants leads to breaks in the time series. Final consumption of geothermal and solid biomass was revised back to 2000 by the New Zealand Administration according to a new study.

Oil: Gas/diesel oil consumption in the road sector includes use by railways. For reasons of confidentiality, beginning in 1994, the New Zealand Administration no longer reports data on the production of methanol. Liquefaction of other hydrocarbons shown as crude oil represents synthetic gasoline production from natural gas. In February 1997, production of synthetic gasoline ceased.

Gas: Main aggregates in transformation, energy, transport, industry and *other sectors* are estimated by the National Administration. In February 1997, production of synthetic gasoline from natural gas ceased. In 1998, two new autoproducer CHP plants came on-stream, accounting for the very large consumption increases in that year.

Electricity and Heat: The classifications used by the Administration of New Zealand were changed in 1991. Prior to 1994, data refer to fiscal year (April 1994 to March 1995 for 1994). From 1994, data refer to calendar year. Electricity production by autoproducers for geothermal is available from 1995.

Data on direct use of geothermal heat are available from 1990.

For electricity, distribution losses include the statistical difference. Electricity consumption in paper, pulp and printing is included in wood and wood products prior to 1991. There are breaks in series between 1996 and 1997 for electricity consumption due to a new NZ Standard Industrial Classification (NZSIC). Blast furnace gas inputs to autoproducer CHP plants refers to manufactured gases coming from multi-hearth-furnaces using iron sand during the steel making process.

Norway

Coal: The decrease of bituminous coal production in 2005 is due to a fire in one of the coal mines that entailed a break in the production for a large part of the year.

Combustible Renewables and Waste: Data for industrial waste and biogas are available from 1991. Data for liquid biofuels are confidential.

Oil: The IEA Secretariat calculates the net calorific value for Norwegian crude oil based on the petroleum product outputs of the oil refineries. Due to revisions from the Norwegian Administration, there are breaks in series between 1989 and 1990. Gas/diesel oil used in fishing is included in agriculture prior to 2000.

Gas: The large increase in own use in 1992 results from the start up of new fields. Before 2000, own use included data normally included under total final consumption. From 2002 onwards, domestic navigation is included under non-specified transport.

Electricity and Heat: Heat production from heat pumps and electric boilers (including the electricity used for this production) is available from 1989. No data on electricity production from solar energy are submitted separately to the IEA by the Norwegian Administration. However, electricity production from wind is available from 1992. Heat production from biogas is available from 1995. Breaks in series between 1996 and 1997 are due to a reclassification of main activity producers and of autoproducers. The electricity generated from waste heat, included with electricity output from coal gases in previous editions, is shown separately from 1990.

The breakdown of heat consumption by industry sub-sector was expanded in 1992, reclassified in 1994 and collected by a new reporting system in 1997. Heat produced by autoproducer heat plants from chemical processes and from other sources and used for electricity production was estimated by the Secretariat for the period 1990 to 2005.

Poland

Combustible Renewables and Waste: Data for biogas refer only to the gas from fermentation of biomass. Due to data availability, there is a large increase in solid biomass between 1992 and 1993. Some changes in the data collection process lead to breaks between 1996 and 1997. Before 2000, industrial wastes were used interchangeably with light fuel oil in some plants, which might result in breaks in the time series. Data on liquid biofuels are available starting in 2003.

Oil: Petroleum coke data are available from 2003 onwards.

Gas: The inputs of gas in the transformation sector have been inferred by the Polish Administration and for some years may be out of line with historical data. Gas used in oil refineries includes natural gas used for hydrogen manufacture in catalytic reforming processes. Prior to 2000, natural gas used in pipeline transport was partly included in own use.

Electricity and Heat: The Polish Administration adopted new methods to estimate the production of heat sold in autoproducer heat plants (1993) and in autoproducer CHP plants (1995). This causes breaks between 1992 and 1993, and between 1994 and 1995 for heat production and fuel inputs in these plants and for heat consumption in industry sub-sectors.

Data for direct use of geothermal become available in 2000.

Own use of heat includes process heat not sold before 1995.

Portugal

Coal: Since 1998, sub-bituminous coal is not used. The iron and steel industry closed in the first quarter of 2001, leading to decreases in supply and consumption of coking coal, coke oven coke, coke oven gas and blast furnace gas.

Combustible Renewables and Waste: Data are available from 1994 for biogas, from 1999 for municipal waste and from 2003 for industrial waste. Solid biomass consumption in the residential sector includes the non-commercial part of solid biomass consumed in households. Data for solid biomass were revised by the National Administration from 1990 to 2001, which may result in breaks in series between 1989 and 1990.

Oil: As of 1995, there is no longer any production and consumption of refinery gas. Consumption of gas/diesel oil in industry and commercial/public services represents diesel use in the mobile fleets of these sectors.

Gas: Portugal started to import natural gas in February 1997. The decrease in natural gas used for gas works in 2001 is due to the closing of the Lisbon gas works plant in May 2001.

Electricity and Heat: To conform to IEA methodology, heat produced from combustible renewables and waste (mainly black liquor) and from coal gases in autoproducer CHP plants is not accounted for since it is not sold, while the electricity produced in these plants is included. New plants fuelled by solid biomass and by municipal waste started in 1999.

Data on direct use of solar thermal and geothermal heat are available from 1989 and 1994 respectively.

Slovak Republic

Data are available starting in 1971. There are some breaks in series between 1992 and 1993. A new survey system in 2001 leads to major breaks in series for most products.

Combustible Renewables and Waste: Municipal waste, biogas and liquid biofuels data become available in 2001. The Slovak Republic is experiencing difficulties in determining the correct end-use classifications for the various elements of combustible renewables and waste. This results in consumption appearing in a given sector for only one year and then being reclassified in the next year. The Slovak Republic is planning to revise the time series.

Oil: For gas/diesel oil, road data include rail use.

Gas: Consumption in *other transformation* between 1994 and 2004 is mainly natural gas used as a feedstock in refineries to make LPG.

Electricity and Heat: Electricity and heat production from combustible fuels from 1990 to 2000 have been estimated based on the data on fuel used for electricity and heat plants reported in the annual fuel questionnaires.

Direct use of geothermal is available from 2001.

Spain

Coal: Other bituminous coal use in the iron and steel industry ceases in 1991 and starts again in 1996. Consumption of BKB also ends in 1991. Consumption of blast furnace gas in the chemical industry stopped in 1993 while chemical industry use of coke oven gas stopped between 1993 and 2000. Natural gas inputs into gas works gas stopped in 1999.

Combustible Renewables and Waste: A new reporting system leads to breaks in final consumption sectors between 1999 and 2000. In 2000, many plants are reclassified from main activity producer to autoproducer or vice versa.

Oil: A change in the reporting system in mid-1996 has resulted in some breaks in series.

Gas: The increase of natural gas used as feedstock starting in 1988 reflects a substitution of naphthas for the production of fertilisers. There is a break in series between 1993 and 1994 in autoproducer CHP consumption, since a new survey revealed a larger number of CHP autoproducers that had previously been included in industry consumption. The large increase in main activity producer electricity consumption in 1997 is due to two main activity producer electricity producers running on natural gas in 1997. From 2001 onwards, the end-use consumption breakdown is estimated by the National Administration.

Electricity and Heat: Production and consumption of heat sold are available from 1989. The large increase in electricity output from main activity producer electricity plants fuelled by natural gas in 1997 is due to the opening of a new plant. Due to a change in the data collection system, heat sold is available only until 1999.

Data on direct use of solar thermal and geothermal heat are available from 1994.

Sweden

Coal: Other bituminous coal production is coal recovered during the quarrying of clay. Autoproducer inputs to waste heat production that is sold are reported in the respective end-use sectors and not in the transformation sector.

Combustible Renewables and Waste: Data for biogas begin in 1992. Transformation data for industrial waste are not available prior to 1998. Heat production from solid biomass in autoproducer CHP includes waste heat and chemical heat.

Oil: Beginning in 1995, Sweden has changed its standard classification of industry sectors. Data are available from 2000 for additives, from 2001 for ethane and from 2003 for refinery gas.

Gas: Prior to 1993, road transport is included in commercial/public services.

Electricity and Heat: In Sweden, heat produced in heat pumps is sold to third parties (as district heat) and is therefore included in transformation. Inputs to heat pumps include heat recovered from industry and from ambient sources (including sewage and seawater). Ambient heat is shown as the indigenous production of heat. The electricity used to drive heat pumps is considered to be transformed and appears as output in the transformation sector rather than own use of electricity. Fuel inputs to the heat that is recovered by the heat pump are reported in the appropriate industry sub-sector (i.e. chemical and paper, pulp and printing). Information on heat for sale produced in heat pumps and electric boilers is available starting in 1992. Heat produced for sale by autoproducer heat plants is reported starting in 1992. However, the associated inputs are included in industry consumption. Heat production from liquid fuels in main activity producer CHP plants includes heat recovered from flue-gas condensing for 1997 and 1998.

Industry consumption of the heat produced by heat pumps has been estimated by the Secretariat based on fuel inputs submitted by the Swedish Administration (2/3 in paper, pulp and printing and 1/3 in chemical). There are breaks in series for heat consumption between 1991 and 1992.

Switzerland

From 1999, data on consumption result from a new survey and are not comparable with data of previous years.

Coal: From 1985, industrial consumption of gas works gas is reported in non-specified industry to prevent the disclosure of commercially confidential data.

Combustible Renewables and Waste: Before 1998, only net imports are reported for solid biomass. In the 2007 edition, the Swiss Administration revised time series of solid biomass and industrial waste in the transformation sector back to 1990.

Oil: As of 1993, the Swiss Administration has reported figures for naphtha that are net of quantities used for blending into motor gasoline. For 1994, 1995, 1997, 1999, 2001 and 2002 this reporting has led to negative production numbers for naphtha. For these years, the IEA Secretariat has moved the data into transfers and reduced the production of motor gasoline by corresponding amounts. Petroleum coke production started in 2004 due to the installation of a cracking unit in a refinery.

Gas: The breakdown of the industry sector was estimated by the Secretariat for 2000 and by the National Administration for 2001 to 2005.

Electricity and Heat: Heat production includes heat produced by nuclear power stations and distributed to other consumers. Solar electricity production by autoproducers is available from 1990. Electricity production from wind and pumped storage by autoproducers is available from 1996. In the 2007 edition, the Swiss Administration revised the times series for electricity and heat production from solid biomass, industrial waste and natural gas from 1990 to 2005.

Direct use of geothermal and solar thermal heat is available from 1990.

Electricity consumption in the transport equipment industry is included with machinery.

Turkey

Coal: Production of gas works gas declined in 1989 due to plant closures; the last plant closed in 1994. Use of gas coke and gas works gas ceased in 1994. Due to government regulations in the industry and residential sectors in particular, there has been a shift from the use of domestically produced coal to imported coal and natural gas.

Combustible Renewables and Waste: The Turkish Administration only surveys renewables and waste used for power and heat intermittently. Due to this fact, some breaks may appear in the combustible renewables and waste series.

Gas: Data for commercial/public services were included in the residential sector prior to 2001. The decrease in natural gas consumption in petrochemical feedstocks between 1999 and 2001 is related to the fertiliser industry.

Electricity and Heat: Data on electricity generated from combustible renewables and waste are available from 1991. In 1995, the Turkish Administration reclassified autoproducer plants by type and source to be consistent with IEA definitions. This causes breaks between 1994 and 1995 for electricity production in these plants. Electricity production from wind is available starting in 1998. In the 2006 edition, the Turkish Statistical Office provided electricity and heat output on the basis of a new survey that revised time series back to 2000. This causes breaks in the time series between 1999 and 2000. Not all of the input series have been revised.

Consumption in the industry sub-sector machinery includes transport equipment. Prior to 1998, consumption in the wood and wood products sub-sector includes that of the paper, pulp and printing industry.

United Kingdom

Coal: Consumption shown for the commercial/public services sector includes consumption of some of the non-specified sector. Prior to 1994, the consumption of substitute natural gas is included with natural gas while its production is included with gas works gas. Due to reclassifications, there are breaks in the series between 1998 and 1999 and between 2000 and 2001 for blast furnace gas.

Oil: Prior to 1995, the product breakdown for transfers is estimated by the U.K. Administration. Beginning with 1995, the U.K. Administration revised their product breakdown for transfers and petrochemical reporting methodology. Breaks in series for LPG occur between 2000 and 2001 due to a re-allocation of data. Heavy fuel oil inputs to heat production are available starting in 2000.

Gas: From 1992 onwards, distribution losses include metering differences and losses due to pipeline leakage. The consumption of natural gas in the commercial sector is included with non-specified *other sectors* while the public services sector is shown separately. Natural gas consumption includes substitute natural gas made at gas works and piped into the natural gas distribution system. Data in the non-specified industry sub-sector refer to sales by independent gas suppliers unallocated by category. The natural gas used to form synthetic coke oven gas is reported under non-specified transformation.

Electricity and Heat: The reorganisation and subsequent privatisation of the electricity supply industry in 1990 has resulted in some breaks in series. Inputs and output from natural gas for main activity producer electricity production are included in autoproducer electricity for 1990 (for reasons of confidentiality). For the United Kingdom, it is necessary to combine figures for main activity producers and autoproducers in order to prevent the disclosure of information relating to less than three electricity generating companies, since this information is considered confidential. For this reason data for main activity producer CHP plants have been included with autoproducer CHP plants from 1988. Prior to 1988, electricity output from CHP plants was included with main activity producer electricity plants. In 1996, the break in electricity production from nuclear is due to a reclassification of plants from autoproducer to main activity producer plants. Electricity production from solar is available from 1999. Heat output is available starting in 1999.

Electricity consumption in coal mines includes consumption in patent fuel plants. Consumption in gas works includes electricity use in the transmission/ distribution of public supply gas. Consumption in the non-metallic mineral products sub-sector includes mining and quarrying. Starting in 1990, small amounts of electricity used in heat pumps have been included in the residential sector.

United States

Due to problems in reporting, there are numerous breaks in series for the U.S. data, particularly in 1992, 1999, 2001 and 2002. Care should be taken when evaluating consumption by sector since inputs of fuel to autoproducers are included in final consumption for some years.

Combustible Renewables and Waste: The Energy Information Administration collects generation and consumption data from all plants 1 MW or more in capacity. Solar thermal electricity production includes generation from natural gas because natural gas units are attached to solar thermal plants and production cannot be separated.

Oil: International marine bunkers of heavy fuel oil show a large increase in 1990 due to a change in the data collection and reporting methodology of the U.S. Administration. From 1992 onwards, the individual components of NGL and LPG have been converted using their respective gravities rather than an average gravity, resulting in a break in series. In 1993, the U.S. Administration made several adjustments to its collection system for oil statistics in order to accommodate the revisions to the Clean Air Act of 1990. As a result, data for oxygenates (i.e. fuel ethanol, MTBE, etc.) were collected in 1993 and reported in the additives category, or in the case of ethanol, in biogasoline. Beginning in 1994, motor gasoline consumption in commercial/public services is based on a new model from the U.S. Department of Transportation. High statistical differences for crude oil represent "unaccounted for crude oil", the difference between the supply and disposition of crude oil. From 1995, LPG inputs to gas works are included in the industry sector. As a result of the new Manufacturing Energy Consumption Survey (MECS), there are breaks in series between 1999 and 2000 for the industry sector, and again between 2000 and 2001 as the MECS percentages were revised due to revisions in electric cogeneration. There were significant revisions to residual fuel oil and unfinished oils for 2001 data. Primarily, the changes are a result of importers misclassifying unfinished oils as residual fuel oil. For 2002 to 2004, the Secretariat has estimated the amounts of refinery gas for electricity production, which includes gases with a low average calorific value.

Gas: The amounts of gas works gas that are blended with natural gas have been estimated from 1990 to 2002 on the basis of the output efficiency of the process. With the exception of petrochemical feedstocks, other non-energy use of natural gas is included in industry prior to 2003.

Electricity and Heat: There are breaks in series concerning the total production of electricity and heat in the United States. Comprehensive data on electricity and heat production and consumption in main activity producer electricity, CHP and heat plants and autoproducer electricity and CHP plants are not available for all years. The selling of main activity producer plants to autoproducers may cause breaks in the series between 1998 and 2000. For the United States, prior to 2000, autoproducers include small and independent power producers, which under IEA definitions are considered main activity producers. In the 2003 edition, the U.S. Administration changed what it was reporting under autoproducers. This reclassification causes more breaks between 1999 and 2000. For 2002, autoproducer electricity output for oil includes generation from refinery gases with a low average calorific value. Prior to 2002, this output was not accounted for.

Data for electricity absorbed by pumping and electricity production from pumped storage plants became available starting in 1987. A new survey for electricity consumption may cause a break in the time series for 2003 and 2004, especially in the industry, transport, commercial and residential sectors. The consumption of heat sold in the industry sector is available from 1991 and own use of heat from 1992. Prior to 1991, total consumption of heat sold referred to consumption in the commercial/public services sector. No data are available for heat sold that is consumed in the residential and agriculture sectors.

Direct use of solar thermal in residential is available from 1999.

4. GEOGRAPHICAL COVERAGE

Australia excludes the overseas territories.

Denmark excludes Greenland and the Danish Faroes, except prior to 1990, where data on oil for Greenland were included with the Danish statistics. The Administration is planning to revise the series back to 1974 to exclude these amounts.

France includes Monaco, and excludes the following overseas departments and territories (Guadeloupe, Guyana, Martinique, New Caledonia, French Polynesia, Reunion, and St.-Pierre and Miquelon).

Germany includes the new federal states of Germany from 1970 onwards.

Italy includes San Marino and the Vatican.

Japan includes Okinawa.

The **Netherlands** excludes Suriname and the Netherlands Antilles.

Portugal includes the Azores and Madeira.

Spain includes the Canary Islands.

Switzerland does not include Liechtenstein.

United States includes the 50 states and the District of Columbia. Oil statistics as well as coal trade statistics also include Puerto Rico, Guam, the Virgin Islands, American Samoa, Johnston Atoll, Midway Islands, Wake Island and the Northern Mariana Islands.

The **International Energy Agency**[5] **(IEA)** includes Australia, Austria, Belgium, Canada, the Czech Republic, Denmark, Finland, France, Germany, Greece, Hungary, Ireland, Italy, Japan, Korea, Luxembourg, the Netherlands, New Zealand, Norway, Portugal, Spain, Sweden, Switzerland, Turkey, the United Kingdom and the United States.

The **Organisation for Economic Co-Operation and Development (OECD)** includes Australia, Austria, Belgium, Canada, the Czech Republic, Denmark, Finland, France, Germany, Greece, Hungary, Iceland, Ireland, Italy, Japan, Korea, Luxembourg, Mexico, the Netherlands, New Zealand, Norway, Poland, Portugal, the Slovak Republic, Spain, Sweden, Switzerland, Turkey, the United Kingdom and the United States.

OECD North America includes Canada, Mexico and the United States.

OECD Pacific includes Australia, Japan, Korea and New Zealand.

OECD Europe includes Austria, Belgium, the Czech Republic, Denmark, Finland, France, Germany, Greece, Hungary, Iceland, Ireland, Italy, Luxembourg, the Netherlands, Norway, Poland, Portugal, the Slovak Republic, Spain, Sweden, Switzerland, Turkey and the United Kingdom.

5. Poland and the Slovak Republic are expected to become Member countries of the IEA in 2007.

1. NOTES EXPLICATIVES

Unité

La méthodologie employée par l'AIE pour établir les bilans énergétiques repose sur le pouvoir calorifique des produits énergétiques et sur une unité commune. Cette unité adoptée par l'AIE est la tonne d'équivalent pétrole (tep) définie comme étant égale à 10^7 kilocalories (41,868 gigajoules). Cette quantité d'énergie est équivalente, à quelques points de pourcentage près, au pouvoir calorifique inférieur d'une tonne de pétrole brut. Tout au long de cette publication, une tonne signifie une tonne métrique, soit 1000 kg.

Conversion (des unités d'origine en tep)

La conversion de l'unité d'origine en tonnes d'équivalent pétrole suppose le choix de coefficients d'équivalence entre les différentes formes et sources d'énergie. Il existe de nombreuses solutions à ce problème. On pourrait notamment adopter une seule équivalence pour chaque grande source d'énergie primaire dans tous les pays, par exemple 29 307 kJ/kg (7 000 kcal/kg) pour la houille, 41 868 kJ/kg (10 000 kcal/kg) pour le pétrole, etc. La principale objection que l'on peut opposer à cette méthode est qu'elle aboutit à des distorsions, car il existe de grandes différences entre les pouvoirs calorifiques des diverses catégories de charbon et de produits dérivés du charbon, ainsi qu'entre les pouvoirs calorifiques de ces combustibles selon les pays. Le Secrétariat a donc adopté les coefficients spécifiques communiqués par les administrations nationales pour les principales catégories de chaque qualité de charbon et pour chaque flux ou utilisation (c'est-à-dire la production, les importations, les exportations, la production d'électricité, les cokeries, les hauts fourneaux et l'industrie). Dans le cas du pétrole brut, les coefficients spécifiques utilisés pour la production, les importations et les exportations ont fait l'objet de consultations avec les experts des administrations nationales, alors que les coefficients de conversion utilisés pour les produits pétroliers sont les mêmes pour tous les pays. Les données relatives au gaz figurant dans la publication *Statistiques de l'énergie des pays de l'OCDE* sont exprimées en térajoules et fondées sur **le pouvoir calorifique supérieur**. Les données concernant les énergies renouvelables combustibles et les déchets sont fournies en térajoules et fondées sur **le pouvoir calorifique inférieur**. Voir également la section 2, Unités et coefficients de conversion.

Les bilans sont exprimés en pouvoir calorifique inférieur (PCI). Pour chaque combustible, la différence entre le pouvoir calorifique inférieur et le pouvoir calorifique supérieur correspond à la chaleur latente de vaporisation de la vapeur d'eau produite pendant la combustion. Pour le charbon et le pétrole, le pouvoir calorifique inférieur représente environ 5 % de moins que le pouvoir calorifique supérieur et, pour la plupart des types de gaz naturel ou manufacturé, la différence est de 9 - 10 %, tandis que, pour l'électricité et la chaleur, il n'y a pas de différence, la notion correspondante n'ayant alors aucune signification. L'emploi du pouvoir calorifique inférieur est conforme à la pratique des Bureaux de statistiques des Communautés Européennes et des Nations Unies.

Les données relatives à l'électricité sont fournies initialement en gigawattheures et sont converties en millions de tonnes d'équivalent pétrole au moyen de la relation suivante : 1 térawattheure = 0,086 Mtep.

Conventions sur l'énergie primaire

La construction d'un bilan énergétique nécessite l'adoption de conventions sur l'énergie primaire relatives à plusieurs sources d'énergie, et notamment à l'énergie nucléaire, géothermique, solaire, hydraulique, éolienne, etc. Les deux types d'hypothèses qui doivent être posées sont décrites ci-après :

Le choix de la forme d'énergie primaire

Pour chacune des sources d'énergie, il convient de définir la forme d'énergie primaire à prendre en compte; par exemple dans le cas de l'énergie hydraulique, le choix doit être fait entre l'énergie cinétique de la chute d'eau et l'électricité produite. Dans le cas de l'énergie nucléaire, le choix est entre le contenu énergétique du combustible nucléaire, la chaleur produite dans les réacteurs et l'électricité produite. Dans le cas de l'électricité photovoltaïque, le choix est entre le rayonnement solaire capté et l'électricité produite.

Le principe adopté par l'AIE est que la forme d'énergie primaire à prendre en compte doit être la première forme d'énergie rencontrée au cours du processus de production pour laquelle il existe plusieurs usages énergétiques possibles. L'application de ce principe conduit au choix des formes d'énergie primaire suivantes :

- la **chaleur** pour le nucléaire, la géothermie et le solaire thermique,
- l'**électricité** pour l'hydraulique, l'éolien, l'énergie des marées, des vagues ou des courants marins, ainsi que pour la photovoltaïque.

Le calcul du contenu en énergie primaire

Il existe essentiellement deux méthodes de calcul du contenu en énergie primaire des sources d'énergie citées plus haut : la méthode de la substitution partielle et celle du contenu énergétique.

La méthode de la substitution partielle : Dans cette méthode, l'équivalent énergétique primaire des sources de production d'électricité susmentionnées est représenté par la quantité d'énergie qui serait nécessaire pour produire la même quantité d'électricité dans une centrale thermique classique. L'équivalent énergétique primaire est calculé sur la base du rendement de conversion moyen de ce type de centrales. Parmi les limitations inhérentes à cette méthode, il convient de citer la difficulté de choisir un rendement de conversion approprié et l'inadaptation de cette méthode dite de la substitution partielle aux pays dont la production d'électricité provient pour une large part de l'hydraulique. Pour ces raisons, l'AIE, à l'instar de la plupart des organisations internationales, n'utilise plus cette méthode et a adopté celle du contenu énergétique.

La méthode du contenu énergétique : Cette méthode utilise comme coefficient d'équivalence énergétique primaire le contenu énergétique de la source d'énergie primaire considérée. En conséquence, il existe une relation évidente entre les principes adoptés pour définir les formes primaires des sources d'énergie considérées et l'équivalent énergétique primaire de ces sources.

Par exemple, dans le cas de la production électronucléaire, la chaleur étant la forme primaire d'énergie retenue par l'AIE, l'équivalent énergétique primaire est la quantité de chaleur produite dans les réacteurs. Néanmoins, comme on ne connaît pas toujours la quantité de chaleur ainsi produite, l'AIE estime l'équivalent énergétique primaire à la production d'électricité en tablant sur un rendement de conversion de 33 %, qui représente la moyenne pour les centrales nucléaires en Europe.

Dans le cas de l'hydroélectricité et l'énergie photovoltaïque, étant donné que la forme primaire d'énergie retenue est l'électricité, l'équivalent énergétique primaire est le contenu énergétique de l'électricité produite à la centrale, ce qui revient à prendre pour hypothèse un rendement de conversion de 100 %. Une présentation plus détaillée des hypothèses utilisées par l'AIE pour la construction de ces bilans énergétiques est donnée en section 2.

Pour l'énergie d'origine géothermique (si aucune information spécifique pour un pays n'est disponible), l'énergie primaire est calculée de la manière suivante :

- 10 % pour l'électricité géothermique ;
- 50 % pour la chaleur géothermique.

En raison des différences significatives de traitement de l'électricité d'origine solaire, hydraulique, éolienne, etc. dans ces deux types de bilans énergétiques, la part des énergies renouvelables dans le total des approvisionnements en énergie différera sensiblement selon la méthode utilisée. Il est par conséquent essentiel de connaître les conventions qui sous-tendent le calcul des bilans énergétiques primaires pour analyser la répartition en pourcentages des diverses sources d'énergie dans l'approvisionnement total.

Indicateurs

Production énergétique : la production énergétique primaire totale, exprimée en Mtep.

Importations nettes : les importations moins les exportations pour l'énergie totale, exprimées en Mtep.

Approvisionnements totaux en énergie primaire : exprimés en Mtep.

Importations nettes de pétrole : les importations moins les exportations de pétrole, exprimées en Mtep.

Approvisionnement de pétrole : l'approvisionnement primaire de pétrole, exprimé en Mtep.

Consommation d'électricité : consommation nationale, c'est-à-dire la production brute + les importations - les exportations - les pertes de distribution, exprimée en TWh.

Population : Ce sont les *Comptes nationaux des pays de l'OCDE, Volume 1*, 2007 qui constituent la source principale de ces séries de 1970 à 2005. Les données pour la période de 1960 à 1969 ont été estimées à partir des taux de croissance des séries de population publiées dans les *Perspectives économiques de l'OCDE No 76*. Pour la **République tchèque**, la **Hongrie** et la **Pologne** (1960 à 1969) et le **Mexique** (1960 à 1962), les données ont été estimées à partir du taux de croissance des séries de population de la Banque mondiale publiées dans le *World Development Indicators CD-ROM*. Pour la **République Slovaque**, les données de population de 1960 à 1989 proviennent du Centre de recherche démographique, Infostat, République slovaque.

PIB : Ce sont les *Comptes nationaux des pays de l'OCDE, Volume 1*, 2007 qui constituent la source principale de ces séries de 1970 à 2005. Les données du PIB pour la période de 1960 à 1969 ont été estimées à partir des taux de croissance des séries publiées dans les *Perspectives économiques de l'OCDE No 76* et des données publiées précédemment par l'OCDE. Les données antérieures à 1990 pour la **République tchèque** et la **Pologne**, antérieures à 1991 pour la **Hongrie**, et antérieures à 1992 pour la **République slovaque** ont été estimées par le Secrétariat de l'AIE à partir des taux de croissance du PIB de la Banque Mondiale.

A l'automne 2006, la **Grèce** a effectué une révision complète de ses comptes nationaux pour les années 2000 à 2005. Cela a entraîné une augmentation de 25.7 % du PIB pour l'année 2000, mais n'a pas eu un effet important sur les taux de croissance. Ces révisions sont dues à l'amélioration des méthodes d'estimation ainsi qu'à la révision des sources de données. Les données avant 2000 ont été calculées en reliant les séries précédentes avec les séries révisées.

Les données relatives au PIB ont été calculées pour chaque pays aux prix du marché en monnaie nationale et compte tenu des taux annuels. Ces données ont ensuite été recalées par rapport aux niveaux des prix de 2000, puis converties en dollars des Etats-Unis en utilisant les taux de change annuels moyens de 2000 ou les parités de pouvoir d'achat (PPA).

Les parités de pouvoir d'achat représentent les taux de conversion monétaire qui égalisent les pouvoirs d'achat des différentes monnaies. Ainsi, une somme donnée, une fois convertie en différentes unités monétaires en appliquant les taux de PPA, permet d'acheter le même panier de biens et de services dans tous les pays. En d'autres termes, les PPA sont les taux de conversion monétaire qui permettent d'éliminer les différences dans les niveaux de prix entre pays. Les PPA retenues pour convertir en dollars des Etats-Unis le PIB exprimé en unités monétaires nationales sont agrégées selon la méthode de Geary-Kharies (GK) et recalées sur les Etats-Unis. Pour une description plus détaillée de cette méthode, il convient de se référer au document suivant : *Parités de pouvoir d'achat et dépenses réelles, Résultats GK, Volume II, 1990, OCDE 1993.*

Indice de production industrielle : C'est la publication de l'OCDE intitulée *Indicateurs des activités industrielles*, 2007 qui constitue la source principale de ces séries de données. La production industrielle désigne les biens produits par les établissements qui se consacrent à des activités extractives (y compris l'extraction de pétrole), à des activités manufacturières, et à la production d'électricité, de gaz et d'eau. Ceci correspond aux catégories C, D et E de la CITI[1] Rév. 3.

Présentation

Les bilans énergétiques sont présentés sous forme de tableaux avec, en colonnes, les diverses sources d'énergie, et en lignes, les différentes origines et utilisations.

1. Classification internationale type par industries de toutes les branches d'activité économique, Série M, N° 4 / Rév. 3, Nations Unies, New York, 1990.

Colonnes

En haut du tableau, et de gauche à droite, on trouve onze colonnes avec les titres suivants :

Colonne 1 : *Charbon* - Comprend tous les charbons (y compris la houille et le lignite) et les produits dérivés (y compris les agglomérés, le coke de cokerie, le coke de gaz, les briquettes de lignite, le gaz de cokerie, le gaz de haut fourneau et le gaz de convertisseur à oxygène ou gaz LD). La tourbe entre également dans cette catégorie.

Colonne 2 : *Pétrole brut* - Comprend le pétrole brut, les liquides de gaz naturel (LGN), les produits d'alimentation des raffineries et les additifs ainsi que les autres hydrocarbures (y compris les huiles émulsionnées, le pétrole brut synthétique, les huiles minérales extraites des roches bitumineuses telles que schistes, sables asphaltiques, etc. ainsi que les huiles issues de la liquéfaction du charbon).

Colonne 3 : *Produits pétroliers* - Comprennent les gaz de raffinerie, l'éthane, les gaz de pétrole liquéfiés (GPL), l'essence aviation, l'essence moteur, les carburéacteurs, le kérosène, le gazole/carburant diesel, le fioul lourd, les naphtas, le white spirit, les lubrifiants, le bitume, les paraffines, le coke de pétrole et autres produits pétroliers.

Colonne 4 : *Gaz* - Comprend le gaz naturel (à l'exception des LGN) et le gaz d'usine à gaz. Ce dernier est comptabilisé dans le tableau, affecté d'un signe positif, à la ligne "usines à gaz", mais il n'entre pas dans la production.

Colonne 5 : *Nucléaire* - Indique le contenu énergétique primaire de l'électricité produite par les centrales nucléaires, sur la base d'un rendement de conversion moyen de 33 %.

Colonne 6 : *Hydraulique* - Indique le contenu énergétique de l'électricité produite par les centrales hydroélectriques. La production hydraulique *ne comprend pas* la production des centrales à accumulation par pompage (également appelées centrale de pompage).

Colonne 7 : *Géothermique, solaire, etc.* - Indique la production d'énergies géothermique, solaire et éolienne ainsi que d'énergie des marées, des vagues ou des courants marins, de même que l'utilisation de ces formes d'énergie pour produire de l'électricité et de la chaleur. Sauf dans les cas où le rendement de conversion effectif du procédé géothermique est connu, la quantité d'énergie géothermique employée pour la production d'électricité est estimée en fonction de la production d'électricité des centrales géothermiques, en tablant sur l'hypothèse d'un rendement de conversion moyen de 10 %. Pour les énergies solaire, éolienne, ainsi que des marées/vagues/courants marins, les quantités utilisées pour la production d'électricité sont égales à celles d'énergie électrique produite. Les autres consommations dans cette colonne représentent la chaleur géothermique et solaire thermique.

Colonne 8 : *Energies renouvelables combustibles et déchets* - Comprend la biomasse solide, le biogaz et les liquides tirés de la biomasse, les déchets industriels ainsi que les déchets urbains et assimilés. La biomasse est, par définition, toute matière végétale utilisée directement comme combustible, ou bien transformée en combustibles (par exemple charbon de bois) ou en électricité et/ou chaleur. Cette définition recouvre le bois, les résidus végétaux (y compris les déchets de bois et les cultures destinées à la production d'énergie), l'éthanol, les matières/déchets d'origine animale et les lessives sulfitiques (également désignées par le terme "liqueur noire" : il s'agit de la liqueur alcaline issue des digesteurs lors de la production de pâte au sulfate ou à la soude dans la fabrication de la pâte à papier, dont le contenu énergétique provient de la lignine extraite de la pâte chimique, généralement solide à 65-70 % sous forme concentrée). Les déchets urbains et assimilés correspondent aux déchets des secteurs résidentiel, commercial et des services publics, collectés par les autorités municipales pour élimination dans une installation centralisée et pour la production de chaleur et/ou d'électricité. Les déchets hospitaliers entrent dans cette catégorie.

Les données figurant sous ce titre sont souvent fondées sur des informations incomplètes. Ainsi, elles ne fournissent qu'une indication générale des évolutions et ne sont pas strictement comparables d'un pays à l'autre. Dans certains cas, des catégories entières de combustibles végétaux sont omises faute d'information. Il est donc conseillé de consulter les données par pays lors de l'utilisation des agrégats régionaux.

Colonne 9 : *Electricité* - Indique la consommation finale et les échanges d'électricité (calculés sur la base du même pouvoir calorifique que l'électricité à la consommation finale, à savoir 1 GWh = 0,000086 Mtep).

Colonne 10 : *Chaleur* - Indique les quantités de chaleur produites pour la vente. La majeure partie de la chaleur figurant dans cette colonne provient de la combustion de combustibles, encore que de faibles quantités soient produites par des pompes à chaleur et des chaudières électriques. La chaleur extraite de l'air ambiant par les pompes à chaleur entre dans la production.

Colonne 11 : *Total* = total des colonnes 1 à 10.

Lignes

Les catégories figurant sur la partie gauche du tableau sont utilisées de la manière suivante :

Ligne 1 : La ligne *Production* concerne la production d'énergie primaire, autrement dit houille, lignite, tourbe, pétrole brut, LGN, gaz naturel, énergies renouvelables combustibles et déchets, énergies nucléaire, hydraulique, géothermique et solaire, ainsi que la chaleur extraite du milieu ambiant par les pompes à chaleur. La production est calculée après élimination des impuretés (par exemple, élimination du soufre contenu dans le gaz naturel). Le mode de calcul de la production d'énergie hydraulique, géothermique, etc., et de la production électronucléaire est expliqué dans la section 2, Unités et coefficients de conversion.

Lignes 2 et 3 : *Importations* et *exportations* représentent les quantités ayant franchi les limites territoriales du pays, que le dédouanement ait été effectué ou non.

Pour le charbon : Les importations et exportations comprennent les quantités de combustibles obtenues d'autres pays ou fournies à d'autres pays, qu'il existe ou non une union économique ou douanière entre les pays en question. Le charbon en transit ne devrait pas être pris en compte.

Pour le pétrole et le gaz : Cette rubrique comprend les quantités de pétrole brut et de produits pétroliers importées ou exportées au titre d'accords de traitement (à savoir, raffinage à façon). Les quantités de pétrole en transit ne sont pas prises en compte. Le pétrole brut, les LGN et le gaz naturel sont indiqués comme provenant de leur pays d'origine. Pour les produits d'alimentation des raffineries et les produits pétroliers, en revanche, c'est le dernier pays de provenance qui est pris en compte. Les réexportations de pétrole importé pour raffinage en zone franche sont comptabilisées comme des exportations de produits raffinés du pays où le traitement est effectué vers leur destination finale.

Pour l'électricité : Les quantités sont considérées comme importées ou exportées lorsqu'elles ont franchi les limites territoriales du pays. Si l'électricité transite par un pays, les quantités concernées sont prises en compte à la fois dans les importations et les exportations.

Ligne 4 : Les *soutes maritimes internationales* correspondent aux quantités fournies aux navires engagés dans la navigation internationale. La navigation internationale peut intervenir en mer, sur des lacs et des cours d'eau, ainsi que dans les eaux côtières. La consommation des navires engagés dans la navigation intérieure n'est pas prise en compte. La différenciation entre navigation intérieure et internationale est fonction du port de départ et du port d'arrivée, et non du pavillon ou de la nationalité du navire. La consommation des navires de pêche et des forces militaires n'est pas prise en compte non plus. Voir les définitions des secteurs de la *navigation intérieure* (ligne 40), de la *pêche* (ligne 46) et des *« autres secteurs » non spécifiés* (ligne 47).

Ligne 5 : La rubrique intitulée *variations des stocks* exprime la différence enregistrée entre le premier jour et le dernier jour de l'année dans le niveau des stocks détenus sur le territoire national par les producteurs, les importateurs, les entreprises de transformation de l'énergie et les gros consommateurs. Une augmentation des stocks est indiquée par un chiffre affecté d'un signe négatif, tandis qu'une diminution apparaît sous la forme d'un chiffre positif.

Ligne 6 : *Les approvisionnements totaux en énergie primaire* (*ATEP*) correspondent à la *production* (ligne 1) + *importations* (ligne 2) - *exportations* (ligne 3) - *soutes maritimes internationales* (ligne 4) ± *variations des stocks* (ligne 5).

Ligne 7 : Les *transferts* couvrent aussi bien le passage d'un produit d'une catégorie à une autre, le transfert matériel d'un produit et les produits recyclés (par exemple, les lubrifiants usés qui sont retraités).

Ligne 8 : Les *écarts statistiques* correspondent à la somme des écarts statistiques inexpliqués pour les différents combustibles, tels qu'ils apparaissent dans les statistiques de base de l'énergie. Cette rubrique comprend également les écarts statistiques qui proviennent de l'utilisation de coefficients de conversion différents dans les colonnes du charbon et du pétrole. Pour plus de détails, se reporter à l'introduction du document intitulé *Statistiques de l'énergie des pays de l'OCDE.*

Ligne 9 : Cette rubrique intitulée *centrales électriques* désigne les centrales conçues pour produire uniquement de l'électricité. Si la centrale compte une unité ou plus de cogénération (et que l'on ne peut pas comptabiliser séparément, sur une base unitaire, les combustibles utilisés et la production), elle est considérée comme une centrale de cogénération. Tant les centrales (auparavant qualifiées de publiques) dont la production concernée constitue l'activité principale[2] que les installations des autoproducteurs[3] entrent dans cette rubrique. Les colonnes 1 à 8 indiquent les quantités de combustibles primaires et secondaires utilisés pour la production d'électricité, les chiffres correspondants étant affectés d'un signe négatif. La chaleur de procédés chimiques utilisée pour la génération de l'électricité est indiquée dans la colonne 10. La production brute d'électricité (qui tient compte de la consommation propre des centrales) figure dans la colonne de l'électricité, affectée d'un signe positif. Les pertes de transformation sont indiquées dans la colonne du total, et sont affectées d'un signe négatif.

Ligne 10 : La rubrique *centrales de cogénération chaleur/électricité* désigne les centrales conçues pour produire de la chaleur et de l'électricité, parfois appelées centrales de production combinée. Dans la mesure du possible, les consommations de combustibles et les productions de chaleur/électricité doivent être exprimées sur la base des unités plutôt que des centrales. Cependant, à défaut de données disponibles exprimées sur une base unitaire, il convient d'adopter la convention indiquée ci-dessus pour la définition d'une centrale de cogénération. Tant les centrales des producteurs dont la production est l'activité principale (auparavant, centrales publiques) que les installations des autoproducteurs entrent dans cette rubrique. *On notera que, dans le cas des installations de cogénération chaleur/électricité des autoproducteurs, sont comptabilisés tous les combustibles utilisés pour la production d'électricité, tandis que seule la partie des combustibles utilisés pour la production de chaleur* ***vendue*** *est indiquée. Les combustibles utilisés pour la production de la chaleur destinée à la consommation interne des autoproducteurs* ***ne sont pas*** *comptabilisés dans cette rubrique mais dans les données concernant la consommation finale de combustibles du secteur de consommation approprié.*

Les colonnes 1 à 8 indiquent les quantités de combustibles primaires et secondaires utilisés pour la production d'électricité et de chaleur ; ces chiffres sont affectés d'un signe négatif. La production brute d'électricité figure dans la colonne de l'électricité, affectée d'un signe positif, et la production de chaleur apparaît dans la colonne de la chaleur, également affectée d'un signe positif. Les pertes de transformation sont indiquées dans la colonne du total, affectées d'un signe négatif.

Ligne 11 : La rubrique *centrales calogènes* désigne les installations (pompes à chaleur et chaudières électriques comprises) conçues pour produire uniquement de la chaleur et qui en vendent à des tiers selon les termes d'un contrat. Cette rubrique comprend aussi bien les centrales des producteurs dont la production est l'activité principale (auparavant, centrales publiques) que les installations des autoproducteurs. Les pompes à chaleur utilisées dans le secteur résidentiel qui ne donnent pas lieu à des ventes de chaleur ne sont pas considérées comme étant une activité de transformation et ne sont pas comptabilisées dans cette rubrique – la consommation d'électricité figurera en tant que consommation résidentielle.

Les colonnes 1 à 8 indiquent les quantités de combustibles primaires et secondaires utilisés par les systèmes de chauffage qui transportent la chaleur, produite à partir d'une ou de plusieurs sources d'énergie, et qui la distribuent à des consommateurs résidentiels, industriels et commerciaux, entre autres, pour le chauffage des locaux, la cuisson des aliments, la production d'eau chaude et les procédés industriels.

Ligne 12 : La production des *usines à gaz* est traitée de la même manière que la production d'électricité : les quantités produites apparaissent affectées d'un signe positif dans la colonne du gaz naturel, les quantités utilisées figurent, affectées d'un signe négatif, dans les colonnes du charbon, des produits pétroliers et du gaz naturel, et les pertes de transformation apparaissent dans la colonne du total.

Ligne 13 : La ligne *raffineries de pétrole* indique les quantités d'énergie primaire utilisées dans les raffineries pour l'élaboration de produits pétroliers finis et la production de produits pétroliers. Le total tient compte des pertes de transformation. Dans certains

---

2. Les producteurs dont la production est l'activité principale (auparavant appelés entreprises de service public) produisent de l'électricité et/ou de la chaleur pour la vente à des tiers. Elles peuvent appartenir au secteur privé ou public. Il convient de noter que les ventes ne se font pas nécessairement par l'intermédiaire du réseau public.

3. L'autoproduction désigne les installations qui produisent de l'électricité et/ou de la chaleur, en totalité ou en partie pour leur consommation propre, en tant qu'activité qui contribue à leur activité principale. Elles peuvent appartenir au secteur privé ou public.

cas, les données dans la colonne total sont des nombres positifs. Cela peut être dû soit à des incohérences du bilan primaire de raffinage, soit au fait que l'AIE utilise des pouvoirs calorifiques inférieurs normalisés pour les produits pétroliers.

Ligne 14 : La *transformation du charbon* comprend les pertes liées à la transformation du charbon pour passer du combustible primaire à un combustible secondaire et d'un combustible secondaire à un combustible tertiaire (transformation de la houille en coke, du coke en gaz de haut fourneau, du lignite en briquettes de lignite, etc.). Il est souvent difficile de prendre en compte correctement l'ensemble des entrées et des sorties des industries de transformation de l'énergie, et de faire la distinction entre énergie transformée et énergie brûlée. Par conséquent, dans certains cas, les données dans la colonne du total sont des chiffres positifs, ce qui laisse supposer qu'il existe un problème dans les données.

Ligne 15 : La ligne *unités de liquéfaction* comprend divers procédés de liquéfaction, notamment ceux qui sont mis en œuvre dans les usines de liquéfaction du charbon et dans les installations de conversion de gaz en hydrocarbures liquides (GTL).

Ligne 16 : La ligne *autres transformations* comprend les transformations non spécifiées ailleurs, telles que la transformation de la biomasse solide en charbon de bois et le mélange d'autres gaz avec le gaz naturel. Elle comprend aussi les retours de l'industrie pétrochimique. Il convient de noter que les retours en raffinerie des produits pétroliers utilisés à des fins non énergétiques (notamment, white spirit et lubrifiants) ne sont pas inclus sous cette rubrique, mais sous celle des utilisations non énergétiques.

Ligne 17 : La ligne *consommation propre* indique la consommation d'énergie primaire et secondaire des industries de transformation pour le chauffage, le pompage, la traction et l'éclairage [Divisions 10-12, 23 et 40 de la CITI[4]], ces chiffres étant affectés d'un signe négatif. Cette rubrique comprend, par exemple, la consommation propre d'énergie des mines de charbon, celle des centrales électriques (y compris la quantité nette d'électricité consommée par les centrales de pompage) et l'énergie employée pour l'extraction du pétrole et du gaz.

4. Classification internationale type par industries de toutes les branches d'activité économique, Série M, N° 4 / Rév. 3, Nations Unies, New York, 1990.

Ligne 18 : Les *pertes de distribution et de transport* comprennent les pertes dans la distribution du gaz ainsi que les pertes dans le transport de l'électricité et du charbon.

Ligne 19 : La ligne *consommation finale totale (CFT)* donne la somme des consommations des différents secteurs d'utilisation finale. Les retours de l'industrie pétrochimique ne sont pas comptabilisés dans la consommation finale (voir ligne 16, *autres transformations* et ligne 50, *dont* : *produits d'alimentation de l'industrie pétrochimique*).

Lignes 20 à 33 : La consommation du *secteur industrie* est répartie entre les sous-secteurs suivants (l'énergie utilisée par l'industrie pour les transports n'est pas prise en compte ici mais figure dans la rubrique transports) :

Industrie sidérurgique [Groupe 271 et Classe 2731 de la CITI] ;

Industrie chimique et pétrochimique [Division 24 de la CITI] à l'exclusion des produits d'alimentation de la pétrochimie. *Avant l'année dernière, les produits d'alimentation de l'industrie pétrochimique étaient comptabilisés avec la consommation d'énergie du secteur industrie :depuis l'année dernière, ils le sont avec les utilisations non énergétiques* ;

Industries de base des *métaux non ferreux* [Groupe 272 et Classe 2732 de la CITI] ;

Produits minéraux non métalliques tels que verre, céramiques, ciment, etc. [Division 26 de la CITI] ;

Matériel de transport [Divisions 34 et 35 de la CITI] ;

Construction mécanique. Ouvrages en métaux, machines et matériels autres que le matériel de transport [Divisions 28 à 32 de la CITI] ;

Industries extractives (à l'exclusion de l'extraction de combustibles) [Divisions 13 et 14 de la CITI] ;

Industrie alimentaire et tabacs [Divisions 15 et 16 de la CITI] ;

Papier, pâte à papier et imprimerie [Divisions 21 et 22 de la CITI] ;

Bois et produits dérivés (sauf pâtes et papiers) [Division 20 de la CITI] ;

Construction [Division 45 de la CITI] ;

Textiles et cuir [Division 17 à 19 de la CITI] ;

Non spécifiés (tout autre secteur industriel non spécifié précédemment) [Division 25, 33, 36 et 37 de la CITI].

Note : La plupart des pays éprouvent des difficultés à fournir une ventilation par branche d'activité pour tous les combustibles. Dans ces cas, la rubrique *non spécifiés* a été utilisée. *Les agrégats régionaux de la consommation industrielle doivent donc être employés avec précaution.*

Lignes 34 à 41 : Le secteur *transports* regroupe tous les carburants utilisés pour les transports, à l'exception des soutes maritimes internationales [Divisions 60 à 62 de la CITI]. Il englobe les transports dans le secteur industriel et couvre *l'aviation internationale, l'aviation intérieure, le transport routier, le transport ferroviaire, le transport par conduites, la navigation intérieure* et les *transports non spécifiés*. L'aviation intérieure recouvre les livraisons de carburants aviation pour les aéronefs utilisés dans l'aviation intérieure - commerciale, privée, agricole, etc. Elle comprend également les quantités utilisées à des fins autres que le vol proprement dit, par exemple, l'essai de moteurs au banc, mais non le carburant utilisé par les compagnies aériennes pour le transport routier. La différenciation entre aviation intérieure et internationale devrait être établie en fonction des aéroports de départ et d'arrivée, et non de la nationalité de la compagnie aérienne. On notera qu'il peut entrer dans cette rubrique des parcours d'une longueur considérable entre deux aéroports d'un même pays (par exemple de San Francisco à Honolulu). Pour nombre de pays, la ventilation entre aviation internationale et aviation intérieure impute, à tort, à l'aviation intérieure la consommation de carburants pour les vols intérieurs et internationaux des transporteurs nationaux. Le carburant utilisé pour les pêches hauturière, côtière et continentale (prise en compte dans le secteur de la pêche) ainsi que pour des activités militaires (prise en compte dans *autres secteurs non spécifiés*) sont exclus du secteur transports.

Lignes 42 à 47 : La rubrique *autres secteurs* couvre les secteurs *résidentiel, commercial et services publics* [Divisions 41, 50-52, 55, 63-67, 70-75, 80, 85, 90-93, 95 et 99 de la CITI], de l'*agriculture/sylviculture* [Divisions 01 et 02 de la CITI], de la *pêche* [Division 05 de la CITI], ainsi que les *consommations non spécifiées*. Il est comptabilisé dans *consommations non spécifiées* la consommation de combustibles ou carburants dans les activités militaires, qu'il s'agisse d'usages mobiles ou stationnaires (par exemple navires, aéronefs, véhicules routiers, énergie consommée dans les quartiers), que les combustibles ou carburants fournis soient destinés à des usages militaires du pays même ou d'un autre pays. Dans bien des cas, les administrations n'arrivent pas à faire la ventilation de la consommation d'énergie entre le secteur *commercial/services publics* et le secteur *résidentiel*. D'autres administrations ne peuvent pas ventiler les consommations des secteurs *agriculture* et *résidentiel*. Dans ces cas, le secteur *résidentiel* comprend également la consommation dans l'agriculture et/ou celle du secteur commercial/services publics. Le total de la ligne *autres secteurs* est donc plus exact que les éléments qui le composent.

Lignes 48 à 52 : La rubrique *utilisations non énergétiques* regroupe la consommation des *autres produits pétroliers* comme le white spirit, les paraffines, les lubrifiants, le bitume et divers autres produits. Elle recouvre également les utilisations non énergétiques du charbon (à l'exclusion de la tourbe). Ces produits sont indiqués à part, dans la consommation finale sous la rubrique des utilisations non énergétiques. Il est supposé que l'usage de ces produits est strictement non énergétique. Le coke de pétrole fait exception à cette règle et ne figure sous la rubrique *utilisations non énergétiques* que si cette utilisation est prouvée ; dans le cas contraire, ce produit est comptabilisé à la rubrique des utilisations énergétiques dans l'*industrie* ou dans d'*autres secteurs*.

dont : produits d'alimentation de l'industrie pétrochimique. L'industrie pétrochimique comprend les opérations de craquage et de reformage destinées à la production de l'éthylène, du propylène, du butylène, des gaz de synthèse, des aromatiques, du butadiène et d'autres matières premières à base d'hydrocarbures dans les procédés mis en œuvre, par exemple, pour le vapocraquage, dans les installations d'élaboration d'aromatiques et pour le reformage à la vapeur [partie du Groupe 241 de la CITI]. *Avant l'année dernière, les produits d'alimentation de l'industrie pétrochimique étaient comptabilisés avec la consommation d'énergie du secteur industrie : depuis l'année dernière ils le sont avec les utilisations non énergétiques.*

Lignes 53 à 55 : La rubrique *électricité produite* indique le nombre total de TWh produits par les centrales thermiques, ventilées entre centrales électriques et installations de cogénération, ainsi que la production des centrales nucléaires, hydroélectriques (à l'exclusion des centrales à accumulation par pompage), géothermiques, etc. (voir cependant les notes relatives aux lignes 9 et 10). L'électricité produite à partir de chaleur de procédés chimiques est indiquée à la colonne *chaleur*.

Lignes 56 à 58 : La rubrique *chaleur produite* indique le nombre total de PJ produits dans les centrales, avec une distinction faite entre centrales de cogénération et centrales calogènes. La chaleur produite au moyen de chaudières électriques est comptabilisée à la colonne *électricité*. La chaleur obtenue au moyen de pompes à chaleur, de procédés chimiques ainsi que la chaleur produite à partir de combustibles non spécifiés figure à la colonne *chaleur*.

2. UNITES ET COEFFICIENTS DE CONVERSION

Coefficients de conversion généraux pour l'énergie

Vers :	TJ	Gcal	Mtep	MBtu	GWh
De :	multiplier par :				
TJ	1	238,8	$2{,}388 \times 10^{-5}$	947,8	0,2778
Gcal	$4{,}1868 \times 10^{-3}$	1	10^{-7}	3,968	$1{,}163 \times 10^{-3}$
Mtep	$4{,}1868 \times 10^{4}$	10^{7}	1	$3{,}968 \times 10^{7}$	11630
MBtu	$1{,}0551 \times 10^{-3}$	0,252	$2{,}52 \times 10^{-8}$	1	$2{,}931 \times 10^{-4}$
GWh	3,6	860	$8{,}6 \times 10^{-5}$	3412	1

Coefficients de conversion pour les mesures de masse

Vers :	kg	t	lt	st	lb
De :	multiplier par :				
kilogramme (kg)	1	0,001	$9{,}84 \times 10^{-4}$	$1{,}102 \times 10^{-3}$	2,2046
tonne (t)	1000	1	0,984	1,1023	2204,6
tonne longue (lt)	1016	1,016	1	1,120	2240,0
tonne courte (st)	907,2	0,9072	0,893	1	2000,0
livre (lb)	0,454	$4{,}54 \times 10^{-4}$	$4{,}46 \times 10^{-4}$	$5{,}0 \times 10^{-4}$	1

Coefficients de conversion pour les mesures de volume

Vers :	gal U.S.	gal U.K.	bbl	ft^3	l	m^3
De :	multiplier par :					
Gallon U.S. (gal)	1	0,8327	0,02381	0,1337	3,785	0,0038
Gallon U.K. (gal)	1,201	1	0,02859	0,1605	4,546	0,0045
Baril (bbl)	42,0	34,97	1	5,615	159,0	0,159
Pied cube (ft^3)	7,48	6,229	0,1781	1	28,3	0,0283
Litre (l)	0,2642	0,220	0,0063	0,0353	1	0,001
Mètre cube (m^3)	264,2	220,0	6,289	35,3147	1000,0	1

Préfixes décimaux

10^1	déca (da)	10^{-1}	déci (d)
10^2	hecto (h)	10^{-2}	centi (c)
10^3	kilo (k)	10^{-3}	milli (m)
10^6	méga (M)	10^{-6}	micro (µ)
10^9	giga (G)	10^{-9}	nano (n)
10^{12}	téra (T)	10^{-12}	pico (p)
10^{15}	péta (P)	10^{-15}	femto (f)
10^{18}	exa (E)	10^{-18}	atto (a)

Gaz

Dans les *Statistiques de l'énergie des pays de l'OCDE*, les gaz indiqués ci-après sont toujours comptabilisés en térajoules et le pouvoir calorifique utilisé est le pouvoir calorifique supérieur (PCS).

1 térajoule = 0,00002388 Mtep.

Pour convertir le pouvoir calorifique supérieur (PCS) d'un gaz en pouvoir calorifique inférieur (PCI), il convient de multiplier le PCS par le coefficient indiqué dans le tableau ci-dessous.

Gaz	Ratio PCI / PCS
Gaz naturel	0,9
Gaz d'usine à gaz	0,9
Gaz de cokerie	0,9
Gaz de haut-fourneau	1,0
Gaz de convertisseur à l'oxygène	1,0

Electricité

Les données relatives à la production, aux échanges et à la consommation finale d'électricité sont calculées en fonction du contenu énergétique de l'électricité, (c'est-à-dire selon le coefficient suivant : 1 TWh = 0,086 Mtep). Pour la production hydroélectrique (production des centrales à accumulation par pompage non comprise) et l'électricité produite par d'autres moyens non thermiques (énergie éolienne, énergie des marées/vagues/courants marins, photovoltaïque, etc.), le même coefficient s'applique. Cependant, le contenu en énergie primaire de l'électricité d'origine nucléaire est calculé à partir de la production brute, compte tenu d'un coefficient hypothétique de rendement de conversion des installations de 33 %. En d'autres termes, 1 TWh = (0,086 ÷ 0,33) Mtep. Dans le cas de l'électricité produite à partir de chaleur géothermique, si le rendement de conversion effectif de l'énergie géothermique n'est pas connu, l'équivalent primaire pris pour hypothèse est de 10 %, soit 1 TWh = (0,086 ÷ 0,1) Mtep.

Pétrole brut

Dans le calcul des bilans, ce sont les pouvoirs calorifiques inférieurs (PCI) spécifiques par pays qui s'appliquent pour la production, les importations et les exportations. La valeur moyenne est utilisée pour convertir en pouvoir calorifique tous les autres flux. Les pouvoirs calorifiques inférieurs spécifiques par pays pour les années 2004 et 2005 sont indiqués dans la deuxième partie.

Produits pétroliers

Les coefficients de conversion suivants sont utilisés pour tous les pays et toutes les années (tep/tonne).

Produit	tep par tonne
Gaz de raffinerie	1,150
Ethane	1,130
GPL	1,130
Naphta	1,075
Essence aviation	1,070
Essence moteur	1,070
Carburéacteur type essence	1,070
Carburéacteur type kérosène	1,065
Autre kérosène	1,045
Gazole/carburant diesel	1,035
Fioul lourd	0,960
Coke de pétrole	0,740
Autres produits	0,960

Charbon

Les pouvoirs calorifiques inférieurs utilisés pour le charbon diffèrent selon qu'il s'agit de la production, des importations, des exportations, de l'alimentation des centrales des producteurs pour lesquels la production d'électricité constitue l'activité principale, ou du charbon employé dans les fours à coke, les hauts fourneaux et l'industrie. Pour tous les autres flux, la conversion est effectuée en utilisant un pouvoir calorifique inférieur (PCI) moyen. Les pouvoirs calorifiques inférieurs spécifiques par pays pour les années 2004 et 2005 sont indiqués dans la deuxième partie.

Energies renouvelables combustibles et déchets

Le pouvoir calorifique de la biomasse solide primaire, du biogaz, des déchets urbains et assimilés ainsi que des déchets industriels, exprimé en térajoules sur la base du pouvoir calorifique inférieur, est présenté dans les *Statistiques de l'énergie des pays de l'OCDE.* Le Secrétariat ne reçoit pas de données sur les volumes et les autres caractéristiques de ces combustibles.

1 térajoule = 0,00002388 Mtep.

Les données sur le charbon de bois exprimées en tonnes sont converties en appliquant les valeurs du pouvoir calorifique inférieur indiquées dans la deuxième partie.

Les données sur la biomasse liquide exprimées en tonnes sont converties en appliquant un coefficient de 0.65 tep par tonne, à moins que les pays n'aient communiqué des précisions à cet égard.

Chaleur

Les données sur la chaleur sont exprimées en térajoules et 1 térajoule = 0,00002388 Mtep.

Pour la chaleur géothermique, les entrées effectives de chaleur doivent être rapportées dans le secteur de la transformation. Si aucune information n'est disponible, alors une efficacité de 50% est supposée.

Exemples

Les exemples ci-après montrent comment calculer le pouvoir calorifique inférieur (en Mtep) des quantités exprimées en unités d'origine dans les *Statistiques de l'énergie des pays de l'OCDE, 2004-2005.*

A partir des unités d'origines	En Mtep (PCI)
Production de charbon à coke (Pologne) pour 2005 en milliers de tonnes	multiplier par 0,0007070
Gaz naturel en térajoules (PCS)	multiplier par 0,00002149
Essence moteur en milliers de tonnes	multiplier par 0,0010700
Chaleur en térajoules (PCI)	multiplier par 0,00002388

3. NOTES RELATIVES AUX DIFFERENTS PAYS

Notes générales

Les notes qui suivent renvoient aux données des années 1960 à 2005 et concernent les tableaux récapitulatifs figurant à la fin de cet ouvrage, ainsi que les données sur CD-ROM et le service de données sur Internet. En général, des notes plus détaillées accompagnent les données à partir de 1990.

S'agissant des données des années antérieures à 1974, la consommation de combustibles et la production d'électricité et de chaleur des autoproducteurs sont comptabilisées, dans la plupart des cas, avec celles des producteurs dont cette production constitue l'activité principale. Les données sur les quantités de combustibles utilisés pour la production d'électricité et de chaleur, et sur les productions correspondantes dans les centrales de cogénération chaleur/électricité et les centrales calogènes, devraient être utilisées avec précaution. Malgré les estimations établies par le Secrétariat, les données sur la consommation et la production ne sont pas toujours compatibles. Le lecteur est invité à se reporter aux notes figurant ci-dessous, sous le titre *Electricité et chaleur*.

En 1996, le Secrétariat a procédé à une révision très détaillée des données sur l'utilisation de charbon et de coke dans les hauts fourneaux et dans l'industrie sidérurgique (dans les pays disposant de hauts fourneaux), sur la base des données fournies par le Comité de l'acier de l'OCDE et d'autres sources. Les quantités de combustibles transformés en gaz de haut fourneau ont été estimées par le Secrétariat à l'aide du modèle de l'AIE relatif au fonctionnement des hauts fourneaux.

De plus, en 1996 et 1997, le Secrétariat a considérablement revu les données sur les énergies renouvelables combustibles et les déchets (c'est-à-dire biomasse solide, biogaz, biomasse liquide, déchets industriels et déchets urbains et assimilés) à partir de données d'EUROSTAT (pour les 15 Etats membres de l'UE) et d'autres sources nationales pour les autres pays membres de l'OCDE. Comme les données sur la consommation d'énergies renouvelables combustibles et de déchets fournies par EUROSTAT sont généralement disponibles à compter de 1989, il peut apparaître des ruptures de séries entre 1988 et 1989 pour certains Etats membres de l'UE.

En décembre 1999, le groupe de travail sur les statistiques de l'énergie — auquel participent l'Agence internationale de l'énergie, l'Organisation des Nations Unies, la Commission économique pour l'Europe des Nations Unies, EUROSTAT et les représentants des administrations de leurs pays membres respectifs — a décidé d'élaborer un questionnaire annuel distinct sur les énergies renouvelables et les déchets afin d'améliorer la qualité des informations soumises par les administrations nationales. L'utilisation de ce nouveau questionnaire risque de donner lieu à des ruptures de séries chronologiques de données sur les énergies renouvelables et les déchets entre 1997 et 1998 tant que les bureaux de statistiques nationaux n'auront pas été à même de réviser leurs séries de données. Afin d'améliorer la qualité des statistiques sur les énergies renouvelables et les déchets et d'assurer la compatibilité des données, l'AIE a lancé en 2002 un projet qui a pour objectif de comparer et d'harmoniser les données rétrospectives de l'AIE avec celles des administrations nationales et/ou d'EUROSTAT, lorsqu'il y a lieu.

Allemagne

Les données relatives à l'Allemagne tiennent compte des nouveaux Länder à partir de 1970.

Charbon : L'administration allemande ayant modifié la classification de plusieurs branches, il se peut que des ruptures de série apparaissent entre 1990 et 1992, notamment pour les BKB, le lignite et le coke de cokerie. Les briquettes de lignite ne sont plus utilisées dans les usines à gaz depuis 1997. Il peut apparaître des ruptures de séries entre 1998 et 1999 en ce qui concerne le coke de cokerie et le gaz de haut fourneau.

Energies renouvelables combustibles et déchets : L'administration allemande a commencé à notifier des données sur la géothermie des nappes phréatiques à faible profondeur en 1995, ce qui entraîne une rupture de la série chronologique par rapport à 1994, année où seule la géothermie des aquifères profonds est prise en compte. L'emploi d'une nouvelle méthode d'enquête pour les énergies renouvelables est à l'origine des ruptures de séries entre 1998 et 1999. L'administration allemande a soumis des réponses incomplètes au questionnaire annuel sur les énergies renouvelables et les déchets pour les années 2001 et 2002. En conséquence, le Secrétariat a estimé les données qui faisaient défaut sur la base des statistiques publiées par le Ministère fédéral de l'Environnement et des données communiquées dans le questionnaire sur l'électricité et la chaleur. Les données de l'année précédente ont été utilisées lorsque l'estimation était impossible pour cause d'informations insuffisantes. L'utilisation d'un nouveau système de notification entraîne des ruptures de séries entre 2002 et 2003. L'administration allemande entreprend actuellement le réajustement des données chronologiques. La série de données communiquées sur les déchets industriels se caractérise par une forte baisse entre 2004 et 2005, qui s'explique parce que de nouvelles informations ont amené à redistribuer les quantités précédemment indiquées à la rubrique des déchets industriels entre les déchets urbains et assimilés, la biomasse solide et le biogaz.

Pétrole : A partir de 1994, les données sur la consommation finale de chaque secteur sont de meilleure qualité, le Minerölwirtschaftsverband ayant instauré de nouvelles méthodes d'enquête. En 1995, il s'est produit une rupture dans la série de données sur la consommation de gazole/carburant diesel parce que la classification a été alignée sur celle de la Nomenclature statistique des activités économiques dans la Communauté Européenne (NACE). Les ruptures de séries dans les données sur la consommation qui se produisent entre 2002 et 2004 s'expliquent par des modifications structurelles des statistiques de l'énergie qui font suite à l'adoption récente de la loi sur les statistiques énergétiques.

Gaz : Avant 1995, les quantités de gaz naturel consommées pour produire de la chaleur dans les centrales calogènes dont cette production constituait l'activité principale sont regroupées avec la consommation pour la cogénération chez les producteurs pour lesquels cette production combinée représentait l'activité principale. Avant 1995 également, les données sur la consommation finale sont fondées sur le bilan énergétique *Arbeitsgemeinschaft Energiebilanzen*. A partir de 1995, la ventilation du secteur industriel repose sur la nouvelle classification de la NACE de 1995. Il en découle un certain nombre de ruptures de séries entre 1994 et 1995. En 2003, on constate une rupture des séries concernant les centrales électriques et les installations de cogénération (s'agissant des autoproducteurs et des producteurs dont c'est l'activité principale). A l'exception des quantités consommées pour produire de l'électricité et/ou de la chaleur, les données sur la consommation ont, pour la plupart, été estimées par l'administration fédérale pour les années 2003 à 2005.

Electricité et chaleur : Il convient d'utiliser les données avec prudence, car de nombreuses ruptures de séries apparaissent entre 1998 et 2005. Dans certains cas, les données concernant la production d'électricité d'origine nucléaire, hydraulique, solaire et éolienne dans les installations de production d'électricité des autoproducteurs sont confidentielles ou non disponibles ; c'est pourquoi elles sont regroupées dans la rubrique des centrales électriques des producteurs dont c'est l'activité principale. Pour les années 2002 et 2003, l'administration allemande n'a pas communiqué la ventilation des données sur la production de chaleur et d'électricité à partir de différentes formes d'énergie combustibles. Les estimations ont alors été effectuées comme suit : les données sur les énergies renouvelables et les déchets sont reprises du questionnaire les concernant et les données sur les autres combustibles ont été estimées au prorata à partir des estimations de 2001. Les données sur la production d'électricité des centrales électriques tiennent compte de la production des installations de cogénération jusqu'en 2003, sauf pour ce qui est de la production d'électricité à partir de gaz naturel ainsi que d'énergies renouvelables combustibles et de déchets en 2003. La totalité de la production de chaleur a été comptabilisée avec celle des installations de cogénération de producteurs dont c'est l'activité principale jusqu'en 2003, sauf en ce qui concerne la production de chaleur à partir de briquettes de lignite ou de tourbe, à partir de gaz naturel depuis 2001 et à partir d'énergies renouvelables combustibles et de déchets en 2003. En raison de l'application de la loi sur les statistiques de l'énergie, la collecte de données sur la chaleur produite dans les centrales calogènes et dans celles de chauffage urbain a été plus efficace et plus complète. Il en résulte des ruptures de séries entre 2002 et 2003 ainsi qu'entre 2004 et 2005. Des données ventilées par combustible ne sont pas disponibles pour la production totale de chaleur. La fraction non affectée est indiquée à la rubrique « autres sources ».

L'Office fédéral des statistiques a modifié la classification de certaines branches d'activité industrielle, ce qui peut entraîner des ruptures de série dans les sous-secteurs de consommation finale de l'industrie entre 1994 et 1995. On ne dispose pas de données sur la consommation propre d'électricité des petites installations industrielles en 2000, ce qui peut donner lieu à des ruptures de séries. La ventilation de la consommation de chaleur n'est pas disponible pour la période 2002 à 2005. Les données ont été estimées de la façon suivante : les pertes de transformation et de distribution sont calculées sur la base de celles des années précédentes, la chaleur produite par les autoproducteurs est comptabilisée avec l'industrie non spécifiés, et le reste de la consommation est comptabilisé à la rubrique *autres secteurs* non spécifiés.

Australie

Toutes les données correspondent à l'exercice budgétaire, qui va de juillet 2004 à juin 2005 pour l'année 2005. En ce qui concerne les données de l'année 2002, l'administration australienne a commencé à utiliser une nouvelle méthode d'enquête qui entraîne des changements dans la structure de la consommation de l'industrie. L'administration australienne procède actuellement aux préparatifs pour la révision des séries chronologiques.

Charbon : On dispose de données sur la consommation de gaz de haut fourneau pour la production d'électricité par les autoproducteurs à partir de 1986. La consommation dans le secteur du bois et de produits dérivés est comptabilisée à la rubrique papier, pâte à papier et imprimerie à partir de 2001. La baisse de la production de briquettes de lignite observée en 2004 est la conséquence d'un incendie survenu dans la principale usine de fabrication de ces briquettes.

Energies renouvelables combustibles et déchets : Pour les énergies renouvelables combustibles et les déchets, on dispose d'une ventilation différente de la consommation de l'industrie à partir de 1996, qui entraîne des ruptures de séries. On manque de données sur la production de biogaz dans les stations d'épuration des eaux usées. Les quantités de biomasse solide utilisées dans les installations de cogénération des autoproducteurs sont des estimations du Secrétariat jusqu'en 1999.

Pétrole : Les pertes en raffinerie, affectées d'un signe négatif, proviennent de différences de traitement des transferts entre raffineries. Les importations de fioul lourd ont été estimées par l'administration australienne. Avant 1992, une partie de la production de LGN était comptabilisée avec le pétrole brut. La baisse de la production de pétrole brut en 1999 s'explique par l'explosion de gaz survenue à l'usine de Longford. Il se produit une rupture des séries concernant le pétrole brut et les LGN entre 2001 et 2002.

Gaz : Avant 1991, les données sur le gaz naturel comprennent l'éthane. Les données pour 1999 et 2000 sont des estimations de l'administration australienne. A partir de 2002, la production intérieure comprend le grisou.

Electricité et chaleur : Les données sur la consommation et la production des installations de cogénération des autoproducteurs ne sont pas disponibles pour les années antérieures à 1986. A partir de 1992 et jusqu'en 2001, la ventilation de la production d'électricité par combustible dans les installations de cogénération des autoproducteurs a été estimée par le Secrétariat. On dispose de données sur la production d'électricité d'origine éolienne à partir de 1994 et sur celle d'origine solaire à compter de 1999. Avant 1995, la production d'électricité à partir de biogaz figure à la rubrique gaz naturel. En 2002, l'administration australienne a commencé à utiliser une nouvelle méthode d'enquête et modifié la classification des types d'installations, en distinguant les producteurs dont la production concernée constitue l'activité principale des autoproducteurs.

Avant 2002, les quantités de pétrole et de gaz utilisées par les autoproducteurs pour la cogénération sont comptabilisées avec la consommation de l'industrie.

Autriche

Par suite des révisions de données chronologiques effectuées par l'administration autrichienne, il se produit des ruptures de séries entre 1989 et 1990.

Charbon : La quantité de gaz d'usine à gaz est négligeable et principalement consommée par les ménages. Aucune production de lignite n'est indiquée en 2005 parce que la dernière mine a été fermée au deuxième trimestre de 2004.

Energies renouvelables combustibles et déchets : Les données de 1986 à 1989 pour les énergies renouvelables combustibles et les déchets sont des estimations du Secrétariat fondées sur les informations publiées par l'OSTAT dans *Ennergieversongung Österreichs Endgültige Energiebilanz.* En raison d'un changement de méthode d'enquête, la chaleur produite dans les petites installations (d'une puissance inférieure à 1 MW) n'est pas notifiée à partir de 2002.

Gaz : La rupture de série entre 1995 et 1996 concernant les données sur les installations de production d'électricité et de cogénération des autoproducteurs s'explique parce que, à partir de 1996, on dispose de données plus détaillées. Les différences de mesure sont prises en compte dans les pertes de distribution avant 2000 et dans l'écart statistique à partir de 2000.

Electricité et chaleur : A partir de 1990, les faibles quantités d'électricité utilisées pour actionner les pompes à chaleur ont été comptabilisées avec la consommation du secteur résidentiel. Des ruptures de série se produisent entre 1995 et 1996, ainsi qu'entre 1998 et 1999, en raison de l'application de nouvelles méthodes d'enquête.

En ce qui concerne la chaleur, la consommation propre est comptabilisée avec les pertes de distribution. La consommation de l'industrie sidérurgique comprend la consommation des fours à coke. Avant 1990, la consommation du secteur commercial/services publics comprend l'énergie électrique utilisée dans le secteur de l'électricité, pour le chauffage urbain et pour la distribution d'eau.

Belgique

Charbon : La production d'autres charbons bitumineux a cessé le 31 août 1992. La production comprend le charbon récupéré des terrils. L'utilisation de gaz de cokerie dans le secteur des produits chimiques et de la pétrochimie a cessé en 1996. La baisse de consommation de charbon bitumineux et de coke de cokerie observée dans l'industrie sidérurgique en 2002 est due à la fermeture de plusieurs usines.

Energies renouvelables combustibles et déchets : En 2003, la combustion de déchets urbains et assimilés pour produire de l'électricité et de la chaleur a sensiblement augmenté. Néanmoins, comme une forte proportion de la chaleur produite n'est pas utilisée (vendue), il en a découlé une diminution notable de rendement des installations entre 2002 et 2003.

Pétrole : La baisse de la consommation de fioul lourd dans l'industrie depuis 1993 est due à l'adoption d'un droit d'accise ainsi qu'à un recours accru au gaz naturel. En 2002, les usines d'agglomérés ont utilisé du fioul résiduel pour augmenter le pouvoir calorifique des agglomérés.

Gaz : La forte diminution observée en 2003 dans la rubrique industrie - non spécifiés est due à des améliorations de la collecte de données. Une nouvelle loi sur la collecte de données a entraîné des ruptures de séries concernant les secteurs de l'industrie et la consommation propre entre 2004 et 2005.

Electricité et chaleur : En 1998 et 1999, la production d'électricité des installations de cogénération dont la production annuelle de chaleur est inférieure à 0.5 TJ est comptabilisée avec celle des centrales qui ne produisent que de l'électricité. A partir de 2000, à la suite d'un changement de classification, les installations de production d'électricité des autoproducteurs entrent dans la rubrique des installations de cogénération des autoproducteurs. Egalement à compter de 2000, la production d'électricité des installations de cogénération est comptabilisée avec celle des installations de cogénération ; la chaleur produite est utilisée pour des procédés industriels internes et n'est pas vendue à des tiers.

Les séries chronologiques de données sur la consommation de chaleur dans l'industrie chimique et dans la rubrique industrie - non spécifiés comportent des ruptures entre 1991 et 1992.

Canada

Les révisions reçues par l'administration canadienne et intégrées dans l'édition de 2002 ont entraîné des ruptures de séries entre 1989 et 1990.

Charbon : Par suite d'une loi canadienne sur la confidentialité des données, à partir de 2002, la ventilation des données sur le charbon primaire a été en partie estimée par le Secrétariat de l'AIE.

Energies renouvelables combustibles et déchets : Le Secrétariat de l'AIE a estimé les données relatives aux déchets urbains, aux déchets industriels et au biogaz pour les années comprises entre 1990 et 2005, ainsi que celles relatives à la biomasse liquide (éthanol) pour les années 1998 à 2004 en se fondant sur des informations communiquées par Ressources naturelles Canada.

Pétrole : Depuis 1988, les données concernant plusieurs sous-secteurs industriels ne sont plus disponibles. Les transferts de naphtas et d'*autres produits pétroliers* tiennent compte des quantités de produits d'alimentation et autres additifs achetées à des entreprises qui ne communiquent pas de données. L'éthane est principalement utilisé comme produit de départ dans la pétrochimie. Avant 1990, l'hydrogène utilisé pour la valorisation du pétrole brut synthétique était comptabilisé avec l'approvisionnement en gaz naturel ; à partir de 1990, l'administration canadienne a adopté une méthode différente. Le Canada a importé de l'orimulsion en provenance du Venezuela entre 1994 et 2000.

Gaz : A partir de 1992, la consommation de gaz naturel dans les centrales de cogénération pour lesquelles il s'agit de l'activité principale comprend celle de trois nouvelles installations de cogénération dans la province de l'Ontario. Les données indiquées dans la rubrique non spécifiés du secteur de la transformation correspondent aux quantités de gaz naturel utilisées pour la valorisation de produits pétroliers raffinés. En 2000, l'augmentation observée dans les données sur la production d'électricité des producteurs dont c'est l'activité principale est due à la mise en service de nouvelles centrales dans l'Alberta et l'Ontario, tandis que la hausse de l'autoproduction d'électricité s'explique par l'accroissement de la production d'électricité assurée par des producteurs indépendants.

Electricité et chaleur : La production de chaleur comprend les quantités produites dans des centrales nucléaires et destinées à la distribution à d'autres consommateurs. La répartition de la production d'électricité et de chaleur entre gaz naturel et produits pétroliers dans les centrales de cogénération dont la production combinée est l'activité principale a été estimée par l'administration canadienne à partir de 1990. Il peut en découler des ruptures de séries chronologiques entre 1989 et 1990. Les données sur les quantités d'énergies renouvelables combustibles et de déchets utilisées dans les installations de production d'électricité des autoproducteurs, ainsi que sur la consommation finale d'énergie dans le secteur des pâtes et papier entre 1981 et 2004, ont été révisées par le Secrétariat de l'AIE.

Corée

On dispose de données à partir de 1971. Les données concernant l'année 2002 ont été notifiées sur une base différente, ce qui entraîne des ruptures de séries entre 2001 et 2002, surtout en ce qui concerne les consommations et les productions dans le secteur de la production d'électricité, ainsi que la consommation de l'industrie sidérurgique. L'administration coréenne prévoit de réviser les séries chronologiques dans la mesure où les délais et les ressources le lui permettront.

Charbon : Les données sur le charbon et les produits houillers entre 1971 et 2000 sont fondées sur des informations fournies par l'administration coréenne, ainsi que sur des données tirées du *Yearbook of Energy Statistics 2001*, du *Yearbook of Coal Statistics 2000* (l'un comme l'autre sont des annuaires statistiques du Ministère du Commerce, de l'Industrie et de l'Energie) et des *Statistics of Electric Power in Korea 2000* (de Korea Electric Power Corporation). Les données sur le charbon sous-bitumineux ont été estimées par le Secrétariat sur la base des statistiques des pays exportateurs.

Energies renouvelables combustibles et déchets : L'administration coréenne entreprend une étude en vue d'améliorer la notification de ses statistiques de l'énergie à partir de 2003. Dans ce cadre, les séries chronologiques concernant les déchets industriels, les déchets urbains et assimilés, la biomasse solide primaire et le biogaz ont été révisées en remontant jusqu'à 1990.

Pétrole : Les quantités de fioul résiduel et de naphtas consommées dans les installations de production d'électricité et de cogénération des autoproducteurs sont comptabilisées avec la consommation au stade de l'utilisation finale.

Gaz : La consommation à la rubrique construction mécanique est comptabilisée avec les matériels de transport.

Electricité et chaleur : Les statistiques sur l'électricité ont été estimées par le Secrétariat à partir des statistiques nationales coréennes pour les années comprises entre 1971 et 1993. Les données de 1994 ont été communiquées par l'administration coréenne. Il s'ensuit des ruptures de séries entre 1993 et 1994. Avant 1994, la production d'électricité des centrales de cogénération dont la production combinée était l'activité principale est comptabilisée avec celle des centrales dont la production d'électricité était l'activité exclusive et principale. Les données sur la chaleur sont disponibles à partir de 1991. Pour ces années, la ventilation de la production de chaleur par type de combustible a été estimée par le Secrétariat. En 2001, l'administration coréenne a commencé à communiquer des statistiques concernant la chaleur produite dans certaines centrales calogènes qui n'étaient pas comptabilisées auparavant, c'est pourquoi il peut se produire des ruptures de séries entre 2000 et 2001 ainsi qu'entre 2001 et 2002. Des données sur la production d'électricité et de chaleur des autoproducteurs utilisant du gaz naturel et des combustibles liquides ont été communiquées pour la première fois en 2002.

Danemark

Dans l'édition de 2004, l'administration danoise a procédé à des révisions importantes des données de 1990 à 2001, ce qui peut entraîner des ruptures de séries entre 1989 et 1990.

Pétrole : Les premières données sur le recyclage et la consommation finale d'huiles usées concernent l'année 1989 et figurent à la rubrique *autres produits pétroliers*. Avant 1990, les données sur le pétrole recouvrent également le Groenland et les îles Féroé danoises. Egalement avant 1990, la consommation de gazole/ carburant diesel et de fioul lourd pour la pêche entrait dans la rubrique navigation intérieure, alors qu'après cette date, elle est indiquée dans le secteur de l'agriculture. Les données relatives à la consommation sont fondées sur une enquête détaillée effectuée auprès d'entreprises danoises une année sur deux. Pour les années non couvertes par l'enquête, l'Agence danoise de l'énergie fournit des estimations de la consommation. Les méthodes d'enquête ayant été améliorées, les apports de combustibles pour la production d'électricité et de chaleur ont fait l'objet d'une nouvelle classification qui entraîne une rupture de série entre 1993 et 1994. L'accroissement prononcé de la consommation de fioul lourd pour la cogénération en 1994 s'explique par l'augmentation des exportations d'électricité à destination de la Norvège. Les données détaillées concernant le secteur industriel en 1994 et 1995 sont fondées sur une nouvelle enquête. Les importations d'orimulsion (utilisées pour la production d'électricité) ont commencé en 1995 et cessé en 2003. Les quantités de produits pétroliers utilisées dans des secteurs industriels pour produire les excédents de chaleur livrés aux réseaux de chauffage urbain sont imputées à ces secteurs.

Electricité et chaleur : A partir de 1984, de faibles quantités de chaleur ont été importées d'Allemagne. La production de chaleur au moyen de pompes à chaleur pour la vente a commencé en 1994. Avant 1994, les données sur la production d'électricité et de chaleur sont des estimations calculées sur la base des quantités de combustibles utilisés.

Espagne

Charbon : La consommation d'autres charbons bitumineux dans l'industrie sidérurgique a cessé en 1991, puis repris en 1996. La consommation de BKB a également pris fin en 1991. La consommation de gaz de haut fourneau a cessé en 1993 dans l'industrie chimique ; cette industrie a également cessé d'utiliser du gaz de cokerie entre 1993 et 2000. Par ailleurs, le gaz naturel n'est plus utilisé dans la fabrication de gaz d'usine à gaz depuis 1999.

Energies renouvelables combustibles et déchets : En raison de l'application d'un nouveau système de notification, il se produit des ruptures de séries dans les données sur les secteurs de consommation finale entre 1999 et 2000. En 2000, de nombreuses installations sont reclassées et passent de la catégorie des producteurs dont la production concernée constitue l'activité principale à celle des autoproducteurs, ou inversement.

Pétrole : Une modification du système de notification intervenue au milieu de 1996 a entraîné certaines ruptures de séries.

Gaz : L'accroissement de l'utilisation du gaz naturel comme produit de base, qui commence en 1988, tient au remplacement des naphtas pour la production d'engrais. On constate une rupture de série entre 1993 et 1994 dans les données concernant la consommation pour la cogénération assurée par les autoproducteurs car, à la suite d'une nouvelle enquête, il est apparu qu'il existe un plus grand nombre d'autoproducteurs de chaleur et d'électricité dont la consommation était antérieurement regroupée avec celle de l'industrie. L'augmentation notable observée en 1997 de la consommation d'électricité des producteurs pour lesquels la production d'électricité représentait l'activité principale découle du fait que deux de ces producteurs d'électricité ont consommé du gaz naturel en 1997. A partir de 2001, la ventilation de la consommation au stade de l'utilisation finale est estimée par l'administration nationale.

Electricité et chaleur : On dispose de données sur la production et la consommation de chaleur vendue à partir de 1989. Le fort accroissement de la production d'électricité observé en 1997 dans les centrales alimentées au gaz naturel des producteurs pour lesquels cette production est l'activité principale est dû à la mise en service d'une nouvelle centrale. En raison d'un changement dans le système de collecte de données, on ne dispose d'informations sur la chaleur vendue que jusqu'en 1999.

Les données sur l'utilisation directe de la chaleur issue du solaire thermique et de la géothermie sont disponibles à partir de 1994.

Etats-Unis

Par suite de problèmes de notification, il se produit de nombreuses ruptures de séries dans les données des Etats-Unis, notamment en 1992, 1999, 2001 et 2002. Il faudrait être vigilant, lors de l'évaluation de la consommation par secteur, car les combustibles utilisés par les autoproducteurs sont comptabilisés, pour certaines années, avec la consommation finale.

Energies renouvelables combustibles et déchets : L'Energy Information Administration collecte des données sur la production et la consommation de toutes les centrales d'une puissance de 1 MW ou plus. La production solaire thermique d'électricité comprend la production à partir de gaz naturel car, des installations au gaz étant couplées aux installations solaires thermiques, il n'est pas possible de comptabiliser la production à part.

Pétrole : Les soutes maritimes internationales de fioul lourd accusent une forte hausse en 1990 par suite d'un changement de méthode de collecte et de notification des données adopté par l'administration américaine. A partir de 1992, les différents composants des LGN et des GPL ont été convertis en utilisant leurs densités respectives au lieu d'une densité moyenne, ce qui a entraîné une rupture dans les séries de données. En 1993, l'administration américaine a adapté à plusieurs reprises son système de collecte des statistiques sur le pétrole afin de prendre en compte les amendements à la loi sur la pureté de l'air (Clean Air Act) de 1990. De ce fait, les données concernant les composés oxygénés (à savoir, l'éthanol utilisé comme carburant, le MTBE, etc.) ont été recueillies en 1993 et notifiées dans la catégorie des additifs, ou bien, pour l'éthanol, dans la catégorie de la biomasse liquide. A partir de 1994, les données sur la consommation d'essence moteur dans le secteur commercial/services publics sont fondées sur un nouveau modèle employé par le Ministère des Transports des Etats-Unis. Les écarts statistiques importants concernant le pétrole brut correspondent aux "quantités non comptabilisées", c'est-à-dire la différence entre les approvisionnements et la demande de pétrole brut. A partir de 1995, le GPL consommé dans les usines à gaz est comptabilisé dans le secteur de l'industrie. Suite à la nouvelle enquête « Manufacturing Energy Consumption Survey » (MECS), il se produit des ruptures de séries entre 1999 et 2000 dans le secteur de l'industrie, ainsi qu'entre 2000 et 2001 parce que les pourcentages de la MECS ont été modifiés suite à des révisions concernant l'électricité produite par cogénération. Des révisions importantes des données de l'année 2001 ont été effectuées pour le fioul résiduel et les produits semi-finis. Les changements tiennent, pour l'essentiel, à une erreur de classification commise par des importateurs, qui ont inclus les produits semi-finis dans la catégorie du fioul résiduel. Pour les années 2002 à 2004, le Secrétariat a estimé les quantités de gaz de raffinerie destinées à la production d'électricité, y compris des gaz dont le pouvoir calorifique est faible, en moyenne.

Gaz : Les quantités de gaz d'usine à gaz mélangées à du gaz naturel ont été estimées pour les années 1990 à 2002 sur la base du rendement du procédé. A l'exception du gaz naturel utilisé comme produit de départ dans la pétrochimie, les utilisations non énergétiques du gaz naturel sont comptabilisées avec l'industrie avant 2003.

Electricité et chaleur : Il apparaît des ruptures de séries concernant la production totale d'électricité et de chaleur aux Etats-Unis. Des données complètes sur la production et la consommation de chaleur et d'électricité dans les centrales électriques, les centrales de cogénération et les centrales calogènes dont ces productions respectives constituent leur activité principale ainsi que dans les installations de production d'électricité et de cogénération des autoproducteurs ne sont pas disponibles pour toutes les années. La cession à des autoproducteurs d'installations de producteurs pour lesquels leur production représentait leur activité principale peut entraîner des ruptures de séries entre 1998 et 2000. Aux Etats-Unis, avant 2000, la rubrique des autoproducteurs comprenait les petits producteurs indépendants d'électricité qui, selon les définitions de l'AIE, entrent dans la catégorie des producteurs dont la production d'électricité constitue l'activité principale. Dans l'édition de 2003, l'administration américaine a modifié la notification des données correspondant à la rubrique des autoproducteurs. Ce changement entraîne davantage de ruptures de séries entre 1999 et 2000. Pour 2002, la production d'électricité des autoproducteurs destinée au secteur pétrolier comprend la production de gaz de raffinerie à pouvoir calorifique faible en moyenne. Avant 2002, cette production n'était pas comptabilisée.

Les données sur l'électricité consommée pour le pompage et la production d'électricité dans les centrales à accumulation par pompage sont disponibles à partir de 1987. Une nouvelle enquête sur la consommation d'électricité peut donner lieu à une rupture de série chronologique en 2003 et 2004, surtout dans les secteurs industriel, commercial et résidentiel, ainsi que dans celui des transports. Il existe des données sur la consommation de chaleur vendue dans le secteur industriel à partir de 1991, et dans le secteur de l'énergie depuis 1992. Avant 1991, la consommation totale de chaleur vendue correspond à la consommation dans le secteur commercial/services publics. On ne dispose pas de données sur la chaleur vendue qui est consommée dans le secteur résidentiel et dans celui de l'agriculture.

Des données sur l'utilisation directe d'énergie solaire thermique dans le secteur résidentiel sont disponibles à partir de 1999.

Finlande

En raison de l'utilisation d'un nouveau système d'enquête et d'un changement de classification des données, il apparaît des ruptures de séries chronologiques concernant la plupart des produits et des secteurs entre 1999 et 2000. Le nouveau système est plus détaillé et assure une meilleure couverture des produits, surtout en ce qui concerne l'électricité, la cogénération et la production de chaleur, ainsi que l'industrie.

Charbon : La première cokerie est entrée en service en 1987, c'est pourquoi les importations de charbon à coke ainsi que la production de coke de cokerie et de gaz de cokerie ont débuté cette année-là. L'augmentation observée entre 1993 et 1994 de la consommation d'autres charbons bitumineux dans les centrales électriques où la production d'électricité constitue l'activité principale tient au remplacement d'électricité importée et d'hydroélectricité par de l'électricité produite à partir de charbon. La production de gaz d'usine à gaz a cessé en avril 1994.

Energies renouvelables combustibles et déchets : Il se produit une rupture de série entre 1991 et 1992, s'agissant des déchets urbains et assimilés. Les données concernant le biogaz et les déchets industriels sont disponibles à partir de 1996. Avant 2004, les déchets industriels comprennent d'autres formes d'énergie, notamment l'hydrogène, la chaleur issue de procédés chimiques, le gaz naturel et le gaz de haut fourneau.

Pétrole : En 1995, il s'est produit une rupture de série pour les échanges de produits pétroliers parce que le système de collecte de données sur les échanges du Conseil national des douanes a été aligné sur le système Intrastat de l'Union européenne. Un nouveau modèle de calcul ayant été utilisé, il se produit une rupture de série pour la consommation de fioul lourd dans les *autres secteurs* entre 1998 et 1999.

Gaz : Pour les années antérieures à 1989, les données concernant la consommation de gaz naturel dans le secteur résidentiel et dans celui de l'agriculture ont été estimées par l'administration finlandaise. La ventilation entre les secteurs résidentiel et commercial/services publics est disponible depuis 1995 parce que l'on applique un nouveau système de collecte de données.

Electricité et chaleur : Avant 1992, la production à partir d'énergies renouvelables combustibles et de déchets pour obtenir de l'électricité et/ou de la chaleur est comptabilisée avec le charbon. On dispose de données sur la production d'électricité et de chaleur à partir de biogaz à compter de 1996. Les données sur la production de chaleur dans les installations de cogénération des autoproducteurs sont disponibles à partir de 1996 et les données sur cette production dans les installations calogènes des autoproducteurs le sont à partir de 2000. Des données sur la chaleur dégagée dans des procédés chimiques et utilisée pour produire de l'électricité sont disponibles depuis 2004. La quantité de chaleur indiquée à la rubrique autres sources correspond à la production de vapeur dans des procédés industriels utilisant de l'hydrogène. La baisse de la production d'électricité en 2005 est principalement due à une production plus faible des centrales au charbon et à la tourbe, qui a été compensée par une augmentation des importations d'électricité en provenance de Suède.

La consommation de chaleur du secteur résidentiel comprend la consommation dans l'agriculture et le secteur commercial/services publics. On ne dispose pas de ventilation de la consommation de chaleur par sous-secteur industriel.

France

Charbon : La consommation de l'industrie des années 1989 à 1998 a été estimée par le Secrétariat sur la base de la publication du SESSI *Les consommations d'énergie dans l'industrie.*

Energies renouvelables combustibles et déchets : Les installations qui consomment des déchets urbains et assimilés ont fait l'objet d'un changement de classification à partir de 1995 et entrent depuis lors dans la catégorie des installations de cogénération des autoproducteurs, d'où une rupture de la série chronologique correspondante. La ventilation de la consommation finale de biogaz a été estimée par l'administration française pour les années comprises entre 1970 et 2003.

Pétrole : Les données sur les additifs et les composés oxygénés sont disponibles à partir de 1991. A partir de 1998, les produits pétroliers importés nécessitant un traitement plus poussé en raffinerie ne sont plus comptabilisés avec les importations de produits d'alimentation des raffineries mais avec les importations de produits pétroliers et les transferts de produits. La consommation de carburéacteur type kérosène comprend les utilisations à des fins militaires à partir de 1998. A compter de l'an 2000, les données sur les métaux non ferreux sont comptabilisées à la rubrique industrie - non spécifiés en ce qui concerne le coke de pétrole. L'éthylène produit à Lacq n'est pas comptabilisé avec les LGN à partir de 2002.

Gaz : Entre 1990 et 1998, l'écart statistique comprend la consommation de gaz non ventilée par secteur. A partir de 1999, une nouvelle méthodologie a été utilisée pour préparer les bilans concernant le gaz naturel, ce qui donne lieu à des ruptures de séries entre 1999 et 2000. Il se produit une rupture de séries concernant les secteurs commercial/services publics et résidentiel en 2001. Les quantités de gaz consommées pour faire fonctionner les conduites sont comptabilisées avec les pertes de distribution.

Electricité et chaleur : Il n'existe pas de données sur la chaleur vendue à des tiers avant 1989. On dispose de données sur la production d'électricité à partir d'énergie éolienne depuis 1993. A partir de 1995, en raison d'une modification de la classification des activités économiques, les données ont été indiquées dans la rubrique *autres secteurs* non spécifiés. L'emploi d'une nouvelle méthode d'enquête et une modification de la classification des centrales qui distingue les producteurs pour lesquels la production d'électricité est l'activité principale des installations de production d'électricité des autoproducteurs peuvent entraîner des ruptures de séries des données concernant les autres charbons bitumineux entre 1998 et 1999. De 2001 à 2004, de nouvelles difficultés de classification se sont posées pour les combustibles utilisés dans la production d'électricité à partir de pétrole et pour la production correspondante. L'administration française s'emploie actuellement à harmoniser ses méthodes de collecte de données sur les consommations et les productions dans la production d'électricité. Grâce à une nouvelle enquête, dans l'édition 2007 l'administration française a révisé les données à partir de 2000 et a inclus la chaleur produite par les combustibles fossiles. Il n'est malheureusement pas possible de distinguer les quantités de chaleur non-vendues pour les autoproducteurs - cogénération ; ces quantités sont donc inclues. Cependant, il n'y a aucun double comptage car les consommations de combustible correspondantes ne sont pas comprises dans la consommation finale.

La consommation des *autres secteurs* non spécifiés comprend les exportations à destination de Monaco avant 1992.

Grèce

Charbon : La production de gaz d'usine à gaz a cessé en 1997. Le lignite est utilisé depuis 1997 dans des installations de cogénération ayant la production combinée comme activité principale.

Energies renouvelables combustibles et déchets : La consommation de bois dans le secteur commercial/ services publics est regroupée avec celle du secteur résidentiel. Les données sur le biogaz sont disponibles à partir de 1990 et celles sur les déchets industriels à partir de 1992. On dispose de nouvelles données sur la biomasse solide à partir de 1996, d'où des ruptures de séries entre 1995 et 1996.

Pétrole : Les données relatives aux produits d'alimentation utilisés pour le craquage dans les raffineries sont disponibles à partir de 1986. A partir de 1993, on dispose d'une répartition plus exacte des produits pétroliers employés dans les différents secteurs de l'industrie. Les méthodes de notification ayant changé, on dispose d'informations plus détaillées sur l'utilisation finale à partir de 1996. La production de pétrole brut, qui avait cessé en novembre 1998, a repris en décembre 1999.

Gaz : Le gaz naturel extrait en Grèce a un pouvoir calorifique supérieur moyen d'environ 53 188 kJ/m^3, en raison de sa forte teneur en hydrocarbures à deux ou quatre atomes de carbone. En 1997, un nouveau gazoduc est entré en service entre la Russie et la Grèce. En 1998, la consommation du secteur résidentiel est comptabilisée avec celle du secteur commercial/ services publics.

Electricité et chaleur : Il apparaît une rupture entre 1991 et 1992 dans la série de données concernant la consommation d'électricité du secteur des transports. On dispose de données sur les énergies renouvelables combustibles et les déchets à partir de 1992. Les données concernant la production ou la consommation de chaleur faisant l'objet d'une distribution (chaleur vendue) produite à partir de lignite sont disponibles à compter de 1997.

Hongrie

Les données sont disponibles à compter de 1965.

Charbon : En raison de la vente d'une installation de production d'électricité appartenant à un autoproducteur, on constate des ruptures de séries pour le gaz de cokerie et le gaz de haut fourneau entre 1997 et 1998.

Energies renouvelables combustibles et déchets : On dispose de données sur le biogaz depuis 2000.

Pétrole : L'administration hongroise a répondu pour la première fois aux questionnaires de l'AIE en communiquant des données de 1993. Les données sur les additifs et l'essence aviation sont disponibles à partir de 1998.

Gaz : Il y a quelques ruptures de séries entre 1996 et 1997 en raison de l'application d'une nouvelle méthodologie. A partir de 1997, deux installations calogènes d'autoproducteurs ont fait l'objet d'une nouvelle classification et entrent désormais dans la catégorie des centrales calogènes de producteurs dont l'activité principale est la production de chaleur. Avant 2004, la transformation de gaz naturel dans les hauts fourneaux est comptabilisée avec la consommation de la sidérurgie.

Electricité et chaleur : La révision des données sur la production de chaleur afin qu'elles soient conformes aux méthodologies de notification de l'AIE peut avoir entraîné une non-concordance entre les données sur les combustibles utilisés et les productions de chaleur et d'électricité par type d'installation, d'où la possibilité qu'apparaissent des rendements élevés. Il se produit une rupture de série chronologique en 1990 en raison d'une nouvelle classification des installations de production de chaleur des autoproducteurs alimentées à la biomasse solide. On dispose de données sur la production de chaleur et d'électricité à partir de biomasse solide dans les installations de cogénération des autoproducteurs depuis 1995. Les données sur la production de chaleur géothermique des centrales calogènes de producteurs dont c'est l'activité principale sont également disponibles à partir de 1995. Quant au gaz naturel, des ruptures de séries se produisent entre 1996 et 1997 pour les données concernant les centrales de producteurs dont la production concernée constituait l'activité principale et les installations des autoproducteurs. L'administration hongroise a modifié la classification de certaines de leurs installations pour les années 1996 et 2000, ce qui peut entraîner des ruptures de séries.

Des données sur l'utilisation directe de chaleur géothermique sont disponibles à compter de 1990. On dispose de données sur l'utilisation directe de chaleur d'origine solaire thermique à partir de 2001.

Irlande

Charbon : La production de gaz d'usine à gaz a cessé en 1987 parce que ce gaz a été remplacé par du gaz naturel. Les quantités d'autres charbons bitumineux utilisées dans les centrales électriques de producteurs pour lesquels la production d'électricité est l'activité principale ont augmenté à partir de 1986, après la mise en service de trois nouvelles tranches à la centrale de Moneypoint. Une nouvelle classification entraîne une rupture de série concernant la consommation de tourbe des usines à briquettes entre 1989 et 1990.

Energies renouvelables combustibles et déchets : Les données sur la biomasse solide et le biogaz sont disponibles à compter de 1990.

Pétrole : La consommation du secteur commercial/ services publics comprend les quantités utilisées par les établissements agricoles appartenant à l'Etat. Les données sur la consommation recueillies pour l'année 1993 sont fondées sur une enquête détaillée. Les données concernant les années antérieures ont été révisées par l'administration nationale en remontant jusqu'à 1990 sur la base des résultats de cette enquête. En raison de ces révisions, il existe des ruptures, entre 1989 et 1990, dans les séries de données détaillées sur la consommation de GPL, de kérosène, de gazole/ carburant diesel et de fioul lourd.

Gaz : La forte augmentation des importations enregistrée depuis 1996 est la conséquence de l'épuisement du gisement de gaz de Kinsale et de l'accessibilité du nouveau gazoduc reliant l'Irlande au Royaume-Uni. La diminution de la consommation de gaz naturel observée dans l'industrie sidérurgique à partir de 2001 s'explique par la fermeture de la principale usine sidérurgique irlandaise. La consommation dans l'industrie chimique a diminué en 2003 en raison de la fermeture d'une usine de fabrication d'engrais. La forte consommation indiquée en 2003 pour le secteur des produits alimentaires, boissons et tabac est due à l'emploi d'une nouvelle méthode.

Electricité et chaleur : La production d'électricité d'origine éolienne débute en 1992.

Les données sur l'utilisation directe de chaleur d'origine géothermique et solaire thermique sont disponibles respectivement à compter de 1989 et de 1990.

La diminution de la consommation d'électricité observée dans l'industrie sidérurgique à partir de 2001 s'explique parce que la principale usine sidérurgique du pays a cessé sa production. L'accroissement de la consommation d'électricité constaté dans le secteur ferroviaire à partir de 2004 est dû à la mise en service du nouveau métro léger de Dublin.

Islande

Charbon : La consommation finale a augmenté en 2000 par suite de l'entrée en service d'une nouvelle usine sidérurgique.

Energies renouvelables combustibles et déchets : Les données sur l'utilisation de déchets urbains et assimilés pour la production de chaleur sont disponibles à compter de 1993.

Electricité et chaleur : Les données sur la production d'électricité d'origine géothermique dans les centrales de cogénération ayant la production combinée comme activité principale sont disponibles à partir de 1992. Les données sur la production de chaleur à partir de déchets urbains et assimilés sont disponibles à partir de 1993. En 1998, une capacité de production d'électricité de 60 MW a été installée dans la centrale géothermique de cogénération de Nesjavellir. Comme cette centrale n'a pas pu fonctionner pendant quatre mois, la production de chaleur d'origine géothermique a diminué par rapport à 1997. En revanche, l'accroissement de sa puissance électrique installée a presque fait doubler la production d'électricité d'origine géothermique au cours de la même période. En 2002, l'augmentation des quantités de chaleur produites au moyen d'énergie géothermique est due à l'installation d'une troisième unité à la centrale de cogénération de Nesjavellir.

La consommation propre d'électricité concerne principalement l'électricité utilisée dans les installations géothermiques pour le pompage des eaux géothermales de sources souterraines. A partir de 1991, la consommation d'électricité pour le transport fait référence au pompage d'eau chaude depuis la centrale géothermique de Nesjavellir jusqu'à Reykjavik. La consommation d'électricité (et de chaleur) de la base de l'OTAN à l'aéroport de Keflavik est indiquée sous la rubrique *autres secteurs*. L'augmentation de la consommation d'électricité observée entre 2003 et 2005 dans le secteur de la construction s'explique par le creusement de tunnels dans le cadre du projet hydroélectrique de Kárahnjúkar.

Italie

Charbon : A partir de 1986, les chiffres concernant le lignite sont calculés en appliquant la même méthode que dans le *Bilancio Energetico Nazionale.* En 1991, toutes les activités industrielles ont fait l'objet d'une nouvelle classification, d'après le système ISTAT/ NACE 91. De ce fait, il se peut que des anomalies apparaissent entre 1991 et les années précédentes par suite de certains transferts d'activités effectués. Le système d'enquête ayant changé, il peut se produire des ruptures de séries entre 1997 et 1998 en ce qui concerne la consommation finale.

Pétrole : Les quantités consommées pour la production de chaleur et d'électricité ont été estimées par le Secrétariat pour les années 1984 à 1997 à partir des données communiquées en réponse au questionnaire sur la chaleur et l'électricité. Toutes les autres données pour les années 1992 à 1997 et la ventilation détaillée de la consommation pour les autres années sont des estimations du Secrétariat établies sur la base du *Bilancio Energetico Nazionale*. De nouvelles enquêtes ayant été réalisées, il apparaît des ruptures dans les séries de données sur la consommation entre 1998 et 1999. Pour le gazole/carburant diesel, la consommation non spécifiée est comptabilisée dans le secteur commercial/services publics.

Gaz : La production de gaz d'usine à gaz à partir de gaz naturel a cessé en 1996.

Electricité et chaleur : Les données sur la production d'électricité à partir d'orimulsion sont confidentielles et elles ont été regroupées avec le fioul résiduel. A partir de l'an 2000, selon la définition de l'administration italienne, la production d'électricité des autoproducteurs recouvre également celle des producteurs qui consomment plus de 70 % de leur propre production. Cependant, dans la période comprise entre 2000 et 2002, la totalité de la production d'électricité des autoproducteurs est regroupée avec celle des producteurs dont c'est l'activité principale. La production d'électricité indiquée dans la catégorie *autres sources* concerne l'électricité produite pendant le procédé de regazéification du GNL ou avec la chaleur récupérée de procédés industriels. A compter de 2000, la production d'électricité à partir de gaz de synthèse obtenu par gazéification de bitume de pétrole figure avec la production à partir de produits pétroliers. La production de chaleur est notifiée à partir de 2004.

Japon

Pour la quatrième année consécutive, l'AIE a reçu des révisions de la part de l'administration japonaise. La première série de révisions reçue en 2004 montre pour les approvisionnements de 1990 une augmentation de 5% dans le cas du charbon, de 2% dans celui du gaz naturel et de 0,7% dans celui des produits pétroliers par rapport aux données antérieures, ce qui entraîne une hausse de 2,5% des émissions de CO_2 en 1990 lorsqu'elles sont calculées avec la méthode de référence, tandis qu'elles restent relativement constantes avec la méthode sectorielle. Pour l'édition 2006, l'AIE a reçu des données révisées concernant le charbon et le pétrole qui ont un impact significatif sur les bilans énergétiques et les émissions de CO_2. Les modifications les plus importantes concernent le coke de cokerie, le naphta, le gaz de haut fourneau et le coke de pétrole, et ce plutôt du côté de la consommation que des approvisionnements. En conséquence, les émissions de CO_2 calculées avec la méthode sectorielle ont augmenté tous les ans, mais dans des proportions différentes. Par exemple, les émissions de CO_2 calculées avec la méthode sectorielle pour 1990 étaient de 4,6% supérieures à celles figurant dans l'édition de 2005, tandis que les émissions de 2003 dépassaient de 1,1% celles figurant dans la précédente édition. En raison de l'impact de ces révisions sur le bilan énergétique final et les émissions de CO_2, l'AIE entretient des contacts étroits avec l'administration japonaise pour mieux comprendre les raisons qui expliquent ces changements. Ces révisions sont surtout le fruit des efforts déployés par le Gouvernement japonais pour préciser les bilans entrées-sorties concernant la production de produits charbonniers et pétroliers afin de communiquer au Secrétariat de la CCNUCC les données demandées. A cet effet, l'administration japonaise a mis en place en mars 2004 un groupe de travail qui a terminé ses travaux en avril 2006. La plupart de ses conclusions avaient déjà été incorporées, mais certaines nouvelles révisions des séries chronologiques (concernant en particulier l'industrie et les *autres secteurs*) ont été communiquées cette année.

A partir de 1990, les données sont indiquées sur la base de l'exercice budgétaire (d'avril 2005 à mars 2006 pour l'année 2005).

Charbon : A partir de 1998, les quantités de gaz de cokerie, de gaz de haut fourneau et de gaz de convertisseur utilisées dans les installations de production d'électricité des autoproducteurs comprennent les quantités utilisées pour produire de l'électricité avec la technologie japonaise TRT (Top pressure Recovery Turbines - cycle à récupération de gaz à haute pression) qui étaient précédemment comptabilisées dans le secteur de l'industrie.

Energies renouvelables combustibles et déchets : Les quantités de combustibles utilisées pour la production de charbon de bois ont été estimées en tablant sur l'hypothèse d'un rendement de 40 %.

Pétrole : Les importations d'orimulsion destinée à la production d'électricité débutent en 1991.

Electricité et chaleur : Les données de l'intégralité des séries chronologiques correspondent à l'exercice budgétaire. La production d'électricité des installations de cogénération des autoproducteurs est comptabilisée avec celle des installations de production d'électricité des autoproducteurs. L'électricité et la chaleur produites dans les installations de cogénération dont cette production combinée constitue l'activité principale ne sont pas prises en compte dans les séries de données. On ne dispose pas de données sur la chaleur produite pour la vente par des autoproducteurs dans des installations calogènes. L'administration japonaise ne communique pas de données sur la production de chaleur à partir d'énergies géothermique et solaire thermique au Japon. La production d'électricité à partir d'énergie éolienne a débuté en 1993. Avant 1998, l'électricité produite avec la technologie TRT (Top pressure Recovery Turbines - cycle à récupération de gaz à haute pression) était comptabilisée avec l'électricité produite à partir de bois, de déchets de bois et d'autres déchets solides. Désormais, elle l'est avec l'électricité produite à partir de gaz de houille.

Luxembourg

Charbon : La production d'acier dans les hauts fourneaux a cessé à la fin de 1997. De ce fait, le Luxembourg ne consomme plus de coke de cokerie ni de gaz de haut fourneau.

Energies renouvelables combustibles et déchets : Les données sur la biomasse solide sont disponibles à partir de 1992.

Gaz : La consommation du secteur résidentiel comprend celle des secteurs commercial et agricole. La forte augmentation de la consommation de gaz dans le secteur de la transformation observée à partir de 2002 s'explique par la mise en service d'une nouvelle centrale à cycle combiné de 350 MW.

Electricité et chaleur : La majeure partie de la production hydroélectrique indiquée pour le Luxembourg est celle de la centrale de pompage de Vianden et elle est exportée directement vers l'Allemagne. Les données sur la production de chaleur et d'électricité à partir de gaz naturel dans les installations de cogénération des autoproducteurs sont disponibles à compter de 1995. On dispose de données sur la production de chaleur et d'électricité à partir de biogaz à compter de 1999. Les données sur l'énergie solaire thermique sont disponibles à partir de 1999. L'augmentation de la production d'électricité en 2002 est due à la mise en service d'une nouvelle centrale à cycle combiné alimentée au gaz naturel.

L'industrie sidérurgique a cessé de produire de l'électricité à la fin de 1997.

Mexique

Les données sont disponibles à partir de 1971 et sont en partie estimées à partir de la publication *Balance Nacional - Energía*. L'administration mexicaine a, pour la première fois, communiqué directement des données à l'aide du questionnaire pour l'année 1992. De ce fait, il existe peut-être quelques ruptures de séries entre 1991 et 1992.

Charbon : Les données sur le gaz de cokerie et le gaz de haut fourneau sont indiquées pour la première fois en 1999.

Energies renouvelables combustibles et déchets : On dispose de données sur le biogaz à partir de 1998.

Pétrole : Le pétrole utilisé pour l'autoproduction d'électricité et de chaleur a été comptabilisé avec l'industrie. En raison d'un changement dans le traitement des données, il se produit des ruptures de séries entre 1998 et 1999.

Gaz : Les chiffres concernant le gaz naturel indiqués dans les publications de l'AIE peuvent différer de ceux qui figurent dans les publications mexicaines sur l'énergie, car l'AIE tient compte du gaz sec uniquement, et non des liquides de gaz naturel. Les pertes de distribution ont été comptabilisées à la rubrique de consommation propre. Depuis 1993, les données sont communiquées par la "Secretaría de Energía".

Electricité et chaleur : On dispose de données sur la production d'électricité à partir d'énergie éolienne à compter de 1994. Les données concernant la production d'électricité à partir d'énergie solaire photovoltaïque et d'énergies renouvelables combustibles et déchets sont disponibles à partir de 1998. Depuis 1998, la CRE (Comisión Reguladora de Energía) publie de nouvelles données sur la production d'électricité des autoproducteurs. Il peut en découler des ruptures de séries chronologiques entre 1997 et 1998. Avant 1998, les données indiquées à la rubrique des produits pétroliers non spécifiés utilisés par les autoproducteurs comprennent toutes les formes d'énergie combustibles. De nouvelles installations de production d'électricité alimentées aux gaz de houille ont été mises en service par des autoproducteurs en 1999. Dans l'édition de 2006, la série chronologique de données sur la production d'électricité des centrales au gaz naturel a été révisée par l'administration mexicaine à compter de 1990.

Les données sur l'utilisation directe d'énergie solaire thermique sont disponibles à partir de 1998.

Une partie de la consommation d'électricité du secteur de l'énergie est comptabilisée avec celle de la branche de l'industrie où elle a été produite (par exemple, chimie ainsi qu'industrie - non spécifiés).

Norvège

Charbon : La diminution de la production de charbon bitumineux observée en 2005 est la conséquence d'un incendie survenu dans l'une des mines de charbon, qui a entraîné une cessation de l'extraction pendant une bonne partie de l'année.

Energies renouvelables combustibles et déchets : Les données sur les déchets industriels et le biogaz sont disponibles à partir de 1991. Les données sur les biocarburants liquides sont confidentielles.

Pétrole : Le Secrétariat de l'AIE calcule le pouvoir calorifique inférieur du pétrole brut norvégien sur la base de la production de produits pétroliers des raffineries. En raison des révisions effectuées par l'administration norvégienne, il apparaît des ruptures de séries entre 1989 et 1990. La consommation de gazole/carburant diesel pour la pêche est comptabilisée avec celle de l'agriculture avant l'an 2000.

Gaz : L'augmentation importante observée en 1992 dans la consommation propre est la conséquence de la mise en production de nouveaux champs. Avant 2000, les données sur la consommation propre comprenaient des données qui normalement figurent dans la consommation finale totale. A partir de 2002, la navigation intérieure est comptabilisée sous la rubrique transports - non spécifiés.

Electricité et chaleur : On dispose de données sur la production de chaleur au moyen de pompes à chaleur et de chaudières électriques (y compris sur l'électricité utilisée pour cette production) à partir de 1989. L'administration norvégienne ne communique pas à l'AIE de données distinctes pour la production d'électricité à partir d'énergie solaire. Cependant, on dispose de données sur la production d'électricité à partir d'énergie éolienne à partir de 1992. Des données sur la production de chaleur au moyen de biogaz sont disponibles à partir de 1995. Les ruptures de séries entre 1996 et 1997 sont dues à une nouvelle classification des producteurs dont la production concernée est l'activité principale et des autoproducteurs. La production d'électricité au moyen de chaleur résiduelle, regroupée avec la production d'électricité à partir de gaz de houille dans les éditions antérieures, est indiquée à part à compter de 1990.

La ventilation de la consommation de chaleur par sous-secteur industriel a été élargie en 1992, elle a fait l'objet d'une nouvelle classification en 1994 et les données correspondantes ont été collectées au moyen d'un nouveau système de notification en 1997. Les données sur la chaleur produite dans les installations calogènes des autoproducteurs moyennant des procédés chimiques ou d'autres sources et utilisée pour produire de l'électricité sont des estimations du Secrétariat dans la période comprise entre 1990 et 2005.

Nouvelle-Zélande

Charbon : La tourbe, quoique produite en Nouvelle-Zélande, n'y est pas utilisée comme combustible mais uniquement à des fins agricoles. Au stade de la consommation finale, les métaux non ferreux sont regroupés avec la sidérurgie ; le bois et les produits dérivés du bois sont comptabilisés avec l'industrie du papier, de la pâte à papier et de l'imprimerie ; les industries extractives sont regroupées avec l'agriculture, et la construction avec le secteur commercial/services publics. Les quantités de charbon sous-bitumineux utilisées dans les hauts fourneaux correspondent au charbon mélangé à du sable ferrugineux qui constitue la charge des fours multisoles (site sidérurgique de Glenbrook).

Energies renouvelables combustibles et déchets : Les données indiquées correspondent à l'exercice budgétaire. En 1999, un changement de classification des installations des autoproducteurs donne lieu à des ruptures de séries chronologiques. Les données sur la consommation finale d'énergie géothermique et de biomasse solide ont été révisées en remontant jusqu'à l'an 2000 par l'administration néo-zélandaise, sur la base d'une nouvelle étude.

Pétrole : La consommation de gazole/carburant diesel dans le secteur du transport routier comprend la consommation du secteur ferroviaire. Pour des raisons de confidentialité, à partir de 1994, l'administration néo-zélandaise ne communique plus de données sur la production de méthanol. La liquéfaction d'autres hydrocarbures, regroupée avec le pétrole brut, correspond à la production d'essence de synthèse à partir de gaz naturel. La production d'essence de synthèse a cessé en février 1997.

Gaz : Les principaux agrégats indiqués pour les secteurs de la transformation, de l'énergie, des transports, de l'industrie et pour les *autres secteurs* sont estimés par l'administration nationale. La production d'essence de synthèse à partir de gaz naturel a cessé en février 1997. En 1998, deux nouvelles installations de cogénération ont été mises en service chez des autoproducteurs et le très fort accroissement de la consommation observé cette année-là leur est imputable.

Electricité et chaleur : Les classifications utilisées par l'administration néo-zélandaise ont été modifiées en 1991. Avant 1994, les données correspondent à l'exercice budgétaire (avril 1994 à mars 1995 pour l'année 1994). Après cette date, elles correspondent à l'année civile. On dispose de données sur la production d'électricité d'origine géothermique assurée par des autoproducteurs à partir de 1995.

Les données sur l'utilisation directe de chaleur d'origine géothermique sont disponibles à partir de 1990.

En ce qui concerne l'électricité, les pertes de distribution comprennent l'écart statistique. La consommation d'électricité de l'industrie de la pâte à papier, du papier et de l'imprimerie est comptabilisée avec celle de l'industrie du bois et des produits dérivés avant 1991. Il apparaît, entre 1996 et 1997, des ruptures dans les séries concernant la consommation d'électricité par suite de l'adoption d'une nouvelle classification-type des industries par branche d'activité (NZSIC-NZ Standard Industrial Classification). Les quantités de gaz de haut fourneau utilisées dans les installations de cogénération des autoproducteurs correspondent aux gaz manufacturés issus des fours multisoles où du sable ferrugineux entre dans l'élaboration de l'acier.

Pays-Bas

Dans le système statistique national des Pays-Bas, la consommation de combustibles pour la cogénération dans les industries manufacturières est traitée comme une consommation du secteur de la transformation. Cependant, dans les statistiques de l'AIE, cette consommation propre destinée à la production de chaleur (chaleur autoproduite) est comptabilisée dans les différents secteurs industriels concernés, sur la base des estimations fournies par le Bureau central de statistiques.

Charbon : La fabrication de meubles est regroupée avec l'industrie de la pâte à papier, du papier et de l'imprimerie.

Energies renouvelables combustibles et déchets : Dans l'édition de 2007, l'administration néerlandaise a modifié la classification d'une partie de la biomasse solide, laquelle entre désormais dans la catégorie des biocarburants liquides, et ce en remontant jusqu'aux données de 2002. Les données sur la production de charbon de bois sont disponibles à partir de 1990.

Pétrole : La consommation de gaz de raffinerie comprend le gaz utilisé par l'industrie chimique : elle est comptabilisée avec la consommation de cette industrie. La série de données sur le gaz de raffinerie utilisé dans les centrales de cogénération pour lesquelles la production combinée constitue l'activité principale commence en 1995.

Gaz : A partir de 2003, une méthode plus précise d'affectation de la chaleur non vendue issue de la cogénération chez les autoproducteurs a été utilisée, de sorte que les données ne sont pas comparables à celles des années antérieures. Toutes les installations calogènes ont été transformées en installations de cogénération en 1990. La consommation du secteur commercial/ services publics comprend celle des *autres secteurs* à compter de 1988.

Electricité et chaleur : L'électricité produite à partir d'*autres sources* comprend la production à partir d'effluents chimiques gazeux et de chaleur achetée à d'autres industries. Les données sur la production d'électricité photovoltaïque sont disponibles à partir de 1992. La baisse de la production d'électricité d'origine nucléaire observée en 1997 tient à l'arrêt d'une centrale nucléaire pendant cinq mois. Des données sur la chaleur produite à partir d'énergies renouvelables combustibles sont disponibles à partir de 1990. Une nouvelle centrale de cogénération alimentée au gaz de raffinerie où la production combinée est l'activité principale a été mise en service en 1999, et une nouvelle classification des combustibles a été appliquée en 2000. Dans l'édition de 2007, l'administration néerlandaise a mis en œuvre une nouvelle méthode de notification, ce qui entraîne des ruptures de séries entre 2004 et 2005. Avant 2005, la totalité de l'électricité et de la chaleur produites à partir de charbon, de pétrole et de gaz naturel est comptabilisée à la rubrique des centrales de cogénération.

La consommation d'électricité du secteur commercial/services publics comprend celle des petits consommateurs. La forte augmentation des échanges d'électricité en 1999 est due à la libéralisation du marché néerlandais de l'électricité. La nouvelle méthode de notification appliquée à partir de 2005 entraîne des ruptures de série pour la consommation de chaleur.

Pologne

Energies renouvelables combustibles et déchets : Les données sur le biogaz ne concernent que le gaz issu de la fermentation de biomasse. Les données disponibles ont entraîné un accroissement important dans la rubrique de la biomasse solide entre 1992 et 1993. En raison de certains changements intervenus dans la procédure de collecte des données, on constate des ruptures de séries entre 1996 et 1997. Avant 2000, les déchets industriels et le fioul léger étaient utilisés de façon interchangeable dans certaines installations, ce qui pourrait entraîner des ruptures de séries chronologiques. Les données sur la consommation de biocombustibles liquides sont disponibles à partir de 2003.

Pétrole : Les données sur le coke de pétrole sont disponibles à partir de 2003.

Gaz : Les quantités de gaz utilisées dans le secteur de la transformation ont été calculées par l'administration polonaise et peuvent ne pas correspondre aux données rétrospectives concernant certaines années. Les quantités de gaz utilisées dans les raffineries de pétrole comprennent le gaz naturel utilisé pour produire de l'hydrogène par reformage catalytique. Avant 2000, le gaz naturel consommé dans le transport par conduites était en partie comptabilisé dans la consommation propre.

Electricité et chaleur : L'administration polonaise a adopté de nouvelles méthodes pour l'estimation de la production de chaleur destinée à la vente dans les installations calogènes des autoproducteurs (1993) et dans les installations de cogénération des autoproducteurs (1995). Il s'ensuit des ruptures de séries entre 1992 et 1993, ainsi qu'entre 1994 et 1995 pour la production de chaleur et les combustibles utilisés dans ces installations ainsi que pour la consommation de chaleur dans les sous-secteurs industriels.

Les données sur l'utilisation directe de l'énergie géothermique sont disponibles à partir de l'an 2000.

La consommation propre de chaleur comprend la chaleur industrielle non vendue avant 1995.

Portugal

Charbon : On ne consomme plus de charbon sous-bitumineux au Portugal depuis 1998. L'industrie sidérurgique a cessé son activité au premier trimestre de 2001, d'où la baisse des approvisionnements et de la consommation de charbon à coke, de coke de cokerie, de gaz de cokerie et de gaz de haut fourneau.

Energies renouvelables combustibles et déchets : On dispose de données sur le biogaz à partir de 1994, sur les déchets urbains et assimilés à partir de 1999 et sur les déchets industriels à partir de 2003. La consommation de biomasse solide dans le secteur résidentiel comprend la fraction non commerciale de la biomasse solide consommée par les ménages. L'administration nationale a révisé les données sur la biomasse solide des années comprises entre 1990 et 2001, ce qui peut entraîner des ruptures de séries entre 1989 et 1990.

Pétrole : En 1995, la production et la consommation de gaz de raffinerie ont cessé. La consommation de gazole/carburant diesel dans l'industrie et le secteur commercial/services publics est celle des parcs de véhicules de ces secteurs.

Gaz : Le Portugal a commencé à importer du gaz naturel en février 1997. La diminution observée en 2001 de la consommation de gaz naturel dans les usines à gaz est due à la fermeture de celle de Lisbonne en mai 2001.

Electricité et chaleur : Conformément à la méthodologie de l'AIE, la chaleur produite à partir d'énergies renouvelables combustibles et de déchets (principalement, de la liqueur noire) ainsi qu'à partir de gaz de houille dans les installations de cogénération des autoproducteurs n'est pas comptabilisée parce qu'elle n'est pas vendue ; en revanche, l'électricité qui y est produite est prise en considération. De nouvelles installations alimentées à la biomasse solide et aux déchets urbains et assimilés sont entrées en service en 1999.

Les données sur l'utilisation directe d'énergie solaire thermique et d'énergie géothermique sont disponibles à partir de 1989 et 1994, respectivement.

République slovaque

Les données sont disponibles à partir de 1971. On constate quelques ruptures de séries entre 1992 et 1993. Un nouveau système d'enquête appliqué en 2001 entraîne des ruptures de séries importantes concernant la plupart des produits.

Energies renouvelables combustibles et déchets : Des données sur les déchets urbains et assimilés, le biogaz et les biocombustibles liquides sont disponibles à partir de 2001. La République slovaque éprouve des difficultés à déterminer la classification correcte au stade de l'utilisation finale des divers éléments entrant dans les énergies renouvelables combustibles et les déchets. De ce fait, des consommations apparaissant dans un secteur donné sur une année seulement sont ensuite reclassées ailleurs l'année suivante. La République slovaque prévoit de revoir ses séries chronologiques.

Pétrole : En ce qui concerne le gazole/carburant diesel, les données relatives au transport routier tiennent comptent de la consommation dans le secteur ferroviaire.

Gaz : La consommation figurant dans la rubrique *transformation - autres* entre 1994 et 2004 concerne essentiellement du gaz naturel utilisé comme produit d'alimentation dans les raffineries pour produire des GPL.

Electricité et chaleur : Les données sur la production de chaleur et d'électricité à partir de formes d'énergie combustibles entre 1990 et 2000 sont des estimations fondées sur les données concernant les combustibles utilisés dans les centrales électriques et calogènes communiquées dans les questionnaires annuels sur les combustibles.

Des données sur l'utilisation directe d'énergie géothermique sont disponibles depuis 2001.

République tchèque

Les données sont disponibles à compter de 1971.

Charbon : L'administration tchèque a communiqué des données sur la consommation finale à partir de 1996. En raison d'une restructuration économique opérée dans les secteurs de consommation finale à la fin des années 90 (scission et/ou privatisation de grandes entreprises d'Etat et utilisation de nouvelles technologies dans les entreprises), il pourrait apparaître des ruptures de séries chronologiques dans ces secteurs. Avant 1993, les données sur la consommation étaient des estimations du Secrétariat. Les données pour les années 1990 à 1995 ont été estimées en se fondant sur la publication tchèque *Energy Economy Year Book*. En 1995, la production de gaz de ville a cessé. A partir de 1996, l'administration tchèque a commencé à comptabiliser le gaz d'usine à gaz avec la cogénération assurée par des autoproducteurs. En 1997, les industries chimique et pétrochimique ont cessé de consommer du gaz de cokerie. Cette même année, on a commencé à extraire d'autres charbons bitumineux à plus grande profondeur, d'où leur pouvoir calorifique plus élevé. Les révisions effectuées par l'administration tchèque ont entraîné quelques ruptures de séries entre 2001 et 2002. En 2004, la production d'autres charbons bitumineux d'autres sources concerne des schlamms.

Energies renouvelables combustibles et déchets : Les données sur les énergies renouvelables combustibles ne sont pas disponibles pour les années antérieures à 1991. La restructuration du marché tchèque de l'électricité entraîne des ruptures des séries chronologiques dans tous les secteurs entre 1998 et 1999. On dispose de données sur la biomasse liquide à partir de 1992 et sur les déchets urbains et assimilés à partir de 1999. En raison de l'utilisation de nouveaux systèmes d'enquête, il apparaît des ruptures de séries dans les données sur la consommation finale en 1999 et en 2002. On observe également en 2003 des ruptures dans les séries concernant les approvisionnements et la consommation d'énergies renouvelables combustibles et de déchets. Les exportations de biodiesel ont augmenté en 2005, stimulées par son prix élevé.

Pétrole : Les données sur les années antérieures à 1994 sont des estimations du Secrétariat. L'administration tchèque a répondu pour la première fois au questionnaire sur le pétrole de l'AIE en communiquant les données de 1994. Les ruptures de série entre 1998 et 1999 dans les données sur la consommation finale de gazole/carburant diesel s'expliquent parce que l'administration tchèque a mis en œuvre un nouveau système de gestion des données.

Gaz : Les données à partir de 1993 ont été officiellement communiquées par le Bureau de statistique tchèque. La rupture de séries entre 1993 et 1994 s'explique parce que les méthodes employées par l'ex-République fédérative tchèque et slovaque et la

République tchèque pour établir les bilans énergétiques ne sont pas les mêmes. Avant 1994, les données indiquées dans le secteur des transports concernent l'ex-République fédérative tchèque et slovaque. Les usines à gaz ne consomment plus de gaz naturel depuis 1996.

Electricité et chaleur : Les statistiques de l'électricité de 1971 à 1989 sont des estimations du Secrétariat, à l'exception des données sur la consommation finale et les échanges, qui ont été communiquées par l'administration tchèque. Les données sur la production de chaleur et les combustibles utilisés à cet effet ont été estimées, pour les années comprises entre 1980 et 1989, sur la base de la consommation des secteurs résidentiel et commercial/services publics. Avant cette période, les combustibles utilisés pour la production de chaleur étaient comptabilisés sous la rubrique industrie. A partir de 1990, des données ont été officiellement communiquées par l'administration tchèque. Il peut en résulter des ruptures de séries entre 1989 et 1990. Avant 1990, les données sur la production d'électricité dans les centrales de cogénération des producteurs pour lesquels cette production combinée était l'activité principale et dans les installations de cogénération des autoproducteurs sont regroupées avec celles des centrales électriques des producteurs dont l'activité principale était la production d'électricité. Avant 1990, la production de chaleur ne comprend pas la chaleur vendue par l'industrie. La ventilation de la production de chaleur entre centrales de cogénération de producteurs pour lesquels cette production combinée était l'activité principale et centrales calogènes n'est pas disponible pour les années antérieures à 1990. En conséquence, toute la production de chaleur est indiquée sous la rubrique des centrales calogènes des producteurs pour lesquels la production de chaleur était l'activité principale. On dispose de données sur le biogaz et les déchets utilisés dans les centrales de cogénération des producteurs dont l'activité principale est cette production combinée ainsi que dans les installations calogènes des autoproducteurs à partir de 1993. En 1999 et 2000, diverses grandes entreprises ont fait l'objet de scissions, de cessions et de fusions. Il en découle des ruptures de séries chronologiques concernant tous les types d'installations et de centrales. La nouvelle méthode de notification utilisée par l'administration tchèque pour les énergies renouvelables combustibles et les déchets entraîne quelques ruptures de séries entre 2002 et 2003. Dans l'édition de 2006, l'administration tchèque a procédé à des révisions considérables des séries chronologiques à partir de 1990.

Royaume-Uni

Charbon : La consommation du secteur commercial/services publics comprend celle d'une partie de la rubrique non spécifiés. Avant 1994, la consommation de gaz de synthèse est regroupée avec celle de gaz naturel, bien que sa production soit comptabilisée avec celle de gaz d'usine à gaz. De nouvelles classifications ont entraîné des ruptures de séries entre 1998 et 1999 ainsi qu'entre 2000 et 2001 pour le gaz de haut fourneau.

Pétrole : Avant 1995, la ventilation des transferts par produit est estimée par l'administration britannique, qui a révisé cette ventilation et la méthode de notification pour les produits pétrochimiques à partir de cette année-là. Il se produit des ruptures de séries concernant les GPL entre 2000 et 2001 en raison d'une redistribution des données. On dispose de données sur le fioul lourd utilisé pour la production de chaleur depuis 2000.

Gaz : A partir de 1992, les pertes de distribution comprennent les différences de comptage et les pertes dues aux fuites dans les conduites. La consommation de gaz naturel du secteur commercial est comptabilisée avec celle des *autres secteurs* non spécifiés, alors que celle du secteur des services publics est indiquée séparément. La consommation de gaz naturel comprend celle de gaz de synthèse, fabriqué dans les usines à gaz et injecté dans le réseau de distribution de gaz naturel. Les données figurant à la rubrique non spécifiés du secteur de l'industrie correspondent aux ventes effectuées par des fournisseurs de gaz indépendants qui ne sont pas réparties par catégorie. Le gaz naturel utilisé pour fabriquer le gaz synthétique de cokerie figure sous la rubrique transformation - non spécifiés.

Electricité et chaleur : La réorganisation, puis la privatisation du secteur de l'électricité en 1990 ont entraîné certaines ruptures de séries. Les quantités de gaz naturel utilisées et la production d'électricité à partir de gaz naturel dans les centrales des producteurs pour lesquels la production d'électricité est l'activité principale sont comptabilisées avec l'autoproduction d'électricité en 1990 (les données étant confidentielles). Dans le cas du Royaume-Uni, il faut regrouper les chiffres concernant les producteurs dont la production qu'ils assurent constitue l'activité principale et les autoproducteurs afin d'éviter la divulgation d'informations relatives à moins de trois entreprises productrices d'électricité, ces données étant considérées confidentielles. C'est pourquoi les données sur les centrales de cogénération de producteurs dont la production combinée représente l'activité principale ont été regroupées avec les données sur les installations de cogénération des autoproducteurs à partir de 1988. Avant 1988, la production d'électricité des installations de cogénération était comptabilisée avec celle des centrales des producteurs pour lesquels la production d'électricité représentait l'activité principale. En 1996, la rupture de la série de données sur la production d'électricité d'origine nucléaire est due à une nouvelle classification des installations des autoproducteurs qui les place dans la catégorie des centrales de producteurs pour lesquels la production d'électricité constitue l'activité principale. On dispose de données sur la production d'électricité à partir d'énergie solaire à compter de 1999. Les données sur la production de chaleur sont disponibles à partir de 1999.

La consommation d'électricité des mines de charbon englobe celle des usines d'agglomérés. La consommation des usines à gaz comprend l'électricité utilisée pour le transport et la distribution du gaz destiné aux petits consommateurs finals. La consommation du sous-secteur des produits minéraux non métalliques comprend celle des industries extractives. A partir de 1990, de faibles quantités d'électricité utilisées pour actionner les pompes à chaleur ont été comptabilisées dans la rubrique du secteur résidentiel.

Suède

Charbon : La production d'autres charbons bitumineux concerne le charbon récupéré lors de l'exploitation de carrières argileuses. Les apports des autoproducteurs à la production de chaleur résiduelle vendue sont indiqués dans les secteurs d'utilisation finale respectifs et non dans le secteur de la transformation.

Energies renouvelables combustibles et déchets : Les données sur le biogaz sont disponibles à partir de 1992. On ne dispose pas de données sur la transformation concernant les déchets industriels avant 1998. La production de chaleur à partir de biomasse solide dans les installations de cogénération des autoproducteurs comprend la chaleur résiduelle et la chaleur issue de réactions chimiques.

Pétrole : A partir de 1995, la Suède a modifié sa classification-type des industries par branche. On dispose de données sur les additifs à partir de 2000, sur l'éthane à partir de 2001 et sur le gaz de raffinerie à partir de 2003.

Gaz : Avant 1993, le transport routier est comptabilisé avec le secteur commercial/services publics.

Electricité et chaleur : En Suède, la chaleur produite au moyen de pompes à chaleur est vendue à des tiers (sous forme de chauffage urbain) et elle figure donc dans le secteur de la transformation. L'énergie consommée par les pompes à chaleur comprend la chaleur récupérée de procédés industriels et du milieu ambiant (eaux usées et eau de mer comprises). La chaleur ambiante est comptabilisée à la rubrique production nationale de chaleur. L'électricité utilisée pour actionner les pompes à chaleur est considérée comme étant transformée et apparaît donc dans la production du secteur de la transformation, au lieu d'être regroupée avec la consommation propre d'électricité. Les combustibles utilisés pour produire la chaleur récupérée par les pompes à chaleur sont indiqués dans le sous-secteur correspondant de l'industrie (par exemple, industrie chimique ou pâte à papier, papier et imprimerie). Les données sur la chaleur destinée à la vente, produite au moyen de pompes à chaleur et de chaudières électriques, sont disponibles depuis 1992. Les données sur la production de chaleur destinée à la vente des installations calogènes des autoproducteurs apparaissent à partir de 1992. Cependant, les apports de combustibles qui y sont associés sont comptabilisés avec la consommation de l'industrie. La production de chaleur à partir de combustibles liquides dans les centrales de cogénération de producteurs pour lesquels la production combinée constituait l'activité principale comprend la chaleur récupérée lors de la condensation des fumées pour les années 1997 et 1998.

La consommation industrielle de chaleur produite par des pompes à chaleur a été estimée par le Secrétariat d'après les données sur les combustibles utilisés à cet effet qui ont été communiquées par l'administration suédoise (2/3 dans l'industrie de la pâte à papier, du papier et de l'imprimerie et 1/3 dans l'industrie chimique). Il se produit des ruptures de séries entre 1991 et 1992 pour les données sur la consommation de chaleur.

Suisse

A partir de 1999, les données sur la consommation sont obtenues au moyen d'une nouvelle enquête et ne sont pas comparables avec les données des années précédentes.

Charbon : A partir de 1985, la consommation industrielle de gaz d'usine à gaz figure à la rubrique industrie - non spécifiés, les données étant confidentielles.

Energies renouvelables combustibles et déchets : Avant 1998, seules les importations nettes sont indiquées à la rubrique de la biomasse solide. Dans l'édition de 2007, les données des séries chronologiques concernant la biomasse solide et les déchets industriels dans le secteur de la transformation ont été révisées par l'administration suisse en remontant jusqu'en 1990.

Pétrole : A compter de 1993, l'administration suisse a notifié des données sur les naphtas après déduction des quantités utilisées en mélange avec de l'essence moteur. Cette notification a entraîné des chiffres négatifs pour la production de naphtas des années 1994, 1995, 1997, 1999, 2001 et 2002. Le Secrétariat de l'AIE a comptabilisé les données concernant les années en question dans la rubrique des transferts et réduit des quantités correspondantes la production d'essence moteur. La production de coke de pétrole a commencé en 2004 avec l'installation d'une unité de craquage dans une raffinerie.

Gaz : La ventilation des données concernant le secteur de l'industrie a été estimée par le Secrétariat pour l'an 2000 et par l'administration nationale pour les années 2001 à 2005.

Electricité et chaleur : La production de chaleur comprend la chaleur produite par les centrales nucléaires et distribuée à d'autres consommateurs. Les données sur la production d'électricité à partir d'énergie solaire assurée par les autoproducteurs sont disponibles à partir de 1990. On dispose de données sur la production d'électricité à partir d'énergie éolienne et sur celle des centrales de pompage des autoproducteurs à partir de 1996. Dans l'édition de 2007, l'administration suisse a révisé les séries chronologiques de données concernant la production d'électricité et de chaleur à partir de biomasse solide, de déchets industriels et de gaz naturel entre 1990 et 2005.

On dispose de données sur l'utilisation directe d'énergie géothermique et d'énergie solaire thermique à partir de 1990.

La consommation d'électricité du sous-secteur des matériels de transport est comptabilisée avec celle du sous-secteur de la construction mécanique.

Turquie

Charbon : La production de gaz d'usine à gaz a diminué en 1989 par suite de fermetures d'usines, la dernière ayant fermé ses portes en 1994. L'utilisation de coke de gaz et de gaz d'usine à gaz a cessé en 1994. La réglementation imposée par les pouvoirs publics, en particulier à l'industrie et au secteur résidentiel, a provoqué un remplacement du charbon extrait dans le pays par du charbon importé et du gaz naturel.

Energies renouvelables combustibles et déchets : L'administration turque procède de manière intermittente à des enquêtes sur les énergies renouvelables et les déchets utilisés pour la production d'électricité et de chaleur. De ce fait, il peut apparaître certaines ruptures dans les séries de données concernant les énergies renouvelables combustibles et les déchets.

Gaz : Les données concernant le secteur commercial/services publics figuraient dans le secteur résidentiel avant 2001. La baisse de la consommation de gaz naturel observée entre 1999 et 2001 dans les produits d'alimentation de l'industrie pétrochimique est imputable à l'industrie des engrais.

Electricité et chaleur : Les données sur l'électricité produite à partir d'énergies renouvelables combustibles et de déchets sont disponibles à partir de 1991. En 1995, l'administration turque a modifié la classification des installations des autoproducteurs, par type et par source, afin de la rendre cohérente avec les définitions de l'AIE. Il s'ensuit des ruptures de séries entre 1994 et 1995, s'agissant des données sur la production d'électricité de ces installations. Des données sur la production d'électricité d'origine éolienne sont disponibles à partir de 1998. Pour l'édition de 2006, l'office statistique turc a fourni des données sur a production d'électricité et de chaleur fondées sur une nouvelle enquête qui a permis de réviser les séries chronologiques à partir de l'an 2000. Il s'ensuit des ruptures de séries chronologiques entre 1999 et 2000. Les séries de données sur les consommations n'ont pas toutes été révisées.

La consommation du sous-secteur industriel de la construction mécanique comprend celle du sous-secteur des matériels de transport. Avant 1998, la consommation du sous-secteur du bois et des produits dérivés comprend celle de l'industrie du papier, de la pâte à papier et de l'imprimerie.

4. COUVERTURE GEOGRAPHIQUE

L'**Allemagne** tient compte des nouveaux Länder à partir de 1970.

L'**Australie** ne comprend pas les territoires d'outre-mer.

Le Groenland et les Iles Féroé danoises ne sont pas pris en compte dans les données relatives au **Danemark**. Cependant, les données sur le pétrole du Groenland sont prises en compte dans les statistiques danoises avant 1990. L'administration danoise envisage de réviser les séries chronologiques en remontant jusqu'en 1974 afin d'en retirer ces quantités.

L'**Espagne** englobe les Iles Canaries.

Les **Etats-Unis** englobent les 50 Etats fédérés et le District de Columbia. Les statistiques sur le pétrole et sur les échanges de charbon concernent également Porto-Rico, l'Ile de Guam, les Iles Vierges des Etats-Unis, le Territoire non incorporé des Samoa américaines, l'Ile Johnston, les Iles Midway, l'Ile de Wake et les Iles Mariannes-du-Nord.

Dans les données relatives à la **France**, Monaco est pris en compte, mais non les départements et territoires d'outre-mer (Guadeloupe, Guyane, Martinique, Nouvelle-Calédonie, Polynésie française, Ile de la Réunion et St.-Pierre et Miquelon).

L'**Italie** englobe Saint Marin et le Vatican.

Le **Japon** englobe Okinawa.

Ni le Suriname ni les Antilles néerlandaises ne sont pris en compte dans les données relatives aux **Pays-Bas**.

Le **Portugal** englobe les Açores et l'Ile de Madère.

La **Suisse** n'englobe pas le Liechtenstein.

L'**Agence internationale de l'énergie**[5] **(AIE)** comprend l'Allemagne, l'Australie, l'Autriche, la Belgique, le Canada, la Corée, le Danemark, l'Espagne, les Etats-Unis, la Finlande, la France, la Grèce, la Hongrie, l'Irlande, l'Italie, le Japon, le Luxembourg, la Norvège, la Nouvelle-Zélande, les Pays-Bas, le Portugal, la République tchèque, le Royaume-Uni, la Suède, la Suisse et la Turquie.

L'**Organisation de coopération et de développement économiques (OCDE)** comprend l'Allemagne, l'Australie, l'Autriche, la Belgique, le Canada, la Corée, le Danemark, l'Espagne, les Etats-Unis, la Finlande, la France, la Grèce, la Hongrie, l'Irlande, l'Islande, l'Italie, le Japon, le Luxembourg, le Mexique, la Norvège, la Nouvelle-Zélande, les Pays-Bas, la Pologne, le Portugal, la République slovaque, la République tchèque, le Royaume-Uni, la Suède, la Suisse et la Turquie.

OCDE Amérique du Nord comprend le Canada, les Etats-Unis et le Mexique.

OCDE Pacifique comprend l'Australie, la Corée, le Japon et la Nouvelle-Zélande.

OCDE Europe comprend l'Allemagne, l'Autriche, la Belgique, le Danemark, l'Espagne, la Finlande, la France, la Grèce, la Hongrie, l'Irlande, l'Islande, l'Italie, le Luxembourg, la Norvège, les Pays-Bas, la Pologne, le Portugal, la République slovaque, la République tchèque, le Royaume-Uni, la Suède, la Suisse et la Turquie.

---

5. La Pologne et la République Slovaque devraient devenir des pays membres de l'AIE en 2007.

PART II

STATISTICAL DATA

PARTIE II

DONNEES STATISTIQUES

COUNTRY-SPECIFIC NET CALORIFIC VALUES

POUVOIRS CALORIFIQUES INFERIEURS SPECIFIQUES PAR PAYS

2004 - 2005

Country Specific Net Calorific Values (tonne of oil equivalent per tonne)

Pouvoirs calorifiques inférieurs spécifiques par pays (tonnes d'équivalent pétrole par tonne)

2004

	Australia	Austria	Belgium	Canada	Czech Republic	Denmark	Finland	France	Germany	Greece
Crude Oil										
Production	1.0506	1.0151	-	1.0220	0.9998	1.0270	-	0.9997	1.0212	0.9114
Imports	1.0188	1.0151	1.0210	1.0220	1.0024	1.0270	1.0516	0.9997	1.0212	0.9922
Exports	1.0506	-	-	1.0220	1.0032	1.0270	-	-	1.0212	0.9922
Average	1.0338	1.0151	1.0210	1.0220	1.0027	1.0270	1.0516	0.9997	1.0212	0.9847
NGL	1.0846	1.0151	-	1.0800	-	-	1.0800	1.0032	-	0.9925
Refinery Feedstocks	1.0338	1.0234	1.0150	1.0150	1.0000	1.0199	1.0150	0.9997	1.0150	0.9869
Additives	-	0.6000	-	-	0.6000	-	0.6000	0.6000	0.6000	0.9869
Other Hydrocarbons	-	-	-	1.0000	1.0000	0.6604	1.0000	-	1.0000	-
Biogasoline	-	-	-	0.6400	-	-	0.6568	0.8567	0.6401	-
Biodiesel	-	-	-	-	0.9076	0.8981	-	0.9044	0.8895	-
Other Liquid Biofuels	-	0.8742	-	-	-	-	-	-	0.8981	-
Anthracite										
Production	-	-	-	-	-	-	-	-	0.7087	-
Imports	-	0.6778	0.6015	0.6616	0.7643	-	-	-	0.7094	-
Exports	-	-	0.6015	-	0.7643	-	-	-	0.7275	-
Electricity Generation	-	-	-	-	-	-	-	-	0.7089	-
Industry	-	0.6901	0.6015	0.6616	-	-	-	-	0.7089	-
Other Uses	-	0.6786	0.6015	0.6616	0.7643	-	-	-	0.7089	-
Coking Coal										
Production	0.6807	-	-	0.5945	0.6857	-	-	-	0.6927	-
Imports	-	0.6943	0.7000	0.6766	0.6688	-	0.6998	0.7285	0.7218	-
Exports	0.6807	-	-	0.5945	0.6807	-	-	0.7285	-	-
Coke Ovens	0.6807	0.6943	0.7000	0.6766	0.6866	-	0.6998	0.7285	0.7013	-
Electricity Generation	-	-	-	-	-	-	-	-	0.6927	-
Industry	-	-	-	-	-	-	-	-	0.6927	-
Other Uses	0.6807	0.6943	0.7000	0.6766	0.6866	-	0.6998	0.7285	0.6927	-
Other Bituminous Coal										
Production	0.6138	-	-	0.6218	0.5851	-	-	0.6210	0.5484	-
Imports	-	0.6778	0.6455	0.6218	0.5732	0.5910	0.6091	0.6210	0.6167	0.6123
Exports	0.6138	0.6760	0.6455	0.6218	0.5947	0.5894	-	0.6210	0.7165	0.6123
Coke Ovens	-	-	-	-	-	-	-	-	-	-
Electricity Generation	0.6138	0.6769	0.6000	0.6218	0.5533	0.5879	0.6091	0.6210	0.5995	-
Industry	0.6138	0.6901	0.7000	0.6218	0.5656	0.6329	0.6091	0.6210	0.5995	0.6123
Other Uses	0.6138	0.6786	0.6455	0.6218	0.5606	0.5908	0.6091	0.6210	0.5971	0.6123
Sub-Bituminous Coal										
Production	0.4413	-	0.5247	0.4256	0.3102	-	-	-	-	-
Imports	-	0.5302	-	0.4256	-	-	-	-	-	-
Exports	-	-	0.4457	0.4256	0.3344	-	-	-	-	-
Electricity Generation	0.4388	-	0.5930	0.4256	0.2995	-	-	-	-	-
Industry	0.4585	0.5302	0.1999	-	0.3027	-	-	-	-	-
Other Uses	0.4413	0.5302	0.5247	0.4256	0.3186	-	-	-	-	-
Lignite										
Production	0.2224	0.2341	-	0.3433	0.1959	-	-	-	0.2177	0.1220
Imports	-	0.2341	0.5150	0.3433	0.1959	-	-	0.4060	0.2037	-
Exports	-	-	-	0.3433	-	-	-	-	0.2568	-
Electricity Generation	0.2224	0.2296	-	0.3433	0.1959	-	-	-	0.2175	0.1238
Industry	0.2224	0.2389	0.5150	0.3433	0.1959	-	-	0.4060	0.2521	0.2342
Other Uses	0.2224	0.2341	0.5150	0.3433	0.1959	-	-	0.4060	0.2516	0.1290
Patent Fuel	-	0.7404	0.7000	-	-	-	-	0.7643	0.7500	-
Coke Oven Coke	0.6126	0.6850	0.6650	0.6542	0.6646	0.6998	0.6998	0.6688	0.6843	0.6999
Coal Tar	-	0.9984	-	-	0.8762	-	0.8837	-	-	-
BKB	0.5015	0.4610	0.4800	-	0.5738	-	-	-	0.4965	0.3330
Peat	-	0.2102	-	-	-	-	0.2436	-	0.2000	-
Charcoal	-	-	-	-	-	-	-	-	-	-

Country Specific Net Calorific Values (tonne of oil equivalent per tonne)

Pouvoirs calorifiques inférieurs spécifiques par pays (tonnes d'équivalent pétrole par tonne)

2004

	Hungary	Iceland	Ireland	Italy	Japan	Korea	Luxem-bourg	Mexico	Nether-lands	New Zealand
Crude Oil										
Production	0.9817	-	-	1.0002	1.0142	-	-	1.0189	1.0199	1.0308
Imports	1.0055	-	1.0230	1.0002	1.0142	1.0200	-	-	1.0199	1.0062
Exports	0.9817	-	-	1.0002	-	-	-	1.0189	1.0199	1.0278
Average	1.0008	-	1.0230	1.0002	1.0142	1.0200	-	1.0189	1.0199	1.0216
NGL	1.0700	-	-	-	1.1207	-	-	1.0189	1.0509	1.0902
Refinery Feedstocks	1.0246	-	1.0150	0.9998	1.0150	1.0700	-	-	1.0150	1.0975
Additives	0.9984	-	-	0.6000	-	1.0000	-	1.0990	-	-
Other Hydrocarbons	0.9554	-	-	-	1.0518	1.0000	-	-	-	-
Biogasoline	-	-	-	-	-	-	-	-	-	-
Biodiesel	-	-	-	0.8800	-	0.8800	0.8800	-	-	-
Other Liquid Biofuels	-	-	-	-	-	-	-	-	0.8816	-
Anthracite										
Production	-	-	-	-	-	0.4286	-	-	-	-
Imports	-	-	0.6650	-	0.6497	0.5714	0.6998	-	0.6998	-
Exports	-	-	-	-	-	-	-	-	0.6998	-
Electricity Generation	-	-	-	-	-	0.4465	-	-	-	-
Industry	-	-	-	-	-	0.4286	0.6998	-	0.6998	-
Other Uses	-	-	0.6650	-	0.6497	0.4286	0.6998	-	0.6998	-
Coking Coal										
Production	-	-	-	-	-	-	-	0.5609	-	0.6821
Imports	0.7252	0.6700	-	0.7400	0.6777	0.6599	-	-	0.6848	-
Exports	-	-	-	-	-	-	-	-	0.6848	0.7227
Coke Ovens	0.7302	-	-	0.7400	0.6777	0.6588	-	0.5609	0.6848	-
Electricity Generation	0.6027	-	-	-	-	-	-	-	-	-
Industry	-	0.6700	-	-	-	0.6599	-	-	0.6848	-
Other Uses	0.7252	0.6700	-	0.7400	0.6730	0.6599	-	0.5609	0.6848	0.6821
Other Bituminous Coal										
Production	-	-	-	0.6350	-	-	-	-	-	0.6821
Imports	0.5856	0.6700	0.6649	0.6350	0.6194	0.6286	0.6998	0.5609	0.6123	0.6821
Exports	0.5653	-	0.6650	-	0.6194	-	-	-	0.6123	-
Coke Ovens	-	-	-	-	0.6194	-	-	0.5609	-	-
Electricity Generation	0.5808	-	0.6194	0.6350	0.6194	0.6286	-	-	0.5990	-
Industry	0.6210	0.6700	0.6650	0.6350	0.6194	0.6286	0.6998	-	0.5990	0.6821
Other Uses	0.5726	0.6700	0.6650	0.6350	0.6194	0.6286	0.6998	0.5609	0.5990	0.6821
Sub-Bituminous Coal										
Production	-	-	-	-	-	-	-	0.4635	-	0.5032
Imports	0.4183	-	-	-	-	0.4713	-	0.4635	-	0.5032
Exports	-	-	-	-	-	-	-	-	-	-
Electricity Generation	0.4227	-	-	-	-	0.4713	-	0.4635	-	0.5032
Industry	0.3822	-	-	-	-	0.4713	-	0.4635	-	0.5032
Other Uses	0.5008	-	-	-	-	0.4713	-	0.4635	-	0.5032
Lignite										
Production	0.1941	-	-	-	-	-	-	-	-	0.3406
Imports	-	-	0.4734	0.2500	-	-	-	0.3368	0.4777	-
Exports	0.2403	-	-	-	-	-	-	-	-	-
Electricity Generation	0.1957	-	-	-	-	-	-	-	-	-
Industry	0.2533	-	-	0.2500	-	-	-	-	0.4777	0.3406
Other Uses	0.3359	-	0.4734	0.2500	-	-	-	0.3368	0.4777	0.3406
Patent Fuel	-	-	0.6700	-	-	0.4744	-	-	-	-
Coke Oven Coke	0.6927	0.6370	-	0.6927	0.7189	0.6500	-	0.6334	0.6807	-
Coal Tar	0.9554	-	-	-	0.8686	-	-	-	1.0008	-
BKB	0.4777	-	0.4430	-	-	-	0.4801	-	-	-
Peat	-	-	0.3130	-	-	-	-	-	-	-
Charcoal	-	-	-	0.7350	0.6998	-	-	-	0.7165	-

Country Specific Net Calorific Values (tonne of oil equivalent per tonne)

Pouvoirs calorifiques inférieurs spécifiques par pays (tonnes d'équivalent pétrole par tonne)

2004

	Norway	Poland	Portugal	Slovak Republic	Spain	Sweden	Switzer-land	Turkey	United Kingdom	United States
Crude Oil										
Production	1.0240	1.0051	-	0.9912	1.0190	-	-	0.9881	1.0369	1.0333
Imports	1.0240	1.0156	1.0198	1.0031	1.0190	1.0070	1.0324	0.9929	1.0369	1.0289
Exports	1.0240	1.0156	-	0.9993	-	-	-	-	1.0369	1.0333
Average	1.0240	1.0150	1.0198	1.0030	1.0190	1.0070	1.0324	0.9917	1.0369	1.0287
NGL	1.0460	-	-	0.9840	-	-	-	-	1.1163	1.1137
Refinery Feedstocks	1.0150	1.0150	1.0744	1.0476	1.0150	1.0567	1.0438	1.0150	1.0150	1.0485
Additives	-	0.9600	-	1.0238	0.6000	-	0.9870	-	0.6000	0.6000
Other Hydrocarbons	-	0.9600	-	0.9912	-	-	-	-	-	1.2182
Biogasoline	-	0.6400	-	-	0.6399	0.7241	-	-	-	0.6388
Biodiesel	-	-	-	0.9190	0.9000	0.7978	0.7653	-	0.8800	0.9777
Other Liquid Biofuels	-	-	-	-	-	0.7978	-	-	-	0.5155
Anthracite										
Production	-	-	-	-	0.4734	-	-	-	-	0.6667
Imports	-	-	0.6999	-	0.6231	-	0.6712	-	-	0.5785
Exports	-	-	-	-	-	-	-	-	-	0.5648
Electricity Generation	-	-	-	-	0.4741	-	-	-	-	0.6667
Industry	-	-	0.6999	-	-	-	0.6712	-	-	0.5830
Other Uses	-	-	0.6999	-	0.6198	-	0.6712	-	-	0.6667
Coking Coal										
Production	-	0.7044	-	-	-	-	-	0.7067	0.6984	0.6849
Imports	-	0.7065	-	0.6970	0.7170	0.7165	-	0.7314	0.6897	0.6614
Exports	-	0.7108	-	-	-	-	-	-	0.6984	0.6465
Coke Ovens	-	0.7059	-	0.6970	0.7170	0.7165	-	0.7405	0.6984	0.6465
Electricity Generation	-	-	-	-	-	-	-	-	-	-
Industry	-	0.6759	-	0.6970	-	-	-	0.6677	0.6984	-
Other Uses	-	0.6888	-	0.6970	0.7170	0.7165	-	0.6716	0.6984	0.6849
Other Bituminous Coal										
Production	0.6712	0.5267	-	-	0.4658	-	-	0.4769	0.5923	0.6323
Imports	0.6712	0.6186	0.6105	0.6054	0.5786	0.6544	0.6712	0.6380	0.6063	0.6614
Exports	0.6712	0.6346	-	-	-	0.6544	-	-	0.7011	0.6465
Coke Ovens	-	0.6664	-	-	-	-	-	-	-	-
Electricity Generation	0.6712	0.5134	0.6105	0.6054	0.5555	0.6664	-	0.5309	0.5945	0.6145
Industry	0.6712	0.5548	0.6105	0.6054	0.5782	0.6415	0.6712	0.6602	0.6172	0.6509
Other Uses	0.6712	0.5829	0.6105	0.6054	0.6210	0.6544	0.6712	0.6567	0.5922	0.6396
Sub-Bituminous Coal										
Production	-	-	-	-	0.2794	-	-	0.4299	-	0.4629
Imports	-	-	-	-	-	-	-	-	-	0.5549
Exports	-	-	-	-	-	-	-	-	-	0.4574
Electricity Generation	-	-	-	-	0.2794	-	-	-	-	0.4651
Industry	-	-	-	-	-	-	-	0.4299	-	0.4918
Other Uses	-	-	-	-	0.2794	-	-	0.4299	-	0.4621
Lignite										
Production	-	0.2112	-	0.2768	0.1617	-	-	0.2091	-	0.3391
Imports	-	-	-	0.3088	-	-	-	-	-	0.3248
Exports	-	0.2035	-	-	-	-	-	-	-	0.3561
Electricity Generation	-	0.2034	-	0.2937	0.1617	-	-	0.1816	-	0.3396
Industry	-	0.2192	-	0.2813	-	-	-	0.2999	-	0.3671
Other Uses	-	0.1993	-	0.2813	0.1617	-	-	0.2998	-	0.3577
Patent Fuel	-	0.5447	-	-	-	-	-	-	0.7216	0.5726
Coke Oven Coke	0.6807	0.6654	0.6698	0.6743	0.7235	0.6707	0.6712	0.6999	0.6694	0.6561
Coal Tar	-	0.9200	-	-	-	-	-	-	-	-
BKB	-	0.4191	-	0.5493	-	0.4800	0.4801	0.4999	-	-
Peat	-	-	-	-	-	0.2986	-	-	-	-
Charcoal	-	-	-	-	-	-	-	-	-	-

Country Specific Net Calorific Values (tonne of oil equivalent per tonne)

Pouvoirs calorifiques inférieurs spécifiques par pays (tonnes d'équivalent pétrole par tonne)

2005

	Australia	Austria	Belgium	Canada	Czech Republic	Denmark	Finland	France	Germany	Greece
Crude Oil										
Production	1.0506	1.0151	-	1.0220	0.9998	1.0270	-	0.9997	1.0212	0.9114
Imports	1.0188	1.0151	1.0210	1.0220	1.0027	1.0270	1.0516	0.9997	1.0212	0.9922
Exports	1.0506	-	-	1.0220	1.0032	1.0270	-	-	1.0212	0.9998
Average	1.0338	1.0151	1.0210	1.0220	1.0027	1.0270	1.0516	0.9997	1.0212	0.9847
NGL	1.0846	1.0151	-	1.0800	-	-	1.0800	1.0032	-	0.9925
Refinery Feedstocks	1.0338	1.0127	1.0150	1.0150	1.0000	1.0199	1.0150	0.9997	1.0150	0.9869
Additives	-	0.6000	-	-	0.6000	-	0.6000	0.6000	0.6000	0.9869
Other Hydrocarbons	-	-	-	1.0000	1.0000	-	1.0000	-	1.0000	-
Biogasoline	0.6400	-	-	0.6400	-	-	-	0.8567	0.6401	-
Biodiesel	-	0.8742	-	-	0.8861	0.8981	-	0.9044	0.8895	-
Other Liquid Biofuels	-	0.8742	0.8837	-	-	-	-	-	0.8981	-
Anthracite										
Production	-	-	-	-	-	-	-	-	0.7094	-
Imports	-	0.6721	0.6015	0.6616	0.7643	-	-	-	0.7094	-
Exports	-	0.6731	0.6015	-	0.7643	-	-	-	0.7285	-
Electricity Generation	-	-	-	-	-	-	-	-	0.7096	-
Industry	-	0.6890	0.6015	0.6616	-	-	-	-	0.7096	-
Other Uses	-	0.6720	0.6015	0.6616	0.7643	-	-	-	0.7096	-
Coking Coal										
Production	0.6807	-	-	0.5945	0.6788	-	-	-	0.6927	-
Imports	-	0.6943	0.7000	0.6766	0.5970	-	0.6998	0.7285	0.7206	-
Exports	0.6807	-	0.7000	0.5945	0.6511	-	-	0.7285	-	-
Coke Ovens	0.6807	0.6943	0.7000	0.6766	0.6883	-	0.6998	0.7285	0.6950	-
Electricity Generation	-	-	-	-	-	-	-	-	0.6950	-
Industry	-	-	-	-	-	-	-	-	0.6950	-
Other Uses	0.6807	0.6943	0.7000	0.6766	0.6883	-	0.6998	0.7285	0.6950	-
Other Bituminous Coal										
Production	0.6138	-	-	0.6094	0.5829	-	-	0.6210	0.5632	-
Imports	-	0.6721	0.6158	0.6094	0.5923	0.5922	0.6091	0.6210	0.6167	0.6119
Exports	0.6138	-	0.6158	0.6094	0.7013	0.5828	-	0.6210	0.7165	0.6119
Coke Ovens	-	-	-	-	-	-	-	-	-	-
Electricity Generation	0.6138	0.6609	0.6000	0.6094	0.5350	0.5831	0.6091	0.6210	0.6043	-
Industry	0.6138	0.6890	0.7000	0.6094	0.5321	0.6329	0.6091	0.6210	0.6043	0.6119
Other Uses	0.6138	0.6720	0.6158	0.6094	0.5030	0.5921	0.6091	0.6210	0.5995	0.6119
Sub-Bituminous Coal										
Production	0.4413	-	0.5247	0.4251	0.3108	-	-	-	-	-
Imports	-	0.5302	-	0.4251	-	-	-	-	-	-
Exports	-	-	0.4457	0.4251	0.3117	-	-	-	-	-
Electricity Generation	0.4388	-	-	0.4251	0.3028	-	-	-	-	-
Industry	0.4585	0.5302	0.1999	-	0.2930	-	-	-	-	-
Other Uses	0.4413	0.5302	0.5247	0.4251	0.3267	-	-	-	-	-
Lignite										
Production	0.2224	-	-	0.3455	0.2090	-	-	-	0.2160	0.1230
Imports	-	0.2153	0.5150	0.3455	0.2025	-	-	0.4060	0.2030	-
Exports	-	-	-	0.3455	-	-	-	-	0.2505	-
Electricity Generation	0.2224	0.2227	-	0.3455	0.2025	-	-	-	0.2138	0.1252
Industry	0.2224	0.2389	0.5150	0.3455	0.2090	-	-	0.4060	0.2451	0.2258
Other Uses	0.2224	0.2187	0.5150	0.3455	0.2090	-	-	0.4060	0.2451	0.1242
Patent Fuel	-	0.7404	0.7000	-	-	-	-	0.7643	0.7500	-
Coke Oven Coke	0.6126	0.6927	0.6615	0.6542	0.6172	0.6998	0.6998	0.6688	0.6843	0.6999
Coal Tar	-	0.9984	-	-	0.8918	-	0.8837	-	-	-
BKB	0.5015	0.4610	0.4800	-	0.5474	-	-	-	0.4697	0.3481
Peat	-	0.2102	-	-	-	-	0.2436	-	0.2000	-
Charcoal	-	-	-	-	-	-	-	-	-	-

Country Specific Net Calorific Values (tonne of oil equivalent per tonne)
Pouvoirs calorifiques inférieurs spécifiques par pays (tonnes d'équivalent pétrole par tonne)

2005

	Hungary	Iceland	Ireland	Italy	Japan	Korea	Luxem-bourg	Mexico	Nether-lands	New Zealand
Crude Oil										
Production	0.9817	-	-	0.9998	1.0142	1.0200	-	1.0536	1.0199	1.0156
Imports	1.0055	-	1.0230	0.9998	1.0142	1.0200	-	-	1.0199	1.0066
Exports	1.0055	-	-	0.9998	-	-	-	1.0536	1.0199	1.0219
Average	1.0032	-	1.0230	0.9998	1.0142	1.0200	-	1.0536	1.0199	1.0147
NGL	1.0509	-	-	-	1.1207	-	-	1.0189	1.0509	1.0903
Refinery Feedstocks	1.0318	-	1.0150	0.9998	1.0150	1.0700	-	-	1.0150	1.0010
Additives	0.9984	-	-	0.6000	-	1.0000	-	1.0990	-	-
Other Hydrocarbons	0.9554	-	-	-	1.0518	1.0000	-	-	-	-
Biogasoline	0.6400	-	-	-	-	-	-	-	-	-
Biodiesel	-	-	0.8903	0.8800	-	0.8800	0.8800	-	-	-
Other Liquid Biofuels	-	-	-	-	-	-	-	-	0.8882	-
Anthracite										
Production	-	-	-	-	-	0.4286	-	-	-	-
Imports	-	-	0.6650	-	0.6497	0.5714	0.6998	-	0.6998	-
Exports	-	-	-	-	-	-	-	-	0.6998	-
Electricity Generation	-	-	-	-	-	0.4286	-	-	-	-
Industry	-	-	-	-	-	0.4286	0.6998	-	0.6998	-
Other Uses	-	-	0.6650	-	0.6497	0.4286	0.6998	-	0.6998	-
Coking Coal										
Production	-	-	-	-	-	-	-	0.5609	-	0.6783
Imports	0.7507	0.6700	-	0.7400	0.6777	0.6600	-	-	0.6848	-
Exports	-	-	-	-	-	-	-	-	0.6848	0.7225
Coke Ovens	0.7507	-	-	0.7400	0.6777	0.6600	-	0.5609	0.6848	-
Electricity Generation	-	-	-	-	-	-	-	-	-	-
Industry	-	0.6700	-	-	-	-	-	-	0.6848	-
Other Uses	0.7507	0.6700	-	0.7400	0.6730	0.6600	-	0.5609	0.6848	0.6783
Other Bituminous Coal										
Production	-	-	-	0.6350	-	-	-	-	-	0.6783
Imports	0.5936	0.6700	0.6649	0.6350	0.6194	0.5947	0.6998	0.5609	0.5989	0.6783
Exports	0.5689	-	0.6650	-	0.6194	-	-	-	0.5989	-
Coke Ovens	-	-	-	-	0.6194	-	-	0.5609	-	-
Electricity Generation	0.6037	-	0.6194	0.6350	0.6194	0.5947	-	-	0.5989	-
Industry	0.5691	0.6700	0.6650	0.6350	0.6194	0.5947	0.6998	-	0.5989	0.6783
Other Uses	0.6184	0.6700	0.6650	0.6350	0.6194	0.5947	0.6998	0.5609	0.5989	0.6783
Sub-Bituminous Coal										
Production	-	-	-	-	-	-	-	0.4635	-	0.5035
Imports	0.4308	-	-	-	-	0.4992	-	0.4635	-	0.5035
Exports	0.4299	-	-	-	-	-	-	-	-	-
Electricity Generation	0.3822	-	-	-	-	0.4992	-	0.4635	-	0.5035
Industry	-	-	-	-	-	0.4992	-	0.4635	-	0.5035
Other Uses	0.5072	-	-	-	-	0.4992	-	0.4635	-	0.5035
Lignite										
Production	0.1827	-	-	-	-	-	-	-	-	0.3430
Imports	-	-	0.4734	0.2500	-	-	-	0.3368	0.4777	-
Exports	0.2104	-	-	-	-	-	-	-	-	-
Electricity Generation	0.1830	-	-	-	-	-	-	-	-	-
Industry	0.3981	-	-	0.2500	-	-	-	-	0.4777	0.3430
Other Uses	0.2861	-	0.4734	0.2500	-	-	-	0.3368	0.4777	0.3430
Patent Fuel	-	-	0.6700	-	-	0.4744	-	-	-	-
Coke Oven Coke	0.7032	0.6370	-	0.6927	0.7189	0.6500	-	0.6334	0.6807	-
Coal Tar	0.9100	-	-	-	0.8686	-	-	-	1.0008	-
BKB	0.4777	-	0.4430	-	-	-	0.4801	-	-	-
Peat	-	-	0.3130	-	-	-	-	-	-	-
Charcoal	-	-	-	0.7350	0.6998	-	-	-	0.7165	-

Country Specific Net Calorific Values (tonne of oil equivalent per tonne)

Pouvoirs calorifiques inférieurs spécifiques par pays (tonnes d'équivalent pétrole par tonne)

2005

	Norway	Poland	Portugal	Slovak Republic	Spain	Sweden	Switzer-land	Turkey	United Kingdom	United States
Crude Oil										
Production	1.0220	0.9974	-	0.9840	1.0190	-	-	0.9881	1.0369	1.0333
Imports	1.0220	1.0149	1.0198	1.0032	1.0190	1.0070	1.0324	0.9929	1.0369	1.0284
Exports	1.0220	0.9584	-	0.9964	-	-	-	-	1.0369	1.0333
Average	1.0220	1.0147	1.0198	1.0029	1.0190	1.0070	1.0324	0.9917	1.0369	1.0285
NGL	1.0460	-	-	0.9984	-	-	-	-	1.1163	1.1137
Refinery Feedstocks	1.0150	1.0150	1.0744	1.0476	1.0150	1.0567	1.0438	1.0150	1.0150	1.0525
Additives	-	0.8007	-	1.0238	0.6000	-	0.9870	-	-	0.6000
Other Hydrocarbons	-	0.9600	-	0.9912	-	-	-	-	-	1.2182
Biogasoline	-	0.6400	-	-	0.6399	0.7241	0.8942	-	0.6400	0.6388
Biodiesel	-	0.8800	-	0.9543	0.9000	0.7978	0.7653	-	0.8800	0.9777
Other Liquid Biofuels	-	-	-	-	-	0.7978	-	-	-	0.5155
Anthracite										
Production	-	-	-	-	0.4601	-	-	-	-	0.6667
Imports	-	-	0.7614	0.6855	0.6042	-	0.6712	-	-	0.5785
Exports	-	-	-	-	-	-	-	-	-	0.5648
Electricity Generation	-	-	-	0.6855	0.4894	-	-	-	-	0.6667
Industry	-	-	0.7614	0.6855	-	-	0.6712	-	-	0.5783
Other Uses	-	-	0.7614	0.6855	0.6376	-	0.6712	-	-	0.6667
Coking Coal										
Production	-	0.7070	-	-	-	-	-	0.6997	0.7373	0.6691
Imports	-	0.7065	-	0.7018	0.7170	0.7165	-	0.7401	0.6894	0.6614
Exports	-	0.7082	-	-	-	-	-	-	0.7373	0.6465
Coke Ovens	-	0.7048	-	0.7018	0.7170	0.7165	-	0.7515	0.6909	0.6952
Electricity Generation	-	-	-	-	-	-	-	-	-	-
Industry	-	0.6874	-	0.7018	-	-	-	0.7078	0.7373	-
Other Uses	-	0.6876	-	0.7018	0.7170	0.7165	-	0.6774	0.7373	0.6691
Other Bituminous Coal										
Production	0.6712	0.5508	-	-	0.5010	-	-	0.4796	0.5718	0.6340
Imports	0.6712	0.5852	0.6105	0.6110	0.5742	0.6544	0.6712	0.6259	0.6061	0.6614
Exports	0.6712	0.5868	-	-	-	0.6544	-	-	0.7469	0.6465
Coke Ovens	-	-	-	-	-	-	-	-	-	-
Electricity Generation	0.6712	0.5148	0.6105	0.6110	0.5594	0.6664	-	0.4796	0.5663	0.6101
Industry	0.6712	0.5832	-	0.6110	0.5782	0.6415	0.6712	0.6722	0.5772	0.6480
Other Uses	0.6712	0.6086	0.6105	0.6110	0.6210	0.6544	0.6712	0.6539	0.5922	0.6365
Sub-Bituminous Coal										
Production	-	-	-	-	0.2876	-	-	0.4299	-	0.4630
Imports	-	-	-	-	-	-	-	-	-	0.5549
Exports	-	-	-	-	-	-	-	-	-	0.4564
Electricity Generation	-	-	-	-	0.2876	-	-	-	-	0.4674
Industry	-	-	-	-	-	-	-	0.4299	-	0.4812
Other Uses	-	-	-	-	0.2876	-	-	0.4299	-	0.4768
Lignite										
Production	-	0.2066	-	0.2537	0.1553	-	-	0.1613	-	0.3394
Imports	-	-	-	0.3116	-	-	-	-	-	0.3248
Exports	-	0.2090	-	-	-	-	-	-	-	0.3561
Electricity Generation	-	0.2088	-	0.2567	0.1553	-	-	0.1418	-	0.3416
Industry	-	0.2204	-	0.2938	-	-	-	0.2999	-	0.4052
Other Uses	-	0.2074	-	0.2938	0.1553	-	-	0.2998	-	0.3501
Patent Fuel	-	-	-	0.7000	-	-	-	-	0.7374	0.5930
Coke Oven Coke	0.6807	0.6669	0.6698	0.6768	0.7235	0.6707	0.6712	0.6999	0.6648	0.6561
Coal Tar	-	0.9200	-	0.7999	-	-	-	-	-	-
BKB	-	0.4602	-	0.5493	-	0.4800	0.4801	0.4999	-	-
Peat	-	-	-	-	-	0.2986	-	-	-	-
Charcoal	-	-	-	0.7350	-	-	-	-	-	-

ENERGY INDICATORS AND BALANCE SHEETS

INDICATEURS ENERGETIQUES ET BILANS ENERGETIQUES

2004 - 2005

OECD Total / OCDE Total
Key Indicators
Indicateurs principaux

	1960	1970	1973	1980	1990	1995
Energy Production (Mtoe)	..	..	2 445.46	2 904.54	3 418.72	3 665.89
Net Imports (Mtoe)	..	..	1 410.07	1 293.78	1 229.00	1 278.90
Total Primary Energy Supply (Mtoe)	..	..	3 762.69	4 076.85	4 525.49	4 890.80
Net Oil Imports (Mtoe)	..	..	1 386.70	1 217.76	1 065.50	1 080.29
Oil Supply (Mtoe)	..	..	1 993.13	1 961.34	1 899.44	2 033.32
Electricity Consumption (TWh)*	..	..	4 124.49	5 237.82	7 055.35	7 950.08
GDP (billion 2000 US$ using exch. rates)	6 274.87	10 421.94	12 147.22	14 689.43	19 901.40	22 007.83
GDP (billion 2000 US$ using PPPs)	6 787.19	11 079.82	12 894.29	15 618.53	20 945.29	23 193.62
Population (millions)	769.91	870.84	902.09	964.58	1 043.65	1 089.17
Industrial Production Index (2000=100)	..	..	..	62.10	78.10	83.40
Energy Production/TPES	..	..	0.6499	0.7124	0.7554	0.7495
Net Oil Imports/GDP (toe per thousand 2000 US$)	..	..	0.1142	0.0829	0.0535	0.0491
TPES/GDP (toe per thousand 2000 US$)	..	..	0.3098	0.2775	0.2274	0.2222
TPES/GDP (toe per thousand 2000 US$ PPP)	..	..	0.2918	0.2610	0.2161	0.2109
TPES/Population (toe per capita)	..	..	4.1711	4.2266	4.3362	4.4904
Oil Supply/GDP (toe per thousand 2000 US$)	..	..	0.1641	0.1335	0.0954	0.0924
Oil Supply/Population (toe per capita)	..	..	2.2095	2.0334	1.8200	1.8668
Elect. Cons./GDP (kWh per 2000 US$)	..	..	0.3395	0.3566	0.3545	0.3612
Elect. Cons./Population (kWh per capita)	..	..	4 572	5 430	6 760	7 299
Industry Cons.**/Industrial Production (2000=100)	..	..	..	150.65	112.52	108.15
Industry Oil Cons.**/Industrial Production (2000=100)	..	..	..	171.94	114.88	114.21

	2000	2001	2002	2003	2004	2005
Energy Production (Mtoe)	3 829.77	3 869.45	3 847.44	3 806.93	3 858.86	3 833.78
Net Imports (Mtoe)	1 531.69	1 568.43	1 564.75	1 662.32	1 739.44	1 812.81
Total Primary Energy Supply (Mtoe)	5 326.37	5 302.61	5 349.04	5 400.40	5 505.39	5 547.60
Net Oil Imports (Mtoe)	1 218.01	1 235.22	1 210.65	1 270.56	1 322.21	1 392.65
Oil Supply (Mtoe)	2 165.51	2 174.04	2 170.52	2 202.07	2 237.22	2 249.00
Electricity Consumption (TWh)*	9 048.60	8 989.41	9 210.32	9 338.84	9 551.24	9 800.22
GDP (billion 2000 US$ using exch. rates)	25 659.84	25 956.09	26 315.06	26 829.70	27 670.56	28 394.27
GDP (billion 2000 US$ using PPPs)	27 277.80	27 609.80	28 045.93	28 609.47	29 536.68	30 320.83
Population (millions)	1 130.28	1 138.75	1 147.14	1 155.72	1 164.11	1 171.52
Industrial Production Index (2000=100)	100.00	97.60	97.90	99.40	102.80	105.10
Energy Production/TPES	0.7190	0.7297	0.7193	0.7049	0.7009	0.6911
Net Oil Imports/GDP (toe per thousand 2000 US$)	0.0475	0.0476	0.0460	0.0474	0.0478	0.0490
TPES/GDP (toe per thousand 2000 US$)	0.2076	0.2043	0.2033	0.2013	0.1990	0.1954
TPES/GDP (toe per thousand 2000 US$ PPP)	0.1953	0.1921	0.1907	0.1888	0.1864	0.1830
TPES/Population (toe per capita)	4.7124	4.6565	4.6629	4.6728	4.7293	4.7354
Oil Supply/GDP (toe per thousand 2000 US$)	0.0844	0.0838	0.0825	0.0821	0.0809	0.0792
Oil Supply/Population (toe per capita)	1.9159	1.9092	1.8921	1.9054	1.9218	1.9197
Elect. Cons./GDP (kWh per 2000 US$)	0.3526	0.3463	0.3500	0.3481	0.3452	0.3451
Elect. Cons./Population (kWh per capita)	8 006	7 894	8 029	8 081	8 205	8 365
Industry Cons.**/Industrial Production (2000=100)	100.00	99.36	99.24	98.29	97.58	94.17
Industry Oil Cons.**/Industrial Production (2000=100)	100.00	103.25	103.31	102.43	103.54	100.45

* Electricity consumption equals domestic supply less distribution losses.
La consommation d'électricité représente l'approvisionnement intérieur diminué des pertes de distribution.

** Includes non-energy use in industry/transformation/energy sectors.
Comprend l'usage non-énergétique dans les secteurs de l'industrie/transformation/énergie.

OECD Total / OCDE Total

Figure 1. TPES* in 1973

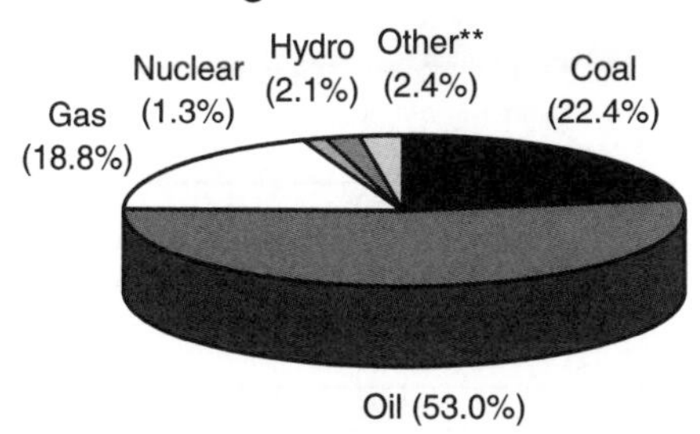

Figure 2. TPES* in 2005

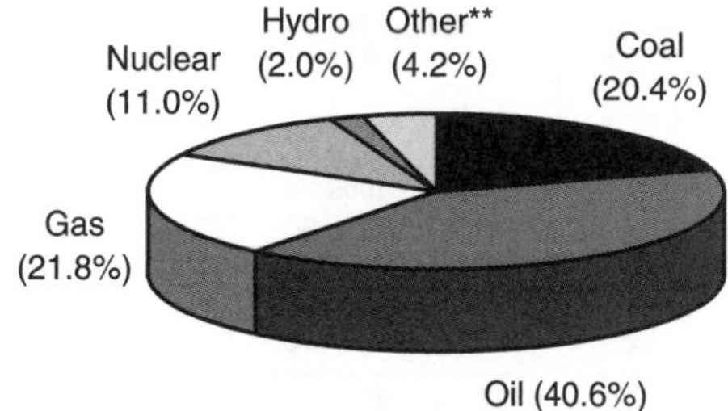

Figure 3. Final Consumption by Sector***

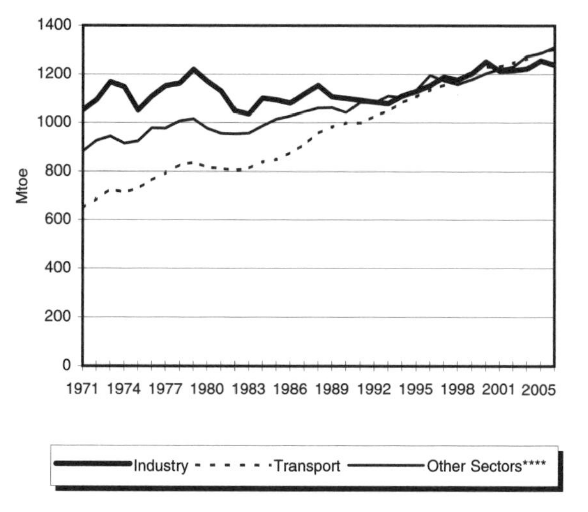

Figure 4. Breakdown of Sectorial Final Consumption by Source in 1973 and 2005***

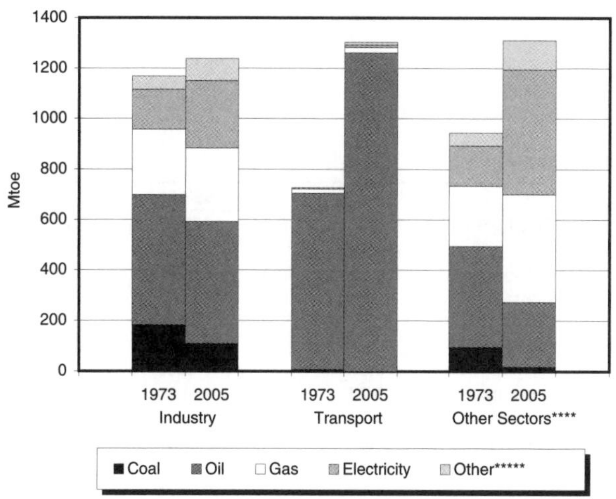

Figure 5. Electricity Generation by Fuel

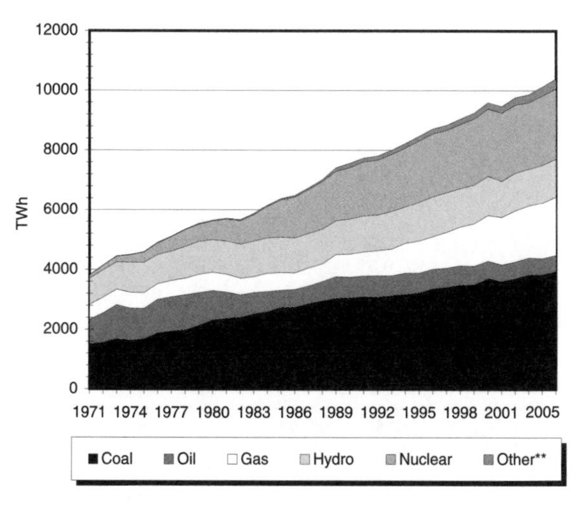

Figure 6. Electricity Consumption/GDP, TPES/GDP and Energy Production/TPES

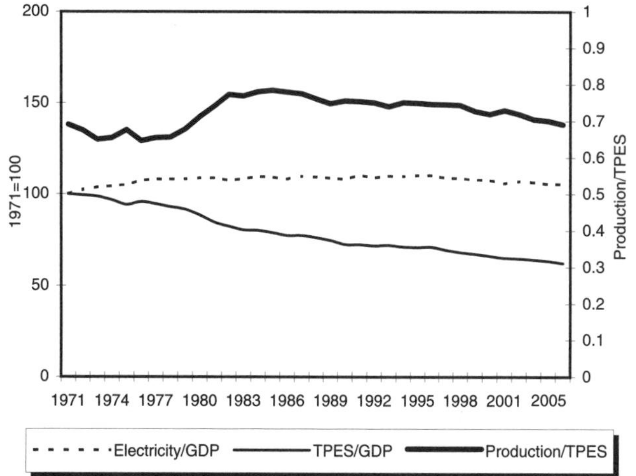

* Excluding electricity trade.

** Includes geothermal, solar, wind, combustible renewables & waste, etc.

*** Includes non-energy use.

**** Includes residential, commercial and public services, agriculture/forestry, fishing and non-specified.

***** Includes comb. renewables & waste, direct use of geothermal/solar thermal and heat produced in CHP/heat plants.

OECD Total / OCDE Total : 2004

Million tonnes of oil equivalent / *Million de tonnes d'équivalent pétrole*

SUPPLY AND CONSUMPTION	Coal	Crude Oil	Petroleum Products	Gas	Nuclear	Hydro	Geotherm. Solar etc.	Combust. Renew. & Waste	Electricity	Heat	Total
APPROVISIONNEMENT ET DEMANDE	*Charbon*	*Pétrole brut*	*Produits pétroliers*	*Gaz*	*Nucléaire*	*Hydro*	*Géotherm. solaire etc.*	*Comb. ren. & déchets*	*Electricité*	*Chaleur*	*Total*
Production	987.72	1009.92	-	923.39	604.35	108.96	37.57	186.50	-	0.45	3858.86
Imports	363.51	1660.86	489.10	515.29	-	-	-	2.38	31.26	0.00	3062.42
Exports	-223.37	-445.33	-382.42	-241.36	-	-	-	-0.70	-29.79	-0.01	-1322.97
Intl. Marine Bunkers	-	-	-88.98	-	-	-	-	-	-	-	-88.98
Stock Changes	3.87	-5.92	-0.01	-1.93	-	-	-	0.06	-	-	-3.93
TPES	**1131.74**	**2219.53**	**17.69**	**1195.39**	**604.35**	**108.96**	**37.57**	**188.25**	**1.47**	**0.45**	**5505.39**
Transfers	-	-41.69	52.26	-	-	-	-	-	-	-	10.57
Statistical Differences	-16.74	-13.29	-1.85	5.03	-	-	0.00	-0.01	-0.13	0.20	-26.79
Electricity Plants	-808.52	-6.30	-90.54	-245.40	-596.69	-108.96	-30.01	-27.57	777.27	-0.11	-1136.83
CHP Plants	-92.76	-0.00	-17.43	-115.93	-7.67	-	-0.88	-28.18	93.36	58.04	-111.46
Heat Plants	-4.77	-	-1.68	-5.06	-	-	-0.18	-3.19	-0.37	13.01	-2.24
Gas Works	-2.28	-	-2.67	3.19	-	-	-	-	-	-	-1.76
Petroleum Refineries	-	-2181.37	2191.62	-0.69	-	-	-	-	-	-	9.56
Coal Transformation	-60.89	0.04	-2.59	-0.26	-	-	-	-0.00	-	-	-63.70
Liquefaction Plants	-	0.56	-	-1.18	-	-	-	-	-	-	-0.62
Other Transformation	0.00	23.99	-24.73	-0.00	-	-	-	-0.12	-	-	-0.86
Own Use	-12.01	-0.02	-121.40	-84.27	-	-	-0.00	-0.10	-62.20	-3.98	-283.98
Distribution Losses	-0.88	-	-	-2.96	-	-	-0.25	-0.01	-57.22	-4.50	-65.82
TFC	**132.90**	**1.46**	**1998.68**	**747.86**	**-**	**-**	**6.25**	**129.06**	**752.18**	**63.09**	**3831.47**
INDUSTRY SECTOR	**112.88**	**0.04**	**143.74**	**264.66**	**-**	**-**	**0.42**	**63.11**	**264.45**	**22.90**	**872.21**
Iron and Steel	42.63	-	6.06	28.28	-	-	-	0.05	30.46	0.46	107.95
Chemical and Petrochem.	11.42	0.04	31.87	73.85	-	-	0.00	1.43	49.77	6.93	175.31
Non-Ferrous Metals	2.38	-	3.45	11.75	-	-	0.00	0.13	26.76	0.18	44.64
Non-Metallic Minerals	22.85	-	19.18	29.64	-	-	0.00	2.35	15.00	0.10	89.13
Transport Equipment	0.46	-	1.96	9.33	-	-	0.00	0.02	9.60	0.27	21.65
Machinery	0.67	-	5.57	18.71	-	-	0.00	0.04	28.80	0.41	54.21
Mining and Quarrying	0.77	-	4.95	6.63	-	-	0.05	0.00	8.42	0.11	20.93
Food and Tobacco	6.24	-	13.25	30.42	-	-	0.01	4.59	19.67	0.79	74.97
Paper, Pulp and Printing	7.60	-	12.20	25.04	-	-	0.13	42.08	33.79	1.45	122.31
Wood and Wood Products	0.19	-	2.83	2.64	-	-	-	8.79	5.02	0.19	19.66
Construction	1.80	-	12.04	1.36	-	-	0.00	0.09	1.47	0.05	16.80
Textile and Leather	0.59	-	3.28	8.37	-	-	0.00	0.10	7.95	0.93	21.23
Non-specified	15.27	-	27.08	18.65	-	-	0.23	3.43	27.75	11.02	103.43
TRANSPORT SECTOR	**0.07**	**-**	**1246.41**	**20.02**	**-**	**-**	**-**	**9.16**	**9.76**	**-**	**1285.43**
International Aviation	-	-	75.80	-	-	-	-	-	-	-	75.80
Domestic Aviation	-	-	87.50	-	-	-	-	-	-	-	87.50
Road	-	-	1043.69	1.25	-	-	-	9.11	-	-	1054.05
Rail	0.01	-	17.61	-	-	-	-	0.00	8.08	-	25.70
Pipeline Transport	-	-	0.02	18.74	-	-	-	-	0.39	-	19.16
Domestic Navigation	0.07	-	20.20	-	-	-	-	0.05	-	-	20.32
Non-specified	-	-	1.60	0.03	-	-	-	-	1.29	-	2.91
OTHER SECTORS	**18.08**	**-**	**258.09**	**425.50**	**-**	**-**	**5.83**	**56.79**	**477.96**	**40.19**	**1282.46**
Residential	11.19	-	122.03	272.85	-	-	4.57	51.35	233.13	15.02	710.14
Comm. and Publ. Services	5.27	-	81.70	140.21	-	-	0.77	3.95	223.18	6.90	461.98
Agriculture/Forestry	1.55	-	47.49	5.24	-	-	0.19	1.47	6.64	0.30	62.87
Fishing	0.00	-	4.79	-	-	-	0.00	-	0.19	0.00	4.99
Non-specified	0.08	-	2.08	7.21	-	-	0.31	0.02	14.82	17.97	42.48
NON-ENERGY USE	**1.86**	**1.41**	**350.43**	**37.67**	**-**	**-**	**-**	**-**	**-**	**-**	**391.37**
in Industry/Transf./Energy	1.71	1.41	342.42	37.67	-	-	-	-	-	-	383.22
of which: Feedstocks	*0.47*	*1.41*	*233.54*	*36.58*	-	-	-	-	-	-	*272.00*
in Transport	-	-	4.70	-	-	-	-	-	-	-	4.70
in Other Sectors	0.14	-	3.31	-	-	-	-	-	-	-	3.45
Electricity Generated - TWh	***3838.33***	***36.41***	***503.14***	***1857.85***	***2318.55***	***1266.99***	***118.88***	***183.01***	**-**	***0.45***	***10123.60***
Electricity Plants	*3498.59*	*36.39*	*419.44*	*1319.70*	*2289.61*	*1266.99*	*114.65*	*92.25*	-	*0.26*	*9037.87*
CHP plants	*339.74*	*0.02*	*83.70*	*538.15*	*28.94*	-	*4.23*	*90.76*	-	*0.19*	*1085.73*
Heat Generated - PJ	***884.36***	***0.11***	***310.45***	***1272.43***	***5.15***	**-**	***18.36***	***339.28***	***7.92***	***156.01***	***2994.05***
CHP plants	*726.55*	*0.11*	*266.43*	*1105.37*	*5.15*	-	*8.81*	*235.08*	*1.78*	*89.64*	*2438.92*
Heat Plants	*157.80*	-	*44.02*	*167.06*	-	-	*9.54*	*104.20*	*6.14*	*66.37*	*555.13*

OECD Total / OCDE Total : 2005

Million tonnes of oil equivalent / *Million de tonnes d'équivalent pétrole*

SUPPLY AND CONSUMPTION / *APPROVISIONNEMENT ET DEMANDE*	Coal / *Charbon*	Crude Oil / *Pétrole brut*	Petroleum Products / *Produits pétroliers*	Gas / *Gaz*	Nuclear / *Nucléaire*	Hydro / *Hydro*	Geotherm. Solar etc. / *Géotherm. solaire etc.*	Combust. Renew. & Waste / *Comb. ren. & déchets*	Electricity / *Electricité*	Heat / *Chaleur*	Total / *Total*
Production	1003.14	965.84	-	911.59	611.43	109.26	39.82	192.19	-	0.50	3833.78
Imports	355.89	1670.05	540.73	539.49	-	-	-	3.21	35.43	0.00	3144.81
Exports	-231.12	-408.35	-409.78	-247.85	-	-	-	-0.96	-33.94	-0.01	-1332.00
Intl. Marine Bunkers	-	-	-96.45	-	-	-	-	-	-	-	-96.45
Stock Changes	2.35	-8.88	-4.17	8.21	-	-	-	-0.05	-	-	-2.54
TPES	**1130.27**	**2218.66**	**30.34**	**1211.44**	**611.43**	**109.26**	**39.82**	**194.39**	**1.49**	**0.49**	**5547.60**
Transfers	-	-34.15	44.39	-	-	-	-	-	-	-	10.24
Statistical Differences	-12.49	-16.44	-8.93	1.86	-	-	0.00	0.11	-0.14	0.19	-35.84
Electricity Plants	-826.07	-8.23	-90.60	-263.43	-603.08	-109.26	-31.94	-27.84	802.41	-0.47	-1158.51
CHP Plants	-87.42	-	-17.33	-113.49	-8.35	-	-0.99	-29.13	91.35	59.86	-105.50
Heat Plants	-3.96	-	-1.61	-5.42	-	-	-0.18	-3.34	-0.37	26.38	11.50
Gas Works	-2.42	-	-2.42	3.09	-	-	-	-	-	-	-1.75
Petroleum Refineries	-	-2183.13	2191.63	-0.71	-	-	-	-	-	-	7.78
Coal Transformation	-59.30	0.02	-2.08	-0.23	-	-	-	-0.00	-	-	-61.59
Liquefaction Plants	-	0.57	-	-1.17	-	-	-	-	-	-	-0.60
Other Transformation	0.00	24.03	-24.87	-0.00	-	-	-	-0.12	-	-	-0.96
Own Use	-11.47	-0.21	-119.92	-88.65	-	-	-0.00	-0.11	-66.74	-4.27	-291.37
Distribution Losses	-0.98	-	-0.01	-3.15	-	-	-0.21	-0.01	-58.17	-5.69	-68.22
TFC	**126.18**	**1.11**	**1998.59**	**740.12**	**-**	**-**	**6.50**	**133.96**	**769.83**	**76.49**	**3852.78**
INDUSTRY SECTOR	**107.11**	**0.04**	**143.26**	**255.02**	**-**	**-**	**0.42**	**65.12**	**266.27**	**23.28**	**860.51**
Iron and Steel	38.48	-	5.99	27.21	-	-	-	0.03	31.25	0.39	103.35
Chemical and Petrochem.	11.83	0.04	32.45	71.01	-	-	0.00	1.50	50.70	6.85	174.37
Non-Ferrous Metals	2.59	-	3.40	11.16	-	-	0.00	0.11	27.79	0.25	45.29
Non-Metallic Minerals	21.33	-	19.75	29.61	-	-	0.00	2.38	14.95	0.13	88.13
Transport Equipment	0.30	-	1.72	8.81	-	-	0.00	0.01	9.63	0.27	20.75
Machinery	0.66	-	6.05	17.94	-	-	0.00	0.04	29.40	0.41	54.49
Mining and Quarrying	0.81	-	5.63	6.68	-	-	0.03	0.00	8.50	0.28	21.92
Food and Tobacco	6.29	-	12.08	28.61	-	-	0.01	4.98	20.06	0.78	72.80
Paper, Pulp and Printing	7.65	-	11.78	23.97	-	-	0.14	43.20	33.37	1.43	121.53
Wood and Wood Products	0.21	-	2.85	2.42	-	-	-	9.13	5.23	0.25	20.09
Construction	1.89	-	12.10	1.48	-	-	0.00	0.11	1.52	0.05	17.16
Textile and Leather	0.73	-	2.97	7.87	-	-	0.00	0.11	7.50	0.92	20.09
Non-specified	14.36	-	26.49	18.26	-	-	0.24	3.54	26.37	11.28	100.54
TRANSPORT SECTOR	**0.10**	**-**	**1255.84**	**21.58**	**-**	**-**	**-**	**11.47**	**9.81**	**-**	**1298.81**
International Aviation	-	-	80.64	-	-	-	-	-	-	-	80.64
Domestic Aviation	-	-	88.50	-	-	-	-	-	-	-	88.50
Road	-	-	1047.83	1.42	-	-	-	11.41	-	-	1060.66
Rail	0.01	-	19.14	-	-	-	-	0.00	8.10	-	27.25
Pipeline Transport	-	-	0.02	20.14	-	-	-	-	0.40	-	20.55
Domestic Navigation	0.09	-	18.36	-	-	-	-	0.05	-	-	18.50
Non-specified	-	-	1.35	0.03	-	-	-	0.00	1.32	-	2.70
OTHER SECTORS	**17.23**	**-**	**251.91**	**427.42**	**-**	**-**	**6.08**	**57.38**	**493.75**	**53.22**	**1306.98**
Residential	11.53	-	119.06	273.90	-	-	4.77	51.79	246.26	15.49	722.80
Comm. and Publ. Services	4.18	-	78.71	142.99	-	-	0.82	3.91	226.74	7.16	464.50
Agriculture/Forestry	1.48	-	47.50	5.18	-	-	0.19	1.66	6.92	0.16	63.10
Fishing	0.00	-	4.52	0.00	-	-	0.00	-	0.20	0.00	4.72
Non-specified	0.04	-	2.11	5.36	-	-	0.31	0.02	13.62	30.40	51.86
NON-ENERGY USE	**1.73**	**1.07**	**347.59**	**36.09**	**-**	**-**	**-**	**-**	**-**	**-**	**386.48**
in Industry/Transf./Energy	1.57	1.07	339.31	36.09	-	-	-	-	-	-	378.04
of which: Feedstocks	*0.45*	*1.07*	*230.05*	*35.08*	-	-	-	-	-	-	*266.65*
in Transport	-	-	4.79	-	-	-	-	-	-	-	4.79
in Other Sectors	0.16	-	3.49	-	-	-	-	-	-	-	3.65
Electricity Generated - TWh	***3946.89***	***43.41***	***494.59***	***1957.68***	***2345.72***	***1270.50***	***140.79***	***192.21***	-	***0.72***	***10392.50***
Electricity Plants	*3626.54*	*43.40*	*416.90*	*1430.00*	*2314.16*	*1270.50*	*134.31*	*93.79*	-	*0.42*	*9330.01*
CHP plants	*320.35*	*0.02*	*77.69*	*527.68*	*31.56*	-	*6.48*	*98.42*	-	*0.30*	*1062.49*
Heat Generated - PJ	***833.10***	***0.11***	***311.16***	***1336.28***	***5.10***	-	***17.53***	***381.24***	***8.10***	***739.53***	***3632.15***
CHP plants	*698.42*	*0.11*	*273.38*	*1147.59*	*5.10*	-	*8.36*	*268.32*	*1.83*	*110.78*	*2513.89*
Heat Plants	*134.69*	-	*37.78*	*188.69*	-	-	*9.16*	*112.92*	*6.27*	*628.75*	*1118.26*

OECD North America / OCDE Amérique du Nord
Key Indicators
Indicateurs principaux

	1960	1970	1973	1980	1990	1995
Energy Production (Mtoe)	..	..	1 700.78	1 908.30	2 118.81	2 214.84
Net Imports (Mtoe)	..	..	268.97	245.96	214.58	246.98
Total Primary Energy Supply (Mtoe)	..	..	1 949.49	2 101.78	2 261.21	2 454.10
Net Oil Imports (Mtoe)	..	..	296.85	301.15	290.02	313.12
Oil Supply (Mtoe)	..	..	936.98	959.29	930.92	964.23
Electricity Consumption (TWh)*	..	..	2 079.90	2 614.98	3 479.28	3 990.22
GDP (billion 2000 US$ using exch. rates)	2 817.48	4 180.74	4 853.12	5 885.07	8 011.45	9 010.19
GDP (billion 2000 US$ using PPPs)	2 903.73	4 336.54	5 041.13	6 157.25	8 347.41	9 373.77
Population (millions)	233.20	274.68	287.70	317.94	359.13	386.05
Industrial Production Index (2000=100)	..	..	..	..	..	..
Energy Production/TPES	..	..	0.8724	0.9079	0.9370	0.9025
Net Oil Imports/GDP (toe per thousand 2000 US$)	..	..	0.0612	0.0512	0.0362	0.0348
TPES/GDP (toe per thousand 2000 US$)	..	..	0.4017	0.3571	0.2822	0.2724
TPES/GDP (toe per thousand 2000 US$ PPP)	..	..	0.3867	0.3414	0.2709	0.2618
TPES/Population (toe per capita)	..	..	6.7760	6.6106	6.2964	6.3569
Oil Supply/GDP (toe per thousand 2000 US$)	..	..	0.1931	0.1630	0.1162	0.1070
Oil Supply/Population (toe per capita)	..	..	3.2568	3.0172	2.5922	2.4976
Elect. Cons./GDP (kWh per 2000 US$)	..	..	0.4286	0.4443	0.4343	0.4429
Elect. Cons./Population (kWh per capita)	..	..	7 229	8 225	9 688	10 336
Industry Cons.**/Industrial Production (2000=100)	..	..	..	..	..	..
Industry Oil Cons.**/Industrial Production (2000=100)	..	..	..	..	..	..

	2000	2001	2002	2003	2004	2005
Energy Production (Mtoe)	2 277.37	2 306.78	2 281.19	2 262.76	2 298.06	2 291.14
Net Imports (Mtoe)	405.05	437.42	421.99	452.59	490.87	519.64
Total Primary Energy Supply (Mtoe)	2 706.14	2 657.87	2 695.40	2 704.91	2 762.48	2 788.77
Net Oil Imports (Mtoe)	434.39	454.15	427.13	451.00	491.49	520.79
Oil Supply (Mtoe)	1 070.60	1 084.76	1 078.91	1 105.96	1 141.54	1 154.05
Electricity Consumption (TWh)*	4 555.75	4 418.78	4 539.31	4 588.66	4 659.21	4 800.83
GDP (billion 2000 US$ using exch. rates)	11 070.51	11 157.35	11 342.26	11 616.44	12 068.54	12 454.35
GDP (billion 2000 US$ using PPPs)	11 535.02	11 624.41	11 816.20	12 097.64	12 568.40	12 968.95
Population (millions)	411.78	416.44	421.02	425.49	429.91	434.25
Industrial Production Index (2000=100)	..	..	..	..	..	..
Energy Production/TPES	0.8416	0.8679	0.8463	0.8365	0.8319	0.8216
Net Oil Imports/GDP (toe per thousand 2000 US$)	0.0392	0.0407	0.0377	0.0388	0.0407	0.0418
TPES/GDP (toe per thousand 2000 US$)	0.2444	0.2382	0.2376	0.2329	0.2289	0.2239
TPES/GDP (toe per thousand 2000 US$ PPP)	0.2346	0.2286	0.2281	0.2236	0.2198	0.2150
TPES/Population (toe per capita)	6.5719	6.3823	6.4020	6.3571	6.4258	6.4221
Oil Supply/GDP (toe per thousand 2000 US$)	0.0967	0.0972	0.0951	0.0952	0.0946	0.0927
Oil Supply/Population (toe per capita)	2.6000	2.6048	2.5626	2.5993	2.6553	2.6576
Elect. Cons./GDP (kWh per 2000 US$)	0.4115	0.3960	0.4002	0.3950	0.3861	0.3855
Elect. Cons./Population (kWh per capita)	11 064	10 611	10 782	10 784	10 838	11 056
Industry Cons.**/Industrial Production (2000=100)	..	..	..	..	..	..
Industry Oil Cons.**/Industrial Production (2000=100)	..	..	..	..	..	..

* Electricity consumption equals domestic supply less distribution losses.
La consommation d'électricité représente l'approvisionnement intérieur diminué des pertes de distribution.

** Includes non-energy use in industry/transformation/energy sectors.
Comprend l'usage non-énergétique dans les secteurs de l'industrie/transformation/énergie.

OECD North America / OCDE Amérique du Nord

Figure 1. TPES* in 1973

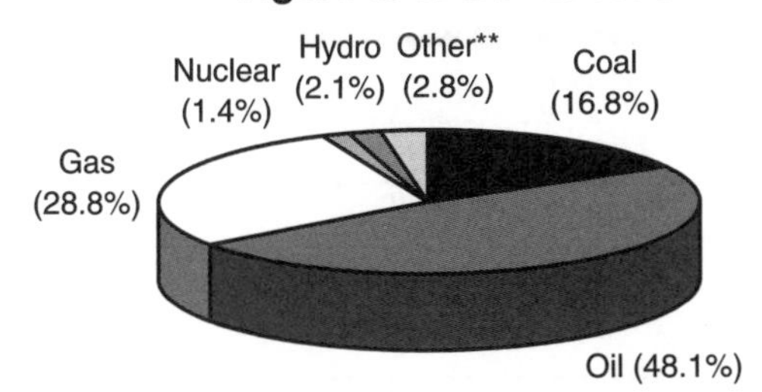

Figure 2. TPES* in 2005

Nuclear (8.5%)
Hydro (2.0%)
Other** (4.2%)
Coal (21.2%)
Gas (22.7%)
Oil (41.4%)

Figure 3. Final Consumption by Sector***

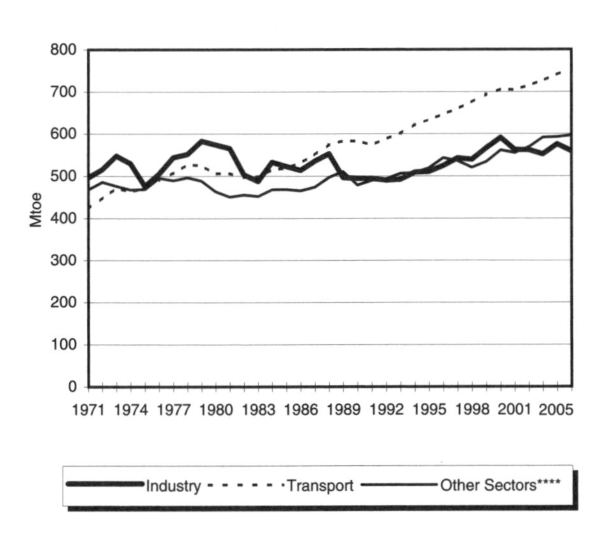

Figure 4. Breakdown of Sectorial Final Consumption by Source in 1973 and 2005***

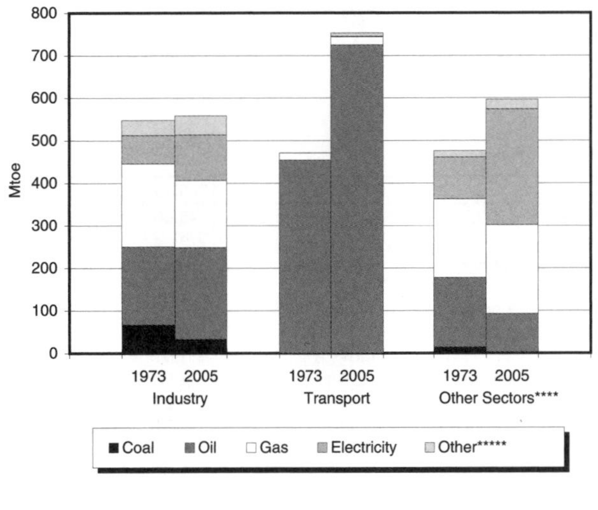

Figure 5. Electricity Generation by Fuel

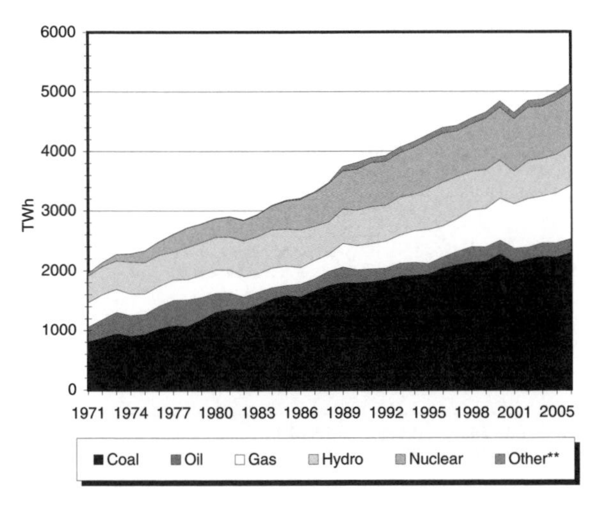

Figure 6. Electricity Consumption/GDP, TPES/GDP and Energy Production/TPES

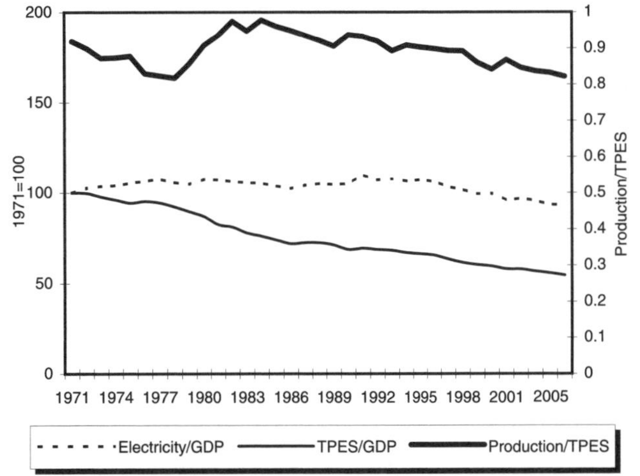

* Excluding electricity trade.

** Includes geothermal, solar, wind, combustible renewables & waste, etc.

*** Includes non-energy use.

**** Includes residential, commercial and public services, agriculture/forestry, fishing and non-specified.

***** Includes comb. renewables & waste, direct use of geothermal/solar thermal and heat produced in CHP/heat plants.

OECD North America / OCDE Amérique du Nord : 2004

Million tonnes of oil equivalent / *Million de tonnes d'équivalent pétrole*

SUPPLY AND CONSUMPTION / *APPROVISIONNEMENT ET DEMANDE*	Coal / *Charbon*	Crude Oil / *Pétrole brut*	Petroleum Products / *Produits pétroliers*	Gas / *Gaz*	Nuclear / *Nucléaire*	Hydro / *Hydro*	Geotherm. Solar etc. / *Géotherm. solaire etc.*	Combust. Renew. & Waste / *Comb. ren. & déchets*	Electricity / *Electricité*	Heat / *Chaleur*	Total / *Total*
Production	590.09	683.40	-	622.11	237.91	54.80	17.05	92.70	-	-	2298.06
Imports	33.58	641.36	124.72	117.33	-	-	-	0.29	4.91	-	922.20
Exports	-45.80	-200.12	-74.47	-105.98	-	-	-	-0.01	-4.95	-	-431.33
Intl. Marine Bunkers	-	-	-25.78	-	-	-	-	-	-	-	-25.78
Stock Changes	6.46	-6.45	-1.12	0.37	-	-	-	0.06	-	-	-0.69
TPES	**584.34**	**1118.20**	**23.35**	**633.83**	**237.91**	**54.80**	**17.05**	**93.04**	**-0.04**	**-**	**2762.48**
Transfers	-	-71.64	77.19	-	-	-	-	-	-	-	5.55
Statistical Differences	-10.62	-10.48	-1.77	4.12	-	-	-	-0.00	-0.02	-	-18.79
Electricity Plants	-507.29	-	-47.51	-120.05	-237.91	-54.80	-14.96	-14.73	396.96	-	-600.30
CHP Plants	-17.33	-	-7.04	-51.93	-	-	-	-11.74	30.63	6.57	-50.85
Heat Plants	-	-	-	-	-	-	-	-	-	-	-
Gas Works	-1.74	-	-	1.04	-	-	-	-	-	-	-0.70
Petroleum Refineries	-	-1036.64	1045.89	-0.56	-	-	-	-	-	-	8.68
Coal Transformation	-6.26	-	-	-	-	-	-	-	-	-	-6.26
Liquefaction Plants	-	0.56	-	-1.18	-	-	-	-	-	-	-0.62
Other Transformation	-	-	-	-	-	-	-	-	-	-	-
Own Use	-2.60	-	-63.91	-64.63	-	-	-	-	-28.80	-1.88	-161.83
Distribution Losses	-	-	-	-	-	-	-	-	-29.17	-0.68	-29.84
TFC	**38.49**	**-**	**1026.19**	**400.62**	**-**	**-**	**2.09**	**66.57**	**369.56**	**4.02**	**1907.53**
INDUSTRY SECTOR	**35.16**	**-**	**46.86**	**149.24**	**-**	**-**	**0.10**	**39.74**	**105.87**	**3.36**	**380.32**
Iron and Steel	7.12	-	2.04	14.56	-	-	-	-	8.03	0.09	31.84
Chemical and Petrochem.	5.24	-	8.82	50.07	-	-	-	0.61	23.84	1.74	90.31
Non-Ferrous Metals	0.26	-	0.76	6.71	-	-	-	-	11.47	0.05	19.24
Non-Metallic Minerals	8.35	-	4.69	10.94	-	-	-	0.51	4.26	0.00	28.75
Transport Equipment	0.21	-	0.74	4.88	-	-	-	0.01	4.36	0.06	10.26
Machinery	0.07	-	1.51	9.82	-	-	-	-	10.19	0.04	21.64
Mining and Quarrying	0.29	-	2.20	5.66	-	-	-	-	5.85	-	14.00
Food and Tobacco	3.76	-	4.24	15.12	-	-	-	1.93	7.47	0.27	32.79
Paper, Pulp and Printing	4.58	-	6.91	15.24	-	-	-	29.23	16.64	0.73	73.33
Wood and Wood Products	0.02	-	2.35	1.99	-	-	-	5.30	2.51	0.12	12.29
Construction	-	-	2.89	0.43	-	-	-	-	0.04	-	3.36
Textile and Leather	0.11	-	0.72	2.95	-	-	-	0.03	2.60	0.07	6.48
Non-specified	5.15	-	8.98	10.89	-	-	0.10	2.12	8.61	0.18	36.02
TRANSPORT SECTOR	**-**	**-**	**713.81**	**17.87**	**-**	**-**	**-**	**7.11**	**1.09**	**-**	**739.88**
International Aviation	-	-	20.48	-	-	-	-	-	-	-	20.48
Domestic Aviation	-	-	69.75	-	-	-	-	-	-	-	69.75
Road	-	-	603.15	0.54	-	-	-	7.06	-	-	610.74
Rail	-	-	13.31	-	-	-	-	-	0.72	-	14.03
Pipeline Transport	-	-	0.02	17.34	-	-	-	-	0.28	-	17.64
Domestic Navigation	-	-	5.90	-	-	-	-	0.05	-	-	5.95
Non-specified	-	-	1.20	-	-	-	-	-	0.08	-	1.28
OTHER SECTORS	**3.06**	**-**	**89.84**	**211.72**	**-**	**-**	**1.99**	**19.72**	**262.60**	**0.66**	**589.58**
Residential	0.03	-	40.92	128.23	-	-	1.62	17.58	127.61	-	315.97
Comm. and Publ. Services	2.46	-	27.92	83.04	-	-	0.38	2.11	119.02	0.66	235.58
Agriculture/Forestry	0.57	-	21.00	0.46	-	-	-	0.03	1.47	0.00	23.54
Fishing	-	-	-	-	-	-	-	-	-	-	-
Non-specified	-	-	-	-	-	-	-	-	14.49	-	14.49
NON-ENERGY USE	**0.28**	**-**	**175.67**	**21.80**	**-**	**-**	**-**	**-**	**-**	**-**	**197.74**
in Industry/Transf./Energy	0.28	-	172.77	21.80	-	-	-	-	-	-	194.84
of which: Feedstocks	-	-	*106.60*	*20.70*	-	-	-	-	-	-	*127.30*
in Transport	-	-	0.39	-	-	-	-	-	-	-	0.39
in Other Sectors	-	-	2.52	-	-	-	-	-	-	-	2.52
Electricity Generated - TWh	***2216.04***	-	***231.90***	***852.96***	***912.92***	***637.16***	***38.70***	***82.24***	-	-	***4971.91***
Electricity Plants	*2156.52*	-	*207.86*	*619.70*	*912.92*	*637.16*	*38.44*	*43.16*	-	-	*4615.76*
CHP plants	*59.52*	-	*24.04*	*233.26*	-	-	*0.26*	*39.08*	-	-	*356.15*
Heat Generated - PJ	***41.37***	-	***14.72***	***206.30***	-	-	-	***12.85***	-	-	***275.24***
CHP plants	*41.37*	-	*14.72*	*206.30*	-	-	-	*12.85*	-	-	*275.24*
Heat Plants	-	-	-	-	-	-	-	-	-	-	-

OECD North America / OCDE Amérique du Nord : 2005

Million tonnes of oil equivalent / *Million de tonnes d'équivalent pétrole*

SUPPLY AND CONSUMPTION *APPROVISIONNEMENT ET DEMANDE*	Coal *Charbon*	Crude Oil *Pétrole brut*	Petroleum Products *Produits pétroliers*	Gas *Gaz*	Nuclear *Nucléaire*	Hydro *Hydro*	Geotherm. Solar etc. *Géotherm. solaire etc.*	Combust. Renew. & Waste *Comb. ren. & déchets*	Electricity *Electricité*	Heat *Chaleur*	Total *Total*
Production	601.14	667.28	-	614.80	238.08	57.08	18.02	94.74	-	-	2291.14
Imports	35.61	646.53	148.88	116.17	-	-	-	0.26	5.53	-	952.98
Exports	-48.89	-196.25	-78.36	-104.28	-	-	-	-0.01	-5.56	-	-433.34
Intl. Marine Bunkers	-	-	-27.38	-	-	-	-	-	-	-	-27.38
Stock Changes	4.51	-7.97	1.32	7.55	-	-	-	-0.03	-	-	5.38
TPES	**592.37**	**1109.59**	**44.46**	**634.24**	**238.08**	**57.08**	**18.02**	**94.96**	**-0.03**	**-**	**2788.77**
Transfers	-	-61.56	66.61	-	-	-	-	-	-	-	5.06
Statistical Differences	-10.73	-14.86	-4.54	2.06	-	-	-	0.12	-0.03	0.00	-27.97
Electricity Plants	-519.37	-	-47.19	-130.75	-238.08	-57.08	-15.86	-14.73	411.69	-	-611.38
CHP Plants	-17.26	-	-6.36	-49.82	-	-	-	-10.30	29.61	6.79	-47.35
Heat Plants	-	-	-	-	-	-	-	-	-	-	-
Gas Works	-1.89	-	-	1.13	-	-	-	-	-	-	-0.76
Petroleum Refineries	-	-1033.74	1040.00	-0.57	-	-	-	-	-	-	5.69
Coal Transformation	-5.82	-	-	-	-	-	-	-	-	-	-5.82
Liquefaction Plants	-	0.57	-	-1.17	-	-	-	-	-	-	-0.60
Other Transformation	-	-	-	-	-	-	-	-	-	-	-
Own Use	-2.21	-	-63.11	-67.97	-	-	-	-	-32.16	-1.99	-167.44
Distribution Losses	-	-	-	-	-	-	-	-	-29.95	-0.72	-30.67
TFC	**35.10**	**-**	**1029.87**	**387.14**	**-**	**-**	**2.16**	**70.05**	**379.12**	**4.08**	**1907.54**
INDUSTRY SECTOR	**32.50**	**-**	**47.74**	**138.07**	**-**	**-**	**0.11**	**41.57**	**106.75**	**3.39**	**370.12**
Iron and Steel	5.00	-	2.01	13.89	-	-	-	-	8.54	0.09	29.54
Chemical and Petrochem.	4.91	-	9.22	45.99	-	-	-	0.75	24.06	1.80	86.73
Non-Ferrous Metals	0.25	-	0.80	6.21	-	-	-	-	12.29	0.05	19.60
Non-Metallic Minerals	8.09	-	5.62	10.20	-	-	-	0.52	4.34	0.00	28.76
Transport Equipment	0.16	-	0.77	4.52	-	-	-	-	4.17	0.06	9.68
Machinery	0.07	-	1.56	9.07	-	-	-	-	9.93	0.05	20.68
Mining and Quarrying	0.31	-	2.59	5.59	-	-	-	-	5.94	-	14.43
Food and Tobacco	3.82	-	4.06	13.99	-	-	-	2.19	7.48	0.28	31.83
Paper, Pulp and Printing	4.59	-	6.80	13.98	-	-	-	30.32	16.11	0.63	72.43
Wood and Wood Products	0.04	-	2.37	1.83	-	-	-	5.49	2.52	0.13	12.38
Construction	-	-	2.80	0.41	-	-	-	-	0.04	-	3.25
Textile and Leather	0.26	-	0.75	2.72	-	-	-	0.03	2.47	0.08	6.30
Non-specified	4.99	-	8.38	9.67	-	-	0.11	2.28	8.85	0.21	34.49
TRANSPORT SECTOR	**-**	**-**	**724.22**	**19.19**	**-**	**-**	**-**	**8.30**	**1.11**	**-**	**752.82**
International Aviation	-	-	21.09	-	-	-	-	-	-	-	21.09
Domestic Aviation	-	-	72.20	-	-	-	-	-	-	-	72.20
Road	-	-	608.58	0.58	-	-	-	8.24	-	-	617.40
Rail	-	-	14.71	-	-	-	-	-	0.75	-	15.45
Pipeline Transport	-	-	0.02	18.61	-	-	-	-	0.28	-	18.91
Domestic Navigation	-	-	6.71	-	-	-	-	0.05	-	-	6.76
Non-specified	-	-	0.91	-	-	-	-	-	0.08	-	0.99
OTHER SECTORS	**2.36**	**-**	**87.21**	**209.61**	**-**	**-**	**2.05**	**20.19**	**271.26**	**0.70**	**593.38**
Residential	0.02	-	38.91	126.89	-	-	1.63	18.00	133.54	0.00	319.00
Comm. and Publ. Services	1.90	-	27.17	82.30	-	-	0.42	2.00	122.91	0.70	237.39
Agriculture/Forestry	0.43	-	21.13	0.43	-	-	-	0.19	1.51	0.00	23.68
Fishing	-	-	-	-	-	-	-	-	-	-	-
Non-specified	-	-	-	-	-	-	-	-	13.30	-	13.30
NON-ENERGY USE	**0.25**	**-**	**170.70**	**20.27**	**-**	**-**	**-**	**-**	**-**	**-**	**191.22**
in Industry/Transf./Energy	0.25	-	167.65	20.27	-	-	-	-	-	-	188.17
of which: Feedstocks	-	-	*101.70*	*19.26*	-	-	-	-	-	-	*120.96*
in Transport	-	-	0.38	-	-	-	-	-	-	-	0.38
in Other Sectors	-	-	2.67	-	-	-	-	-	-	-	2.67
Electricity Generated - TWh	***2293.05***	**-**	***229.49***	***903.91***	***913.57***	***663.69***	***44.79***	***82.87***	**-**	**-**	***5131.36***
Electricity Plants	*2232.80*	-	*205.88*	*682.86*	*913.57*	*663.69*	*44.42*	*43.88*	-	-	*4787.11*
CHP plants	*60.24*	-	*23.61*	*221.05*	-	-	*0.37*	*38.99*	-	-	*344.25*
Heat Generated - PJ	***50.81***	**-**	***29.29***	***187.51***	**-**	**-**	**-**	***16.72***	**-**	**-**	***284.33***
CHP plants	*50.81*	-	*29.29*	*187.51*	-	-	-	*16.72*	-	-	*284.33*
Heat Plants	-	-	-	-	-	-	-	-	-	-	-

OECD Pacific / OCDE Pacifique
Key Indicators
Indicateurs principaux

	1960	1970	1973	1980	1990	1995
Energy Production (Mtoe)	..	..	108.28	144.12	267.38	319.62
Net Imports (Mtoe)	..	..	327.09	336.33	385.62	456.49
Total Primary Energy Supply (Mtoe)	..	..	411.15	467.47	639.16	757.25
Net Oil Imports (Mtoe)	..	..	300.76	294.32	322.09	385.22
Oil Supply (Mtoe)	..	..	297.15	297.56	341.53	403.37
Electricity Consumption (TWh)*	..	..	528.66	692.43	1 077.15	1 293.72
GDP (billion 2000 US$ using exch. rates)	808.61	2 050.79	2 497.67	3 158.99	4 715.64	5 220.30
GDP (billion 2000 US$ using PPPs)	658.56	1 595.51	1 934.21	2 453.26	3 714.96	4 206.09
Population (millions)	131.25	151.45	159.36	172.88	186.88	192.43
Industrial Production Index (2000=100)	..	..	..	..	..	..
Energy Production/TPES	..	..	0.2634	0.3083	0.4183	0.4221
Net Oil Imports/GDP (toe per thousand 2000 US$)	..	..	0.1204	0.0932	0.0683	0.0738
TPES/GDP (toe per thousand 2000 US$)	..	..	0.1646	0.1480	0.1355	0.1451
TPES/GDP (toe per thousand 2000 US$ PPP)	..	..	0.2126	0.1905	0.1721	0.1800
TPES/Population (toe per capita)	..	..	2.5801	2.7040	3.4202	3.9351
Oil Supply/GDP (toe per thousand 2000 US$)	..	..	0.1190	0.0942	0.0724	0.0773
Oil Supply/Population (toe per capita)	..	..	1.8647	1.7212	1.8276	2.0962
Elect. Cons./GDP (kWh per 2000 US$)	..	..	0.2117	0.2192	0.2284	0.2478
Elect. Cons./Population (kWh per capita)	..	..	3 318	4 005	5 764	6 723
Industry Cons.**/Industrial Production (2000=100)	..	..	..	..	..	..
Industry Oil Cons.**/Industrial Production (2000=100)	..	..	..	..	..	..

	2000	2001	2002	2003	2004	2005
Energy Production (Mtoe)	386.85	401.88	400.62	388.79	405.04	425.89
Net Imports (Mtoe)	472.33	449.57	462.51	479.02	486.89	472.14
Total Primary Energy Supply (Mtoe)	846.15	838.71	852.34	852.94	876.51	883.10
Net Oil Imports (Mtoe)	388.62	364.27	372.11	380.88	378.07	382.70
Oil Supply (Mtoe)	409.11	392.53	399.20	400.74	396.62	392.55
Electricity Consumption (TWh)*	1 488.94	1 498.36	1 577.20	1 585.43	1 651.61	1 701.68
GDP (billion 2000 US$ using exch. rates)	5 613.58	5 668.23	5 727.13	5 847.13	5 998.45	6 164.59
GDP (billion 2000 US$ using PPPs)	4 607.22	4 672.06	4 753.06	4 863.10	4 999.85	5 143.90
Population (millions)	196.98	197.91	198.75	199.55	200.10	200.63
Industrial Production Index (2000=100)	..	..	..	..	..	..
Energy Production/TPES	0.4572	0.4792	0.4700	0.4558	0.4621	0.4823
Net Oil Imports/GDP (toe per thousand 2000 US$)	0.0692	0.0643	0.0650	0.0651	0.0630	0.0621
TPES/GDP (toe per thousand 2000 US$)	0.1507	0.1480	0.1488	0.1459	0.1461	0.1433
TPES/GDP (toe per thousand 2000 US$ PPP)	0.1837	0.1795	0.1793	0.1754	0.1753	0.1717
TPES/Population (toe per capita)	4.2956	4.2377	4.2885	4.2743	4.3803	4.4016
Oil Supply/GDP (toe per thousand 2000 US$)	0.0729	0.0693	0.0697	0.0685	0.0661	0.0637
Oil Supply/Population (toe per capita)	2.0769	1.9833	2.0086	2.0082	1.9821	1.9566
Elect. Cons./GDP (kWh per 2000 US$)	0.2652	0.2643	0.2754	0.2711	0.2753	0.2760
Elect. Cons./Population (kWh per capita)	7 559	7 571	7 936	7 945	8 254	8 482
Industry Cons.**/Industrial Production (2000=100)	..	..	..	..	..	..
Industry Oil Cons.**/Industrial Production (2000=100)	..	..	..	..	..	..

* Electricity consumption equals domestic supply less distribution losses.
La consommation d'électricité représente l'approvisionnement intérieur diminué des pertes de distribution.

** Includes non-energy use in industry/transformation/energy sectors.
Comprend l'usage non-énergétique dans les secteurs de l'industrie/transformation/énergie.

OECD Pacific / OCDE Pacifique

Figure 1. TPES* in 1973

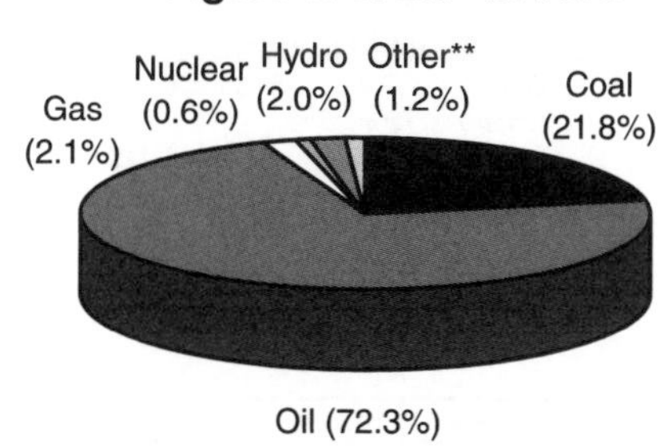

Figure 2. TPES* in 2005

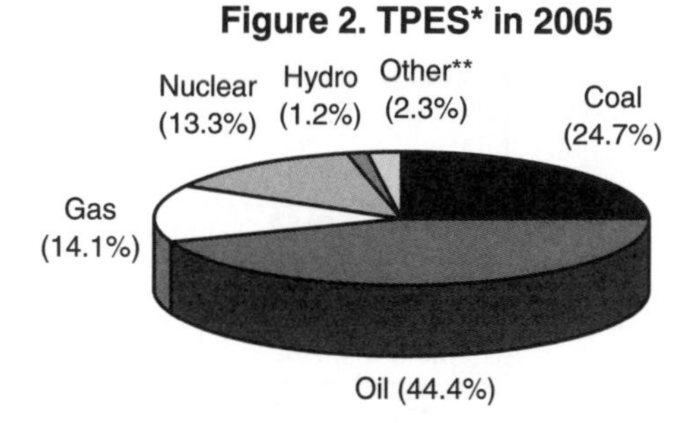

Figure 3. Final Consumption by Sector***

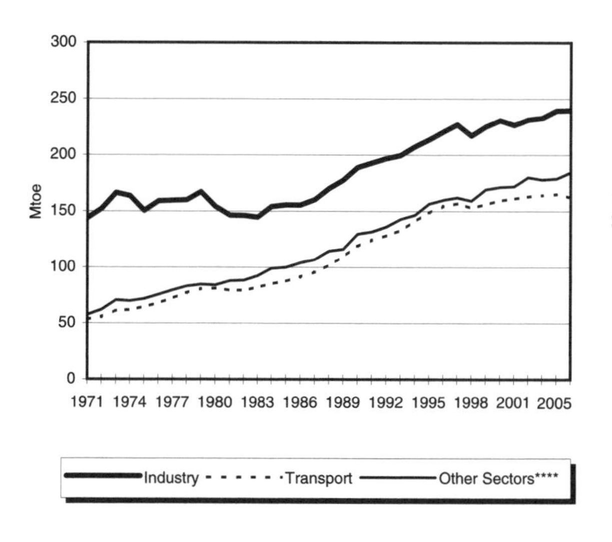

Figure 4. Breakdown of Sectorial Final Consumption by Source in 1973 and 2005***

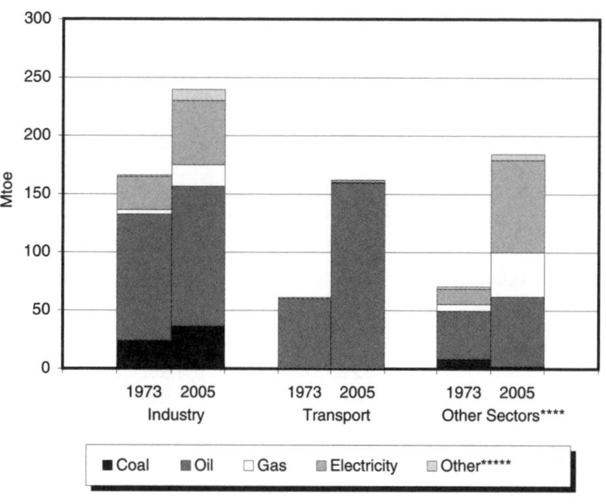

Figure 5. Electricity Generation by Fuel

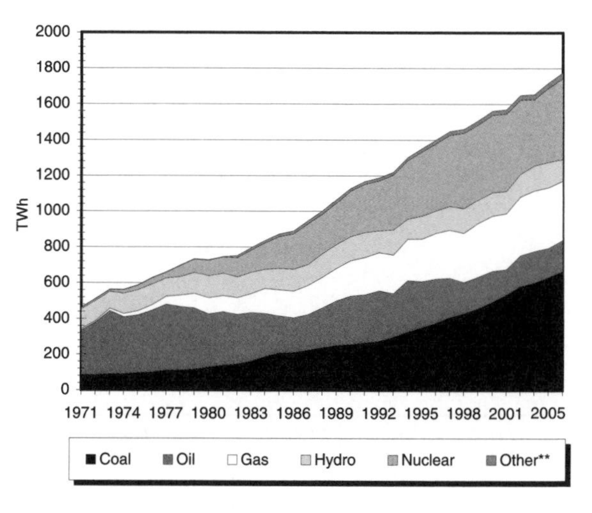

Figure 6. Electricity Consumption/GDP, TPES/GDP and Energy Production/TPES

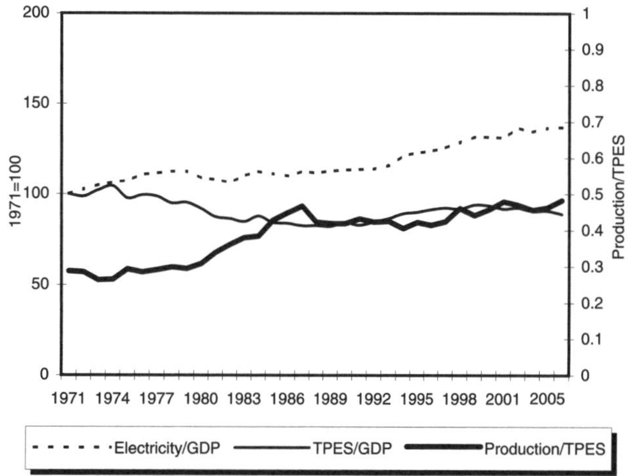

* Excluding electricity trade.

** Includes geothermal, solar, wind, combustible renewables & waste, etc.

*** Includes non-energy use.

**** Includes residential, commercial and public services, agriculture/forestry, fishing and non-specified.

***** Includes comb. renewables & waste, direct use of geothermal/solar thermal and heat produced in CHP/heat plants.

OECD Pacific / OCDE Pacifique : 2004

Million tonnes of oil equivalent / *Million de tonnes d'équivalent pétrole*

SUPPLY AND CONSUMPTION / *APPROVISIONNEMENT ET DEMANDE*	Coal / *Charbon*	Crude Oil / *Pétrole brut*	Petroleum Products / *Produits pétroliers*	Gas / *Gaz*	Nuclear / *Nucléaire*	Hydro / *Hydro*	Geotherm. Solar etc. / *Géotherm. solaire etc.*	Combust. Renew. & Waste / *Comb. ren. & déchets*	Electricity / *Electricité*	Heat / *Chaleur*	Total / *Total*
Production	196.99	29.94	-	38.14	107.67	12.15	5.92	14.21	-	0.02	405.04
Imports	168.64	352.76	83.74	93.95	-	-	-	0.03	-	-	699.13
Exports	-144.55	-19.38	-39.05	-9.25	-	-	-	-	-	-	-212.24
Intl. Marine Bunkers	-	-	-13.21	-	-	-	-	-	-	-	-13.21
Stock Changes	-3.23	2.62	-0.80	-0.80	-	-	-	-	-	-	-2.21
TPES	**217.85**	**365.95**	**30.68**	**122.04**	**107.67**	**12.15**	**5.92**	**14.23**	**-**	**0.02**	**876.51**
Transfers	-	1.93	1.62	-	-	-	-	-	-	-	3.55
Statistical Differences	-6.17	-3.41	-0.52	1.26	-	-	-	-0.01	-0.10	-0.02	-8.97
Electricity Plants	-133.29	-6.30	-21.63	-61.50	-107.67	-12.15	-4.63	-3.96	143.42	-0.02	-207.73
CHP Plants	-5.99	-	-1.23	-4.83	-	-	-0.01	-1.15	4.45	4.06	-4.70
Heat Plants	-0.01	-	-0.66	-0.40	-	-	-	-0.27	-0.10	0.97	-0.46
Gas Works	-0.06	-	-2.53	1.75	-	-	-	-	-	-	-0.84
Petroleum Refineries	-	-369.84	367.19	-	-	-	-	-	-	-	-2.65
Coal Transformation	-31.20	-	-0.81	-0.15	-	-	-	-	-	-	-32.16
Liquefaction Plants	-	-	-	-	-	-	-	-	-	-	-
Other Transformation	-	13.13	-13.43	-	-	-	-	-0.02	-	-	-0.33
Own Use	-2.90	-0.02	-16.08	-4.33	-	-	-	-	-8.50	-	-31.83
Distribution Losses	-	-	-	-0.02	-	-	-0.14	-	-6.77	-0.08	-7.01
TFC	**38.23**	**1.43**	**342.59**	**53.82**	**-**	**-**	**1.13**	**8.83**	**132.41**	**4.94**	**583.38**
INDUSTRY SECTOR	**36.23**	**0.03**	**44.47**	**15.63**	**-**	**-**	**0.13**	**6.72**	**54.35**	**2.89**	**160.46**
Iron and Steel	16.90	-	2.32	3.33	-	-	-	0.00	10.08	-	32.63
Chemical and Petrochem.	3.05	0.03	13.14	1.85	-	-	0.00	0.31	8.49	1.84	28.71
Non-Ferrous Metals	1.52	-	1.24	1.79	-	-	-	0.08	5.85	0.02	10.50
Non-Metallic Minerals	8.42	-	3.08	1.63	-	-	-	0.50	3.15	-	16.78
Transport Equipment	-	-	0.35	0.79	-	-	-	0.01	1.16	-	2.32
Machinery	0.27	-	1.38	1.12	-	-	-	0.01	9.57	0.07	12.43
Mining and Quarrying	0.18	-	1.65	0.37	-	-	-	0.00	1.22	-	3.42
Food and Tobacco	0.24	-	3.97	0.89	-	-	-	1.92	2.71	0.03	9.76
Paper, Pulp and Printing	1.70	-	2.83	0.62	-	-	0.13	2.64	4.36	0.20	12.50
Wood and Wood Products	-	-	0.07	0.03	-	-	-	0.75	0.39	-	1.24
Construction	0.00	-	4.76	0.06	-	-	-	-	0.15	-	4.97
Textile and Leather	0.11	-	1.13	0.51	-	-	-	0.01	1.37	0.72	3.85
Non-specified	3.85	-	8.54	2.63	-	-	0.00	0.48	5.84	0.01	21.35
TRANSPORT SECTOR	**0.07**	**-**	**161.19**	**0.57**	**-**	**-**	**-**	**0.00**	**2.06**	**-**	**163.89**
International Aviation	-	-	11.71	-	-	-	-	-	-	-	11.71
Domestic Aviation	-	-	8.28	-	-	-	-	-	-	-	8.28
Road	-	-	132.05	0.26	-	-	-	0.00	-	-	132.31
Rail	-	-	1.04	-	-	-	-	-	2.02	-	3.06
Pipeline Transport	-	-	0.00	0.30	-	-	-	-	0.00	-	0.30
Domestic Navigation	0.07	-	7.87	-	-	-	-	-	-	-	7.93
Non-specified	-	-	0.24	0.01	-	-	-	-	0.04	-	0.29
OTHER SECTORS	**1.52**	**-**	**61.35**	**34.85**	**-**	**-**	**1.00**	**2.10**	**75.99**	**2.04**	**178.86**
Residential	0.68	-	19.05	19.64	-	-	0.66	1.81	33.73	1.31	76.88
Comm. and Publ. Services	0.83	-	31.20	15.19	-	-	0.25	0.29	41.29	0.73	89.78
Agriculture/Forestry	0.01	-	6.90	0.02	-	-	0.09	-	0.82	-	7.85
Fishing	-	-	3.10	-	-	-	-	-	0.14	-	3.24
Non-specified	-	-	1.11	-	-	-	-	-	-	-	1.11
NON-ENERGY USE	**0.41**	**1.40**	**75.58**	**2.77**	**-**	**-**	**-**	**-**	**-**	**-**	**80.16**
in Industry/Transf./Energy	0.41	1.40	74.33	2.77	-	-	-	-	-	-	78.91
of which: Feedstocks	*0.37*	*1.40*	*60.08*	*2.77*	-	-	-	-	-	-	*64.63*
in Transport	-	-	1.22	-	-	-	-	-	-	-	1.22
in Other Sectors	-	-	0.03	-	-	-	-	-	-	-	0.03
Electricity Generated - TWh	***631.23***	***35.21***	***128.08***	***340.44***	***413.16***	***141.27***	***8.56***	***21.45***	**-**	***0.09***	***1719.50***
Electricity Plants	*609.83*	*35.21*	*120.85*	*319.07*	*413.16*	*141.27*	*8.54*	*19.70*	-	*0.09*	*1667.72*
CHP plants	*21.40*	-	*7.24*	*21.37*	-	-	*0.03*	*1.75*	-	-	*51.78*
Heat Generated - PJ	***35.01***	**-**	***102.25***	***56.79***	**-**	**-**	**-**	***12.90***	***3.99***	***1.00***	***211.94***
CHP plants	*34.57*	-	*92.36*	*40.70*	-	-	-	*2.55*	-	-	*170.17*
Heat Plants	*0.45*	-	*9.89*	*16.10*	-	-	-	*10.35*	*3.99*	*1.00*	*41.77*

OECD Pacific / OCDE Pacifique : 2005

Million tonnes of oil equivalent / *Million de tonnes d'équivalent pétrole*

SUPPLY AND CONSUMPTION *APPROVISIONNEMENT ET DEMANDE*	Coal *Charbon*	Crude Oil *Pétrole brut*	Petroleum Products *Produits pétroliers*	Gas *Gaz*	Nuclear *Nucléaire*	Hydro *Hydro*	Geotherm. Solar etc. *Géotherm. solaire etc.*	Combust. Renew. & Waste *Comb. ren. & déchets*	Electricity *Electricité*	Heat *Chaleur*	Total *Total*
Production	208.97	26.47	-	41.92	117.67	10.41	5.90	14.52	-	0.02	425.89
Imports	161.13	359.80	84.45	93.89	-	-	-	0.03	-	-	699.30
Exports	-153.23	-15.45	-46.10	-12.38	-	-	-	-	-	-	-227.16
Intl. Marine Bunkers	-	-	-16.83	-	-	-	-	-	-	-	-16.83
Stock Changes	0.98	-0.22	0.42	0.72	-	-	-	-	-	-	1.90
TPES	**217.86**	**370.60**	**21.95**	**124.14**	**117.67**	**10.41**	**5.90**	**14.54**	**-**	**0.02**	**883.10**
Transfers	-	2.02	1.62	-	-	-	-	-	-	-	3.64
Statistical Differences	0.62	2.48	-4.85	1.13	-	-	-	-0.00	-0.17	0.00	-0.79
Electricity Plants	-140.20	-8.23	-22.44	-59.60	-117.67	-10.41	-4.61	-4.10	148.14	-0.02	-219.15
CHP Plants	-6.42	-	-0.73	-4.88	-	-	-0.02	-1.16	4.59	4.10	-4.52
Heat Plants	-0.02	-	-0.67	-0.48	-	-	-	-0.34	-0.10	1.13	-0.46
Gas Works	-0.04	-	-2.29	1.54	-	-	-	-	-	-	-0.79
Petroleum Refineries	-	-378.20	376.00	-	-	-	-	-	-	-	-2.21
Coal Transformation	-31.05	-	-0.39	-0.13	-	-	-	-	-	-	-31.58
Liquefaction Plants	-	-	-	-	-	-	-	-	-	-	-
Other Transformation	-	12.57	-12.96	-	-	-	-	-0.02	-	-	-0.41
Own Use	-2.67	-0.15	-17.02	-4.42	-	-	-	-	-8.94	-	-33.19
Distribution Losses	-	-	-	-0.02	-	-	-0.14	-	-7.23	-0.09	-7.48
TFC	**38.07**	**1.08**	**338.21**	**57.29**	**-**	**-**	**1.13**	**8.92**	**136.28**	**5.14**	**586.13**
INDUSTRY SECTOR	**35.76**	**0.03**	**44.22**	**16.34**	**-**	**-**	**0.14**	**6.95**	**54.87**	**2.87**	**161.17**
Iron and Steel	16.30	-	2.43	3.40	-	-	-	0.00	10.26	-	32.39
Chemical and Petrochem.	3.82	0.03	13.68	1.71	-	-	0.00	0.26	8.41	1.85	29.75
Non-Ferrous Metals	1.52	-	1.22	1.89	-	-	-	0.08	6.05	0.03	10.78
Non-Metallic Minerals	7.55	-	2.85	1.87	-	-	-	0.43	3.18	-	15.89
Transport Equipment	-	-	0.15	0.86	-	-	-	0.01	1.27	-	2.29
Machinery	0.27	-	1.32	1.27	-	-	-	0.01	10.21	0.07	13.16
Mining and Quarrying	0.20	-	1.94	0.38	-	-	-	-	1.21	-	3.74
Food and Tobacco	0.22	-	3.53	0.90	-	-	-	2.00	2.77	0.03	9.44
Paper, Pulp and Printing	1.73	-	2.63	0.74	-	-	0.14	2.80	4.36	0.17	12.57
Wood and Wood Products	-	-	0.06	0.01	-	-	-	0.81	0.40	-	1.28
Construction	0.00	-	4.79	0.07	-	-	-	-	0.12	-	4.98
Textile and Leather	0.11	-	0.92	0.49	-	-	-	0.02	1.29	0.70	3.54
Non-specified	4.04	-	8.69	2.76	-	-	0.00	0.53	5.32	0.02	21.38
TRANSPORT SECTOR	**0.09**	**-**	**157.85**	**0.68**	**-**	**-**	**-**	**0.02**	**2.07**	**-**	**160.71**
International Aviation	-	-	13.29	-	-	-	-	-	-	-	13.29
Domestic Aviation	-	-	7.11	-	-	-	-	-	-	-	7.11
Road	-	-	131.00	0.36	-	-	-	0.02	-	-	131.38
Rail	-	-	1.18	-	-	-	-	-	2.01	-	3.19
Pipeline Transport	-	-	0.00	0.31	-	-	-	-	0.00	-	0.31
Domestic Navigation	0.09	-	5.00	-	-	-	-	-	-	-	5.09
Non-specified	-	-	0.27	0.01	-	-	-	-	0.06	-	0.34
OTHER SECTORS	**1.82**	**-**	**59.76**	**38.16**	**-**	**-**	**0.99**	**1.95**	**79.34**	**2.27**	**184.31**
Residential	0.98	-	19.65	20.82	-	-	0.66	1.66	39.43	1.48	84.69
Comm. and Publ. Services	0.81	-	29.34	17.32	-	-	0.24	0.28	38.96	0.79	87.75
Agriculture/Forestry	0.03	-	6.72	0.03	-	-	0.09	-	0.80	-	7.67
Fishing	-	-	2.87	-	-	-	-	-	0.15	-	3.02
Non-specified	-	-	1.18	-	-	-	-	-	-	-	1.18
NON-ENERGY USE	**0.40**	**1.05**	**76.39**	**2.10**	**-**	**-**	**-**	**-**	**-**	**-**	**79.94**
in Industry/Transf./Energy	0.40	1.05	75.00	2.10	-	-	-	-	-	-	78.55
of which: Feedstocks	*0.36*	*1.05*	*61.86*	*2.10*	-	-	-	-	-	-	*65.38*
in Transport	-	-	1.32	-	-	-	-	-	-	-	1.32
in Other Sectors	-	-	0.06	-	-	-	-	-	-	-	0.06
Electricity Generated - TWh	***665.03***	***43.39***	***130.52***	***332.31***	***451.53***	***121.04***	***9.49***	***22.55***	**-**	***0.09***	***1775.94***
Electricity Plants	*641.09*	*43.39*	*124.87*	*310.47*	*451.53*	*121.04*	*9.46*	*20.60*	-	*0.09*	*1722.55*
CHP plants	*23.94*	-	*5.65*	*21.83*	-	-	*0.03*	*1.94*	-	-	*53.39*
Heat Generated - PJ	***35.80***	**-**	***101.58***	***62.66***	**-**	**-**	**-**	***14.90***	***4.05***	***1.02***	***220.00***
CHP plants	*35.23*	-	*90.37*	*43.42*	-	-	-	*2.53*	-	-	*171.54*
Heat Plants	*0.57*	-	*11.22*	*19.23*	-	-	-	*12.37*	*4.05*	*1.02*	*48.45*

OECD Europe / OCDE Europe
Key Indicators
Indicateurs principaux

	1960	1970	1973	1980	1990	1995
Energy Production (Mtoe)	..	..	636.39	852.12	1 032.54	1 131.43
Net Imports (Mtoe)	..	..	814.01	711.49	628.80	575.43
Total Primary Energy Supply (Mtoe)	..	..	1 402.06	1 507.60	1 625.12	1 679.46
Net Oil Imports (Mtoe)	..	..	789.09	622.30	453.39	381.95
Oil Supply (Mtoe)	..	..	759.00	704.50	626.99	665.72
Electricity Consumption (TWh)*	..	..	1 515.94	1 930.41	2 498.92	2 666.13
GDP (billion 2000 US$ using exch. rates)	2 648.78	4 190.42	4 796.43	5 645.37	7 174.32	7 777.35
GDP (billion 2000 US$ using PPPs)	3 224.90	5 147.77	5 918.96	7 008.02	8 882.92	9 613.76
Population (millions)	405.46	444.71	455.03	473.76	497.64	510.68
Industrial Production Index (2000=100)	..	..	..	70.10	83.80	86.50
Energy Production/TPES	..	..	0.4539	0.5652	0.6354	0.6737
Net Oil Imports/GDP (toe per thousand 2000 US$)	..	..	0.1645	0.1102	0.0632	0.0491
TPES/GDP (toe per thousand 2000 US$)	..	..	0.2923	0.2671	0.2265	0.2159
TPES/GDP (toe per thousand 2000 US$ PPP)	..	..	0.2369	0.2151	0.1829	0.1747
TPES/Population (toe per capita)	..	..	3.0813	3.1822	3.2656	3.2887
Oil Supply/GDP (toe per thousand 2000 US$)	..	..	0.1582	0.1248	0.0874	0.0856
Oil Supply/Population (toe per capita)	..	..	1.6680	1.4870	1.2599	1.3036
Elect. Cons./GDP (kWh per 2000 US$)	..	..	0.3161	0.3419	0.3483	0.3428
Elect. Cons./Population (kWh per capita)	..	..	3 332	4 075	5 022	5 221
Industry Cons.**/Industrial Production (2000=100)	..	..	..	146.83	115.55	108.69
Industry Oil Cons.**/Industrial Production (2000=100)	..	..	..	182.70	113.45	113.96

	2000	2001	2002	2003	2004	2005
Energy Production (Mtoe)	1 165.55	1 160.79	1 165.62	1 155.37	1 155.75	1 116.75
Net Imports (Mtoe)	654.30	681.44	680.26	730.70	761.68	821.03
Total Primary Energy Supply (Mtoe)	1 774.08	1 806.04	1 801.30	1 842.56	1 866.41	1 875.72
Net Oil Imports (Mtoe)	395.00	416.80	411.41	438.68	452.65	489.16
Oil Supply (Mtoe)	685.81	696.75	692.41	695.36	699.05	702.40
Electricity Consumption (TWh)*	3 003.91	3 072.27	3 093.81	3 164.75	3 240.43	3 297.71
GDP (billion 2000 US$ using exch. rates)	8 975.76	9 130.51	9 245.67	9 366.13	9 603.57	9 775.33
GDP (billion 2000 US$ using PPPs)	11 135.56	11 313.32	11 476.68	11 648.73	11 968.44	12 207.98
Population (millions)	521.53	524.39	527.36	530.68	534.10	536.64
Industrial Production Index (2000=100)	100.00	99.80	99.70	100.70	103.80	105.20
Energy Production/TPES	0.6570	0.6427	0.6471	0.6270	0.6192	0.5954
Net Oil Imports/GDP (toe per thousand 2000 US$)	0.0440	0.0456	0.0445	0.0468	0.0471	0.0500
TPES/GDP (toe per thousand 2000 US$)	0.1977	0.1978	0.1948	0.1967	0.1943	0.1919
TPES/GDP (toe per thousand 2000 US$ PPP)	0.1593	0.1596	0.1570	0.1582	0.1559	0.1536
TPES/Population (toe per capita)	3.4017	3.4441	3.4157	3.4721	3.4945	3.4953
Oil Supply/GDP (toe per thousand 2000 US$)	0.0764	0.0763	0.0749	0.0742	0.0728	0.0719
Oil Supply/Population (toe per capita)	1.3150	1.3287	1.3130	1.3103	1.3088	1.3089
Elect. Cons./GDP (kWh per 2000 US$)	0.3347	0.3365	0.3346	0.3379	0.3374	0.3374
Elect. Cons./Population (kWh per capita)	5 760	5 859	5 867	5 964	6 067	6 145
Industry Cons.**/Industrial Production (2000=100)	100.00	98.99	98.63	101.12	98.72	97.33
Industry Oil Cons.**/Industrial Production (2000=100)	100.00	100.13	99.81	100.57	97.21	96.06

* Electricity consumption equals domestic supply less distribution losses.
La consommation d'électricité représente l'approvisionnement intérieur diminué des pertes de distribution.

** Includes non-energy use in industry/transformation/energy sectors.
Comprend l'usage non-énergétique dans les secteurs de l'industrie/transformation/énergie.

OECD Europe / OCDE Europe

Figure 1. TPES* in 1973

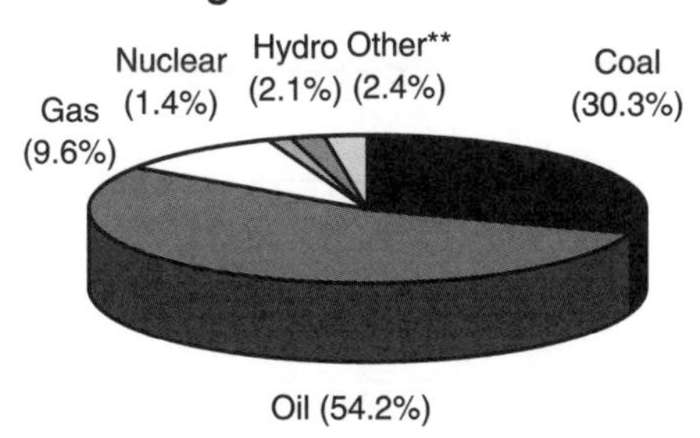

Figure 2. TPES* in 2005

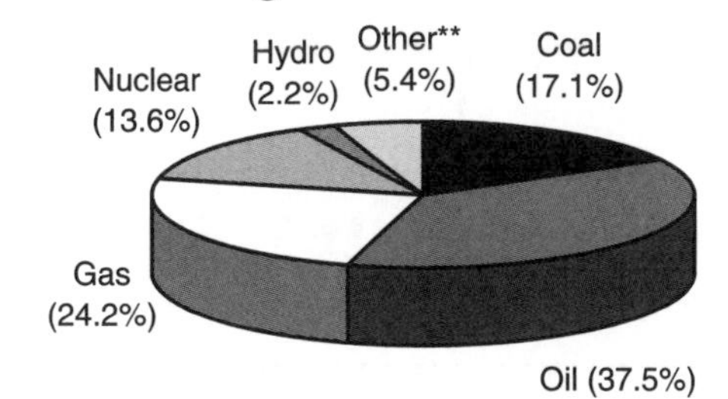

Figure 3. Final Consumption by Sector***

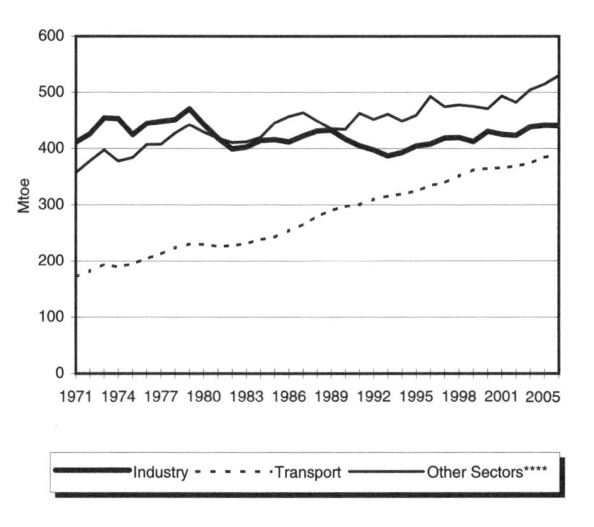

Figure 4. Breakdown of Sectorial Final Consumption by Source in 1973 and 2005***

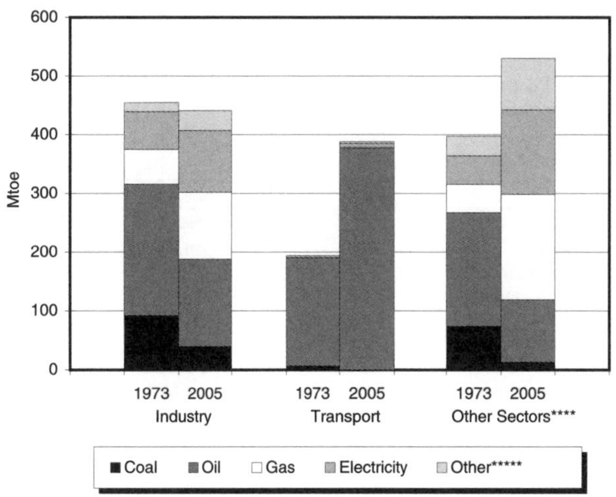

Figure 5. Electricity Generation by Fuel

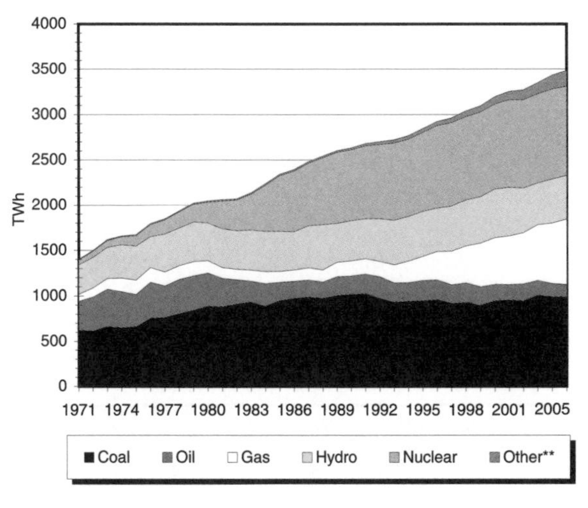

Figure 6. Electricity Consumption/GDP, TPES/GDP and Energy Production/TPES

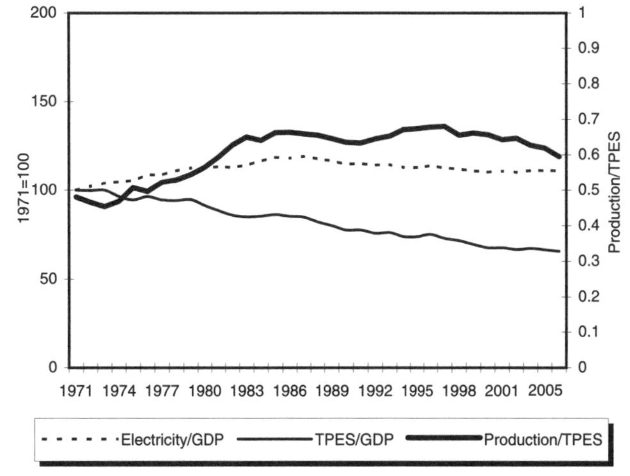

* Excluding electricity trade.

** Includes geothermal, solar, wind, combustible renewables & waste, etc.

*** Includes non-energy use.

**** Includes residential, commercial and public services, agriculture/forestry, fishing and non-specified.

***** Includes comb. renewables & waste, direct use of geothermal/solar thermal and heat produced in CHP/heat plants.

OECD Europe / OCDE Europe : 2004

Million tonnes of oil equivalent / *Million de tonnes d'équivalent pétrole*

SUPPLY AND CONSUMPTION *APPROVISIONNEMENT ET DEMANDE*	Coal *Charbon*	Crude Oil *Pétrole brut*	Petroleum Products *Produits pétroliers*	Gas *Gaz*	Nuclear *Nucléaire*	Hydro *Hydro*	Geotherm. Solar etc. *Géotherm. solaire etc.*	Combust. Renew. & Waste *Comb. ren. & déchets*	Electricity *Electricité*	Heat *Chaleur*	Total *Total*
Production	200.65	296.57	-	263.14	258.77	42.02	14.60	79.59	-	0.43	1155.75
Imports	161.29	666.74	280.64	304.01	-	-	-	2.06	26.35	0.00	1441.09
Exports	-33.03	-225.83	-268.90	-126.13	-	-	-	-0.68	-24.84	-0.01	-679.41
Intl. Marine Bunkers	-	-	-49.99	-	-	-	-	-	-	-	-49.99
Stock Changes	0.64	-2.09	1.92	-1.49	-	-	-	0.00	-	-	-1.03
TPES	**329.55**	**735.39**	**-36.34**	**439.52**	**258.77**	**42.02**	**14.60**	**80.97**	**1.51**	**0.42**	**1866.41**
Transfers	-	28.02	-26.56	-	-	-	-	-	-	-	1.46
Statistical Differences	0.05	0.61	0.44	-0.34	-	-	0.00	0.01	-0.01	0.21	0.97
Electricity Plants	-167.93	-	-21.40	-63.84	-251.10	-42.02	-10.42	-8.89	236.89	-0.09	-328.80
CHP Plants	-69.45	-0.00	-9.16	-59.17	-7.67	-	-0.87	-15.29	58.27	47.41	-55.91
Heat Plants	-4.76	-	-1.01	-4.66	-	-	-0.18	-2.92	-0.27	12.03	-1.77
Gas Works	-0.48	-	-0.14	0.40	-	-	-	-	-	-	-0.22
Petroleum Refineries	-	-774.89	778.54	-0.13	-	-	-	-	-	-	3.53
Coal Transformation	-23.43	0.04	-1.78	-0.11	-	-	-	-0.00	-	-	-25.28
Liquefaction Plants	-	-	-	-	-	-	-	-	-	-	-
Other Transformation	0.00	10.87	-11.30	-0.00	-	-	-	-0.10	-	-	-0.53
Own Use	-6.50	-0.00	-41.41	-15.31	-	-	-0.00	-0.10	-24.90	-2.10	-90.32
Distribution Losses	-0.88	-	-	-2.94	-	-	-0.11	-0.01	-21.28	-3.74	-28.97
TFC	**56.18**	**0.03**	**629.89**	**293.41**	**-**	**-**	**3.03**	**53.66**	**250.22**	**54.14**	**1340.57**
INDUSTRY SECTOR	**41.49**	**0.01**	**52.41**	**99.80**	**-**	**-**	**0.19**	**16.64**	**104.23**	**16.65**	**331.42**
Iron and Steel	18.61	-	1.70	10.40	-	-	-	0.05	12.35	0.37	43.48
Chemical and Petrochem.	3.13	0.01	9.92	21.93	-	-	-	0.51	17.44	3.34	56.28
Non-Ferrous Metals	0.60	-	1.46	3.24	-	-	0.00	0.05	9.44	0.11	14.90
Non-Metallic Minerals	6.09	-	11.41	17.07	-	-	0.00	1.34	7.59	0.10	43.59
Transport Equipment	0.25	-	0.87	3.65	-	-	0.00	0.00	4.08	0.22	9.07
Machinery	0.34	-	2.68	7.76	-	-	0.00	0.02	9.04	0.30	20.14
Mining and Quarrying	0.30	-	1.09	0.60	-	-	0.05	0.00	1.34	0.11	3.50
Food and Tobacco	2.24	-	5.04	14.42	-	-	0.01	0.74	9.48	0.49	32.42
Paper, Pulp and Printing	1.32	-	2.46	9.18	-	-	-	10.20	12.79	0.53	36.48
Wood and Wood Products	0.17	-	0.40	0.62	-	-	-	2.74	2.12	0.07	6.12
Construction	1.80	-	4.38	0.87	-	-	0.00	0.09	1.28	0.05	8.47
Textile and Leather	0.38	-	1.43	4.91	-	-	0.00	0.06	3.98	0.14	10.91
Non-specified	6.28	-	9.57	5.13	-	-	0.13	0.83	13.29	10.83	46.06
TRANSPORT SECTOR	**0.01**	**-**	**371.41**	**1.58**	**-**	**-**	**-**	**2.05**	**6.61**	**-**	**381.66**
International Aviation	-	-	43.60	-	-	-	-	-	-	-	43.60
Domestic Aviation	-	-	9.47	-	-	-	-	-	-	-	9.47
Road	-	-	308.48	0.46	-	-	-	2.05	-	-	310.99
Rail	0.01	-	3.26	-	-	-	-	0.00	5.34	-	8.62
Pipeline Transport	-	-	0.00	1.11	-	-	-	-	0.11	-	1.22
Domestic Navigation	-	-	6.43	-	-	-	-	-	-	-	6.43
Non-specified	-	-	0.16	0.01	-	-	-	-	1.16	-	1.33
OTHER SECTORS	**13.51**	**-**	**106.90**	**178.93**	**-**	**-**	**2.84**	**34.97**	**139.38**	**37.49**	**514.01**
Residential	10.48	-	62.06	124.99	-	-	2.29	31.96	71.79	13.71	317.29
Comm. and Publ. Services	1.98	-	22.58	41.98	-	-	0.15	1.55	62.87	5.51	136.62
Agriculture/Forestry	0.96	-	19.59	4.76	-	-	0.10	1.44	4.34	0.30	31.48
Fishing	0.00	-	1.69	-	-	-	0.00	-	0.05	0.00	1.74
Non-specified	0.08	-	0.98	7.21	-	-	0.31	0.02	0.33	17.97	26.89
NON-ENERGY USE	**1.17**	**0.01**	**99.18**	**13.11**	**-**	**-**	**-**	**-**	**-**	**-**	**113.47**
in Industry/Transf./Energy	1.03	0.01	95.32	13.11	-	-	-	-	-	-	109.48
of which: Feedstocks	*0.10*	*0.01*	*66.85*	*13.11*	-	-	-	-	-	-	*80.07*
in Transport	-	-	3.09	-	-	-	-	-	-	-	3.09
in Other Sectors	0.14	-	0.77	-	-	-	-	-	-	-	0.91
Electricity Generated - TWh	***991.06***	***1.20***	***143.16***	***664.46***	***992.47***	***488.56***	***71.62***	***79.31***	-	***0.36***	***3432.19***
Electricity Plants	*732.24*	*1.18*	*90.73*	*380.93*	*963.53*	*488.56*	*67.68*	*29.39*	-	*0.17*	*2754.40*
CHP plants	*258.82*	*0.02*	*52.43*	*283.53*	*28.94*	-	*3.94*	*49.92*	-	*0.19*	*677.79*
Heat Generated - PJ	***807.98***	***0.11***	***193.49***	***1009.33***	***5.15***	-	***18.36***	***313.53***	***3.93***	***155.01***	***2506.88***
CHP plants	*650.62*	*0.11*	*159.35*	*858.37*	*5.15*	-	*8.81*	*219.68*	*1.78*	*89.64*	*1993.52*
Heat Plants	*157.36*	-	*34.13*	*150.96*	-	-	*9.54*	*93.85*	*2.15*	*65.36*	*513.36*

OECD Europe / OCDE Europe : 2005

Million tonnes of oil equivalent / *Million de tonnes d'équivalent pétrole*

SUPPLY AND CONSUMPTION ***APPROVISIONNEMENT ET DEMANDE***	Coal *Charbon*	Crude Oil *Pétrole brut*	Petroleum Products *Produits pétroliers*	Gas *Gaz*	Nuclear *Nucléaire*	Hydro *Hydro*	Geotherm. Solar etc. *Géotherm. solaire etc.*	Combust. Renew. & Waste *Comb. ren. & déchets*	Electricity *Electricité*	Heat *Chaleur*	Total *Total*
Production	193.03	272.09	-	254.88	255.67	41.78	15.90	82.93	-	0.47	1116.75
Imports	159.15	663.72	307.40	329.44	-	-	-	2.92	29.90	0.00	1492.54
Exports	-29.01	-196.65	-285.32	-131.19	-	-	-	-0.95	-28.38	-0.01	-671.50
Intl. Marine Bunkers	-	-	-52.24	-	-	-	-	-	-	-	-52.24
Stock Changes	-3.14	-0.69	-5.91	-0.06	-	-	-	-0.02	-	-	-9.82
TPES	**320.04**	**738.47**	**-36.07**	**453.06**	**255.67**	**41.78**	**15.90**	**84.88**	**1.52**	**0.47**	**1875.72**
Transfers	-	25.39	-23.84	-	-	-	-	-	-	-	1.54
Statistical Differences	-2.38	-4.06	0.46	-1.33	-	-	0.00	-0.01	0.06	0.19	-7.07
Electricity Plants	-166.49	-	-20.98	-73.08	-247.33	-41.78	-11.46	-9.00	242.58	-0.45	-327.98
CHP Plants	-63.73	-	-10.24	-58.78	-8.35	-	-0.98	-17.67	57.15	48.97	-53.63
Heat Plants	-3.95	-	-0.94	-4.95	-	-	-0.18	-3.00	-0.27	25.25	11.97
Gas Works	-0.49	-	-0.13	0.42	-	-	-	-	-	-	-0.20
Petroleum Refineries	-	-771.19	775.63	-0.14	-	-	-	-	-	-	4.30
Coal Transformation	-22.43	0.02	-1.68	-0.10	-	-	-	-0.00	-	-	-24.20
Liquefaction Plants	-	-	-	-	-	-	-	-	-	-	-
Other Transformation	0.00	11.46	-11.91	-0.00	-	-	-	-0.10	-	-	-0.55
Own Use	-6.59	-0.06	-39.79	-16.26	-	-	-0.00	-0.11	-25.64	-2.28	-90.73
Distribution Losses	-0.98	-	-0.01	-3.14	-	-	-0.07	-0.01	-20.98	-4.89	-30.07
TFC	**53.00**	**0.03**	**630.51**	**295.69**	**-**	**-**	**3.21**	**54.99**	**254.42**	**67.27**	**1359.11**
INDUSTRY SECTOR	**38.85**	**0.01**	**51.30**	**100.61**	**-**	**-**	**0.17**	**16.60**	**104.65**	**17.02**	**329.22**
Iron and Steel	17.18	-	1.55	9.93	-	-	-	0.03	12.44	0.30	41.42
Chemical and Petrochem.	3.10	0.01	9.55	23.31	-	-	-	0.49	18.23	3.20	57.89
Non-Ferrous Metals	0.82	-	1.38	3.06	-	-	0.00	0.03	9.44	0.18	14.91
Non-Metallic Minerals	5.68	-	11.28	17.54	-	-	0.00	1.43	7.43	0.13	43.48
Transport Equipment	0.14	-	0.81	3.44	-	-	0.00	0.00	4.19	0.21	8.78
Machinery	0.33	-	3.17	7.59	-	-	0.00	0.03	9.25	0.28	20.65
Mining and Quarrying	0.29	-	1.09	0.71	-	-	0.03	0.00	1.35	0.28	3.75
Food and Tobacco	2.24	-	4.49	13.72	-	-	0.01	0.79	9.81	0.47	31.52
Paper, Pulp and Printing	1.33	-	2.35	9.25	-	-	-	10.08	12.90	0.62	36.53
Wood and Wood Products	0.16	-	0.42	0.58	-	-	-	2.83	2.32	0.12	6.43
Construction	1.89	-	4.50	1.01	-	-	0.00	0.11	1.36	0.05	8.93
Textile and Leather	0.36	-	1.30	4.66	-	-	0.00	0.06	3.74	0.14	10.26
Non-specified	5.33	-	9.42	5.83	-	-	0.13	0.72	12.20	11.05	44.67
TRANSPORT SECTOR	**0.01**	**-**	**373.77**	**1.71**	**-**	**-**	**-**	**3.15**	**6.63**	**-**	**385.28**
International Aviation	-	-	46.25	-	-	-	-	-	-	-	46.25
Domestic Aviation	-	-	9.19	-	-	-	-	-	-	-	9.19
Road	-	-	308.24	0.48	-	-	-	3.15	-	-	311.88
Rail	0.01	-	3.26	-	-	-	-	0.00	5.34	-	8.61
Pipeline Transport	-	-	0.00	1.21	-	-	-	-	0.11	-	1.33
Domestic Navigation	-	-	6.65	-	-	-	-	-	-	-	6.65
Non-specified	-	-	0.17	0.02	-	-	-	0.00	1.17	-	1.36
OTHER SECTORS	**13.05**	**-**	**104.94**	**179.64**	**-**	**-**	**3.04**	**35.24**	**143.14**	**50.24**	**529.30**
Residential	10.52	-	60.50	126.19	-	-	2.48	32.13	73.29	14.01	319.12
Comm. and Publ. Services	1.46	-	22.20	43.37	-	-	0.16	1.62	64.87	5.67	139.36
Agriculture/Forestry	1.03	-	19.65	4.73	-	-	0.10	1.47	4.61	0.16	31.75
Fishing	0.00	-	1.65	0.00	-	-	0.00	-	0.04	0.00	1.70
Non-specified	0.04	-	0.93	5.36	-	-	0.31	0.02	0.32	30.40	37.37
NON-ENERGY USE	**1.09**	**0.01**	**100.50**	**13.72**	**-**	**-**	**-**	**-**	**-**	**-**	**115.32**
in Industry/Transf./Energy	0.92	0.01	96.66	13.72	-	-	-	-	-	-	111.32
of which: Feedstocks	*0.09*	*0.01*	*66.49*	*13.72*	-	-	-	-	-	-	*80.31*
in Transport	-	-	3.09	-	-	-	-	-	-	-	3.09
in Other Sectors	0.16	-	0.75	-	-	-	-	-	-	-	0.92
Electricity Generated - TWh	***988.82***	***0.02***	***134.57***	***721.47***	***980.61***	***485.76***	***86.52***	***86.80***	**-**	***0.63***	***3485.20***
Electricity Plants	*752.65*	*0.01*	*86.15*	*436.67*	*949.05*	*485.76*	*80.44*	*29.31*	-	*0.33*	*2820.35*
CHP plants	*236.17*	*0.02*	*48.43*	*284.81*	*31.56*	-	*6.08*	*57.49*	-	*0.30*	*664.85*
Heat Generated - PJ	***746.50***	***0.11***	***180.28***	***1086.12***	***5.10***	**-**	***17.53***	***349.62***	***4.06***	***738.51***	***3127.83***
CHP plants	*612.39*	*0.11*	*153.72*	*916.66*	*5.10*	-	*8.36*	*249.08*	*1.83*	*110.78*	*2058.02*
Heat Plants	*134.11*	-	*26.56*	*169.46*	-	-	*9.16*	*100.55*	*2.23*	*627.74*	*1069.81*

IEA / AIE
Key Indicators
Indicateurs principaux

	1960	1970	1973	1980	1990	1995
Energy Production (Mtoe)	..	..	2 287.65	2 630.36	3 117.89	3 357.59
Net Imports (Mtoe)	..	..	1 403.61	1 323.69	1 279.15	1 335.14
Total Primary Energy Supply (Mtoe)	..	..	3 599.68	3 834.22	4 277.78	4 638.25
Net Oil Imports (Mtoe)	..	..	1 363.24	1 239.54	1 115.87	1 131.64
Oil Supply (Mtoe)	..	..	1 943.07	1 869.90	1 797.64	1 928.57
Electricity Consumption (TWh)*	..	..	4 000.00	5 043.67	6 789.39	7 665.93
GDP (billion 2000 US$ using exch. rates)	6 114.12	10 141.01	11 803.98	14 203.91	19 344.86	21 406.87
GDP (billion 2000 US$ using PPPs)	6 481.58	10 560.74	12 261.52	14 749.93	19 965.27	22 135.85
Population (millions)	701.57	785.32	810.59	858.09	918.73	954.79
Industrial Production Index (2000=100)	..	..	..	..	..	..
Energy Production/TPES	..	..	0.6355	0.6860	0.7289	0.7239
Net Oil Imports/GDP (toe per thousand 2000 US$)	..	..	0.1155	0.0873	0.0577	0.0529
TPES/GDP (toe per thousand 2000 US$)	..	..	0.3050	0.2699	0.2211	0.2167
TPES/GDP (toe per thousand 2000 US$ PPP)	..	..	0.2936	0.2599	0.2143	0.2095
TPES/Population (toe per capita)	..	..	4.4408	4.4683	4.6562	4.8579
Oil Supply/GDP (toe per thousand 2000 US$)	..	..	0.1646	0.1316	0.0929	0.0901
Oil Supply/Population (toe per capita)	..	..	2.3971	2.1791	1.9567	2.0199
Elect. Cons./GDP (kWh per 2000 US$)	..	..	0.3389	0.3551	0.3510	0.3581
Elect. Cons./Population (kWh per capita)	..	..	4 935	5 878	7 390	8 029
Industry Cons.**/Industrial Production (2000=100)	..	..	..	..	..	..
Industry Oil Cons.**/Industrial Production (2000=100)	..	..	..	..	..	..

	2000	2001	2002	2003	2004	2005
Energy Production (Mtoe)	3 515.47	3 549.78	3 528.09	3 475.71	3 517.46	3 486.69
Net Imports (Mtoe)	1 582.30	1 623.38	1 614.28	1 719.81	1 798.53	1 864.02
Total Primary Energy Supply (Mtoe)	5 065.64	5 038.54	5 082.28	5 127.17	5 226.56	5 255.64
Net Oil Imports (Mtoe)	1 271.31	1 294.26	1 268.58	1 340.79	1 394.64	1 458.58
Oil Supply (Mtoe)	2 050.56	2 057.63	2 053.81	2 086.10	2 115.30	2 118.67
Electricity Consumption (TWh)*	8 714.14	8 651.14	8 868.98	8 993.35	9 197.56	9 438.50
GDP (billion 2000 US$ using exch. rates)	24 878.63	25 172.17	25 523.39	26 022.00	26 826.62	27 523.63
GDP (billion 2000 US$ using PPPs)	25 904.83	26 230.35	26 651.31	27 183.33	28 045.25	28 781.40
Population (millions)	987.69	994.76	1 001.84	1 009.15	1 016.25	1 022.37
Industrial Production Index (2000=100)	..	..	..	..	..	..
Energy Production/TPES	0.6940	0.7045	0.6942	0.6779	0.6730	0.6634
Net Oil Imports/GDP (toe per thousand 2000 US$)	0.0511	0.0514	0.0497	0.0515	0.0520	0.0530
TPES/GDP (toe per thousand 2000 US$)	0.2036	0.2002	0.1991	0.1970	0.1948	0.1910
TPES/GDP (toe per thousand 2000 US$ PPP)	0.1955	0.1921	0.1907	0.1886	0.1864	0.1826
TPES/Population (toe per capita)	5.1288	5.0651	5.0729	5.0807	5.1430	5.1406
Oil Supply/GDP (toe per thousand 2000 US$)	0.0824	0.0817	0.0805	0.0802	0.0789	0.0770
Oil Supply/Population (toe per capita)	2.0761	2.0685	2.0500	2.0672	2.0815	2.0723
Elect. Cons./GDP (kWh per 2000 US$)	0.3503	0.3437	0.3475	0.3456	0.3429	0.3429
Elect. Cons./Population (kWh per capita)	8 823	8 697	8 853	8 912	9 051	9 232
Industry Cons.**/Industrial Production (2000=100)	..	..	..	..	..	..
Industry Oil Cons.**/Industrial Production (2000=100)	..	..	..	..	..	..

* Electricity consumption equals domestic supply less distribution losses.
La consommation d'électricité représente l'approvisionnement intérieur diminué des pertes de distribution.

** Includes non-energy use in industry/transformation/energy sectors.
Comprend l'usage non-énergétique dans les secteurs de l'industrie/transformation/énergie.

IEA / AIE

Figure 1. TPES* in 1973

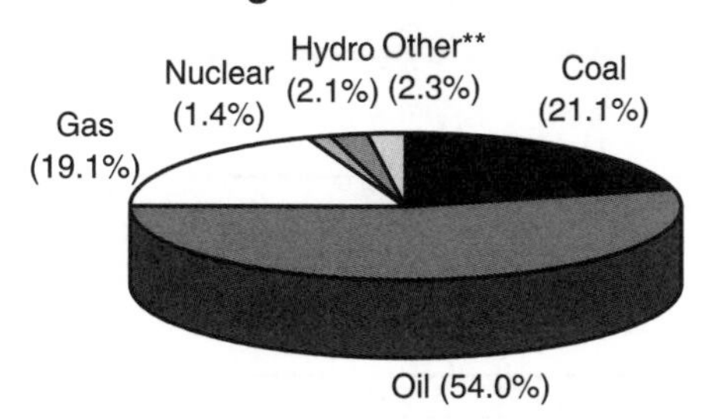

Figure 2. TPES* in 2005

Hydro Other**
Nuclear (2.0%) (4.1%)
(11.5%)
Coal
(20.2%)
Gas
(21.9%)
Oil (40.3%)

Figure 3. Final Consumption by Sector***

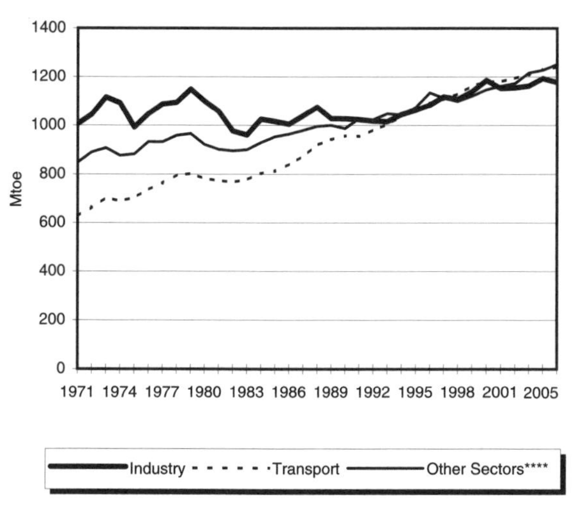

Figure 4. Breakdown of Sectorial Final Consumption by Source in 1973 and 2005***

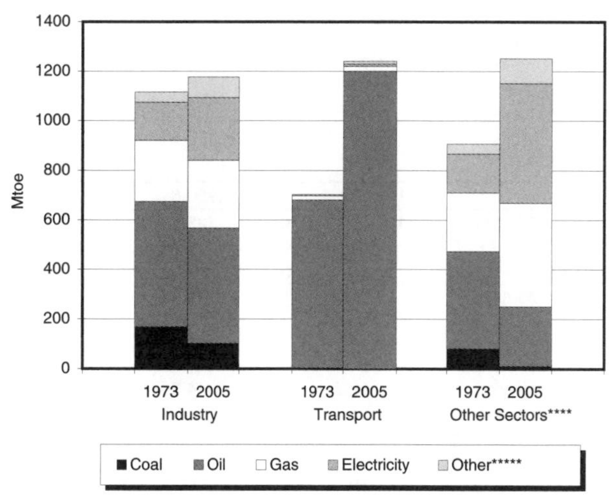

Figure 5. Electricity Generation by Fuel

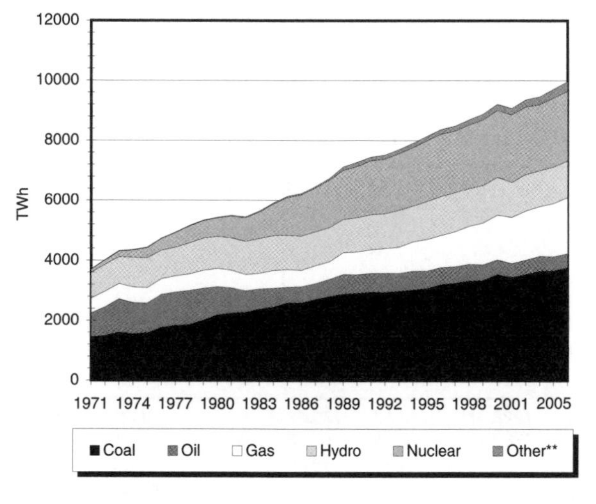

Figure 6. Electricity Consumption/GDP, TPES/GDP and Energy Production/TPES

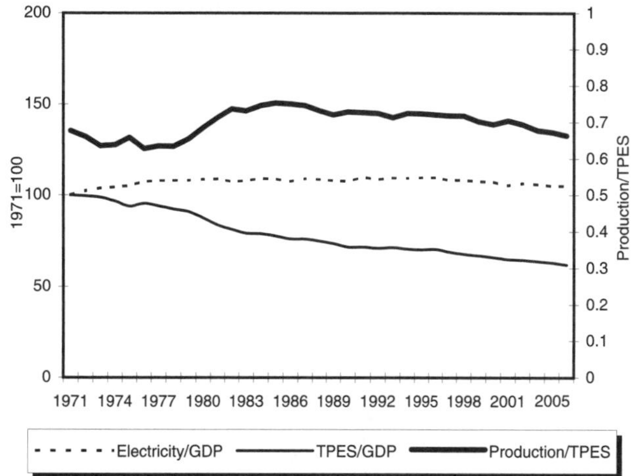

* Excluding electricity trade.

** Includes geothermal, solar, wind, combustible renewables & waste, etc.

*** Includes non-energy use.

**** Includes residential, commercial and public services, agriculture/forestry, fishing and non-specified.

***** Includes comb. renewables & waste, direct use of geothermal/solar thermal and heat produced in CHP/heat plants.

IEA / AIE : 2004

Million tonnes of oil equivalent / *Million de tonnes d'équivalent pétrole*

SUPPLY AND CONSUMPTION / ***APPROVISIONNEMENT ET DEMANDE***	Coal / *Charbon*	Crude Oil / *Pétrole brut*	Petroleum Products / *Produits pétroliers*	Gas / *Gaz*	Nuclear / *Nucléaire*	Hydro / *Hydro*	Geotherm. Solar etc. / *Géotherm. solaire etc.*	Combust. Renew. & Waste / *Comb. ren. & déchets*	Electricity / *Electricité*	Heat / *Chaleur*	Total / *Total*
Production	912.98	813.76	-	883.83	597.46	105.65	29.91	173.42	-	0.45	3517.46
Imports	355.61	1636.51	468.20	492.12	-	-	-	2.38	30.05	0.00	2984.87
Exports	-206.72	-337.84	-372.23	-241.32	-	-	-	-0.68	-27.54	-0.01	-1186.34
Intl. Marine Bunkers	-	-	-87.87	-	-	-	-	-	-	-	-87.87
Stock Changes	3.92	-5.23	0.00	-0.31	-	-	-	0.06	-	-	-1.56
TPES	**1065.79**	**2107.20**	**8.09**	**1134.31**	**597.46**	**105.65**	**29.91**	**175.18**	**2.51**	**0.45**	**5226.56**
Transfers	-	-29.06	38.34	-	-	-	-	-	-	-	9.29
Statistical Differences	-17.17	-13.57	0.98	7.30	-	-	0.00	-0.01	-0.13	0.00	-22.60
Electricity Plants	-802.68	-6.30	-74.62	-226.88	-594.29	-105.65	-23.97	-26.46	756.73	-0.11	-1104.23
CHP Plants	-54.80	-0.00	-16.77	-114.24	-3.17	-	-0.01	-27.85	78.15	51.93	-86.77
Heat Plants	-1.52	-	-1.60	-4.08	-	-	-0.15	-3.11	-0.36	9.33	-1.48
Gas Works	-2.28	-	-2.66	3.19	-	-	-	-	-	-	-1.76
Petroleum Refineries	-	-2080.86	2095.30	-0.56	-	-	-	-	-	-	13.88
Coal Transformation	-57.79	0.04	-2.59	-0.26	-	-	-	-	-	-	-60.59
Liquefaction Plants	-	0.56	-	-1.18	-	-	-	-	-	-	-0.62
Other Transformation	0.00	23.46	-24.28	-0.00	-	-	-	-0.12	-	-	-0.94
Own Use	-9.98	-0.02	-113.58	-74.39	-	-	-0.00	-0.09	-57.92	-2.57	-258.56
Distribution Losses	-0.80	-	-	-2.63	-	-	-0.14	-0.01	-52.77	-4.32	-60.68
TFC	**118.78**	**1.46**	**1906.61**	**720.57**	**-**	**-**	**5.63**	**117.53**	**726.21**	**54.72**	**3651.50**
INDUSTRY SECTOR	**105.08**	**0.04**	**135.57**	**250.88**	**-**	**-**	**0.36**	**60.65**	**250.62**	**20.91**	**824.12**
Iron and Steel	39.04	-	5.69	24.66	-	-	-	0.01	28.86	0.24	98.50
Chemical and Petrochem.	10.66	0.04	30.36	70.81	-	-	0.00	1.20	48.41	5.82	167.31
Non-Ferrous Metals	2.21	-	3.43	11.54	-	-	0.00	0.08	25.82	0.13	43.20
Non-Metallic Minerals	21.73	-	18.71	27.76	-	-	0.00	2.30	14.14	0.06	84.70
Transport Equipment	0.41	-	1.95	9.15	-	-	0.00	0.02	9.28	0.18	20.98
Machinery	0.54	-	5.52	18.44	-	-	0.00	0.03	28.44	0.30	53.27
Mining and Quarrying	0.63	-	4.54	5.87	-	-	-	0.00	7.81	0.03	18.87
Food and Tobacco	5.35	-	12.00	29.67	-	-	0.00	3.56	19.06	0.71	70.34
Paper, Pulp and Printing	7.19	-	11.80	24.57	-	-	0.13	41.39	33.21	1.37	119.67
Wood and Wood Products	0.05	-	2.76	2.56	-	-	-	8.51	4.86	0.18	18.91
Construction	1.79	-	11.71	1.32	-	-	0.00	0.09	1.38	0.03	16.31
Textile and Leather	0.50	-	3.26	8.26	-	-	0.00	0.10	7.83	0.89	20.84
Non-specified	15.00	-	23.85	16.27	-	-	0.23	3.36	21.52	10.97	91.20
TRANSPORT SECTOR	**0.07**	**-**	**1188.89**	**18.64**	**-**	**-**	**-**	**9.15**	**9.20**	**-**	**1225.95**
International Aviation	-	-	72.78	-	-	-	-	-	-	-	72.78
Domestic Aviation	-	-	87.47	-	-	-	-	-	-	-	87.47
Road	-	-	990.77	1.23	-	-	-	9.09	-	-	1001.10
Rail	0.01	-	16.86	-	-	-	-	0.00	7.56	-	24.43
Pipeline Transport	-	-	0.02	17.39	-	-	-	-	0.36	-	17.77
Domestic Navigation	0.07	-	19.41	-	-	-	-	0.05	-	-	19.52
Non-specified	-	-	1.59	0.02	-	-	-	-	1.28	-	2.89
OTHER SECTORS	**11.91**	**-**	**241.68**	**417.89**	**-**	**-**	**5.27**	**47.73**	**466.38**	**33.81**	**1224.68**
Residential	6.68	-	113.33	267.48	-	-	4.18	42.93	226.95	9.63	671.19
Comm. and Publ. Services	4.47	-	79.39	138.03	-	-	0.65	3.79	218.57	5.95	450.84
Agriculture/Forestry	0.69	-	42.32	5.17	-	-	0.13	0.99	5.86	0.27	55.44
Fishing	0.00	-	4.55	-	-	-	0.00	-	0.19	0.00	4.75
Non-specified	0.08	-	2.08	7.21	-	-	0.31	0.02	14.81	17.96	42.46
NON-ENERGY USE	**1.71**	**1.41**	**340.47**	**33.16**	**-**	**-**	**-**	**-**	**-**	**-**	**376.75**
in Industry/Transf./Energy	1.57	1.41	332.84	33.16	-	-	-	-	-	-	368.98
of which: Feedstocks	*0.47*	*1.41*	*226.33*	*32.07*	-	-	-	-	-	-	*260.29*
in Transport	-	-	4.51	-	-	-	-	-	-	-	4.51
in Other Sectors	0.14	-	3.12	-	-	-	-	-	-	-	3.26
Electricity Generated - TWh	***3664.80***	***36.41***	***430.30***	***1765.24***	***2292.33***	***1228.47***	***110.63***	***179.27***	**-**	***0.45***	***9707.89***
Electricity Plants	*3473.84*	*36.39*	*349.84*	*1232.65*	*2280.41*	*1228.47*	*107.45*	*89.73*	-	*0.26*	*8799.04*
CHP plants	*190.97*	*0.02*	*80.46*	*532.59*	*11.92*	-	*3.17*	*89.54*	-	*0.19*	*908.85*
Heat Generated - PJ	***558.91***	***0.11***	***303.72***	***1212.95***	***2.88***	**-**	***8.88***	***333.59***	***7.30***	***156.00***	***2584.34***
CHP plants	*514.08*	*0.11*	*262.43*	*1080.10*	*2.88*	-	-	*231.96*	*1.78*	*89.64*	*2182.98*
Heat Plants	*44.84*	-	*41.29*	*132.85*	-	-	*8.88*	*101.63*	*5.52*	*66.36*	*401.36*

IEA / AIE : 2005

Million tonnes of oil equivalent / *Million de tonnes d'équivalent pétrole*

SUPPLY AND CONSUMPTION ***APPROVISIONNEMENT ET DEMANDE***	Coal *Charbon*	Crude Oil *Pétrole brut*	Petroleum Products *Produits pétroliers*	Gas *Gaz*	Nuclear *Nucléaire*	Hydro *Hydro*	Geotherm. Solar etc. *Géotherm. solaire etc.*	Combust. Renew. & Waste *Comb. ren. & déchets*	Electricity *Electricité*	Heat *Chaleur*	Total *Total*
Production	928.49	767.41	-	870.69	603.94	105.69	31.41	178.58	-	0.50	3486.69
Imports	345.98	1645.66	514.92	517.39	-	-	-	3.20	34.30	0.00	3061.47
Exports	-215.82	-302.52	-399.48	-247.29	-	-	-	-0.85	-31.47	-0.01	-1197.44
Intl. Marine Bunkers	-	-	-95.17	-	-	-	-	-	-	-	-95.17
Stock Changes	3.94	-8.53	-3.62	8.35	-	-	-	-0.04	-	-	0.09
TPES	**1062.59**	**2102.01**	**16.66**	**1149.13**	**603.94**	**105.69**	**31.41**	**180.89**	**2.84**	**0.49**	**5255.64**
Transfers	-	-22.13	31.15	-	-	-	-	-	-	-	9.02
Statistical Differences	-11.57	-16.41	-5.13	3.08	-	-	0.00	0.11	-0.14	0.00	-30.07
Electricity Plants	-818.71	-8.23	-74.98	-245.47	-600.27	-105.69	-25.21	-26.69	780.89	-0.47	-1124.81
CHP Plants	-49.37	-	-16.71	-111.79	-3.67	-	-0.02	-28.54	75.86	53.79	-80.45
Heat Plants	-0.86	-	-1.55	-4.50	-	-	-0.14	-3.23	-0.35	22.84	12.20
Gas Works	-2.42	-	-2.42	3.09	-	-	-	-	-	-	-1.75
Petroleum Refineries	-	-2077.89	2094.76	-0.57	-	-	-	-	-	-	16.31
Coal Transformation	-56.77	0.02	-2.08	-0.22	-	-	-	-	-	-	-59.05
Liquefaction Plants	-	0.57	-	-1.17	-	-	-	-	-	-	-0.60
Other Transformation	0.00	23.38	-24.32	-0.00	-	-	-	-0.12	-	-	-1.05
Own Use	-9.65	-0.21	-111.84	-76.53	-	-	-0.00	-0.09	-62.22	-2.83	-263.37
Distribution Losses	-0.91	-	-0.01	-3.00	-	-	-0.14	-0.01	-53.47	-5.53	-63.06
TFC	**112.32**	**1.11**	**1903.54**	**712.06**	**-**	**-**	**5.90**	**122.32**	**743.41**	**68.29**	**3668.94**
INDUSTRY SECTOR	**100.04**	**0.04**	**135.31**	**241.28**	**-**	**-**	**0.38**	**62.49**	**252.14**	**21.35**	**813.03**
Iron and Steel	35.46	-	5.69	23.58	-	-	-	0.01	29.76	0.23	94.71
Chemical and Petrochem.	11.05	0.04	31.07	68.09	-	-	0.00	1.31	49.33	5.74	166.64
Non-Ferrous Metals	2.45	-	3.37	10.95	-	-	0.00	0.08	26.84	0.18	43.87
Non-Metallic Minerals	20.26	-	18.46	27.61	-	-	0.00	2.29	14.07	0.09	82.78
Transport Equipment	0.26	-	1.69	8.62	-	-	0.00	0.01	9.29	0.17	20.04
Machinery	0.54	-	6.00	17.67	-	-	0.00	0.03	29.03	0.30	53.55
Mining and Quarrying	0.66	-	5.23	5.92	-	-	-	0.00	7.87	0.20	19.88
Food and Tobacco	5.40	-	11.19	27.78	-	-	0.00	3.71	19.43	0.72	68.23
Paper, Pulp and Printing	7.25	-	11.43	23.49	-	-	0.14	42.52	32.77	1.34	118.94
Wood and Wood Products	0.07	-	2.79	2.32	-	-	-	8.84	5.08	0.24	19.34
Construction	1.88	-	11.73	1.43	-	-	0.00	0.11	1.42	0.03	16.61
Textile and Leather	0.65	-	2.95	7.78	-	-	0.00	0.11	7.39	0.87	19.75
Non-specified	14.12	-	23.70	16.03	-	-	0.24	3.48	19.86	11.24	88.67
TRANSPORT SECTOR	**0.10**	**-**	**1194.91**	**20.02**	**-**	**-**	**-**	**11.41**	**9.28**	**-**	**1235.72**
International Aviation	-	-	77.46	-	-	-	-	-	-	-	77.46
Domestic Aviation	-	-	88.46	-	-	-	-	-	-	-	88.46
Road	-	-	991.76	1.40	-	-	-	11.35	-	-	1004.52
Rail	0.01	-	18.36	-	-	-	-	0.00	7.61	-	25.98
Pipeline Transport	-	-	0.02	18.60	-	-	-	-	0.36	-	18.97
Domestic Navigation	0.09	-	17.50	-	-	-	-	0.05	-	-	17.65
Non-specified	-	-	1.35	0.02	-	-	-	0.00	1.31	-	2.69
OTHER SECTORS	**10.57**	**-**	**235.59**	**419.07**	**-**	**-**	**5.52**	**48.42**	**481.99**	**46.93**	**1248.09**
Residential	6.50	-	110.55	268.39	-	-	4.38	43.45	239.98	10.16	683.41
Comm. and Publ. Services	3.48	-	76.58	140.21	-	-	0.69	3.75	222.08	6.25	453.04
Agriculture/Forestry	0.55	-	42.06	5.11	-	-	0.13	1.20	6.12	0.14	55.31
Fishing	0.00	-	4.29	0.00	-	-	0.00	-	0.19	0.00	4.49
Non-specified	0.04	-	2.11	5.36	-	-	0.31	0.02	13.62	30.38	51.84
NON-ENERGY USE	**1.61**	**1.07**	**337.73**	**31.69**	**-**	**-**	**-**	**-**	**-**	**-**	**372.09**
in Industry/Transf./Energy	1.44	1.07	329.82	31.69	-	-	-	-	-	-	364.02
of which: Feedstocks	*0.45*	*1.07*	*223.10*	*30.68*	-	-	-	-	-	-	*255.30*
in Transport	-	-	4.60	-	-	-	-	-	-	-	4.60
in Other Sectors	0.16	-	3.31	-	-	-	-	-	-	-	3.47
Electricity Generated - TWh	***3762.80***	***43.41***	***422.72***	***1867.17***	***2317.18***	***1228.91***	***131.64***	***187.65***	**-**	***0.72***	***9962.21***
Electricity Plants	*3592.90*	*43.40*	*348.16*	*1345.24*	*2303.35*	*1228.91*	*126.31*	*91.19*	-	*0.42*	*9079.88*
CHP plants	*169.90*	*0.02*	*74.57*	*521.93*	*13.83*	-	*5.33*	*96.47*	-	*0.30*	*882.34*
Heat Generated - PJ	***513.87***	***0.11***	***305.74***	***1278.11***	***2.87***	**-**	***8.67***	***373.18***	***7.54***	***739.52***	***3229.60***
CHP plants	*487.24*	*0.11*	*269.78*	*1123.03*	*2.87*	-	*0.29*	*263.77*	*1.83*	*110.78*	*2259.70*
Heat Plants	*26.63*	-	*35.96*	*155.08*	-	-	*8.38*	*109.41*	*5.71*	*628.75*	*969.90*

Australia / Australie
Key Indicators
Indicateurs principaux

	1960	1970	1973	1980	1990	1995
Energy Production (Mtoe)	21.31	47.70	67.97	86.10	157.53	186.91
Net Imports (Mtoe)	11.99	6.59	- 8.49	- 17.34	- 64.67	- 89.38
Total Primary Energy Supply (Mtoe)	31.55	51.33	57.62	70.37	87.55	94.39
Net Oil Imports (Mtoe)	12.74	17.75	9.16	11.15	4.94	7.46
Oil Supply (Mtoe)	11.22	24.42	27.15	30.84	32.52	34.38
Electricity Consumption (TWh)*	18.76	45.15	56.60	86.91	144.29	161.85
GDP (billion 2000 US$ using exch. rates)	93.49 e	156.95	174.25	210.03	280.98	330.11
GDP (billion 2000 US$ using PPPs)	122.73 e	206.03	228.75	275.72	368.85	433.35
Population (millions)	10.40 e	12.66	13.61	14.81	17.17	18.19
Industrial Production Index (2000=100)	..	..	..	61.90	80.40	87.00
Energy Production/TPES	0.6753	0.9291	1.1797	1.2235	1.7995	1.9803
Net Oil Imports/GDP (toe per thousand 2000 US$)	0.1363 e	0.1131	0.0525	0.0531	0.0176	0.0226
TPES/GDP (toe per thousand 2000 US$)	0.3375 e	0.3271	0.3307	0.3351	0.3116	0.2859
TPES/GDP (toe per thousand 2000 US$ PPP)	0.2571 e	0.2492	0.2519	0.2552	0.2373	0.2178
TPES/Population (toe per capita)	3.0327 e	4.0538	4.2324	4.7526	5.0988	5.1880
Oil Supply/GDP (toe per thousand 2000 US$)	0.1200 e	0.1556	0.1558	0.1468	0.1157	0.1041
Oil Supply/Population (toe per capita)	1.0786 e	1.9286	1.9940	2.0830	1.8940	1.8895
Elect. Cons./GDP (kWh per 2000 US$)	0.2007 e	0.2877	0.3248	0.4138	0.5135	0.4903
Elect. Cons./Population (kWh per capita)	1 803 e	3 566	4 158	5 869	8 404	8 897
Industry Cons.**/Industrial Production (2000=100)	..	..	..	116.54	102.15	102.58
Industry Oil Cons.**/Industrial Production (2000=100)	..	..	..	166.25	104.17	103.82

	2000	2001	2002	2003	2004	2005
Energy Production (Mtoe)	233.61	249.18	254.54	253.89	259.02	270.98
Net Imports (Mtoe)	- 127.26	- 133.91	- 139.69	- 138.81	- 143.76	- 148.02
Total Primary Energy Supply (Mtoe)	110.49	108.34	111.96	113.05	113.54	121.96
Net Oil Imports (Mtoe)	3.45	- 0.08	1.78	5.84	7.19	14.70
Oil Supply (Mtoe)	36.50	33.22	34.57	35.93	34.56	37.87
Electricity Consumption (TWh)*	192.58	201.23 e	211.59	212.91	224.76	234.20
GDP (billion 2000 US$ using exch. rates)	399.61	414.66	427.73	445.07	456.98	469.81
GDP (billion 2000 US$ using PPPs)	524.59	544.35	561.51	584.26	599.90	616.75
Population (millions)	19.27	19.53	19.75	19.98	20.20	20.47
Industrial Production Index (2000=100)	100.00	100.10	103.30	103.40	103.70	104.90
Energy Production/TPES	2.1143	2.2999	2.2736	2.2459	2.2813	2.2220
Net Oil Imports/GDP (toe per thousand 2000 US$)	0.0086	- 0.0002	0.0042	0.0131	0.0157	0.0313
TPES/GDP (toe per thousand 2000 US$)	0.2765	0.2613	0.2617	0.2540	0.2485	0.2596
TPES/GDP (toe per thousand 2000 US$ PPP)	0.2106	0.1990	0.1994	0.1935	0.1893	0.1977
TPES/Population (toe per capita)	5.7336	5.5484	5.6681	5.6580	5.6196	5.9566
Oil Supply/GDP (toe per thousand 2000 US$)	0.0913	0.0801	0.0808	0.0807	0.0756	0.0806
Oil Supply/Population (toe per capita)	1.8942	1.7012	1.7502	1.7984	1.7107	1.8497
Elect. Cons./GDP (kWh per 2000 US$)	0.4819	0.4853 e	0.4947	0.4784	0.4918	0.4985
Elect. Cons./Population (kWh per capita)	9 994	10 305 e	10 712	10 656	11 125	11 439
Industry Cons.**/Industrial Production (2000=100)	100.00	102.26	88.44	88.77	92.74	95.38
Industry Oil Cons.**/Industrial Production (2000=100)	100.00	98.87	75.27	76.67	75.57	83.78

* Electricity consumption equals domestic supply less distribution losses.
La consommation d'électricité représente l'approvisionnement intérieur diminué des pertes de distribution.

** Includes non-energy use in industry/transformation/energy sectors.
Comprend l'usage non-énergétique dans les secteurs de l'industrie/transformation/énergie.

Australia / Australie

Figure 1. TPES* in 1973

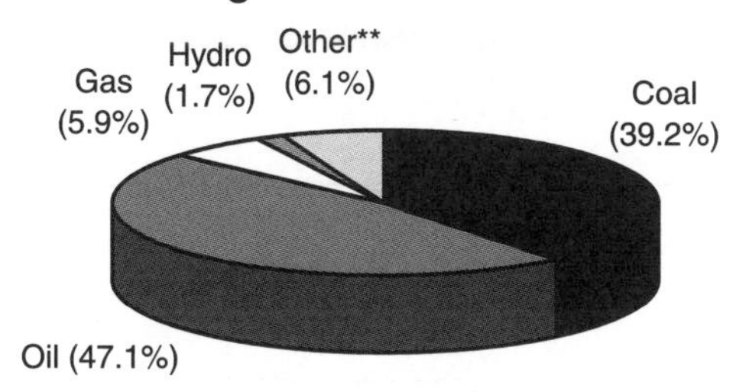

Figure 2. TPES* in 2005

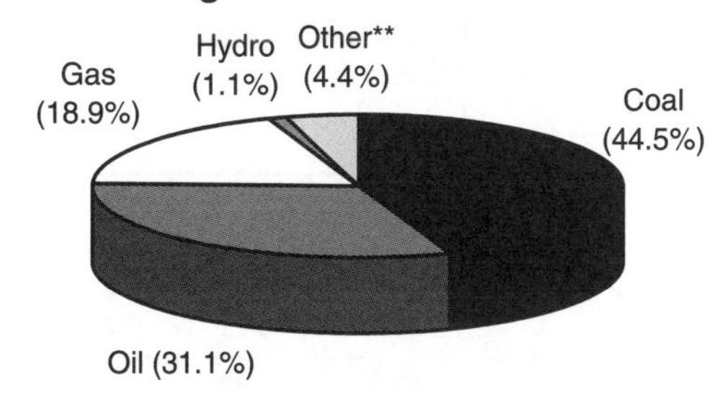

Figure 3. Final Consumption by Sector***

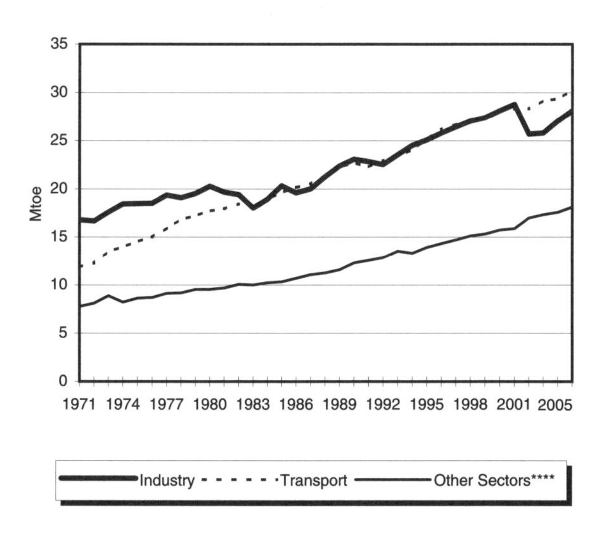

Figure 4. Breakdown of Sectorial Final Consumption by Source in 1973 and 2005***

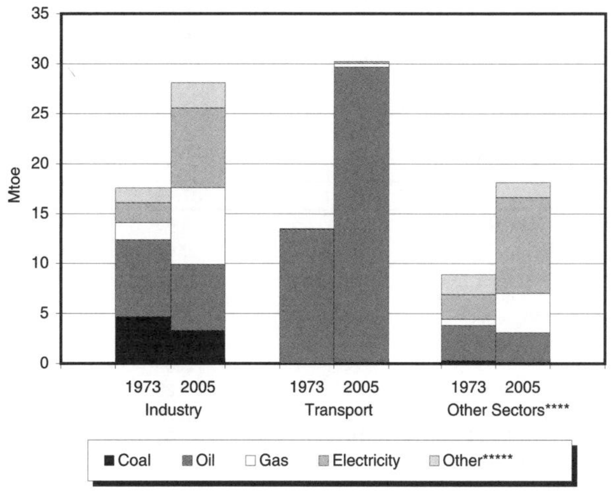

Figure 5. Electricity Generation by Fuel

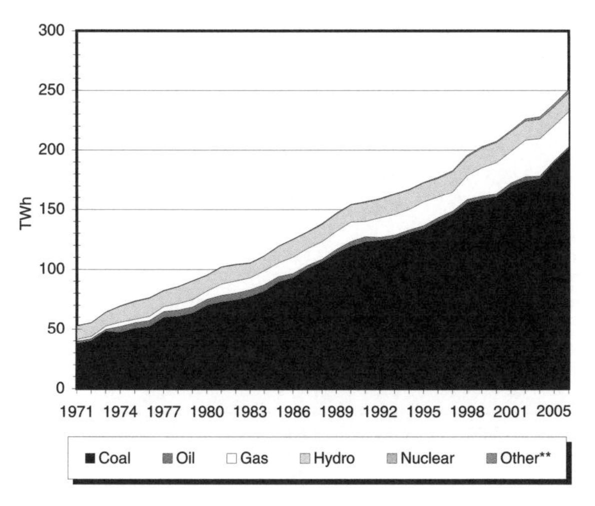

Figure 6. Electricity Consumption/GDP, TPES/GDP and Energy Production/TPES

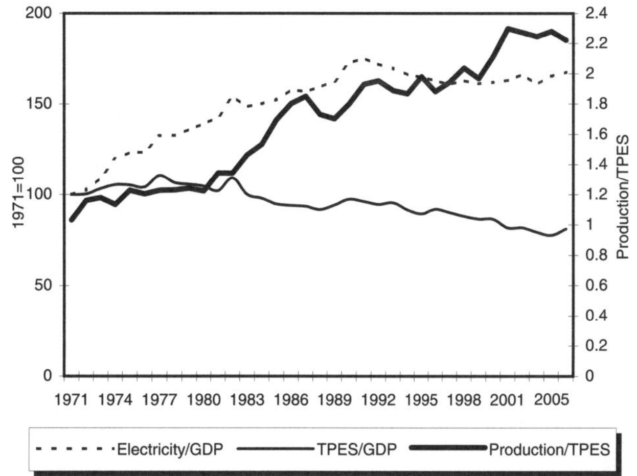

* Excluding electricity trade.

** Includes geothermal, solar, wind, combustible renewables & waste, etc.

*** Includes non-energy use.

**** Includes residential, commercial and public services, agriculture/forestry, fishing and non-specified.

***** Includes comb. renewables & waste, direct use of geothermal/solar thermal and heat produced in CHP/heat plants.

Australia / Australie : 2004

Million tonnes of oil equivalent / *Million de tonnes d'équivalent pétrole*

SUPPLY AND CONSUMPTION	Coal	Crude Oil	Petroleum Products	Gas	Nuclear	Hydro	Geotherm. Solar etc.	Combust. Renew. & Waste	Electricity	Heat	Total
APPROVISIONNEMENT ET DEMANDE	*Charbon*	*Pétrole brut*	*Produits pétroliers*	*Gaz*	*Nucléaire*	*Hydro*	*Géotherm. solaire etc.*	*Comb. ren. & déchets*	*Electricité*	*Chaleur*	*Total*
Production	192.61	27.64	-	31.99	-	1.35	0.12	5.30	-	-	259.02
Imports	-	21.65	6.45	-	-	-	-	-	-	-	28.10
Exports	-141.70	-18.63	-2.27	-9.25	-	-	-	-	-	-	-171.86
Intl. Marine Bunkers	-	-	-0.82	-	-	-	-	-	-	-	-0.82
Stock Changes	-1.44	0.78	-0.24	-	-	-	-	-	-	-	-0.90
TPES	**49.47**	**31.45**	**3.12**	**22.74**	**-**	**1.35**	**0.12**	**5.30**	**-**	**-**	**113.54**
Transfers	-	2.51	1.03	-	-	-	-	-	-	-	3.54
Statistical Differences	-0.03	1.61	0.86	-	-	-	-	-	-	-	2.45
Electricity Plants	-42.84	-	-0.43	-6.24	-	-1.35	-0.06	-0.30	19.36	-	-31.86
CHP Plants	-1.64	-	-0.40	-1.57	-	-	-	-0.85	1.18 e	-	-3.28
Heat Plants	-	-	-	-	-	-	-	-	-	-	-
Gas Works	-	-	-0.03	-0.17	-	-	-	-	-	-	-0.20
Petroleum Refineries	-	-35.55	35.85	-	-	-	-	-	-	-	0.30
Coal Transformation	-1.33 e	-	-0.02	-0.15	-	-	-	-	-	-	-1.51
Liquefaction Plants	-	-	-	-	-	-	-	-	-	-	-
Other Transformation	-	-	-	-	-	-	-	-	-	-	-
Own Use	-0.31	-0.02	-2.48	-2.77	-	-	-	-	-2.22	-	-7.80
Distribution Losses	-	-	-	-	-	-	-	-	-1.23	-	-1.23
TFC	**3.32**	**-**	**37.49**	**11.83**	**-**	**-**	**0.06**	**4.15**	**17.09**	**-**	**73.95**
INDUSTRY SECTOR	**3.16**	**-**	**3.08**	**6.39**	**-**	**-**	**-**	**2.55**	**7.69**	**-**	**22.86**
Iron and Steel	0.66 e	-	0.04	1.08	-	-	-	-	0.55	-	2.33
Chemical and Petrochem.	0.11	-	0.16	0.78	-	-	-	0.17	0.35	-	1.58
Non-Ferrous Metals	1.22	-	0.78	1.78	-	-	-	0.06	4.12	-	7.96
Non-Metallic Minerals	0.61	-	0.12	1.17	-	-	-	-	0.33	-	2.23
Transport Equipment	-	-	-	..	-	-	-	-	..	-	-
Machinery	-	-	0.02	0.11	-	-	-	-	0.22	-	0.35
Mining and Quarrying	0.16	-	1.28	0.31	-	-	-	-	1.01	-	2.77
Food and Tobacco	0.22	-	0.05	0.64	-	-	-	1.89	0.58	-	3.39
Paper, Pulp and Printing	0.15	-	0.03	0.31	-	-	-	0.20	0.33	-	1.04
Wood and Wood Products	-	-	0.01	..	-	-	-	0.22	0.10	-	0.34
Construction	-	-	0.56	0.05	-	-	-	-	0.01	-	0.62
Textile and Leather	0.02	-	0.01	0.14	-	-	-	-	0.07	-	0.25
Non-specified	-	-	-	0.01	-	-	-	-	0.01	-	0.02
TRANSPORT SECTOR	**0.07**	**-**	**28.74**	**0.34**	**-**	**-**	**-**	**-**	**0.20**	**-**	**29.34**
International Aviation	-	-	2.34	-	-	-	-	-	-	-	2.34
Domestic Aviation	-	-	2.03	-	-	-	-	-	-	-	2.03
Road	-	-	23.59	0.03	-	-	-	-	-	-	23.62
Rail	-	-	0.54	-	-	-	-	-	0.18	-	0.72
Pipeline Transport	-	-	-	0.30	-	-	-	-	0.00	-	0.30
Domestic Navigation	0.07	-	0.25	-	-	-	-	-	-	-	0.31
Non-specified	-	-	0.00	0.01	-	-	-	-	0.01	-	0.03
OTHER SECTORS	**0.09**	**-**	**2.84**	**3.77**	**-**	**-**	**0.06**	**1.60**	**9.21**	**-**	**17.58**
Residential	0.00	-	0.35	2.82	-	-	0.06	1.59	4.89	-	9.71
Comm. and Publ. Services	0.09	-	0.50	0.95	-	-	0.00	0.01	4.16	-	5.71
Agriculture/Forestry	-	-	2.00	0.00	-	-	-	-	0.16	-	2.16
Fishing	-	-	-	-	-	-	-	-	-	-	-
Non-specified	-	-	-	-	-	-	-	-	-	-	-
NON-ENERGY USE	**-**	**-**	**2.83**	**1.33**	**-**	**-**	**-**	**-**	**-**	**-**	**4.16**
in Industry/Transf./Energy	-	-	2.83	1.33	-	-	-	-	-	-	4.16
of which: Feedstocks	-	-	*0.88*	*1.33*	-	-	-	-	-	-	*2.22*
in Transport	-	-	-	-	-	-	-	-	-	-	-
in Other Sectors	-	-	-	-	-	-	-	-	-	-	-
Electricity Generated - TWh	***189.67***	-	***1.55***	***29.41***	-	***15.68***	***0.71***	***1.83***	-	-	***238.84***
Electricity Plants	*183.72 e*	-	*1.55*	*22.81*	-	*15.68*	*0.71*	*0.65*	-	-	*225.12*
CHP plants	*5.94 e*	-	-	*6.60*	-	-	-	*1.18*	-	-	*13.72*
Heat Generated - PJ	-	-	-	-	-	-	-	-	-	-	-
CHP plants	-	-	-	-	-	-	-	-	-	-	-
Heat Plants	-	-	-	-	-	-	-	-	-	-	-

Australia / Australie : 2005

Million tonnes of oil equivalent / *Million de tonnes d'équivalent pétrole*

SUPPLY AND CONSUMPTION / ***APPROVISIONNEMENT ET DEMANDE***	Coal / *Charbon*	Crude Oil / *Pétrole brut*	Petroleum Products / *Produits pétroliers*	Gas / *Gaz*	Nuclear / *Nucléaire*	Hydro / *Hydro*	Geotherm. Solar etc. / *Géotherm. solaire etc.*	Combust. Renew. & Waste / *Comb. ren. & déchets*	Electricity / *Electricité*	Heat / *Chaleur*	Total / *Total*
Production	204.70	24.13	-	35.42	-	1.35	0.14	5.24	-	-	270.98
Imports	-	21.38	9.65	-	-	-	-	-	-	-	31.03
Exports	-150.34	-14.83	-1.50	-12.38	-	-	-	-	-	-	-179.05
Intl. Marine Bunkers	-	-	-0.83	-	-	-	-	-	-	-	-0.83
Stock Changes	-0.05	-0.30	0.18	-	-	-	-	-	-	-	-0.17
TPES	**54.32**	**30.38**	**7.49**	**23.04**	**-**	**1.35**	**0.14**	**5.24**	**-**	**-**	**121.96**
Transfers	-	2.70	0.91	-	-	-	-	-	-	-	3.61
Statistical Differences	-0.04	0.88	-0.39	-	-	-	-	-	-	-	0.45
Electricity Plants	-46.68	-	-0.42	-6.19	-	-1.35	-0.08	-0.33	20.11	-	-34.93
CHP Plants	-2.35	-	-0.15	-1.68	-	-	-	-0.86	1.47	-	-3.57
Heat Plants	-	-	-	-	-	-	-	-	-	-	-
Gas Works	-	-	-0.03	-0.15	-	-	-	-	-	-	-0.18
Petroleum Refineries	-	-33.94	34.29	-	-	-	-	-	-	-	0.35
Coal Transformation	-1.47 e	-	-0.02	-0.13	-	-	-	-	-	-	-1.62
Liquefaction Plants	-	-	-	-	-	-	-	-	-	-	-
Other Transformation	-	-	-	-	-	-	-	-	-	-	-
Own Use	-0.31	-0.03	-2.52	-2.92	-	-	-	-	-2.37	-	-8.14
Distribution Losses	-	-	-	-	-	-	-	-	-1.46	-	-1.46
TFC	**3.47**	**-**	**39.16**	**11.98**	**-**	**-**	**0.06**	**4.04**	**17.76**	**-**	**76.48**
INDUSTRY SECTOR	**3.27**	**-**	**3.42**	**6.37**	**-**	**-**	**-**	**2.59**	**7.94**	**-**	**23.59**
Iron and Steel	0.63 e	-	0.05	0.91	-	-	-	-	0.57	-	2.15
Chemical and Petrochem.	0.11	-	0.16	0.53	-	-	-	0.12	0.36	-	1.29
Non-Ferrous Metals	1.23	-	0.78	1.87	-	-	-	0.06	4.29	-	8.23
Non-Metallic Minerals	0.70	-	0.14	1.34	-	-	-	-	0.34	-	2.51
Transport Equipment	-	-	-	..	-	-	-	-	..	-	-
Machinery	-	-	0.04	0.11	-	-	-	-	0.22	-	0.37
Mining and Quarrying	0.18	-	1.60	0.32	-	-	-	-	1.00	-	3.10
Food and Tobacco	0.20	-	0.06	0.68	-	-	-	1.98	0.60	-	3.53
Paper, Pulp and Printing	0.19	-	0.02	0.40	-	-	-	0.20	0.36	-	1.17
Wood and Wood Products	-	-	0.01	..	-	-	-	0.23	0.10	-	0.34
Construction	-	-	0.55	0.07	-	-	-	-	0.01	-	0.63
Textile and Leather	0.02	-	0.01	0.14	-	-	-	-	0.07	-	0.25
Non-specified	-	-	-	0.01	-	-	-	-	0.02	-	0.03
TRANSPORT SECTOR	**0.09**	**-**	**29.56**	**0.35**	**-**	**-**	**-**	**0.01**	**0.21**	**-**	**30.24**
International Aviation	-	-	2.74	-	-	-	-	-	-	-	2.74
Domestic Aviation	-	-	1.83	-	-	-	-	-	-	-	1.83
Road	-	-	24.05	0.03	-	-	-	0.01	-	-	24.09
Rail	-	-	0.69	-	-	-	-	-	0.19	-	0.88
Pipeline Transport	-	-	-	0.31	-	-	-	-	0.00	-	0.31
Domestic Navigation	0.09	-	0.25	-	-	-	-	-	-	-	0.34
Non-specified	-	-	0.00	0.01	-	-	-	-	0.03	-	0.04
OTHER SECTORS	**0.11**	**-**	**2.98**	**3.93**	**-**	**-**	**0.06**	**1.45**	**9.61**	**-**	**18.13**
Residential	0.01	-	0.35	2.94	-	-	0.06	1.44	5.24	-	10.04
Comm. and Publ. Services	0.10	-	0.51	0.98	-	-	0.00	0.01	4.21	-	5.82
Agriculture/Forestry	-	-	2.12	0.00	-	-	-	-	0.15	-	2.27
Fishing	-	-	-	-	-	-	-	-	-	-	-
Non-specified	-	-	-	-	-	-	-	-	-	-	-
NON-ENERGY USE	**-**	**-**	**3.20**	**1.32**	**-**	**-**	**-**	**-**	**-**	**-**	**4.53**
in Industry/Transf./Energy	-	-	3.20	1.32	-	-	-	-	-	-	4.53
of which: Feedstocks	-	-	*1.21*	*1.32*	-	-	-	-	-	-	*2.53*
in Transport	-	-	-	-	-	-	-	-	-	-	-
in Other Sectors	-	-	-	-	-	-	-	-	-	-	-
Electricity Generated - TWh	***201.09***	-	***1.93***	***29.30***	-	***15.69***	***0.89***	***2.03***	-	-	***250.92***
Electricity Plants	*192.48*	-	*1.93*	*22.10*	-	*15.69*	*0.89*	*0.80*	-	-	*233.88*
CHP plants	*8.61*	-	-	*7.20*	-	-	-	*1.23*	-	-	*17.04*
Heat Generated - PJ	-	-	-	-	-	-	-	-	-	-	-
CHP plants	-	-	-	-	-	-	-	-	-	-	-
Heat Plants	-	-	-	-	-	-	-	-	-	-	-

Austria / Autriche
Key Indicators
Indicateurs principaux

	1960	1970	1973	1980	1990	1995
Energy Production (Mtoe)	7.36	7.95	7.93	7.63	8.10	8.73
Net Imports (Mtoe)	3.77	10.68	13.97	16.15	17.27	18.08
Total Primary Energy Supply (Mtoe)	10.93	18.18	21.65	23.30	25.07	27.15
Net Oil Imports (Mtoe)	0.56	6.75	9.74	11.02	9.65	10.23
Oil Supply (Mtoe)	3.01	9.20	12.28	12.23	10.63	11.45
Electricity Consumption (TWh)*	12.79	22.54	27.47	35.37	46.87	50.79
GDP (billion 2000 US$ using exch. rates)	53.35 e	84.52	98.97	120.44	150.67	167.72
GDP (billion 2000 US$ using PPPs)	63.33 e	100.34	117.49	142.98	178.87	199.11
Population (millions)	7.05 e	7.47	7.59	7.55	7.68	7.95
Industrial Production Index (2000=100)	20.60	35.60	42.90	52.60	69.00	74.50
Energy Production/TPES	0.6735	0.4374	0.3664	0.3275	0.3232	0.3216
Net Oil Imports/GDP (toe per thousand 2000 US$)	0.0106 e	0.0798	0.0984	0.0915	0.0640	0.0610
TPES/GDP (toe per thousand 2000 US$)	0.2048 e	0.2151	0.2188	0.1935	0.1664	0.1619
TPES/GDP (toe per thousand 2000 US$ PPP)	0.1725 e	0.1812	0.1843	0.1630	0.1402	0.1364
TPES/Population (toe per capita)	1.5504 e	2.4349	2.8540	3.0869	3.2653	3.4166
Oil Supply/GDP (toe per thousand 2000 US$)	0.0565 e	0.1088	0.1241	0.1015	0.0706	0.0683
Oil Supply/Population (toe per capita)	0.4276 e	1.2319	1.6189	1.6201	1.3851	1.4407
Elect. Cons./GDP (kWh per 2000 US$)	0.2397 e	0.2667	0.2775	0.2936	0.3111	0.3028
Elect. Cons./Population (kWh per capita)	1 815 e	3 019	3 621	4 685	6 104	6 390
Industry Cons.**/Industrial Production (2000=100)	233.15	185.54	179.18	149.59	122.87	113.61
Industry Oil Cons.**/Industrial Production (2000=100)	241.17	302.36	293.07	148.22	121.02	116.91

	2000	2001	2002	2003	2004	2005
Energy Production (Mtoe)	9.75	9.89	10.06	9.79	10.04	9.81
Net Imports (Mtoe)	19.12	20.03	21.22	23.17	23.55	24.76
Total Primary Energy Supply (Mtoe)	29.04	30.86	31.37	32.99	33.25	34.36
Net Oil Imports (Mtoe)	11.03	11.77	12.61	13.35	13.57	13.38
Oil Supply (Mtoe)	12.27	13.16	13.47	14.28	14.30	14.50
Electricity Consumption (TWh)*	56.94	58.87	60.02	62.42	63.80	64.95
GDP (billion 2000 US$ using exch. rates)	193.84	195.45	197.12	199.27	204.14	208.31
GDP (billion 2000 US$ using PPPs)	230.12	232.03	234.02	236.57	242.35	247.30
Population (millions)	8.01	8.04	8.08	8.12	8.18	8.23
Industrial Production Index (2000=100)	100.00	102.80	103.60	105.60	112.30	117.30
Energy Production/TPES	0.3358	0.3205	0.3208	0.2969	0.3020	0.2854
Net Oil Imports/GDP (toe per thousand 2000 US$)	0.0569	0.0602	0.0639	0.0670	0.0665	0.0642
TPES/GDP (toe per thousand 2000 US$)	0.1498	0.1579	0.1591	0.1655	0.1629	0.1650
TPES/GDP (toe per thousand 2000 US$ PPP)	0.1262	0.1330	0.1340	0.1394	0.1372	0.1390
TPES/Population (toe per capita)	3.6241	3.8370	3.8800	4.0636	4.0677	4.1738
Oil Supply/GDP (toe per thousand 2000 US$)	0.0633	0.0673	0.0683	0.0716	0.0700	0.0696
Oil Supply/Population (toe per capita)	1.5314	1.6359	1.6657	1.7586	1.7487	1.7609
Elect. Cons./GDP (kWh per 2000 US$)	0.2938	0.3012	0.3045	0.3132	0.3125	0.3118
Elect. Cons./Population (kWh per capita)	7 107	7 319	7 425	7 689	7 805	7 889
Industry Cons.**/Industrial Production (2000=100)	100.00	102.77	102.35	101.34	98.76	96.78
Industry Oil Cons.**/Industrial Production (2000=100)	100.00	105.76	105.52	108.32	103.65	95.93

* Electricity consumption equals domestic supply less distribution losses.
La consommation d'électricité représente l'approvisionnement intérieur diminué des pertes de distribution.

** Includes non-energy use in industry/transformation/energy sectors.
Comprend l'usage non-énergétique dans les secteurs de l'industrie/transformation/énergie.

Austria / Autriche

Figure 1. TPES* in 1973

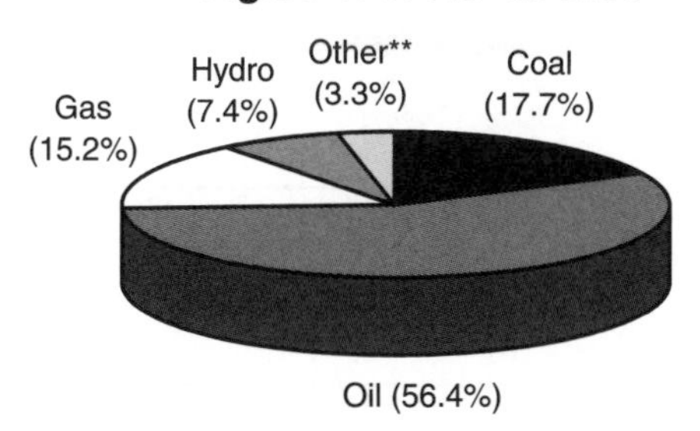

Figure 2. TPES* in 2005

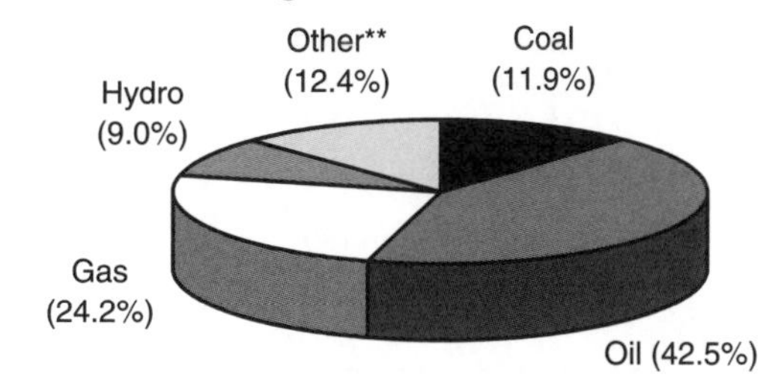

Figure 3. Final Consumption by Sector***

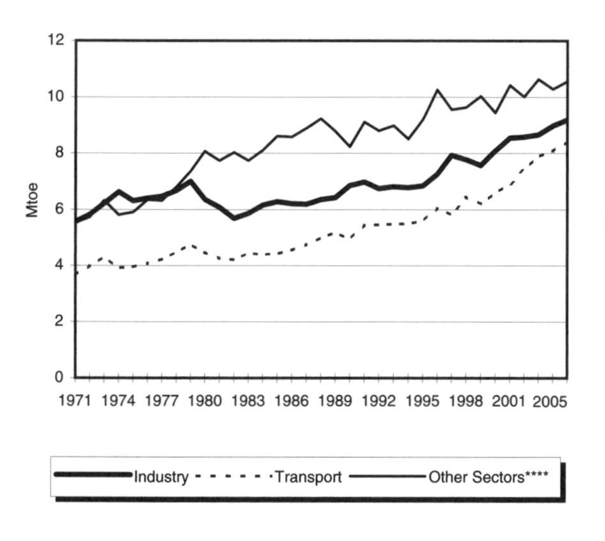

Figure 4. Breakdown of Sectorial Final Consumption by Source in 1973 and 2005***

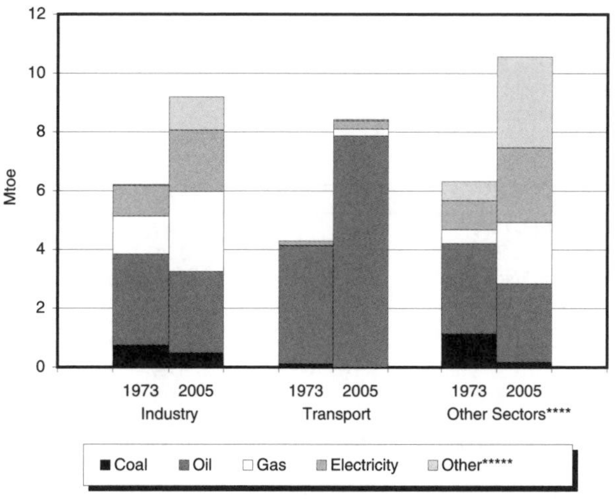

Figure 5. Electricity Generation by Fuel

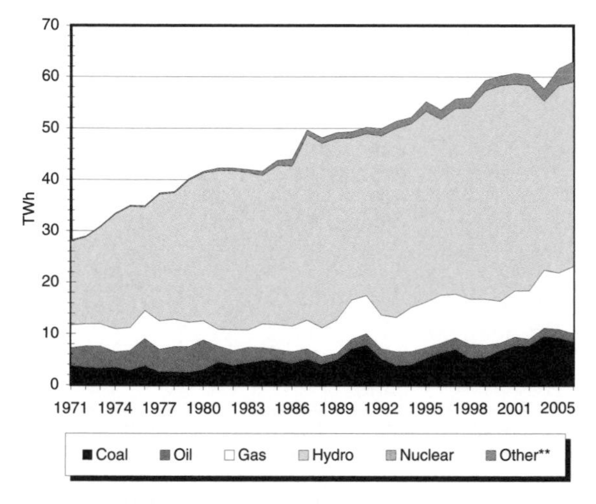

Figure 6. Electricity Consumption/GDP, TPES/GDP and Energy Production/TPES

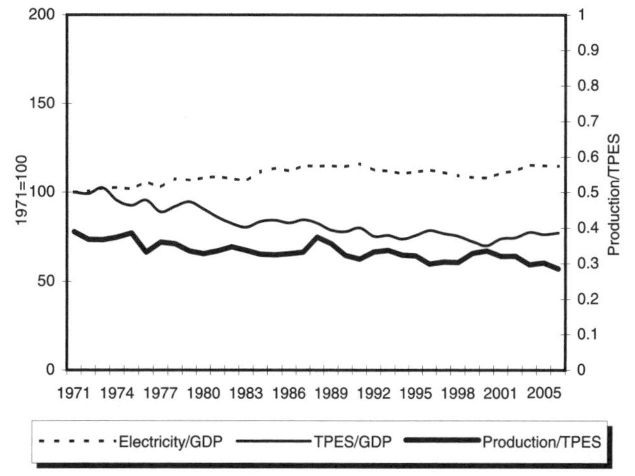

* Excluding electricity trade.

** Includes geothermal, solar, wind, combustible renewables & waste, etc.

*** Includes non-energy use.

**** Includes residential, commercial and public services, agriculture/forestry, fishing and non-specified.

***** Includes comb. renewables & waste, direct use of geothermal/solar thermal and heat produced in CHP/heat plants.

Austria / Autriche : 2004

Million tonnes of oil equivalent / *Million de tonnes d'équivalent pétrole*

SUPPLY AND CONSUMPTION ***APPROVISIONNEMENT ET DEMANDE***	Coal *Charbon*	Crude Oil *Pétrole brut*	Petroleum Products *Produits pétroliers*	Gas *Gaz*	Nuclear *Nucléaire*	Hydro *Hydro*	Geotherm. Solar etc. *Géotherm. solaire etc.*	Combust. Renew. & Waste *Comb. ren. & déchets*	Electricity *Electricité*	Heat *Chaleur*	Total *Total*
Production	0.06	1.08	-	1.67	-	3.13	0.20	3.91	-	0.00	10.04
Imports	3.98	7.91	7.31	7.12	-	-	-	0.24	1.43	-	27.99
Exports	-0.05	-0.00	-1.64	-1.27	-	-	-	-0.30	-1.17	-	-4.43
Intl. Marine Bunkers	-	-	-	-	-	-	-	-	-	-	-
Stock Changes	0.07	0.02	-0.38	-0.06	-	-	-	-	-	-	-0.34
TPES	**4.05**	**9.00**	**5.29**	**7.46**	**-**	**3.13**	**0.20**	**3.84**	**0.26**	**0.00**	**33.25**
Transfers	-	0.04	-0.02	-	-	-	-	-	-	-	0.01
Statistical Differences	-0.00	-0.00	-	-0.09	-	-	-	-	-	-	-0.09
Electricity Plants	-1.81	-	-0.16	-0.74	-	-3.13	-0.08 e	-0.36	4.44	-0.00	-1.86
CHP Plants	-0.20	-	-0.35	-1.51	-	-	-	-0.36	0.86	0.92	-0.63
Heat Plants	-	-	-0.06	-0.18	-	-	-0.03	-0.34	-	0.41	-0.20
Gas Works	-	-	-	-	-	-	-	-	-	-	-
Petroleum Refineries	-	-9.04	9.02	-	-	-	-	-	-	-	-0.02
Coal Transformation	-0.76 e	-	-	-	-	-	-	-	-	-	-0.76
Liquefaction Plants	-	-	-	-	-	-	-	-	-	-	-
Other Transformation	-	-	-	-	-	-	-	-	-	-	-
Own Use	-0.55	-	-0.70	-0.21	-	-	-	-	-0.46	-	-1.93
Distribution Losses	-0.05	-	-	..	-	-	-	-	-0.29	-0.11	-0.45
TFC	**0.68**	**-**	**13.01**	**4.73**	**-**	**-**	**0.09**	**2.79**	**4.80**	**1.23**	**27.33**
INDUSTRY SECTOR	**0.50**	**-**	**1.50**	**2.17**	**-**	**-**	**-**	**0.98**	**2.03**	**0.17**	**7.35**
Iron and Steel	0.27 e	-	0.01	0.32	-	-	-	-	0.26	0.00	0.86
Chemical and Petrochem.	0.05	-	0.03	0.32	-	-	-	0.14	0.30	0.03	0.88
Non-Ferrous Metals	0.00	-	0.01	0.07	-	-	-	-	0.07	0.00	0.15
Non-Metallic Minerals	0.09	-	0.13	0.33	-	-	-	0.13	0.19	0.00	0.87
Transport Equipment	-	-	0.14	0.05	-	-	-	0.00	0.08	0.02	0.30
Machinery	-	-	0.05	0.13	-	-	-	0.01	0.22	0.02	0.42
Mining and Quarrying	-	-	0.09	0.07	-	-	-	0.00	0.06	0.00	0.21
Food and Tobacco	0.01	-	0.06	0.32	-	-	-	0.01	0.13	0.02	0.55
Paper, Pulp and Printing	0.08	-	0.03	0.38	-	-	-	0.43	0.43	0.02	1.36
Wood and Wood Products	-	-	0.03	0.04	-	-	-	0.23	0.11	0.03	0.44
Construction	-	-	0.87	0.04	-	-	-	0.01	0.03	0.00	0.97
Textile and Leather	-	-	0.03	0.06	-	-	-	0.00	0.05	0.00	0.15
Non-specified	-	-	0.02	0.04	-	-	-	0.02	0.11	0.01	0.19
TRANSPORT SECTOR	**-**	**-**	**7.57**	**0.19**	**-**	**-**	**-**	**0.01**	**0.27**	**-**	**8.05**
International Aviation	-	-	0.52	-	-	-	-	-	-	-	0.52
Domestic Aviation	-	-	0.10	-	-	-	-	-	-	-	0.10
Road	-	-	6.90	-	-	-	-	0.01	-	-	6.91
Rail	-	-	0.05	-	-	-	-	-	0.17	-	0.21
Pipeline Transport	-	-	-	0.19	-	-	-	-	0.01	-	0.20
Domestic Navigation	-	-	0.01	-	-	-	-	-	-	-	0.01
Non-specified	-	-	-	-	-	-	-	-	0.09	-	0.09
OTHER SECTORS	**0.16**	**-**	**2.55**	**2.13**	**-**	**-**	**0.09**	**1.79**	**2.50**	**1.06**	**10.28**
Residential	0.12	-	1.62	1.33	-	-	0.05	1.53	1.15	0.59	6.39
Comm. and Publ. Services	0.04	-	0.62	0.79	-	-	0.04	0.10	1.24	0.46	3.30
Agriculture/Forestry	0.00	-	0.30	0.02	-	-	0.00	0.16	0.10	0.01	0.59
Fishing	-	-	-	-	-	-	-	-	-	-	-
Non-specified	-	-	-	-	-	-	-	-	-	-	-
NON-ENERGY USE	**0.01**	**-**	**1.39**	**0.24**	**-**	**-**	**-**	**-**	**-**	**-**	**1.65**
in Industry/Transf./Energy	0.01	-	1.36	0.24	-	-	-	-	-	-	1.62
of which: Feedstocks	-	-	*0.67*	*0.24*	-	-	-	-	-	-	*0.91*
in Transport	-	-	0.03	-	-	-	-	-	-	-	0.03
in Other Sectors	-	-	0.00	-	-	-	-	-	-	-	0.00
Electricity Generated - TWh	***9.11***	**-**	***1.82***	***10.97***	**-**	***36.42***	***0.94***	***2.33***	**-**	***0.02***	***61.60***
Electricity Plants	*8.49*	-	*0.77*	*4.02*	-	*36.42*	*0.94*	*0.94*	-	*0.02*	*51.60*
CHP plants	*0.62*	-	*1.05*	*6.95*	-	-	-	*1.39*	-	-	*10.00*
Heat Generated - PJ	***3.60***	**-**	***8.80***	***28.54***	**-**	**-**	***0.56***	***14.42***	**-**	***0.16***	***56.07***
CHP plants	*3.60*	-	*6.63*	*23.00*	-	-	-	*5.34*	-	-	*38.57*
Heat Plants	-	-	*2.17*	*5.54*	-	-	*0.56*	*9.08*	-	*0.16*	*17.50*

Austria / Autriche : 2005

Million tonnes of oil equivalent / *Million de tonnes d'équivalent pétrole*

SUPPLY AND CONSUMPTION ***APPROVISIONNEMENT ET DEMANDE***	Coal *Charbon*	Crude Oil *Pétrole brut*	Petroleum Products *Produits pétroliers*	Gas *Gaz*	Nuclear *Nucléaire*	Hydro *Hydro*	Geotherm. Solar etc. *Géotherm. solaire etc.*	Combust. Renew. & Waste *Comb. ren. & déchets*	Electricity *Electricité*	Heat *Chaleur*	Total *Total*
Production	0.00	0.98	-	1.40	-	3.09	0.24	4.10	-	0.00	9.81
Imports	4.00	8.22	7.38	8.12	-	-	-	0.26	1.75	-	29.73
Exports	-0.02	-0.03	-2.19	-0.84	-	-	-	-0.37	-1.52	-	-4.97
Intl. Marine Bunkers	-	-	-	-	-	-	-	-	-	-	-
Stock Changes	0.09	0.17	-0.04	-0.43	-	-	-	-0.00	-	-	-0.20
TPES	**4.06**	**9.35**	**5.15**	**8.26**	**-**	**3.09**	**0.24**	**3.98**	**0.23**	**0.00**	**34.36**
Transfers	-	-0.01	0.02	-	-	-	-	-	-	-	0.01
Statistical Differences	-0.01	0.00	0.00	-0.07	-	-	-	0.00	-	-	-0.07
Electricity Plants	-1.64	-	-0.11	-1.14	-	-3.09	-0.12	-0.36	4.59	-0.00	-1.88
CHP Plants	-0.19	-	-0.34	-1.42	-	-	-	-0.42	0.82	0.91	-0.64
Heat Plants	-	-	-0.07	-0.22	-	-	-0.03	-0.30	-	0.46	-0.16
Gas Works	-	-	-	-	-	-	-	-	-	-	-
Petroleum Refineries	-	-9.34	9.43	-	-	-	-	-	-	-	0.09
Coal Transformation	-0.98 e	-	-	-	-	-	-	-	-	-	-0.98
Liquefaction Plants	-	-	-	-	-	-	-	-	-	-	-
Other Transformation	-	-	-	-	-	-	-	-	-	-	-
Own Use	-0.56	-	-0.78	-0.34	-	-	-	-	-0.45	-	-2.14
Distribution Losses	-0.03	-	-	..	-	-	-	-	-0.30	-0.11	-0.44
TFC	**0.64**	**-**	**13.30**	**5.07**	**-**	**-**	**0.10**	**2.90**	**4.90**	**1.26**	**28.16**
INDUSTRY SECTOR	**0.47**	**-**	**1.51**	**2.48**	**-**	**-**	**-**	**0.96**	**2.08**	**0.17**	**7.66**
Iron and Steel	0.25 e	-	0.01	0.32	-	-	-	-	0.26	0.00	0.85
Chemical and Petrochem.	0.03	-	0.03	0.57	-	-	-	0.14	0.31	0.03	1.12
Non-Ferrous Metals	-	-	0.01	0.08	-	-	-	-	0.07	0.00	0.16
Non-Metallic Minerals	0.11	-	0.11	0.35	-	-	-	0.12	0.19	0.00	0.88
Transport Equipment	-	-	0.14	0.05	-	-	-	0.00	0.08	0.02	0.30
Machinery	-	-	0.05	0.13	-	-	-	0.01	0.22	0.02	0.42
Mining and Quarrying	-	-	0.09	0.07	-	-	-	0.00	0.06	0.00	0.23
Food and Tobacco	0.00	-	0.05	0.26	-	-	-	0.01	0.14	0.01	0.47
Paper, Pulp and Printing	0.07	-	0.04	0.36	-	-	-	0.42	0.42	0.03	1.34
Wood and Wood Products	-	-	0.03	0.08	-	-	-	0.22	0.13	0.04	0.50
Construction	-	-	0.92	0.05	-	-	-	0.01	0.04	0.00	1.03
Textile and Leather	-	-	0.03	0.07	-	-	-	0.00	0.06	0.00	0.15
Non-specified	-	-	0.01	0.07	-	-	-	0.02	0.11	0.01	0.23
TRANSPORT SECTOR	**-**	**-**	**7.83**	**0.23**	**-**	**-**	**-**	**0.04**	**0.28**	**-**	**8.39**
International Aviation	-	-	0.58	-	-	-	-	-	-	-	0.58
Domestic Aviation	-	-	0.12	-	-	-	-	-	-	-	0.12
Road	-	-	7.08	-	-	-	-	0.04	-	-	7.12
Rail	-	-	0.05	-	-	-	-	-	0.17	-	0.21
Pipeline Transport	-	-	-	0.23	-	-	-	-	0.01	-	0.25
Domestic Navigation	-	-	0.01	-	-	-	-	-	-	-	0.01
Non-specified	-	-	-	-	-	-	-	-	0.10	-	0.10
OTHER SECTORS	**0.17**	**-**	**2.67**	**2.10**	**-**	**-**	**0.10**	**1.90**	**2.54**	**1.09**	**10.56**
Residential	0.13	-	1.71	1.44	-	-	0.06	1.63	1.17	0.63	6.76
Comm. and Publ. Services	0.04	-	0.66	0.64	-	-	0.04	0.10	1.26	0.46	3.20
Agriculture/Forestry	0.00	-	0.29	0.02	-	-	0.00	0.17	0.10	0.01	0.60
Fishing	-	-	-	-	-	-	-	-	-	-	-
Non-specified	-	-	-	-	-	-	-	-	-	-	-
NON-ENERGY USE	**0.01**	**-**	**1.29**	**0.26**	**-**	**-**	**-**	**-**	**-**	**-**	**1.55**
in Industry/Transf./Energy	0.01	-	1.25	0.26	-	-	-	-	-	-	1.52
of which: Feedstocks	-	-	*0.56*	*0.26*	-	-	-	-	-	-	*0.81*
in Transport	-	-	0.03	-	-	-	-	-	-	-	0.03
in Other Sectors	-	-	0.00	-	-	-	-	-	-	-	0.00
Electricity Generated - TWh	***8.48***	**-**	***1.64***	***13.04***	**-**	***35.87***	***1.34***	***2.59***	**-**	***0.02***	***62.98***
Electricity Plants	*7.86*	-	*0.59*	*6.70*	-	*35.87*	*1.34*	*1.03*	-	*0.02*	*53.42*
CHP plants	*0.62*	-	*1.05*	*6.34*	-	-	-	*1.56*	-	-	*9.56*
Heat Generated - PJ	***3.27***	**-**	***9.12***	***28.62***	**-**	**-**	***0.56***	***15.80***	**-**	***0.16***	***57.52***
CHP plants	*3.27*	-	*6.56*	*22.04*	-	-	-	*6.38*	-	-	*38.25*
Heat Plants	-	-	*2.56*	*6.58*	-	-	*0.56*	*9.42*	-	*0.16*	*19.27*

Belgium / Belgique
Key Indicators
Indicateurs principaux

	1960	1970	1973	1980	1990	1995
Energy Production (Mtoe)	14.00	7.12	6.51	8.09	13.10	11.93
Net Imports (Mtoe)	8.25	35.75	42.89	42.11	40.10	45.14
Total Primary Energy Supply (Mtoe)	23.24	40.24	46.32	47.01	49.16	52.38
Net Oil Imports (Mtoe)	7.75	27.28	31.29	26.26	22.51	24.79
Oil Supply (Mtoe)	7.22	24.42	28.02	23.58	18.75	20.98
Electricity Consumption (TWh)*	14.43	29.27	38.40	48.25	63.60	74.81
GDP (billion 2000 US$ using exch. rates)	69.26 e	110.54	128.11	153.98	187.89	203.34
GDP (billion 2000 US$ using PPPs)	81.57 e	130.18	150.87	181.35	221.28	239.48
Population (millions)	9.13 e	9.63	9.73	9.83	9.97	10.14
Industrial Production Index (2000=100)	34.70	56.60	65.60	70.60	85.90	86.50
Energy Production/TPES	0.6024	0.1769	0.1405	0.1721	0.2666	0.2278
Net Oil Imports/GDP (toe per thousand 2000 US$)	0.1118 e	0.2468	0.2443	0.1706	0.1198	0.1219
TPES/GDP (toe per thousand 2000 US$)	0.3355 e	0.3641	0.3616	0.3053	0.2616	0.2576
TPES/GDP (toe per thousand 2000 US$ PPP)	0.2848 e	0.3091	0.3070	0.2592	0.2222	0.2187
TPES/Population (toe per capita)	2.5464 e	4.1810	4.7628	4.7808	4.9319	5.1669
Oil Supply/GDP (toe per thousand 2000 US$)	0.1043 e	0.2209	0.2187	0.1532	0.0998	0.1032
Oil Supply/Population (toe per capita)	0.7914 e	2.5374	2.8810	2.3981	1.8807	2.0697
Elect. Cons./GDP (kWh per 2000 US$)	0.2083 e	0.2648	0.2997	0.3133	0.3385	0.3679
Elect. Cons./Population (kWh per capita)	1 581 e	3 041	3 948	4 906	6 380	7 380
Industry Cons.**/Industrial Production (2000=100)	111.54	133.20	136.09	103.53	83.46	86.16
Industry Oil Cons.**/Industrial Production (2000=100)	104.26	198.19	175.25	93.40	71.17	72.57

	2000	2001	2002	2003	2004	2005
Energy Production (Mtoe)	13.73	13.32	13.50	13.70	13.75	13.90
Net Imports (Mtoe)	50.20	51.61	49.33	52.68	52.02	50.89
Total Primary Energy Supply (Mtoe)	59.09	58.84	56.79	59.44	58.10	56.65
Net Oil Imports (Mtoe)	29.20	29.79	29.43	31.93	30.72	30.72
Oil Supply (Mtoe)	23.77	24.26	22.90	24.76	23.02	22.79
Electricity Consumption (TWh)*	84.55	85.04	85.89	87.28	89.37	89.17
GDP (billion 2000 US$ using exch. rates)	231.93	234.36	237.89	240.06	246.28	249.35
GDP (billion 2000 US$ using PPPs)	273.16	276.02	280.17	282.73	290.05	293.67
Population (millions)	10.25	10.28	10.33	10.37	10.42	10.47
Industrial Production Index (2000=100)	100.00	99.00	100.30	101.10	104.30	103.90
Energy Production/TPES	0.2324	0.2264	0.2376	0.2304	0.2367	0.2453
Net Oil Imports/GDP (toe per thousand 2000 US$)	0.1259	0.1271	0.1237	0.1330	0.1247	0.1232
TPES/GDP (toe per thousand 2000 US$)	0.2548	0.2511	0.2387	0.2476	0.2359	0.2272
TPES/GDP (toe per thousand 2000 US$ PPP)	0.2163	0.2132	0.2027	0.2102	0.2003	0.1929
TPES/Population (toe per capita)	5.7667	5.7236	5.4978	5.7296	5.5768	5.4095
Oil Supply/GDP (toe per thousand 2000 US$)	0.1025	0.1035	0.0963	0.1031	0.0935	0.0914
Oil Supply/Population (toe per capita)	2.3202	2.3599	2.2166	2.3864	2.2100	2.1762
Elect. Cons./GDP (kWh per 2000 US$)	0.3645	0.3629	0.3610	0.3636	0.3629	0.3576
Elect. Cons./Population (kWh per capita)	8 252	8 272	8 314	8 414	8 579	8 515
Industry Cons.**/Industrial Production (2000=100)	100.00	102.13	91.90	89.73	80.81	78.80
Industry Oil Cons.**/Industrial Production (2000=100)	100.00	107.27	92.77	85.91	68.68	71.38

* Electricity consumption equals domestic supply less distribution losses.
La consommation d'électricité représente l'approvisionnement intérieur diminué des pertes de distribution.

** Includes non-energy use in industry/transformation/energy sectors.
Comprend l'usage non-énergétique dans les secteurs de l'industrie/transformation/énergie.

Belgium / Belgique

Figure 1. TPES* in 1973

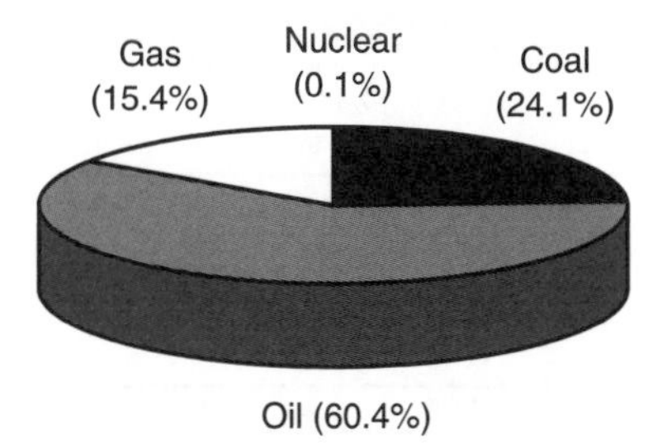

Figure 2. TPES* in 2005

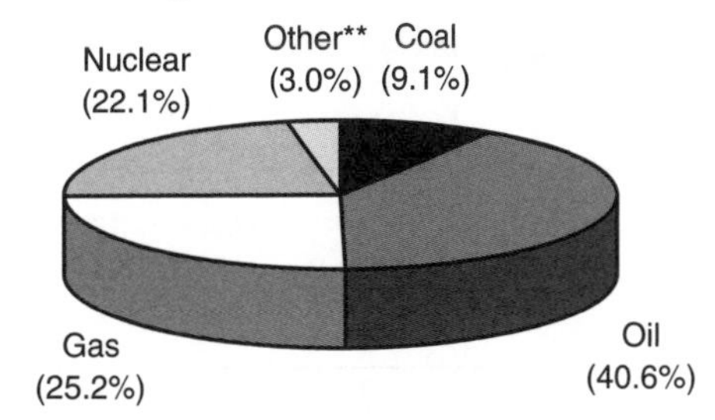

Figure 3. Final Consumption by Sector***

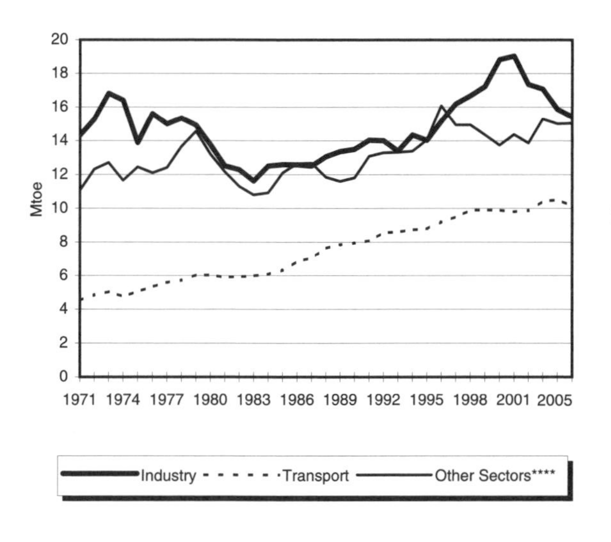

Figure 4. Breakdown of Sectorial Final Consumption by Source in 1973 and 2005***

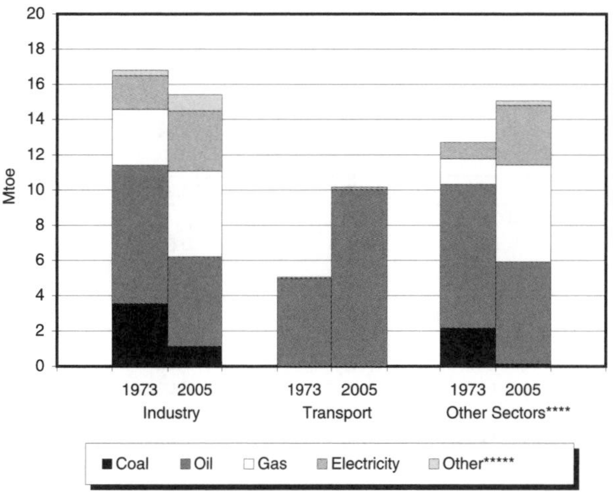

Figure 5. Electricity Generation by Fuel

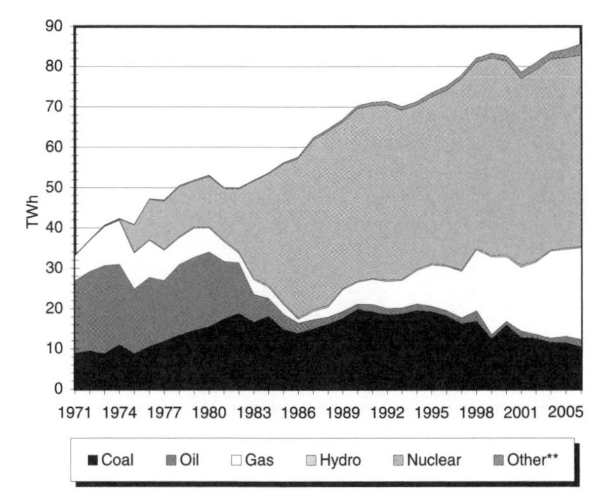

Figure 6. Electricity Consumption/GDP, TPES/GDP and Energy Production/TPES

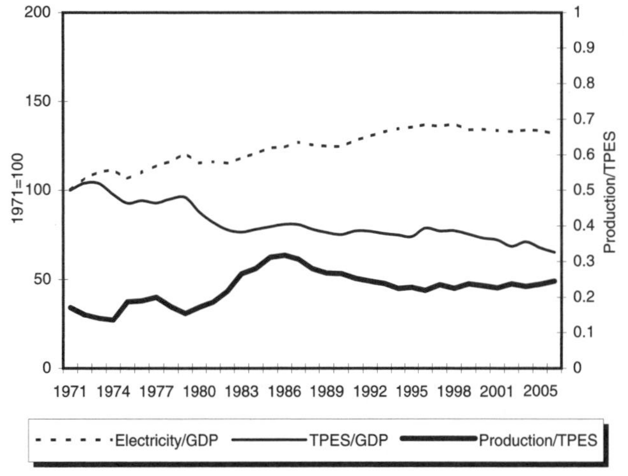

* Excluding electricity trade.

** Includes geothermal, solar, wind, combustible renewables & waste, etc.

*** Includes non-energy use.

**** Includes residential, commercial and public services, agriculture/forestry, fishing and non-specified.

***** Includes comb. renewables & waste, direct use of geothermal/solar thermal and heat produced in CHP/heat plants.

Belgium / Belgique : 2004

Million tonnes of oil equivalent / *Million de tonnes d'équivalent pétrole*

SUPPLY AND CONSUMPTION / ***APPROVISIONNEMENT ET DEMANDE***	Coal / *Charbon*	Crude Oil / *Pétrole brut*	Petroleum Products / *Produits pétroliers*	Gas / *Gaz*	Nuclear / *Nucléaire*	Hydro / *Hydro*	Geotherm. Solar etc. / *Géotherm. solaire etc.*	Combust. Renew. & Waste / *Comb. ren. & déchets*	Electricity / *Electricité*	Heat / *Chaleur*	Total / *Total*
Production	0.09	-	-	-	12.33	0.03	0.02	1.28	-	-	13.75
Imports	6.73	38.96	17.53	14.55	-	-	-	0.21	1.25	-	79.24
Exports	-0.86	-3.10	-22.68	-	-	-	-	-	-0.58	-	-27.22
Intl. Marine Bunkers	-	-	-7.75	-	-	-	-	-	-	-	-7.75
Stock Changes	-0.18	0.00	0.05	0.20	-	-	-	-	-	-	0.08
TPES	**5.79**	**35.87**	**-12.85**	**14.76**	**12.33**	**0.03**	**0.02**	**1.49**	**0.67**	**-**	**58.10**
Transfers	-	8.51	-8.05	-	-	-	-	-	-	-	0.46
Statistical Differences	-0.28	0.05	-0.07	0.02	-	-	-	0.00	-0.00	-	-0.28
Electricity Plants	-2.22	-	-0.38	-2.85	-12.33	-0.03	-0.01	-0.39	6.59	-	-11.63
CHP Plants	-0.12	-	-0.05	-1.06	-	-	-	-0.35 e	0.67	0.56	-0.36
Heat Plants	-	-	-	-	-	-	-	-0.04	-	0.00	-0.03
Gas Works	-	-	-	-	-	-	-	-	-	-	-
Petroleum Refineries	-	-44.44	43.69	-	-	-	-	-	-	-	-0.75
Coal Transformation	-1.47 e	-	-	-	-	-	-	-	-	-	-1.47
Liquefaction Plants	-	-	-	-	-	-	-	-	-	-	-
Other Transformation	-	-	-	-	-	-	-	-	-	-	-
Own Use	-0.22	-	-1.36	-0.06	-	-	-	-	-0.64	-	-2.29
Distribution Losses	-	-	-	-	-	-	-0.00	-	-0.35	-0.04	-0.39
TFC	**1.47**	**-**	**20.93**	**10.81**	**-**	**-**	**0.00**	**0.71**	**6.93**	**0.52**	**41.37**
INDUSTRY SECTOR	**1.30**	**-**	**1.10**	**4.42**	**-**	**-**	**-**	**0.52**	**3.47**	**0.40**	**11.21**
Iron and Steel	0.99 e	-	0.03	0.77	-	-	-	-	0.61	0.02	2.42
Chemical and Petrochem.	0.01	-	0.15	1.74	-	-	-	0.01	1.16	0.13	3.19
Non-Ferrous Metals	0.02	-	0.03	0.11	-	-	-	-	0.18	-	0.34
Non-Metallic Minerals	0.16	-	0.28	0.61	-	-	-	0.22	0.22	-	1.49
Transport Equipment	-	-	-	0.13	-	-	-	-	0.09	-	0.22
Machinery	0.00	-	0.02	0.16	-	-	-	-	0.18	-	0.37
Mining and Quarrying	-	-	0.01	-	-	-	-	-	0.04	-	0.06
Food and Tobacco	0.05	-	0.17	0.47	-	-	-	0.00	0.35	-	1.05
Paper, Pulp and Printing	0.03	-	0.04	0.15	-	-	-	0.19	0.22	-	0.64
Wood and Wood Products	-	-	-	-	-	-	-	0.10	0.05	-	0.15
Construction	-	-	0.09	-	-	-	-	-	0.03	-	0.12
Textile and Leather	-	-	0.01	0.17	-	-	-	-	0.17	-	0.35
Non-specified	0.03	-	0.26	0.11	-	-	-	-	0.16	0.26	0.82
TRANSPORT SECTOR	**-**	**-**	**10.32**	**-**	**-**	**-**	**-**	**-**	**0.13**	**-**	**10.45**
International Aviation	-	-	1.40	-	-	-	-	-	-	-	1.40
Domestic Aviation	-	-	0.08	-	-	-	-	-	-	-	0.08
Road	-	-	8.68	-	-	-	-	-	-	-	8.68
Rail	-	-	0.04	-	-	-	-	-	0.13	-	0.17
Pipeline Transport	-	-	-	-	-	-	-	-	0.00	-	0.00
Domestic Navigation	-	-	0.12	-	-	-	-	-	-	-	0.12
Non-specified	-	-	-	-	-	-	-	-	-	-	-
OTHER SECTORS	**0.16**	**-**	**5.59**	**5.53**	**-**	**-**	**0.00**	**0.19**	**3.33**	**0.12**	**14.93**
Residential	0.13	-	3.70	3.76	-	-	0.00	0.19	2.28	0.02	10.08
Comm. and Publ. Services	-	-	1.27	1.77	-	-	0.00	0.00	1.03	0.01	4.08
Agriculture/Forestry	-	-	0.63	-	-	-	-	0.00	0.02	-	0.65
Fishing	-	-	-	-	-	-	-	-	-	-	-
Non-specified	0.03	-	-	-	-	-	-	-	-	0.09	0.12
NON-ENERGY USE	**-**	**-**	**3.91**	**0.85**	**-**	**-**	**-**	**-**	**-**	**-**	**4.76**
in Industry/Transf./Energy	-	-	3.80	0.85	-	-	-	-	-	-	4.65
of which: Feedstocks	-	-	*3.40*	*0.85*	-	-	-	-	-	-	*4.26*
in Transport	-	-	0.04	-	-	-	-	-	-	-	0.04
in Other Sectors	-	-	0.07	-	-	-	-	-	-	-	0.07
Electricity Generated - TWh	***11.48***	-	***1.68***	***21.48***	***47.31***	***0.32***	***0.14***	***1.95***	-	-	***84.35***
Electricity Plants	*10.87*	-	*1.36*	*15.48*	*47.31*	*0.32*	*0.14*	*1.14*	-	-	*76.62*
CHP plants	*0.61*	-	*0.31*	*6.00*	-	-	-	*0.81 e*	-	-	*7.74*
Heat Generated - PJ	-	-	-	***21.02***	-	-	-	***2.35***	-	-	***23.37***
CHP plants	-	-	-	*21.02*	-	-	-	*2.24 e*	-	-	*23.26*
Heat Plants	-	-	-	-	-	-	-	*0.11*	-	-	*0.11*

Belgium / Belgique : 2005

Million tonnes of oil equivalent / *Million de tonnes d'équivalent pétrole*

SUPPLY AND CONSUMPTION ***APPROVISIONNEMENT ET DEMANDE***	Coal *Charbon*	Crude Oil *Pétrole brut*	Petroleum Products *Produits pétroliers*	Gas *Gaz*	Nuclear *Nucléaire*	Hydro *Hydro*	Geotherm. Solar etc. *Géotherm. solaire etc.*	Combust. Renew. & Waste *Comb. ren. & déchets*	Electricity *Electricité*	Heat *Chaleur*	Total *Total*
Production	0.06	-	-	-	12.40	0.02	0.02	1.32 e	-	0.07	13.90
Imports	5.92	36.29	20.49	14.19	-	-	-	0.28	1.23	-	78.39
Exports	-0.77	-3.28	-22.77	-	-	-	-	-	-0.69	-	-27.51
Intl. Marine Bunkers	-	-	-7.67	-	-	-	-	-	-	-	-7.67
Stock Changes	-0.13	0.16	-0.41	-0.08	-	-	-	-	-	-	-0.46
TPES	**5.09**	**33.16**	**-10.37**	**14.11**	**12.40**	**0.02**	**0.02**	**1.60**	**0.54**	**0.07**	**56.65**
Transfers	-	5.09	-4.82	-	-	-	-	-	-	-	0.27
Statistical Differences	-0.04	-0.01	0.14	0.42	-	-	-	0.00	-0.01	-	0.50
Electricity Plants	-2.27	-	-0.38	-2.92	-12.40	-0.02	-0.02	-0.50 e	6.72	-0.07 e	-11.87
CHP Plants	-0.08	-	-0.03	-1.14	-	-	-	-0.31 e	0.65	0.46	-0.46
Heat Plants	-	-	-	-0.00	-	-	-	-0.02	-	0.01	-0.02
Gas Works	-	-	-	-	-	-	-	-	-	-	-
Petroleum Refineries	-	-38.24	37.50	-	-	-	-	-	-	-	-0.74
Coal Transformation	-1.21 e	-	-	-	-	-	-	-	-	-	-1.21
Liquefaction Plants	-	-	-	-	-	-	-	-	-	-	-
Other Transformation	-	-	-	-	-	-	-	-	-	-	-
Own Use	-0.23	-	-1.16	-0.07	-	-	-	-	-0.65	-	-2.11
Distribution Losses	-	-	-	-	-	-	-0.00	-	-0.36	-0.04	-0.39
TFC	**1.25**	**-**	**20.87**	**10.40**	**-**	**-**	**0.00**	**0.77**	**6.90**	**0.43**	**40.62**
INDUSTRY SECTOR	**1.13**	**-**	**1.08**	**4.00**	**-**	**-**	**-**	**0.57**	**3.39**	**0.37**	**10.53**
Iron and Steel	0.83 e	-	0.03	0.73	-	-	-	-	0.52	0.01	2.12
Chemical and Petrochem.	0.01	-	0.17	1.90	-	-	-	0.02	1.18	0.12	3.39
Non-Ferrous Metals	0.01	-	0.03	0.11	-	-	-	-	0.15	-	0.30
Non-Metallic Minerals	0.15	-	0.28	0.37	-	-	-	0.22	0.20	-	1.22
Transport Equipment	-	-	-	0.10	-	-	-	-	0.09	-	0.19
Machinery	0.02	-	0.03	0.00	-	-	-	0.00	0.19	-	0.24
Mining and Quarrying	-	-	0.01	0.00	-	-	-	-	0.05	-	0.06
Food and Tobacco	0.02	-	0.14	0.43	-	-	-	0.00	0.34	-	0.94
Paper, Pulp and Printing	0.03	-	0.04	0.09	-	-	-	0.22	0.23	-	0.62
Wood and Wood Products	-	-	-	0.02	-	-	-	0.10	0.16	-	0.27
Construction	-	-	0.07	0.08	-	-	-	-	0.03	-	0.18
Textile and Leather	-	-	0.00	0.10	-	-	-	-	0.11	-	0.21
Non-specified	0.05	-	0.27	0.08	-	-	-	-	0.15	0.24	0.79
TRANSPORT SECTOR	**-**	**-**	**9.98**	**-**	**-**	**-**	**-**	**-**	**0.15**	**-**	**10.12**
International Aviation	-	-	1.33	-	-	-	-	-	-	-	1.33
Domestic Aviation	-	-	0.00	-	-	-	-	-	-	-	0.00
Road	-	-	8.38	-	-	-	-	-	-	-	8.38
Rail	-	-	0.04	-	-	-	-	-	0.14	-	0.19
Pipeline Transport	-	-	-	-	-	-	-	-	0.00	-	0.00
Domestic Navigation	-	-	0.22	-	-	-	-	-	-	-	0.22
Non-specified	-	-	-	-	-	-	-	-	-	-	-
OTHER SECTORS	**0.13**	**-**	**5.77**	**5.51**	**-**	**-**	**0.00**	**0.20**	**3.36**	**0.06**	**15.03**
Residential	0.13	-	3.68	3.73	-	-	0.00	0.19	2.24	0.01	9.98
Comm. and Publ. Services	-	-	1.29	1.77	-	-	0.00	0.01	1.09	0.01	4.17
Agriculture/Forestry	-	-	0.79	0.02	-	-	-	0.00	0.03	-	0.85
Fishing	-	-	-	-	-	-	-	-	-	-	-
Non-specified	-	-	-	-	-	-	-	-	-	0.03	0.03
NON-ENERGY USE	**-**	**-**	**4.05**	**0.89**	**-**	**-**	**-**	**-**	**-**	**-**	**4.93**
in Industry/Transf./Energy	-	-	3.99	0.89	-	-	-	-	-	-	4.88
of which: Feedstocks	-	-	*3.27*	*0.89*	-	-	-	-	-	-	*4.16*
in Transport	-	-	0.04	-	-	-	-	-	-	-	0.04
in Other Sectors	-	-	0.01	-	-	-	-	-	-	-	0.01
Electricity Generated - TWh	***10.49***	**-**	***1.74***	***22.85***	***47.60***	***0.29***	***0.23***	***2.25***	**-**	***0.27***	***85.71***
Electricity Plants	*10.16*	-	*1.58*	*16.49*	*47.60*	*0.29*	*0.23*	*1.57*	-	*0.15*	*78.05*
CHP plants	*0.34*	-	*0.16*	*6.36*	-	-	-	*0.68*	-	*0.11*	*7.66*
Heat Generated - PJ	**-**	**-**	***0.06***	***15.79***	**-**	**-**	**-**	***3.56***	**-**	***2.90***	***22.32***
CHP plants	-	-	*0.06*	*15.68*	-	-	-	*3.43*	-	-	*19.17*
Heat Plants	-	-	-	*0.11*	-	-	-	*0.13*	-	*2.90 e*	*3.14*

Canada
Key Indicators
Indicateurs principaux

	1960	1970	1973	1980	1990	1995
Energy Production (Mtoe)	57.09	144.76	198.02	207.42	273.73	348.82
Net Imports (Mtoe)	20.44	- 3.98	- 35.43	- 11.99	- 59.38	- 119.86
Total Primary Energy Supply (Mtoe)	76.27	138.52	159.84	193.00	209.41	231.44
Net Oil Imports (Mtoe)	16.16	4.25	- 14.28	8.39	- 14.94	- 35.82
Oil Supply (Mtoe)	42.11	71.06	79.89	88.92	77.33	77.96
Electricity Consumption (TWh)*	100.84	191.11	230.36	313.90	447.60	484.30
GDP (billion 2000 US$ using exch. rates)	168.91 e	276.91	325.18	411.94	543.65	592.05
GDP (billion 2000 US$ using PPPs)	203.43 e	333.49	391.63	496.13	654.75	713.05
Population (millions)	17.89 e	21.32	22.49	24.52	27.70	29.30
Industrial Production Index (2000=100)	..	39.80	50.90	55.80	69.10	78.60
Energy Production/TPES	0.7485	1.0450	1.2388	1.0747	1.3072	1.5072
Net Oil Imports/GDP (toe per thousand 2000 US$)	0.0957 e	0.0153	- 0.0439	0.0204	- 0.0275	- 0.0605
TPES/GDP (toe per thousand 2000 US$)	0.4515 e	0.5002	0.4915	0.4685	0.3852	0.3909
TPES/GDP (toe per thousand 2000 US$ PPP)	0.3749 e	0.4154	0.4081	0.3890	0.3198	0.3246
TPES/Population (toe per capita)	4.2623 e	6.4960	7.1066	7.8724	7.5605	7.8984
Oil Supply/GDP (toe per thousand 2000 US$)	0.2493 e	0.2566	0.2457	0.2159	0.1422	0.1317
Oil Supply/Population (toe per capita)	2.3534 e	3.3322	3.5518	3.6271	2.7919	2.6606
Elect. Cons./GDP (kWh per 2000 US$)	0.5970 e	0.6902	0.7084	0.7620	0.8233	0.8180
Elect. Cons./Population (kWh per capita)	5 636 e	8 962	10 242	12 804	16 160	16 528
Industry Cons.**/Industrial Production (2000=100)	..	146.65	140.61	149.97	120.77	116.70
Industry Oil Cons.**/Industrial Production (2000=100)	..	187.04	202.40	179.30	121.51	112.49

	2000	2001	2002	2003	2004	2005
Energy Production (Mtoe)	372.51	376.92	383.98	385.93	397.44	401.26
Net Imports (Mtoe)	- 130.52	- 131.63	- 134.99	- 127.20	- 134.72	- 133.96
Total Primary Energy Supply (Mtoe)	249.18	246.07	250.14	262.36	268.70	271.95
Net Oil Imports (Mtoe)	- 39.12	- 39.34	- 49.08	- 49.32	- 51.81	- 47.15
Oil Supply (Mtoe)	87.77	88.36	86.37	92.84	97.95	97.37
Electricity Consumption (TWh)*	522.66	522.26	531.75	544.86	551.71	558.50
GDP (billion 2000 US$ using exch. rates)	724.91	737.85	759.58	773.42	798.93	822.39
GDP (billion 2000 US$ using PPPs)	873.06	888.64	914.81	931.48	962.21	990.45
Population (millions)	30.69	31.02	31.37	31.67	31.97	32.27
Industrial Production Index (2000=100)	100.00	96.00	97.50	98.10	100.10	101.40
Energy Production/TPES	1.4950	1.5318	1.5350	1.4710	1.4791	1.4755
Net Oil Imports/GDP (toe per thousand 2000 US$)	- 0.0540	- 0.0533	- 0.0646	- 0.0638	- 0.0648	- 0.0573
TPES/GDP (toe per thousand 2000 US$)	0.3437	0.3335	0.3293	0.3392	0.3363	0.3307
TPES/GDP (toe per thousand 2000 US$ PPP)	0.2854	0.2769	0.2734	0.2817	0.2793	0.2746
TPES/Population (toe per capita)	8.1195	7.9324	7.9732	8.2846	8.4037	8.4272
Oil Supply/GDP (toe per thousand 2000 US$)	0.1211	0.1198	0.1137	0.1200	0.1226	0.1184
Oil Supply/Population (toe per capita)	2.8600	2.8485	2.7531	2.9315	3.0635	3.0173
Elect. Cons./GDP (kWh per 2000 US$)	0.7210	0.7078	0.7001	0.7045	0.6906	0.6791
Elect. Cons./Population (kWh per capita)	17 031	16 836	16 949	17 205	17 255	17 307
Industry Cons.**/Industrial Production (2000=100)	100.00	98.88	100.03	104.50	106.32	102.00
Industry Oil Cons.**/Industrial Production (2000=100)	100.00	105.73	102.61	111.66	117.83	113.90

* Electricity consumption equals domestic supply less distribution losses.
La consommation d'électricité représente l'approvisionnement intérieur diminué des pertes de distribution.

** Includes non-energy use in industry/transformation/energy sectors.
Comprend l'usage non-énergétique dans les secteurs de l'industrie/transformation/énergie.

Canada

Figure 1. TPES* in 1973

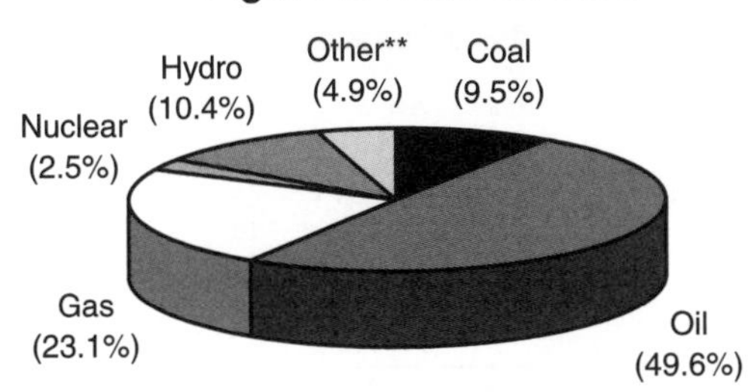

Figure 2. TPES* in 2005

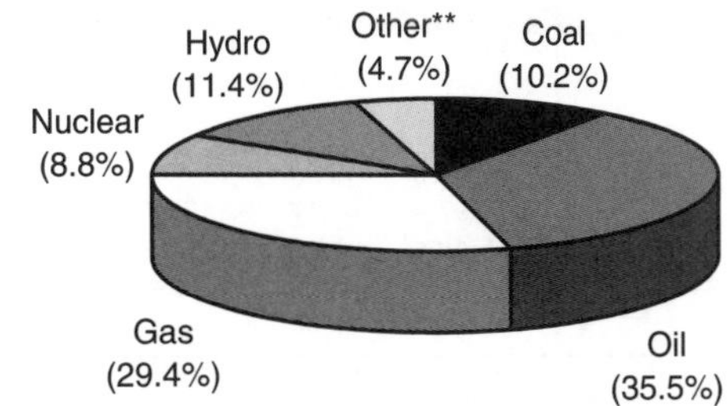

Figure 3. Final Consumption by Sector***

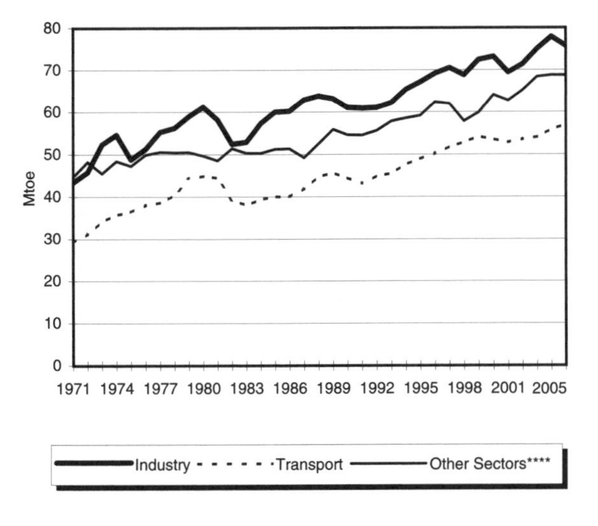

Figure 4. Breakdown of Sectorial Final Consumption by Source in 1973 and 2005***

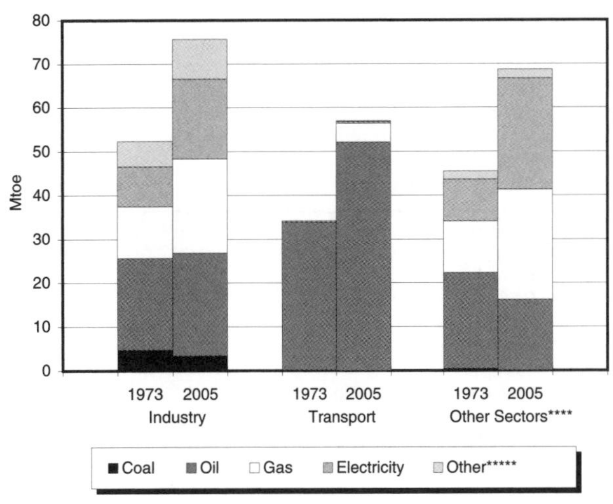

Figure 5. Electricity Generation by Fuel

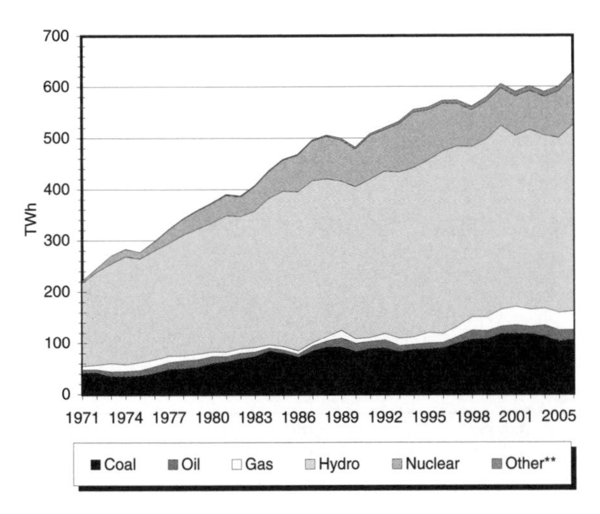

Figure 6. Electricity Consumption/GDP, TPES/GDP and Energy Production/TPES

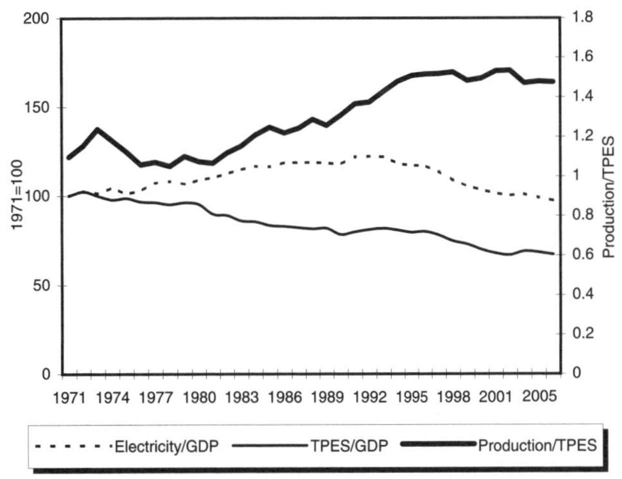

* Excluding electricity trade.

** Includes geothermal, solar, wind, combustible renewables & waste, etc.

*** Includes non-energy use.

**** Includes residential, commercial and public services, agriculture/forestry, fishing and non-specified.

***** Includes comb. renewables & waste, direct use of geothermal/solar thermal and heat produced in CHP/heat plants.

Canada : 2004

Million tonnes of oil equivalent / *Million de tonnes d'équivalent pétrole*

SUPPLY AND CONSUMPTION ***APPROVISIONNEMENT ET DEMANDE***	Coal *Charbon*	Crude Oil *Pétrole brut*	Petroleum Products *Produits pétroliers*	Gas *Gaz*	Nuclear *Nucléaire*	Hydro *Hydro*	Geotherm. Solar etc. *Géotherm. solaire etc.*	Combust. Renew. & Waste *Comb. ren. & déchets*	Electricity *Electricité*	Heat *Chaleur*	Total *Total*
Production	32.18 e	149.29	-	150.79	23.56	29.31	0.09	12.23 e	-	-	397.44
Imports	10.97 e	47.17	12.27	8.92	-	-	-	0.06 e	1.97	-	81.35
Exports	-15.48 e	-89.13	-22.12	-86.43	-	-	-	-0.01 e	-2.90	-	-216.07
Intl. Marine Bunkers	-	-	-0.60	-	-	-	-	-	-	-	-0.60
Stock Changes	0.77 e	1.32	-0.25	4.73	-	-	-	-	-	-	6.58
TPES	**28.44**	**108.66**	**-10.70**	**78.00**	**23.56**	**29.31**	**0.09**	**12.28**	**-0.93**	**-**	**268.70**
Transfers	-	-2.37	5.56	-	-	-	-	-	-	-	3.19
Statistical Differences	-0.24	-1.07	1.88	-1.84	-	-	-	-	-0.02	-	-1.29
Electricity Plants	-23.39 e	-	-4.55	-4.69	-23.56	-29.31	-0.09	-2.01 e	50.74	-	-36.85
CHP Plants	-	-	-0.16	-2.70	-	-	-	-0.01	0.87	0.93	-1.07
Heat Plants	-	-	-	-	-	-	-	-	-	-	-
Gas Works	-	-	-	-	-	-	-	-	-	-	-
Petroleum Refineries	-	-105.79	108.45	-0.56	-	-	-	-	-	-	2.10
Coal Transformation	-1.15 e	-	-	-	-	-	-	-	-	-	-1.15
Liquefaction Plants	-	0.56	-	-1.18	-	-	-	-	-	-	-0.62
Other Transformation	-	-	-	-	-	-	-	-	-	-	-
Own Use	-0.16 e	-	-8.86	-14.46	-	-	-	-	-3.83	-	-27.32
Distribution Losses	-	-	-	-	-	-	-	-	-3.24	-	-3.24
TFC	**3.50**	**-**	**91.62**	**52.56**	**-**	**-**	**-**	**10.26**	**43.58**	**0.93**	**202.46**
INDUSTRY SECTOR	**3.20**	**-**	**6.42**	**19.92**	**-**	**-**	**-**	**8.27**	**17.81**	**0.92**	**56.55**
Iron and Steel	1.76 e	-	0.17	1.53	-	-	-	-	0.87	-	4.34
Chemical and Petrochem.	-	-	0.11	2.74	-	-	-	-	1.66	0.25	4.76
Non-Ferrous Metals	0.26 e	-	0.24	0.57	-	-	-	-	4.76	-	5.84
Non-Metallic Minerals	0.75 e	-	0.07	0.04	-	-	-	0.10 e	0.17	-	1.14
Transport Equipment	-	-	-	-	-	-	-	-	-	-	-
Machinery	-	-	-	-	-	-	-	-	-	-	-
Mining and Quarrying	0.16 e	-	1.85	4.95	-	-	-	-	3.16	-	10.12
Food and Tobacco	-	-	-	-	-	-	-	-	-	-	-
Paper, Pulp and Printing	0.03 e	-	1.48	1.77	-	-	-	8.17	5.41	0.50	17.36
Wood and Wood Products	-	-	0.52	-	-	-	-	-	-	-	0.52
Construction	-	-	0.92	0.43	-	-	-	-	-	-	1.35
Textile and Leather	-	-	-	-	-	-	-	-	-	-	-
Non-specified	0.23 e	-	1.07	7.88	-	-	-	-	1.78	0.17	11.13
TRANSPORT SECTOR	**-**	**-**	**51.53**	**3.60**	**-**	**-**	**-**	**0.14**	**0.37**	**-**	**55.65**
International Aviation	-	-	0.91	-	-	-	-	-	-	-	0.91
Domestic Aviation	-	-	4.77	-	-	-	-	-	-	-	4.77
Road	-	-	42.15	0.04	-	-	-	0.14	-	-	42.33
Rail	-	-	1.73	-	-	-	-	-	-	-	1.73
Pipeline Transport	-	-	0.02	3.57	-	-	-	-	0.28	-	3.87
Domestic Navigation	-	-	1.95	-	-	-	-	-	-	-	1.95
Non-specified	-	-	-	-	-	-	-	-	0.08	-	0.08
OTHER SECTORS	**0.03**	**-**	**13.44**	**25.50**	**-**	**-**	**-**	**1.85**	**25.41**	**0.01**	**66.23**
Residential	0.03 e	-	2.69	13.99	-	-	-	1.85 e	12.98	-	31.54
Comm. and Publ. Services	-	-	8.45	11.05	-	-	-	-	11.55	0.01	31.06
Agriculture/Forestry	-	-	2.31	0.46	-	-	-	-	0.87	0.00	3.64
Fishing	-	-	-	-	-	-	-	-	-	-	-
Non-specified	-	-	-	-	-	-	-	-	-	-	-
NON-ENERGY USE	**0.28**	**-**	**20.22**	**3.54**	**-**	**-**	**-**	**-**	**-**	**-**	**24.03**
in Industry/Transf./Energy	0.28 e	-	17.50	3.54	-	-	-	-	-	-	21.32
of which: Feedstocks	-	-	*12.33*	*3.54*	-	-	-	-	-	-	*15.88*
in Transport	-	-	0.20	-	-	-	-	-	-	-	0.20
in Other Sectors	-	-	2.52	-	-	-	-	-	-	-	2.52
Electricity Generated - TWh	***101.65***	**-**	***23.21***	***34.36***	***90.39***	***340.84***	***1.00***	***8.69***	**-**	**-**	***600.13***
Electricity Plants	*101.65 e*	-	*23.20*	*24.30*	*90.39*	*340.84*	*1.00*	*8.67*	-	-	*590.04*
CHP plants	-	-	*0.01*	*10.06*	-	-	-	*0.02*	-	-	*10.09*
Heat Generated - PJ	**-**	**-**	***4.05***	***35.07***	**-**	**-**	**-**	***0.01***	**-**	**-**	***39.13***
CHP plants	-	-	*4.05*	*35.07*	-	-	-	*0.01*	-	-	*39.13*
Heat Plants	-	-	-	-	-	-	-	-	-	-	-

Canada : 2005

Million tonnes of oil equivalent / *Million de tonnes d'équivalent pétrole*

SUPPLY AND CONSUMPTION *APPROVISIONNEMENT ET DEMANDE*	Coal *Charbon*	Crude Oil *Pétrole brut*	Petroleum Products *Produits pétroliers*	Gas *Gaz*	Nuclear *Nucléaire*	Hydro *Hydro*	Geotherm. Solar etc. *Géotherm. solaire etc.*	Combust. Renew. & Waste *Comb. ren. & déchets*	Electricity *Electricité*	Heat *Chaleur*	Total *Total*
Production	31.77 e	147.44	-	154.06	23.99	31.26	0.13	12.60 e	-	-	401.26
Imports	11.68 e	46.64	13.99	7.83	-	-	-	0.05	1.69	-	81.88
Exports	-16.93 e	-85.86	-21.91	-87.38	-	-	-	-0.01	-3.74	-	-215.84
Intl. Marine Bunkers	-	-	-0.59	-	-	-	-	-	-	-	-0.59
Stock Changes	1.46 e	-2.37	0.05	6.11	-	-	-	-	-	-	5.25
TPES	**27.98**	**105.84**	**-8.47**	**80.63**	**23.99**	**31.26**	**0.13**	**12.64**	**-2.05**	**-**	**271.95**
Transfers	-	-3.08	6.06	-	-	-	-	-	-	-	2.98
Statistical Differences	0.34	-1.74	1.91	-4.96	-	-	-	-	-0.03	0.00	-4.47
Electricity Plants	-23.66 e	-	-4.05	-4.94	-23.99	-31.26	-0.13	-2.10 e	52.97	-	-37.15
CHP Plants	-	-	-0.13	-3.07	-	-	-	-0.01	1.04	0.83	-1.34
Heat Plants	-	-	-	-	-	-	-	-	-	-	-
Gas Works	-	-	-	-	-	-	-	-	-	-	-
Petroleum Refineries	-	-101.59	105.47	-0.57	-	-	-	-	-	-	3.31
Coal Transformation	-1.11 e	-	-	-	-	-	-	-	-	-	-1.11
Liquefaction Plants	-	0.57	-	-1.17	-	-	-	-	-	-	-0.60
Other Transformation	-	-	-	-	-	-	-	-	-	-	-
Own Use	-0.13 e	-	-9.18	-14.92	-	-	-	-	-4.07	-	-28.30
Distribution Losses	-	-	-	-	-	-	-	-	-3.94	-0.00	-3.94
TFC	**3.41**	**-**	**91.60**	**51.02**	**-**	**-**	**-**	**10.54**	**43.93**	**0.83**	**201.33**
INDUSTRY SECTOR	**3.14**	**-**	**6.45**	**18.07**	**-**	**-**	**-**	**8.33**	**18.17**	**0.81**	**54.97**
Iron and Steel	1.73 e	-	0.15	1.62	-	-	-	-	0.92	-	4.42
Chemical and Petrochem.	-	-	0.06	2.20	-	-	-	-	1.68	0.22	4.16
Non-Ferrous Metals	0.25 e	-	0.26	0.54	-	-	-	-	5.14	-	6.19
Non-Metallic Minerals	0.68 e	-	0.06	0.04	-	-	-	0.10 e	0.17	-	1.06
Transport Equipment	-	-	-	-	-	-	-	-	-	-	-
Machinery	-	-	-	-	-	-	-	-	-	-	-
Mining and Quarrying	0.18 e	-	2.26	4.88	-	-	-	-	3.22	-	10.54
Food and Tobacco	-	-	-	-	-	-	-	-	-	-	-
Paper, Pulp and Printing	0.03 e	-	1.16	1.50	-	-	-	8.22	5.28	0.39	16.58
Wood and Wood Products	-	-	0.48	-	-	-	-	-	-	-	0.48
Construction	-	-	0.94	0.41	-	-	-	-	-	-	1.34
Textile and Leather	-	-	-	-	-	-	-	-	-	-	-
Non-specified	0.27 e	-	1.08	6.89	-	-	-	-	1.76	0.20	10.20
TRANSPORT SECTOR	**-**	**-**	**51.90**	**4.30**	**-**	**-**	**-**	**0.17**	**0.37**	**-**	**56.74**
International Aviation	-	-	0.86	-	-	-	-	-	-	-	0.86
Domestic Aviation	-	-	5.06	-	-	-	-	-	-	-	5.06
Road	-	-	42.25	0.04	-	-	-	0.17	-	-	42.46
Rail	-	-	1.82	-	-	-	-	-	-	-	1.82
Pipeline Transport	-	-	0.02	4.26	-	-	-	-	0.28	-	4.56
Domestic Navigation	-	-	1.89	-	-	-	-	-	-	-	1.89
Non-specified	-	-	-	-	-	-	-	-	0.08	-	0.08
OTHER SECTORS	**0.02**	**-**	**13.41**	**25.17**	**-**	**-**	**-**	**2.04**	**25.39**	**0.01**	**66.05**
Residential	0.02 e	-	2.41	13.90	-	-	-	2.04	12.98	0.00	31.35
Comm. and Publ. Services	-	-	8.70	10.85	-	-	-	-	11.52	0.01	31.09
Agriculture/Forestry	-	-	2.30	0.43	-	-	-	-	0.88	0.00	3.61
Fishing	-	-	-	-	-	-	-	-	-	-	-
Non-specified	-	-	-	-	-	-	-	-	-	-	-
NON-ENERGY USE	**0.25**	**-**	**19.85**	**3.48**	**-**	**-**	**-**	**-**	**-**	**-**	**23.58**
in Industry/Transf./Energy	0.25 e	-	16.98	3.48	-	-	-	-	-	-	20.71
of which: Feedstocks	-	-	*11.58*	*3.48*	-	-	-	-	-	-	*15.06*
in Transport	-	-	0.19	-	-	-	-	-	-	-	0.19
in Other Sectors	-	-	2.67	-	-	-	-	-	-	-	2.67
Electricity Generated - TWh	***106.19***	***-***	***19.44***	***36.32***	***92.04***	***363.52***	***1.52***	***9.06***	***-***	***-***	***628.08***
Electricity Plants	*106.19 e*	-	*19.43*	*24.25*	*92.04*	*363.52*	*1.52*	*9.04 e*	-	-	*615.98*
CHP plants	-	-	*0.01*	*12.08*	-	-	-	*0.02*	-	-	*12.11*
Heat Generated - PJ	***-***	***-***	***3.10***	***31.44***	***-***	***-***	***-***	***0.01***	***-***	***-***	***34.55***
CHP plants	-	-	*3.10*	*31.44*	-	-	-	*0.01*	-	-	*34.55*
Heat Plants	-	-	-	-	-	-	-	-	-	-	-

Czech Republic / République tchèque
Key Indicators
Indicateurs principaux

	1960	1970	1973	1980	1990	1995
Energy Production (Mtoe)	..	..	38.51	41.21	40.10	31.84
Net Imports (Mtoe)	..	..	6.99	6.41	7.63	8.59
Total Primary Energy Supply (Mtoe)	..	..	45.42	47.25	48.99	41.11
Net Oil Imports (Mtoe)	..	..	8.87	10.91	8.60	7.89
Oil Supply (Mtoe)	..	..	8.91	11.15	8.96	8.01
Electricity Consumption (TWh)*	..	..	37.01	47.25	57.87	56.50
GDP (billion 2000 US$ using exch. rates)	27.82 e	37.14 e	41.03 e	48.67 e	55.30	52.69
GDP (billion 2000 US$ using PPPs)	74.74 e	99.76 e	110.23 e	130.75 e	148.56	141.55
Population (millions)	9.58 e	9.81	9.92	10.33	10.36	10.33
Industrial Production Index (2000=100)	..	..	..	..	119.90	90.60
Energy Production/TPES	..	..	0.8478	0.8721	0.8185	0.7746
Net Oil Imports/GDP (toe per thousand 2000 US$)	..	..	0.2162 e	0.2242 e	0.1555	0.1498
TPES/GDP (toe per thousand 2000 US$)	..	..	1.1069 e	0.9709 e	0.8860	0.7803
TPES/GDP (toe per thousand 2000 US$ PPP)	..	..	0.4120 e	0.3614 e	0.3298	0.2904
TPES/Population (toe per capita)	..	..	4.5774	4.5757	4.7277	3.9794
Oil Supply/GDP (toe per thousand 2000 US$)	..	..	0.2173 e	0.2290 e	0.1620	0.1520
Oil Supply/Population (toe per capita)	..	..	0.8984	1.0794	0.8644	0.7752
Elect. Cons./GDP (kWh per 2000 US$)	..	..	0.9020 e	0.9708 e	1.0466	1.0723
Elect. Cons./Population (kWh per capita)	..	..	3 730	4 575	5 584	5 469
Industry Cons.**/Industrial Production (2000=100)	..	..	..	..	132.52	136.06
Industry Oil Cons.**/Industrial Production (2000=100)	..	..	..	..	145.71	157.72

	2000	2001	2002	2003	2004	2005
Energy Production (Mtoe)	29.88	30.51	30.69	33.36	34.49	32.87
Net Imports (Mtoe)	9.41	10.64	11.30	11.31	11.71	12.72
Total Primary Energy Supply (Mtoe)	40.39	41.39	41.96	44.58	45.77	45.21
Net Oil Imports (Mtoe)	7.54	8.20	7.99	8.42	9.02	9.75
Oil Supply (Mtoe)	7.89	8.39	8.52	8.77	9.62	9.98
Electricity Consumption (TWh)*	58.49	60.20	60.10	61.93	63.53	64.92
GDP (billion 2000 US$ using exch. rates)	56.72	58.11	59.21	61.35	63.93	67.82
GDP (billion 2000 US$ using PPPs)	152.37	156.12	159.08	164.81	171.75	182.19
Population (millions)	10.27	10.22	10.20	10.20	10.21	10.23
Industrial Production Index (2000=100)	100.00	106.70	108.70	114.70	125.70	134.00
Energy Production/TPES	0.7397	0.7370	0.7315	0.7484	0.7535	0.7271
Net Oil Imports/GDP (toe per thousand 2000 US$)	0.1329	0.1411	0.1350	0.1372	0.1410	0.1437
TPES/GDP (toe per thousand 2000 US$)	0.7122	0.7123	0.7087	0.7266	0.7159	0.6666
TPES/GDP (toe per thousand 2000 US$ PPP)	0.2651	0.2651	0.2638	0.2705	0.2665	0.2481
TPES/Population (toe per capita)	3.9319	4.0485	4.1134	4.3693	4.4842	4.4172
Oil Supply/GDP (toe per thousand 2000 US$)	0.1392	0.1444	0.1440	0.1430	0.1504	0.1472
Oil Supply/Population (toe per capita)	0.7684	0.8208	0.8357	0.8598	0.9422	0.9753
Elect. Cons./GDP (kWh per 2000 US$)	1.0313	1.0359	1.0150	1.0095	0.9938	0.9573
Elect. Cons./Population (kWh per capita)	5 694	5 888	5 892	6 070	6 224	6 343
Industry Cons.**/Industrial Production (2000=100)	100.00	91.80	89.00	83.95	82.99	77.22
Industry Oil Cons.**/Industrial Production (2000=100)	100.00	96.98	86.53	79.16	95.54	86.40

* Electricity consumption equals domestic supply less distribution losses.
La consommation d'électricité représente l'approvisionnement intérieur diminué des pertes de distribution.

** Includes non-energy use in industry/transformation/energy sectors.
Comprend l'usage non-énergétique dans les secteurs de l'industrie/transformation/énergie.

Czech Republic / République tchèque

Figure 1. TPES* in 1973

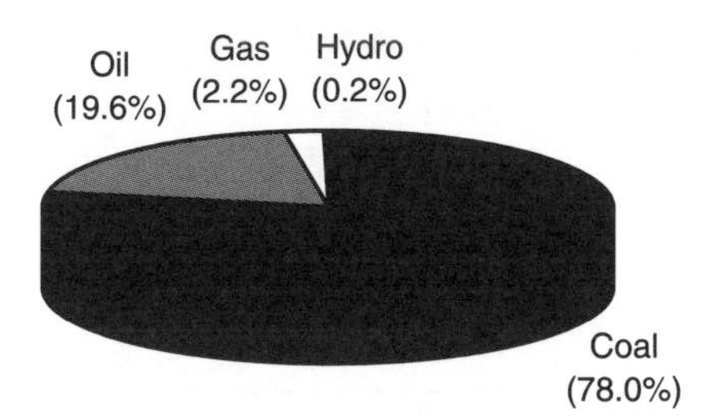

Figure 2. TPES* in 2005

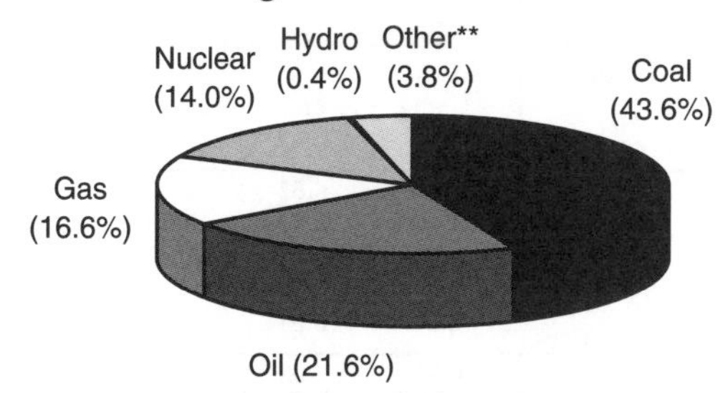

Figure 3. Final Consumption by Sector***

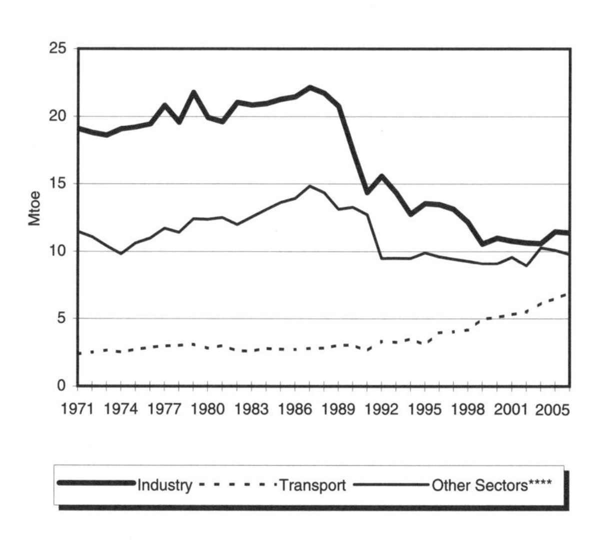

Figure 4. Breakdown of Sectorial Final Consumption by Source in 1973 and 2005***

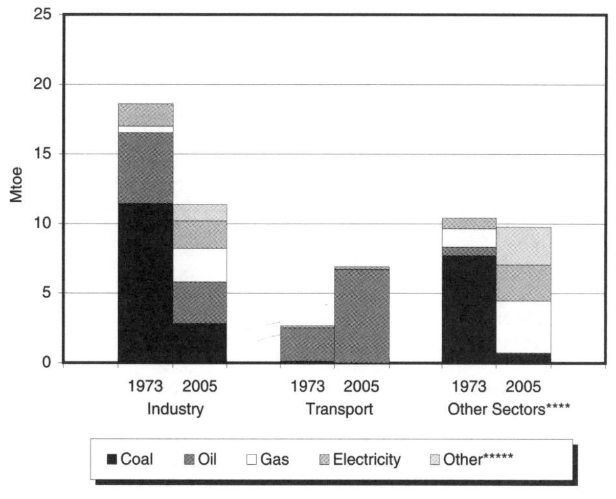

Figure 5. Electricity Generation by Fuel

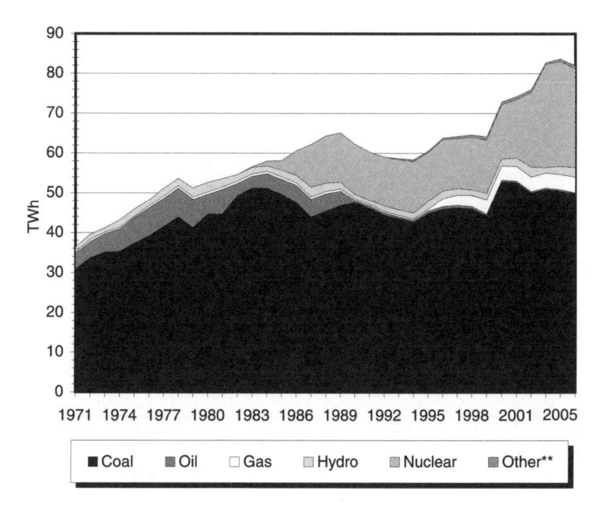

Figure 6. Electricity Consumption/GDP, TPES/GDP and Energy Production/TPES

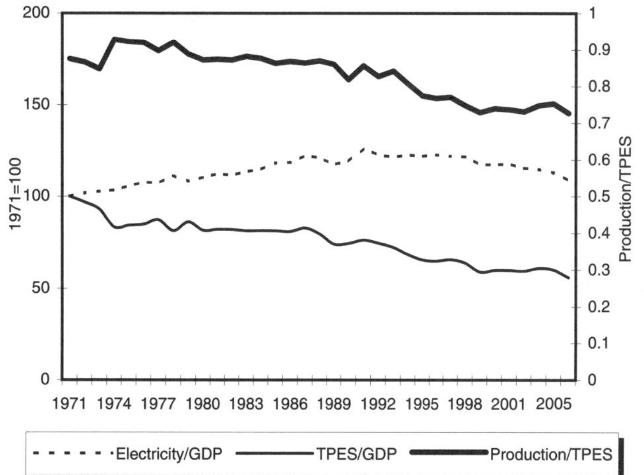

* Excluding electricity trade.

** Includes geothermal, solar, wind, combustible renewables & waste, etc.

*** Includes non-energy use.

**** Includes residential, commercial and public services, agriculture/forestry, fishing and non-specified.

***** Includes comb. renewables & waste, direct use of geothermal/solar thermal and heat produced in CHP/heat plants.

Czech Republic / République tchèque : 2004

Million tonnes of oil equivalent / *Million de tonnes d'équivalent pétrole*

SUPPLY AND CONSUMPTION *APPROVISIONNEMENT ET DEMANDE*	Coal *Charbon*	Crude Oil *Pétrole brut*	Petroleum Products *Produits pétroliers*	Gas *Gaz*	Nuclear *Nucléaire*	Hydro *Hydro*	Geotherm. Solar etc. *Géotherm. solaire etc.*	Combust. Renew. & Waste *Comb. ren. & déchets*	Electricity *Electricité*	Heat *Chaleur*	Total *Total*
Production	24.84	0.57	-	0.16	6.89	0.17	0.00	1.84	-	0.00	34.49
Imports	1.80	6.50	3.50	7.16	-	-	-	0.01	0.84	-	19.82
Exports	-4.70	-0.06	-0.92	-0.07	-	-	-	-0.15	-2.19	-0.00	-8.10
Intl. Marine Bunkers	-	-	-	-	-	-	-	-	-	-	-
Stock Changes	-0.99	0.01	0.02	0.53	-	-	-	-	-	-	-0.43
TPES	**20.96**	**7.02**	**2.60**	**7.79**	**6.89**	**0.17**	**0.00**	**1.70**	**-1.35**	**-0.00**	**45.77**
Transfers	-	-	0.01	-	-	-	-	-	-	-	0.01
Statistical Differences	-0.52	0.00	0.09	-0.00	-	-	-	-	-	-	-0.42
Electricity Plants	-8.67	-	-0.04	-0.04	-6.86	-0.17	-0.00	-0.06	5.48	-0.00 e	-10.37
CHP Plants	-5.48	-	-0.12	-1.00	-0.03	-	-	-0.25	1.73	2.65	-2.50
Heat Plants	-0.23	-	-0.09	-0.64	-	-	-	-0.06	-	0.80 e	-0.22
Gas Works	-0.48	-	-	0.30	-	-	-	-	-	-	-0.18
Petroleum Refineries	-	-7.03	7.20	-	-	-	-	-	-	-	0.16
Coal Transformation	-1.17 e	-	-	-	-	-	-	-	-	-	-1.17
Liquefaction Plants	-	-	-	-	-	-	-	-	-	-	-
Other Transformation	-	0.02	-0.02	-	-	-	-	-	-	-	-0.00
Own Use	-0.43	-	-0.23	-0.11	-	-	-	-	-0.79	-0.36	-1.92
Distribution Losses	-0.11	-	-	-0.08	-	-	-	-	-0.44	-0.47	-1.10
TFC	**3.86**	**-**	**9.40**	**6.21**	**-**	**-**	**0.00**	**1.33**	**4.63**	**2.61**	**28.05**
INDUSTRY SECTOR	**2.41**	**-**	**0.73**	**2.48**	**-**	**-**	**-**	**0.35**	**1.92**	**0.80**	**8.69**
Iron and Steel	1.10 e	-	0.13	0.29	-	-	-	0.00	0.31	0.10	1.93
Chemical and Petrochem.	0.93	-	0.17	0.24	-	-	-	0.00	0.32	0.20	1.87
Non-Ferrous Metals	0.00	-	-	0.06	-	-	-	-	0.03	0.00	0.08
Non-Metallic Minerals	0.16	-	0.06	0.64	-	-	-	0.08	0.21	0.03	1.18
Transport Equipment	0.01	-	0.00	0.11	-	-	-	0.00	0.13	0.07	0.33
Machinery	0.06	-	0.02	0.18	-	-	-	0.00	0.27	0.11	0.65
Mining and Quarrying	0.00	-	0.01	0.02	-	-	-	0.00	0.02	0.00	0.06
Food and Tobacco	0.06	-	0.07	0.39	-	-	-	0.00	0.14	0.13	0.79
Paper, Pulp and Printing	0.03	-	0.01	0.06	-	-	-	0.11	0.15	0.07	0.43
Wood and Wood Products	0.00	-	0.01	0.02	-	-	-	0.12	0.04	0.01	0.20
Construction	0.01	-	0.04	0.06	-	-	-	0.00	0.04	0.03	0.17
Textile and Leather	0.04	-	0.01	0.08	-	-	-	0.00	0.10	0.04	0.27
Non-specified	0.01	-	0.20	0.33	-	-	-	0.02	0.18	0.00	0.74
TRANSPORT SECTOR	**0.00**	**-**	**6.08**	**0.03**	**-**	**-**	**-**	**0.03**	**0.19**	**-**	**6.34**
International Aviation	-	-	0.30	-	-	-	-	-	-	-	0.30
Domestic Aviation	-	-	0.05	-	-	-	-	-	-	-	0.05
Road	-	-	5.63	0.01	-	-	-	0.03	-	-	5.67
Rail	0.00	-	0.09	-	-	-	-	0.00	0.10	-	0.20
Pipeline Transport	-	-	-	0.02	-	-	-	-	0.00	-	0.03
Domestic Navigation	-	-	0.01	-	-	-	-	-	-	-	0.01
Non-specified	-	-	-	-	-	-	-	-	0.09	-	0.09
OTHER SECTORS	**1.03**	**-**	**0.09**	**3.69**	**-**	**-**	**0.00**	**0.95**	**2.52**	**1.81**	**10.09**
Residential	0.52	-	0.06	2.35	-	-	0.00	0.88	1.25	1.19	6.25
Comm. and Publ. Services	0.48	-	0.01	1.24	-	-	0.00	0.05	1.05	0.61	3.44
Agriculture/Forestry	0.02	-	0.02	0.07	-	-	-	0.02	0.09	0.01	0.23
Fishing	-	-	-	-	-	-	-	-	0.00	0.00	0.00
Non-specified	0.00	-	0.00	0.03	-	-	-	-	0.13	0.00	0.17
NON-ENERGY USE	**0.42**	**-**	**2.51**	**-**	**-**	**-**	**-**	**-**	**-**	**-**	**2.93**
in Industry/Transf./Energy	0.42	-	2.36	-	-	-	-	-	-	-	2.77
of which: Feedstocks	-	-	*1.78*	-	-	-	-	-	-	-	*1.78*
in Transport	-	-	0.15	-	-	-	-	-	-	-	0.15
in Other Sectors	-	-	0.01	-	-	-	-	-	-	-	0.01
Electricity Generated - TWh	***50.54***	**-**	***0.35***	***3.83***	***26.33***	***2.02***	***0.01***	***0.72***	**-**	***0.00***	***83.79***
Electricity Plants	*34.72*	-	*0.17*	*0.19*	*26.33*	*2.02*	*0.01*	*0.26*	-	-	*63.70*
CHP plants	*15.82*	-	*0.18*	*3.63*	-	-	-	*0.46*	-	*0.00*	*20.09*
Heat Generated - PJ	***90.02***	**-**	***5.78***	***38.36***	***1.07***	**-**	**-**	***9.17***	**-**	***0.01***	***144.40***
CHP plants	*84.03*	-	*3.01*	*15.74*	*1.07*	-	-	*7.22*	-	-	*111.08*
Heat Plants	*5.98*	-	*2.77*	*22.62*	-	-	-	*1.95*	-	*0.01 e*	*33.33*

Czech Republic / République tchèque : 2005

Million tonnes of oil equivalent / *Million de tonnes d'équivalent pétrole*

SUPPLY AND CONSUMPTION ***APPROVISIONNEMENT ET DEMANDE***	Coal *Charbon*	Crude Oil *Pétrole brut*	Petroleum Products *Produits pétroliers*	Gas *Gaz*	Nuclear *Nucléaire*	Hydro *Hydro*	Geotherm. Solar etc. *Géotherm. solaire etc.*	Combust. Renew. & Waste *Comb. ren. & déchets*	Electricity *Electricité*	Heat *Chaleur*	Total *Total*
Production	23.52	0.58	-	0.15	6.47	0.20	0.00	1.93	-	0.00	32.87
Imports	1.34	7.81	3.22	7.60	-	-	-	0.04	1.06	-	21.08
Exports	-4.62	-0.06	-1.23	-0.07	-	-	-	-0.23	-2.15	-0.00	-8.35
Intl. Marine Bunkers	-	-	-	-	-	-	-	-	-	-	-
Stock Changes	-0.05	-0.26	-0.09	0.01	-	-	-	-	-	-	-0.38
TPES	**20.19**	**8.08**	**1.90**	**7.70**	**6.47**	**0.20**	**0.00**	**1.75**	**-1.09**	**-0.00**	**45.21**
Transfers	-	-	0.01	-	-	-	-	-	-	-	0.01
Statistical Differences	-0.39	0.02	0.01	-0.00	-	-	-	-	-	-	-0.36
Electricity Plants	-8.63	-	-0.04	-0.04	-6.44	-0.20	-0.00	-0.06	5.31	-0.01	-10.12
CHP Plants	-5.65	-	-0.11	-0.94	-0.03	-	-	-0.16	1.73	2.56	-2.61
Heat Plants	-0.15	-	-0.09	-0.62	-	-	-	-0.06	-	0.77	-0.15
Gas Works	-0.49	-	-	0.32	-	-	-	-	-	-	-0.17
Petroleum Refineries	-	-8.16	8.35	-	-	-	-	-	-	-	0.19
Coal Transformation	-0.95 e	-	-	-	-	-	-	-	-	-	-0.95
Liquefaction Plants	-	-	-	-	-	-	-	-	-	-	-
Other Transformation	-	0.06	-0.06	-	-	-	-	-	-	-	0.00
Own Use	-0.41	-	-0.25	-0.13	-	-	-	-	-0.77	-0.34	-1.90
Distribution Losses	-0.06	-	-	-0.09	-	-	-	-	-0.43	-0.50	-1.08
TFC	**3.47**	**-**	**9.72**	**6.18**	**-**	**-**	**0.00**	**1.46**	**4.76**	**2.48**	**28.06**
INDUSTRY SECTOR	**2.48**	**-**	**0.48**	**2.42**	**-**	**-**	**-**	**0.49**	**1.99**	**0.69**	**8.56**
Iron and Steel	1.20 e	-	0.10	0.28	-	-	-	0.00	0.30	0.08	1.96
Chemical and Petrochem.	0.89	-	0.14	0.28	-	-	-	0.00	0.33	0.20	1.85
Non-Ferrous Metals	-	-	-	0.06	-	-	-	-	0.03	0.00	0.09
Non-Metallic Minerals	0.15	-	0.05	0.62	-	-	-	0.11	0.22	0.03	1.17
Transport Equipment	0.01	-	0.00	0.12	-	-	-	0.00	0.14	0.06	0.33
Machinery	0.05	-	0.02	0.29	-	-	-	0.00	0.29	0.08	0.73
Mining and Quarrying	0.00	-	0.01	0.02	-	-	-	0.00	0.02	0.00	0.05
Food and Tobacco	0.06	-	0.05	0.37	-	-	-	0.00	0.14	0.10	0.72
Paper, Pulp and Printing	0.07	-	0.02	0.10	-	-	-	0.23	0.16	0.06	0.65
Wood and Wood Products	0.00	-	0.01	0.02	-	-	-	0.12	0.05	0.01	0.21
Construction	0.00	-	0.04	0.06	-	-	-	0.01	0.03	0.03	0.17
Textile and Leather	0.04	-	0.01	0.08	-	-	-	0.00	0.10	0.03	0.26
Non-specified	0.01	-	0.03	0.13	-	-	-	0.01	0.19	0.00	0.37
TRANSPORT SECTOR	**0.00**	**-**	**6.52**	**0.04**	**-**	**-**	**-**	**0.00**	**0.19**	**-**	**6.75**
International Aviation	-	-	0.33	-	-	-	-	-	-	-	0.33
Domestic Aviation	-	-	0.03	-	-	-	-	-	-	-	0.03
Road	-	-	6.06	0.01	-	-	-	0.00	-	-	6.08
Rail	0.00	-	0.09	-	-	-	-	0.00	0.10	-	0.19
Pipeline Transport	-	-	-	0.03	-	-	-	-	0.00	-	0.03
Domestic Navigation	-	-	0.01	-	-	-	-	-	-	-	0.01
Non-specified	-	-	-	-	-	-	-	-	0.08	-	0.08
OTHER SECTORS	**0.66**	**-**	**0.06**	**3.73**	**-**	**-**	**0.00**	**0.96**	**2.58**	**1.79**	**9.78**
Residential	0.39	-	0.03	2.31	-	-	0.00	0.89	1.27	1.17	6.05
Comm. and Publ. Services	0.25	-	0.01	1.27	-	-	0.00	0.06	1.08	0.61	3.27
Agriculture/Forestry	0.02	-	0.02	0.07	-	-	-	0.02	0.09	0.01	0.22
Fishing	-	-	-	-	-	-	-	-	0.00	0.00	0.00
Non-specified	0.00	-	0.00	0.08	-	-	-	-	0.15	0.00	0.23
NON-ENERGY USE	**0.32**	**-**	**2.65**	**-**	**-**	**-**	**-**	**-**	**-**	**-**	**2.97**
in Industry/Transf./Energy	0.32	-	2.49	-	-	-	-	-	-	-	2.82
of which: Feedstocks	-	-	*1.90*	-	-	-	-	-	-	-	*1.90*
in Transport	-	-	0.15	-	-	-	-	-	-	-	0.15
in Other Sectors	-	-	0.01	-	-	-	-	-	-	-	0.01
Electricity Generated - TWh	***49.78***	**-**	***0.33***	***3.95***	***24.73***	***2.38***	***0.02***	***0.74***	**-**	***0.00***	***81.93***
Electricity Plants	*34.03*	-	*0.17*	*0.17*	*24.73*	*2.38*	*0.02*	*0.26*	-	-	*61.76*
CHP plants	*15.75*	-	*0.16*	*3.78*	-	-	-	*0.48*	-	*0.00*	*20.17*
Heat Generated - PJ	***89.43***	**-**	***5.67***	***37.45***	***1.10***	**-**	***0.29***	***5.28***	**-**	***0.02***	***139.24***
CHP plants	*84.94*	-	*2.93*	*14.55*	*1.10*	-	*0.29*	*3.25*	-	-	*107.06*
Heat Plants	*4.49*	-	*2.74*	*22.90*	-	-	-	*2.03*	-	*0.02*	*32.18*

Denmark / Danemark
Key Indicators
Indicateurs principaux

	1960	1970	1973	1980	1990	1995
Energy Production (Mtoe)	1.00	0.38	0.43	0.95	10.04	15.59
Net Imports (Mtoe)	8.68	21.22	20.54	19.30	8.65	7.28
Total Primary Energy Supply (Mtoe)	9.03	20.27	19.83	19.78	17.90	20.00
Net Oil Imports (Mtoe)	5.24	19.34	18.69	13.36	2.75	1.17
Oil Supply (Mtoe)	4.91	18.12	17.57	13.36	8.18	8.86
Electricity Consumption (TWh)*	4.99	14.26	17.22	23.56	30.56	33.52
GDP (billion 2000 US$ using exch. rates)	52.17 e	80.80	89.96	101.00	123.89	139.06
GDP (billion 2000 US$ using PPPs)	50.14 e	77.66	86.46	97.08	119.07	133.65
Population (millions)	4.59 e	4.94	5.02	5.12	5.14	5.23
Industrial Production Index (2000=100)	..	..	..	57.50	75.80	86.50
Energy Production/TPES	0.1102	0.0186	0.0215	0.0481	0.5610	0.7793
Net Oil Imports/GDP (toe per thousand 2000 US$)	0.1004 e	0.2394	0.2077	0.1322	0.0222	0.0084
TPES/GDP (toe per thousand 2000 US$)	0.1732 e	0.2509	0.2205	0.1959	0.1445	0.1438
TPES/GDP (toe per thousand 2000 US$ PPP)	0.1802 e	0.2610	0.2294	0.2038	0.1503	0.1497
TPES/Population (toe per capita)	1.9680 e	4.1052	3.9495	3.8608	3.4816	3.8247
Oil Supply/GDP (toe per thousand 2000 US$)	0.0941 e	0.2242	0.1953	0.1323	0.0660	0.0637
Oil Supply/Population (toe per capita)	1.0700 e	3.6692	3.4979	2.6081	1.5914	1.6942
Elect. Cons./GDP (kWh per 2000 US$)	0.0957 e	0.1765	0.1914	0.2333	0.2467	0.2410
Elect. Cons./Population (kWh per capita)	1 087 e	2 888	3 428	4 598	5 945	6 409
Industry Cons.**/Industrial Production (2000=100)	..	..	..	195.42	122.55	119.05
Industry Oil Cons.**/Industrial Production (2000=100)	..	..	..	438.72	155.92	131.80

	2000	2001	2002	2003	2004	2005
Energy Production (Mtoe)	27.73	27.14	28.58	28.47	31.10	31.30
Net Imports (Mtoe)	- 7.46	- 6.07	- 8.76	- 6.88	- 9.99	- 10.52
Total Primary Energy Supply (Mtoe)	19.36	19.94	19.64	20.78	20.20	19.61
Net Oil Imports (Mtoe)	- 8.48	- 7.12	- 9.41	- 9.29	- 10.70	- 9.41
Oil Supply (Mtoe)	8.74	8.86	8.55	8.39	8.40	8.21
Electricity Consumption (TWh)*	34.61	34.78	35.12	35.59	35.75	36.09
GDP (billion 2000 US$ using exch. rates)	160.08	161.21	161.96	163.08	166.13	171.08
GDP (billion 2000 US$ using PPPs)	153.86	154.94	155.66	156.74	159.68	164.43
Population (millions)	5.34	5.36	5.38	5.39	5.40	5.42
Industrial Production Index (2000=100)	100.00	101.60	103.00	103.20	103.20	104.90
Energy Production/TPES	1.4325	1.3609	1.4553	1.3699	1.5396	1.5962
Net Oil Imports/GDP (toe per thousand 2000 US$)	- 0.0530	- 0.0442	- 0.0581	- 0.0569	- 0.0644	- 0.0550
TPES/GDP (toe per thousand 2000 US$)	0.1209	0.1237	0.1213	0.1274	0.1216	0.1146
TPES/GDP (toe per thousand 2000 US$ PPP)	0.1258	0.1287	0.1262	0.1326	0.1265	0.1193
TPES/Population (toe per capita)	3.6270	3.7224	3.6536	3.8560	3.7384	3.6187
Oil Supply/GDP (toe per thousand 2000 US$)	0.0546	0.0549	0.0528	0.0515	0.0506	0.0480
Oil Supply/Population (toe per capita)	1.6379	1.6531	1.5898	1.5570	1.5548	1.5144
Elect. Cons./GDP (kWh per 2000 US$)	0.2162	0.2157	0.2168	0.2182	0.2152	0.2109
Elect. Cons./Population (kWh per capita)	6 484	6 492	6 533	6 602	6 617	6 659
Industry Cons.**/Industrial Production (2000=100)	100.00	100.23	93.45	93.97	96.34	91.93
Industry Oil Cons.**/Industrial Production (2000=100)	100.00	99.73	96.91	97.76	102.81	95.27

* Electricity consumption equals domestic supply less distribution losses.
La consommation d'électricité représente l'approvisionnement intérieur diminué des pertes de distribution.

** Includes non-energy use in industry/transformation/energy sectors.
Comprend l'usage non-énergétique dans les secteurs de l'industrie/transformation/énergie.

Denmark / Danemark

Figure 1. TPES* in 1973

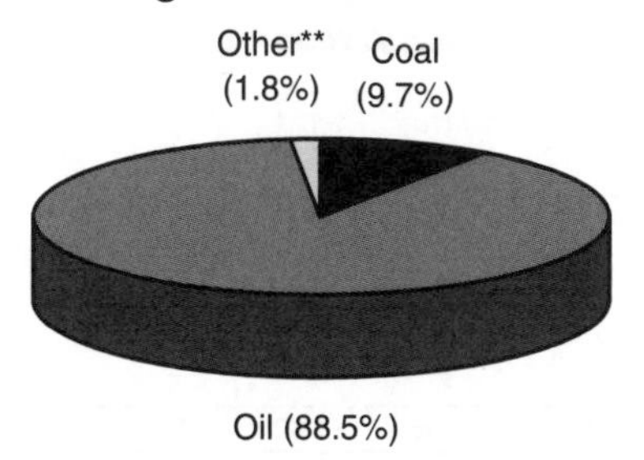

Figure 2. TPES* in 2005

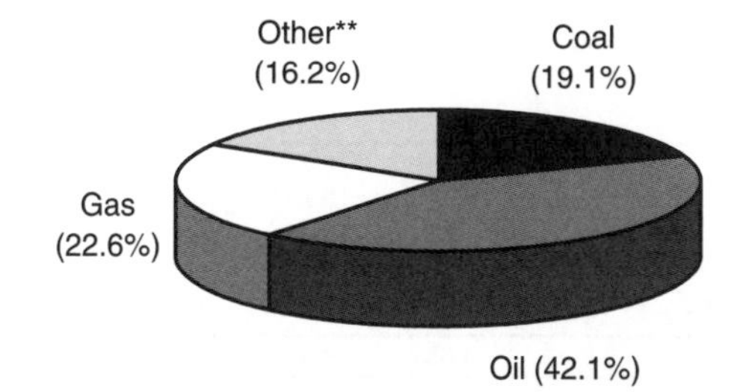

Figure 3. Final Consumption by Sector***

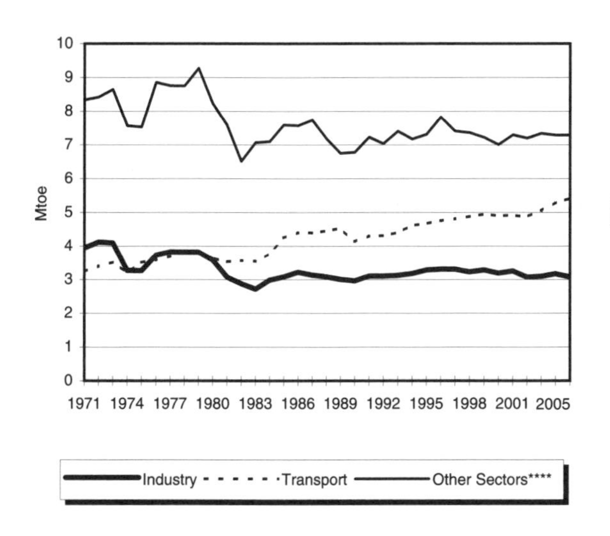

Figure 4. Breakdown of Sectorial Final Consumption by Source in 1973 and 2005***

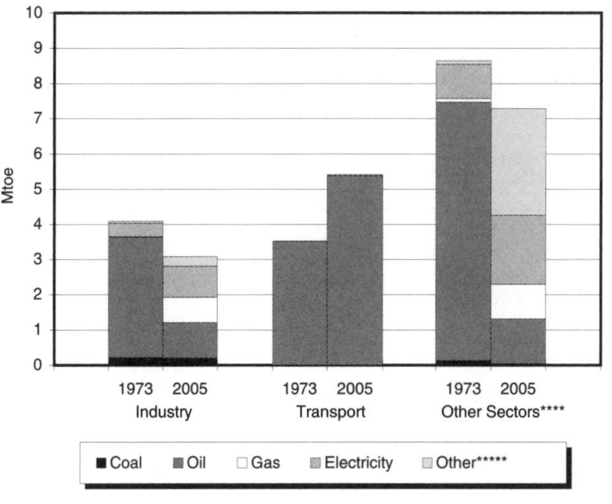

Figure 5. Electricity Generation by Fuel

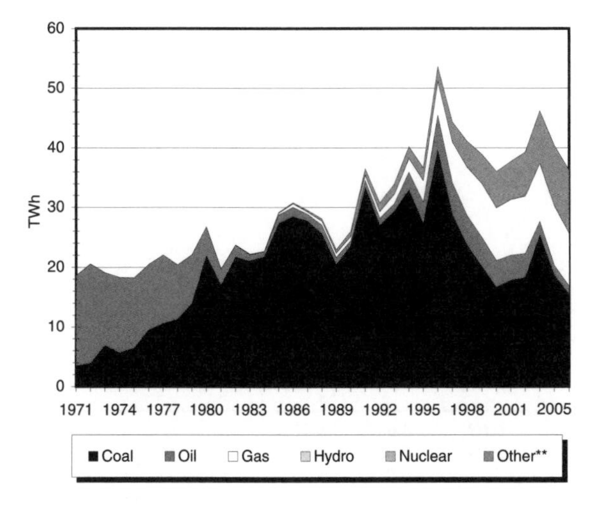

Figure 6. Electricity Consumption/GDP, TPES/GDP and Energy Production/TPES

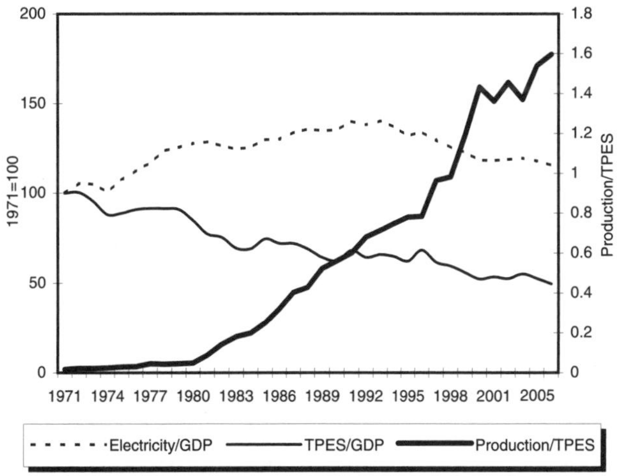

* Excluding electricity trade.

** Includes geothermal, solar, wind, combustible renewables & waste, etc.

*** Includes non-energy use.

**** Includes residential, commercial and public services, agriculture/forestry, fishing and non-specified.

***** Includes comb. renewables & waste, direct use of geothermal/solar thermal and heat produced in CHP/heat plants.

Denmark / Danemark : 2004

Million tonnes of oil equivalent / *Million de tonnes d'équivalent pétrole*

SUPPLY AND CONSUMPTION / *APPROVISIONNEMENT ET DEMANDE*	Coal / *Charbon*	Crude Oil / *Pétrole brut*	Petroleum Products / *Produits pétroliers*	Gas / *Gaz*	Nuclear / *Nucléaire*	Hydro / *Hydro*	Geotherm. Solar etc. / *Géotherm. solaire etc.*	Combust. Renew. & Waste / *Comb. ren. & déchets*	Electricity / *Electricité*	Heat / *Chaleur*	Total / *Total*
Production	-	19.78	-	8.49	-	0.00	0.58 e	2.25	-	0.00	31.10
Imports	4.52	3.96	4.92	-	-	-	-	0.28	0.75	0.00	14.42
Exports	-0.09	-15.46	-4.12	-3.69	-	-	-	-0.06	-0.99	-	-24.41
Intl. Marine Bunkers	-	-	-0.80	-	-	-	-	-	-	-	-0.80
Stock Changes	-0.06	-0.06	0.18	-0.17	-	-	-	-	-	-	-0.11
TPES	**4.36**	**8.23**	**0.17**	**4.63**	**-**	**0.00**	**0.58**	**2.47**	**-0.25**	**0.00**	**20.20**
Transfers	-	-	0.01	-	-	-	-	-	-	-	0.01
Statistical Differences	0.02	0.05	-0.02	0.03	-	-	0.00	0.00	0.00	0.00	0.08
Electricity Plants	-	-	-0.02	-	-	-0.00	-0.57	-0.00	0.57	-	-0.02
CHP Plants	-4.12	-0.00	-0.36	-2.23	-	-	-	-1.21	2.90	2.53	-2.50
Heat Plants	-0.00	-	-0.04	-0.07	-	-	-0.01 e	-0.43	-0.00	0.58	0.02
Gas Works	-	-	-	-0.00	-	-	-	-	-	-	-0.00
Petroleum Refineries	-	-8.27	8.25	-	-	-	-	-	-	-	-0.02
Coal Transformation	-	-	-	-	-	-	-	-	-	-	-
Liquefaction Plants	-	-	-	-	-	-	-	-	-	-	-
Other Transformation	-	-	-	-	-	-	-	-	-	-	-
Own Use	-	-	-0.33	-0.65	-	-	-	-0.00	-0.23	-0.03	-1.24
Distribution Losses	-	-	-	-0.00	-	-	-	-	-0.16	-0.62	-0.78
TFC	**0.26**	**-**	**7.65**	**1.70**	**-**	**-**	**0.01**	**0.82**	**2.84**	**2.46**	**15.75**
INDUSTRY SECTOR	**0.24**	**-**	**0.81**	**0.72**	**-**	**-**	**-**	**0.11**	**0.86**	**0.18**	**2.91**
Iron and Steel	-	-	0.01	0.02	-	-	-	-	0.03	0.01	0.06
Chemical and Petrochem.	0.02	-	0.03	0.09	-	-	-	0.00	0.11	0.02	0.26
Non-Ferrous Metals	-	-	0.00	0.00	-	-	-	-	0.01	0.00	0.01
Non-Metallic Minerals	0.16	-	0.25	0.13	-	-	-	0.02	0.08	0.02	0.66
Transport Equipment	-	-	0.01	0.01	-	-	-	0.00	0.02	0.00	0.04
Machinery	-	-	0.07	0.10	-	-	-	0.00	0.14	0.03	0.34
Mining and Quarrying	0.00	-	0.05	0.02	-	-	-	-	0.01	0.00	0.09
Food and Tobacco	0.06	-	0.17	0.20	-	-	-	0.00	0.20	0.04	0.67
Paper, Pulp and Printing	-	-	0.01	0.06	-	-	-	0.00	0.07	0.02	0.17
Wood and Wood Products	0.00	-	0.02	0.00	-	-	-	0.04	0.03	0.01	0.09
Construction	-	-	0.16	0.01	-	-	-	-	0.03	-	0.19
Textile and Leather	-	-	0.01	0.02	-	-	-	0.00	0.02	0.00	0.05
Non-specified	-	-	0.03	0.05	-	-	-	0.04	0.13	0.03	0.28
TRANSPORT SECTOR	**-**	**-**	**5.23**	**-**	**-**	**-**	**-**	**-**	**0.03**	**-**	**5.26**
International Aviation	-	-	0.85	-	-	-	-	-	-	-	0.85
Domestic Aviation	-	-	0.03	-	-	-	-	-	-	-	0.03
Road	-	-	4.08	-	-	-	-	-	-	-	4.08
Rail	-	-	0.07	-	-	-	-	-	0.03	-	0.10
Pipeline Transport	-	-	-	-	-	-	-	-	-	-	-
Domestic Navigation	-	-	0.12	-	-	-	-	-	-	-	0.12
Non-specified	-	-	0.08	-	-	-	-	-	-	-	0.08
OTHER SECTORS	**0.02**	**-**	**1.31**	**0.99**	**-**	**-**	**0.01**	**0.71**	**1.94**	**2.28**	**7.27**
Residential	0.00	-	0.66	0.71	-	-	0.01	0.60	0.89	1.53	4.40
Comm. and Publ. Services	-	-	0.12	0.21	-	-	0.00	0.06	0.89	0.71	1.99
Agriculture/Forestry	0.02	-	0.35	0.05	-	-	-	0.05	0.16	0.05	0.69
Fishing	-	-	0.18	-	-	-	-	-	-	-	0.18
Non-specified	-	-	-	0.01	-	-	-	-	-	-	0.01
NON-ENERGY USE	**-**	**-**	**0.31**	**-**	**-**	**-**	**-**	**-**	**-**	**-**	**0.31**
in Industry/Transf./Energy	-	-	0.26	-	-	-	-	-	-	-	0.26
of which: Feedstocks	-	-	-	-	-	-	-	-	-	-	-
in Transport	-	-	0.03	-	-	-	-	-	-	-	0.03
in Other Sectors	-	-	0.02	-	-	-	-	-	-	-	0.02
Electricity Generated - TWh	***18.68***	***0.00***	***1.63***	***9.94***	***-***	***0.03***	***6.60***	***3.56***	***-***	***-***	***40.43***
Electricity Plants	*-*	*-*	*0.05*	*-*	*-*	*0.03*	*6.59*	*0.00*	*-*	*-*	*6.66*
CHP plants	*18.68*	*0.00*	*1.58*	*9.94*	*-*	*-*	*0.01*	*3.56*	*-*	*-*	*33.77*
Heat Generated - PJ	***36.45***	***0.00***	***6.15***	***40.65***	***-***	***-***	***3.54***	***43.00***	***-***	***0.08***	***129.88***
CHP plants	*36.43*	*0.00*	*4.68*	*37.61*	*-*	*-*	*-*	*27.02*	*-*	*-*	*105.74*
Heat Plants	*0.02*	*-*	*1.47*	*3.04*	*-*	*-*	*3.54*	*15.98*	*-*	*0.08*	*24.14*

Denmark / Danemark : 2005

Million tonnes of oil equivalent / *Million de tonnes d'équivalent pétrole*

SUPPLY AND CONSUMPTION / *APPROVISIONNEMENT ET DEMANDE*	Coal / *Charbon*	Crude Oil / *Pétrole brut*	Petroleum Products / *Produits pétroliers*	Gas / *Gaz*	Nuclear / *Nucléaire*	Hydro / *Hydro*	Geotherm. Solar etc. / *Géotherm. solaire etc.*	Combust. Renew. & Waste / *Comb. ren. & déchets*	Electricity / *Electricité*	Heat / *Chaleur*	Total / *Total*
Production	-	19.02	-	9.38	-	0.00	0.58 e	2.32	-	0.00 e	31.30
Imports	3.56	2.86	5.99	-	-	-	-	0.33	1.11	0.00	13.86
Exports	-0.06	-14.12	-4.14	-5.01	-	-	-	-0.06	-1.00	-	-24.38
Intl. Marine Bunkers	-	-	-0.83	-	-	-	-	-	-	-	-0.83
Stock Changes	0.21	0.11	-0.69	0.03	-	-	-	-	-	-	-0.34
TPES	**3.72**	**7.87**	**0.34**	**4.40**	**-**	**0.00**	**0.58**	**2.58**	**0.12**	**0.00**	**19.61**
Transfers	-	-	0.01	-	-	-	-	-	-	-	0.01
Statistical Differences	-0.03	0.07	0.22	0.08	-	-	0.00	0.00	0.00	0.00	0.33
Electricity Plants	-	-	-0.01	-	-	-0.00	-0.57	-0.00	0.57	-	-0.01
CHP Plants	-3.44	-	-0.34	-2.00	-	-	-	-1.34	2.55	2.51	-2.07
Heat Plants	-0.00	-	-0.03	-0.10	-	-	-0.00	-0.37	-0.00 e	0.54 e	0.02
Gas Works	-	-	-	-0.00	-	-	-	-	-	-	-0.00
Petroleum Refineries	-	-7.93	7.79	-	-	-	-	-	-	-	-0.15
Coal Transformation	-	-	-	-	-	-	-	-	-	-	-
Liquefaction Plants	-	-	-	-	-	-	-	-	-	-	-
Other Transformation	-	-	-	-	-	-	-	-	-	-	-
Own Use	-	-	-0.32	-0.66	-	-	-	-0.00	-0.22	-0.04	-1.24
Distribution Losses	-	-	-	-0.00	-	-	-	-	-0.13	-0.60	-0.74
TFC	**0.24**	**-**	**7.65**	**1.70**	**-**	**-**	**0.01**	**0.88**	**2.88**	**2.41**	**15.77**
INDUSTRY SECTOR	**0.20**	**-**	**0.77**	**0.72**	**-**	**-**	**-**	**0.11**	**0.88**	**0.16**	**2.84**
Iron and Steel	-	-	0.01	0.02	-	-	-	-	0.03	0.01	0.06
Chemical and Petrochem.	0.01	-	0.02	0.09	-	-	-	0.00	0.11	0.02	0.26
Non-Ferrous Metals	-	-	0.00	0.00	-	-	-	-	0.01	0.00	0.01
Non-Metallic Minerals	0.13	-	0.24	0.13	-	-	-	0.02	0.08	0.02	0.62
Transport Equipment	-	-	0.01	0.01	-	-	-	0.00	0.02	0.00	0.04
Machinery	-	-	0.07	0.10	-	-	-	0.00	0.14	0.03	0.34
Mining and Quarrying	0.00	-	0.05	0.02	-	-	-	-	0.01	0.00	0.08
Food and Tobacco	0.05	-	0.15	0.20	-	-	-	0.00	0.21	0.04	0.64
Paper, Pulp and Printing	-	-	0.01	0.06	-	-	-	0.00	0.08	0.01	0.17
Wood and Wood Products	0.00	-	0.01	0.00	-	-	-	0.04	0.03	0.01	0.09
Construction	-	-	0.16	0.01	-	-	-	-	0.03	-	0.20
Textile and Leather	-	-	0.01	0.02	-	-	-	0.00	0.02	0.00	0.05
Non-specified	-	-	0.03	0.06	-	-	-	0.04	0.13	0.03	0.28
TRANSPORT SECTOR	**-**	**-**	**5.35**	**-**	**-**	**-**	**-**	**-**	**0.03**	**-**	**5.38**
International Aviation	-	-	0.89	-	-	-	-	-	-	-	0.89
Domestic Aviation	-	-	0.03	-	-	-	-	-	-	-	0.03
Road	-	-	4.12	-	-	-	-	-	-	-	4.12
Rail	-	-	0.08	-	-	-	-	-	0.03	-	0.11
Pipeline Transport	-	-	-	-	-	-	-	-	-	-	-
Domestic Navigation	-	-	0.14	-	-	-	-	-	-	-	0.14
Non-specified	-	-	0.09	-	-	-	-	-	-	-	0.09
OTHER SECTORS	**0.04**	**-**	**1.25**	**0.98**	**-**	**-**	**0.01**	**0.77**	**1.97**	**2.24**	**7.27**
Residential	-	-	0.63	0.70	-	-	0.01	0.67	0.90	1.50	4.41
Comm. and Publ. Services	-	-	0.10	0.21	-	-	0.00	0.05	0.90	0.69	1.97
Agriculture/Forestry	0.04	-	0.33	0.05	-	-	-	0.05	0.17	0.05	0.69
Fishing	-	-	0.18	-	-	-	-	-	-	-	0.18
Non-specified	-	-	-	0.01	-	-	-	-	-	-	0.01
NON-ENERGY USE	**-**	**-**	**0.28**	**-**	**-**	**-**	**-**	**-**	**-**	**-**	**0.28**
in Industry/Transf./Energy	-	-	0.24	-	-	-	-	-	-	-	0.24
of which: Feedstocks	-	-	-	-	-	-	-	-	-	-	-
in Transport	-	-	0.03	-	-	-	-	-	-	-	0.03
in Other Sectors	-	-	0.02	-	-	-	-	-	-	-	0.02
Electricity Generated - TWh	*15.47*	*-*	*1.37*	*8.82*	*-*	*0.02*	*6.62*	*3.98*	*-*	*-*	*36.28*
Electricity Plants	*-*	*-*	*0.01*	*-*	*-*	*0.02*	*6.62*	*0.00*	*-*	*-*	*6.66*
CHP plants	*15.47*	*-*	*1.36*	*8.82*	*-*	*-*	*-*	*3.98*	*-*	*-*	*29.62*
Heat Generated - PJ	*34.25*	*-*	*6.10*	*38.95*	*-*	*-*	*3.15*	*45.04*	*-*	*0.07*	*127.56*
CHP plants	*34.20*	*-*	*4.88*	*34.69*	*-*	*-*	*-*	*31.30*	*-*	*-*	*105.07*
Heat Plants	*0.04*	*-*	*1.22*	*4.26*	*-*	*-*	*3.15*	*13.74*	*-*	*0.07*	*22.49*

Finland / Finlande
Key Indicators
Indicateurs principaux

	1960	1970	1973	1980	1990	1995
Energy Production (Mtoe)	5.29	5.00	4.88	6.91	12.08	13.16
Net Imports (Mtoe)	4.75	15.17	16.64	19.01	18.28	16.13
Total Primary Energy Supply (Mtoe)	9.78	18.07	21.35	25.41	29.17	29.63
Net Oil Imports (Mtoe)	2.70	12.51	13.84	14.35	10.79	8.73
Oil Supply (Mtoe)	2.55	10.71	13.57	13.41	10.25	8.88
Electricity Consumption (TWh)*	8.30	21.06	28.22	39.65	62.26	69.42
GDP (billion 2000 US$ using exch. rates)	32.36 e	51.73	61.03	74.45	100.29	96.54
GDP (billion 2000 US$ using PPPs)	35.87 e	57.34	67.65	82.53	111.17	107.01
Population (millions)	4.43 e	4.61	4.67	4.78	4.99	5.11
Industrial Production Index (2000=100)	14.20	29.20	35.60	45.50	60.30	69.10
Energy Production/TPES	0.5412	0.2764	0.2288	0.2720	0.4141	0.4441
Net Oil Imports/GDP (toe per thousand 2000 US$)	0.0835 e	0.2418	0.2268	0.1927	0.1076	0.0905
TPES/GDP (toe per thousand 2000 US$)	0.3022 e	0.3493	0.3498	0.3413	0.2909	0.3070
TPES/GDP (toe per thousand 2000 US$ PPP)	0.2726 e	0.3152	0.3155	0.3079	0.2624	0.2769
TPES/Population (toe per capita)	2.2075 e	3.9235	4.5748	5.3165	5.8506	5.8011
Oil Supply/GDP (toe per thousand 2000 US$)	0.0787 e	0.2070	0.2224	0.1801	0.1022	0.0920
Oil Supply/Population (toe per capita)	0.5751 e	2.3253	2.9091	2.8058	2.0560	1.7380
Elect. Cons./GDP (kWh per 2000 US$)	0.2564 e	0.4070	0.4623	0.5326	0.6208	0.7191
Elect. Cons./Population (kWh per capita)	1 873 e	4 571	6 047	8 295	12 487	13 591
Industry Cons.**/Industrial Production (2000=100)	146.27	149.78	175.74	130.94	142.96	125.55
Industry Oil Cons.**/Industrial Production (2000=100)	307.39	623.67	763.98	446.55	231.96	167.51

	2000	2001	2002	2003	2004	2005
Energy Production (Mtoe)	15.08	15.01	16.01	15.92	15.77	16.56
Net Imports (Mtoe)	18.77	19.17	19.08	22.67	21.21	19.51
Total Primary Energy Supply (Mtoe)	32.98	33.67	35.43	37.55	37.85	34.96
Net Oil Imports (Mtoe)	10.78	10.40	10.44	11.59	11.38	11.18
Oil Supply (Mtoe)	9.63	9.43	10.43	10.75	11.23	10.70
Electricity Consumption (TWh)*	79.12	81.39	83.89	85.64	87.76	84.57
GDP (billion 2000 US$ using exch. rates)	121.87	125.08	127.13	129.39	133.93	137.84
GDP (billion 2000 US$ using PPPs)	135.08	138.65	140.92	143.42	148.45	152.80
Population (millions)	5.18	5.19	5.20	5.21	5.23	5.25
Industrial Production Index (2000=100)	100.00	99.80	102.00	103.20	108.40	108.30
Energy Production/TPES	0.4573	0.4457	0.4519	0.4239	0.4166	0.4737
Net Oil Imports/GDP (toe per thousand 2000 US$)	0.0885	0.0831	0.0822	0.0895	0.0850	0.0811
TPES/GDP (toe per thousand 2000 US$)	0.2706	0.2692	0.2786	0.2902	0.2826	0.2536
TPES/GDP (toe per thousand 2000 US$ PPP)	0.2441	0.2428	0.2514	0.2618	0.2550	0.2288
TPES/Population (toe per capita)	6.3717	6.4895	6.8112	7.2034	7.2419	6.6655
Oil Supply/GDP (toe per thousand 2000 US$)	0.0790	0.0754	0.0820	0.0831	0.0838	0.0776
Oil Supply/Population (toe per capita)	1.8597	1.8167	2.0044	2.0618	2.1476	2.0406
Elect. Cons./GDP (kWh per 2000 US$)	0.6493	0.6507	0.6598	0.6619	0.6553	0.6135
Elect. Cons./Population (kWh per capita)	15 287	15 687	16 129	16 427	16 789	16 123
Industry Cons.**/Industrial Production (2000=100)	100.00	96.79	100.78	103.43	101.09	95.13
Industry Oil Cons.**/Industrial Production (2000=100)	100.00	93.66	114.64	130.51	120.62	119.33

* Electricity consumption equals domestic supply less distribution losses.
La consommation d'électricité représente l'approvisionnement intérieur diminué des pertes de distribution.

** Includes non-energy use in industry/transformation/energy sectors.
Comprend l'usage non-énergétique dans les secteurs de l'industrie/transformation/énergie.

Finland / Finlande

Figure 1. TPES* in 1973

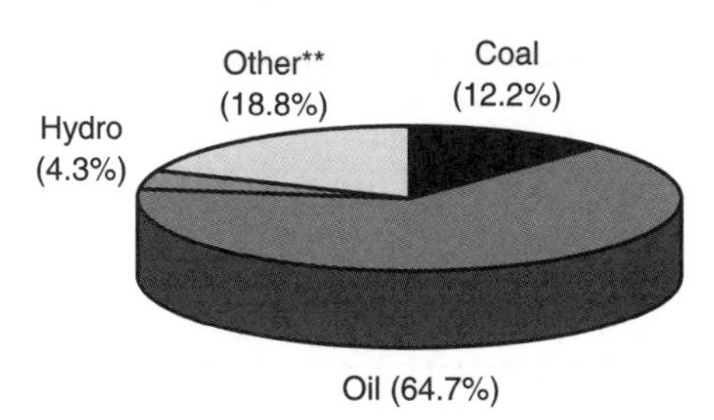

Figure 2. TPES* in 2005

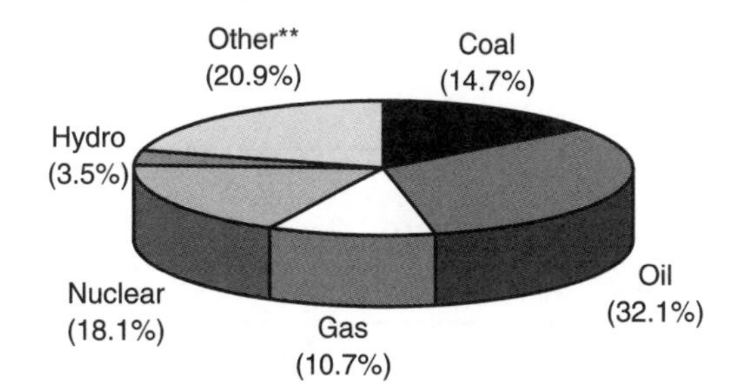

Figure 3. Final Consumption by Sector***

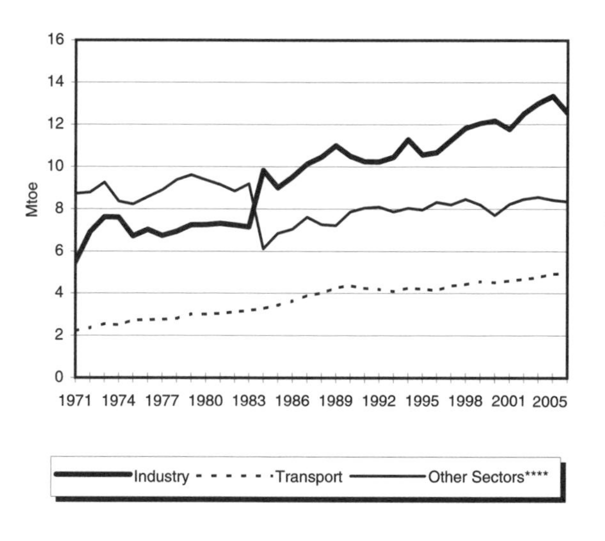

Figure 4. Breakdown of Sectorial Final Consumption by Source in 1973 and 2005***

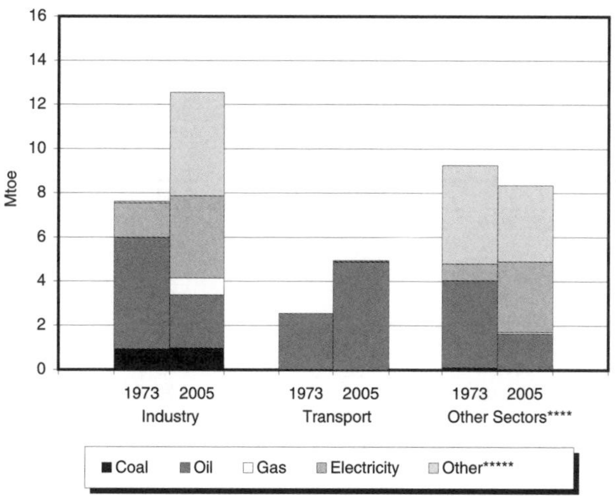

Figure 5. Electricity Generation by Fuel

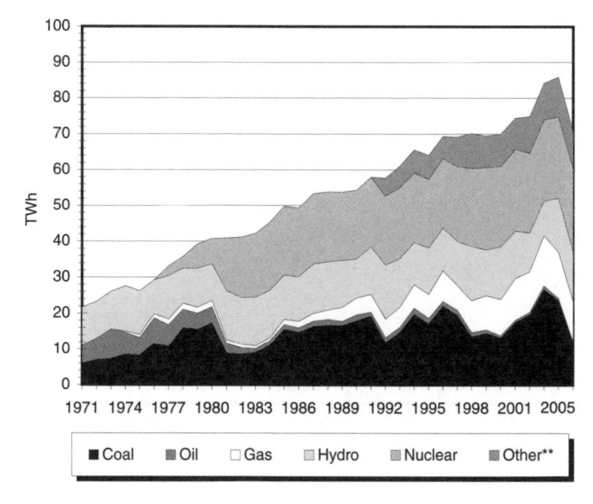

Figure 6. Electricity Consumption/GDP, TPES/GDP and Energy Production/TPES

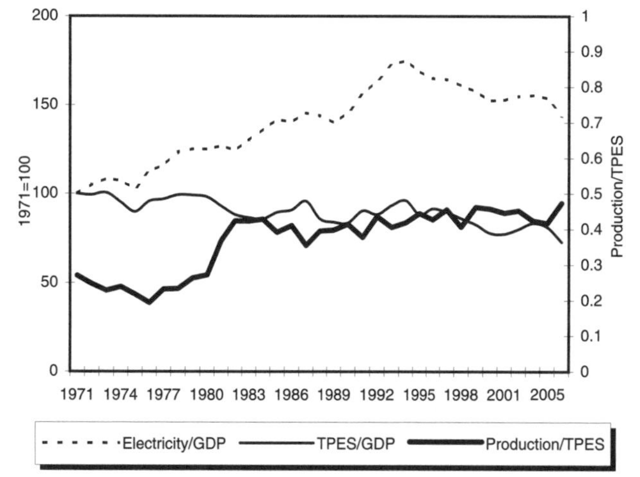

* Excluding electricity trade.

** Includes geothermal, solar, wind, combustible renewables & waste, etc.

*** Includes non-energy use.

**** Includes residential, commercial and public services, agriculture/forestry, fishing and non-specified.

***** Includes comb. renewables & waste, direct use of geothermal/solar thermal and heat produced in CHP/heat plants.

Finland / Finlande : 2004

Million tonnes of oil equivalent / *Million de tonnes d'équivalent pétrole*

SUPPLY AND CONSUMPTION / ***APPROVISIONNEMENT ET DEMANDE***	Coal / *Charbon*	Crude Oil / *Pétrole brut*	Petroleum Products / *Produits pétroliers*	Gas / *Gaz*	Nuclear / *Nucléaire*	Hydro / *Hydro*	Geotherm. Solar etc. / *Géotherm. solaire etc.*	Combust. Renew. & Waste / *Comb. ren. & déchets*	Electricity / *Electricité*	Heat / *Chaleur*	Total / *Total*
Production	0.88	0.08	-	-	5.92	1.30	0.10	7.41	-	0.07	15.77
Imports	5.53	13.00	4.13	3.95	-	-	-	0.00	1.00	-	27.62
Exports	-0.00	-	-5.75	-	-	-	-	-0.06	-0.58	-	-6.40
Intl. Marine Bunkers	-	-	-0.51	-	-	-	-	-	-	-	-0.51
Stock Changes	1.11	-0.07	0.35	-	-	-	-	-	-	-	1.38
TPES	**7.52**	**13.01**	**-1.79**	**3.95**	**5.92**	**1.30**	**0.10**	**7.35**	**0.42**	**0.07**	**37.85**
Transfers	-	1.08	-1.03	-	-	-	-	-	-	-	0.05
Statistical Differences	-0.06	0.01	-0.72	-0.02	-	-	-	-	-	-	-0.79
Electricity Plants	-3.40	-	-0.05	-0.28	-5.92	-1.30	-0.01	-0.33	4.89	-0.04	-6.45
CHP Plants	-2.43	-	-0.14	-2.21	-	-	-	-1.83	2.49	3.06	-1.06
Heat Plants	-0.17	-	-0.28	-0.32	-	-	-0.09	-0.20	-0.00	0.93	-0.13
Gas Works	-	-	-	-	-	-	-	-	-	-	-
Petroleum Refineries	-	-14.24	13.98	-	-	-	-	-	-	-	-0.26
Coal Transformation	-0.43 e	-	-0.30	-	-	-	-	-	-	-	-0.73
Liquefaction Plants	-	-	-	-	-	-	-	-	-	-	-
Other Transformation	-	0.14	-0.15	-	-	-	-	-	-	-	-0.01
Own Use	-	-	-0.57	-0.26	-	-	-	-0.00	-0.40	-	-1.22
Distribution Losses	-0.03	-	-	-	-	-	-	-	-0.25	-0.25	-0.54
TFC	**0.99**	**-**	**8.94**	**0.86**	**-**	**-**	**0.00**	**4.99**	**7.15**	**3.76**	**26.70**
INDUSTRY SECTOR	**0.96**	**-**	**1.48**	**0.71**	**-**	**-**	**-**	**3.82**	**3.97**	**1.41**	**12.35**
Iron and Steel	0.55 e	-	0.14	0.06	-	-	-	-	0.29	-	1.04
Chemical and Petrochem.	0.09	-	0.17	0.03	-	-	-	0.02	0.41	-	0.72
Non-Ferrous Metals	0.03	-	0.02	-	-	-	-	-	0.18	-	0.23
Non-Metallic Minerals	0.08	-	0.10	0.04	-	-	-	0.00	0.08	-	0.32
Transport Equipment	-	-	0.02	-	-	-	-	-	0.02	-	0.04
Machinery	-	-	0.02	0.01	-	-	-	0.00	0.19	-	0.22
Mining and Quarrying	-	-	0.01	-	-	-	-	-	0.05	-	0.06
Food and Tobacco	0.01	-	0.07	0.04	-	-	-	0.01	0.14	-	0.26
Paper, Pulp and Printing	0.20	-	0.31	0.52	-	-	-	3.62	2.26	-	6.91
Wood and Wood Products	-	-	0.04	0.01	-	-	-	0.11	0.14	-	0.30
Construction	-	-	0.32	-	-	-	-	-	0.02	-	0.34
Textile and Leather	-	-	0.03	0.01	-	-	-	0.00	0.02	-	0.06
Non-specified	-	-	0.23	-	-	-	-	0.05	0.16	1.41	1.85
TRANSPORT SECTOR	**-**	**-**	**4.84**	**0.02**	**-**	**-**	**-**	**0.00**	**0.05**	**-**	**4.92**
International Aviation	-	-	0.43	-	-	-	-	-	-	-	0.43
Domestic Aviation	-	-	0.14	-	-	-	-	-	-	-	0.14
Road	-	-	4.01	0.00	-	-	-	0.00	-	-	4.02
Rail	-	-	0.04	-	-	-	-	-	0.05	-	0.09
Pipeline Transport	-	-	-	0.02	-	-	-	-	-	-	0.02
Domestic Navigation	-	-	0.21	-	-	-	-	-	-	-	0.21
Non-specified	-	-	-	-	-	-	-	-	0.01	-	0.01
OTHER SECTORS	**0.03**	**-**	**1.68**	**0.07**	**-**	**-**	**0.00**	**1.16**	**3.13**	**2.35**	**8.43**
Residential	0.02	-	0.69	0.03	-	-	0.00	0.98	1.75	1.39	4.85
Comm. and Publ. Services	0.01	-	0.32	0.03	-	-	-	0.07	1.30	-	1.73
Agriculture/Forestry	-	-	0.51	0.01	-	-	-	0.12	0.07	-	0.72
Fishing	0.00	-	0.04	-	-	-	-	-	-	-	0.04
Non-specified	-	-	0.11	-	-	-	-	0.00	-	0.97	1.08
NON-ENERGY USE	**-**	**-**	**0.94**	**0.05**	**-**	**-**	**-**	**-**	**-**	**-**	**0.99**
in Industry/Transf./Energy	-	-	0.94	0.05	-	-	-	-	-	-	0.99
of which: Feedstocks	-	-	*0.44*	*0.05*	-	-	-	-	-	-	*0.49*
in Transport	-	-	-	-	-	-	-	-	-	-	-
in Other Sectors	-	-	-	-	-	-	-	-	-	-	-
Electricity Generated - TWh	***23.66***	**-**	***0.62***	***12.78***	***22.72***	***15.07***	***0.12***	***10.63***	**-**	***0.26***	***85.85***
Electricity Plants	*15.74*	-	*0.16*	*1.38*	*22.72*	*15.07*	*0.12*	*1.40*	-	*0.08*	*56.66*
CHP plants	*7.92*	-	*0.46*	*11.40*	-	-	-	*9.23*	-	*0.18*	*29.19*
Heat Generated - PJ	***63.34***	**-**	***13.45***	***51.55***	**-**	**-**	***3.72***	***34.81***	***0.08***	***3.05***	***170.00***
CHP plants	*57.36*	-	*2.99*	*39.80*	-	-	-	*28.03*	-	*0.60*	*128.78*
Heat Plants	*5.98*	-	*10.46*	*11.75*	-	-	*3.72*	*6.78*	*0.08*	*2.45*	*41.22*

Finland / Finlande : 2005

Million tonnes of oil equivalent / *Million de tonnes d'équivalent pétrole*

SUPPLY AND CONSUMPTION ***APPROVISIONNEMENT ET DEMANDE***	Coal *Charbon*	Crude Oil *Pétrole brut*	Petroleum Products *Produits pétroliers*	Gas *Gaz*	Nuclear *Nucléaire*	Hydro *Hydro*	Geotherm. Solar etc. *Géotherm. solaire etc.*	Combust. Renew. & Waste *Comb. ren. & déchets*	Electricity *Electricité*	Heat *Chaleur*	Total *Total*
Production	2.13	0.09	-	-	6.06	1.19	0.10	6.92	-	0.07	16.56
Imports	3.36	11.27	5.12	3.60	-	-	-	0.00	1.54	-	24.88
Exports	-0.01	-	-5.21	-	-	-	-	-0.08	-0.08	-	-5.38
Intl. Marine Bunkers	-	-	-0.50	-	-	-	-	-	-	-	-0.50
Stock Changes	-0.54	0.18	-0.25	-	-	-	-	-	-	-	-0.61
TPES	**4.93**	**11.54**	**-0.83**	**3.60**	**6.06**	**1.19**	**0.10**	**6.84**	**1.46**	**0.07**	**34.96**
Transfers	-	1.55	-1.53	-	-	-	-	-	-	-	0.03
Statistical Differences	-0.09	0.15	-0.60	0.01	-	-	-	-	-	-	-0.53
Electricity Plants	-0.96	-	-0.03	-0.06	-6.06	-1.19	-0.01	-0.29	3.72	-0.04	-4.92
CHP Plants	-2.23	-	-0.13	-2.13	-	-	-	-1.78	2.35	2.89	-1.03
Heat Plants	-0.17	-	-0.27	-0.29	-	-	-0.08	-0.22	-0.00	0.93	-0.11
Gas Works	-	-	-	-	-	-	-	-	-	-	-
Petroleum Refineries	-	-13.40	13.30	-	-	-	-	-	-	-	-0.10
Coal Transformation	-0.46 e	-	-0.30	-	-	-	-	-	-	-	-0.75
Liquefaction Plants	-	-	-	-	-	-	-	-	-	-	-
Other Transformation	-	0.16	-0.18	-	-	-	-	-	-	-	-0.02
Own Use	-	-	-0.58	-0.25	-	-	-	-0.00	-0.31	-	-1.14
Distribution Losses	-0.03	-	-	-	-	-	-	-	-0.26	-0.26	-0.54
TFC	**1.00**	**-**	**8.87**	**0.87**	**-**	**-**	**0.00**	**4.55**	**6.96**	**3.60**	**25.85**
INDUSTRY SECTOR	**0.97**	**-**	**1.39**	**0.72**	**-**	**-**	**-**	**3.39**	**3.72**	**1.29**	**11.49**
Iron and Steel	0.54 e	-	0.12	0.06	-	-	-	-	0.28	-	1.00
Chemical and Petrochem.	0.10	-	0.20	0.03	-	-	-	0.02	0.40	-	0.75
Non-Ferrous Metals	0.03	-	0.02	-	-	-	-	-	0.18	-	0.22
Non-Metallic Minerals	0.10	-	0.10	0.05	-	-	-	0.00	0.09	-	0.34
Transport Equipment	-	-	0.02	-	-	-	-	-	0.03	-	0.04
Machinery	-	-	0.02	0.01	-	-	-	0.00	0.19	-	0.22
Mining and Quarrying	-	-	0.01	-	-	-	-	-	0.05	-	0.07
Food and Tobacco	0.01	-	0.06	0.04	-	-	-	0.01	0.14	-	0.25
Paper, Pulp and Printing	0.19	-	0.29	0.52	-	-	-	3.22	2.03	-	6.24
Wood and Wood Products	-	-	0.04	0.01	-	-	-	0.11	0.14	-	0.30
Construction	-	-	0.32	-	-	-	-	-	0.02	-	0.34
Textile and Leather	-	-	0.03	0.01	-	-	-	0.00	0.02	-	0.06
Non-specified	-	-	0.17	-	-	-	-	0.03	0.16	1.29	1.66
TRANSPORT SECTOR	**-**	**-**	**4.87**	**0.02**	**-**	**-**	**-**	**-**	**0.06**	**-**	**4.94**
International Aviation	-	-	0.43	-	-	-	-	-	-	-	0.43
Domestic Aviation	-	-	0.16	-	-	-	-	-	-	-	0.16
Road	-	-	4.04	0.00	-	-	-	-	-	-	4.04
Rail	-	-	0.04	-	-	-	-	-	0.05	-	0.09
Pipeline Transport	-	-	-	0.02	-	-	-	-	-	-	0.02
Domestic Navigation	-	-	0.20	-	-	-	-	-	-	-	0.20
Non-specified	-	-	-	-	-	-	-	-	0.01	-	0.01
OTHER SECTORS	**0.03**	**-**	**1.60**	**0.07**	**-**	**-**	**0.00**	**1.16**	**3.18**	**2.30**	**8.35**
Residential	0.02	-	0.65	0.03	-	-	0.00	0.97	1.77	1.43	4.86
Comm. and Publ. Services	0.01	-	0.30	0.03	-	-	-	0.07	1.34	-	1.74
Agriculture/Forestry	-	-	0.51	0.01	-	-	-	0.12	0.07	-	0.72
Fishing	0.00	-	0.04	-	-	-	-	-	-	-	0.04
Non-specified	-	-	0.11	-	-	-	-	0.00	-	0.87	0.99
NON-ENERGY USE	**-**	**-**	**1.01**	**0.05**	**-**	**-**	**-**	**-**	**-**	**-**	**1.06**
in Industry/Transf./Energy	-	-	1.01	0.05	-	-	-	-	-	-	1.06
of which: Feedstocks	-	-	*0.46*	*0.05*	-	-	-	-	-	-	*0.52*
in Transport	-	-	-	-	-	-	-	-	-	-	-
in Other Sectors	-	-	-	-	-	-	-	-	-	-	-
Electricity Generated - TWh	***11.66***	-	***0.50***	***11.25***	***23.27***	***13.78***	***0.17***	***9.66***	-	***0.25***	***70.55***
Electricity Plants	*4.24*	-	*0.13*	*0.25*	*23.27*	*13.78*	*0.17*	*1.19*	-	*0.07*	*43.09*
CHP plants	*7.42*	-	*0.37*	*11.00*	-	-	-	*8.48*	-	*0.18*	*27.46*
Heat Generated - PJ	***58.43***	-	***12.43***	***49.49***	-	-	***3.43***	***36.18***	***0.06***	***3.06***	***163.09***
CHP plants	*52.05*	-	*2.49*	*38.21*	-	-	-	*28.42*	-	*0.51*	*121.68*
Heat Plants	*6.38*	-	*9.94*	*11.28*	-	-	*3.43*	*7.76*	*0.06*	*2.56*	*41.41*

France
Key Indicators
Indicateurs principaux

	1960	1970	1973	1980	1990	1995
Energy Production (Mtoe)	45.30	50.09	44.21	52.60	112.43	128.53
Net Imports (Mtoe)	38.45	111.82	148.15	148.96	119.62	115.60
Total Primary Energy Supply (Mtoe)	79.47	154.69	184.65	193.57	227.82	241.37
Net Oil Imports (Mtoe)	28.96	98.87	131.35	112.28	86.16	84.99
Oil Supply (Mtoe)	28.80	93.64	124.32	108.12	87.28	85.00
Electricity Consumption (TWh)*	68.19	136.49	168.28	243.92	347.59	394.07
GDP (billion 2000 US$ using exch. rates)	351.91 e	604.94	697.97	841.13	1 088.25	1 156.70
GDP (billion 2000 US$ using PPPs)	417.32 e	717.39	827.71	997.49	1 290.53	1 371.70
Population (millions)	46.71 e	51.91	53.30	55.11	58.17	59.42
Industrial Production Index (2000=100)	33.80	57.20	69.00	75.90	86.50	87.00
Energy Production/TPES	0.5700	0.3238	0.2394	0.2717	0.4935	0.5325
Net Oil Imports/GDP (toe per thousand 2000 US$)	0.0823 e	0.1634	0.1882	0.1335	0.0792	0.0735
TPES/GDP (toe per thousand 2000 US$)	0.2258 e	0.2557	0.2646	0.2301	0.2093	0.2087
TPES/GDP (toe per thousand 2000 US$ PPP)	0.1904 e	0.2156	0.2231	0.1941	0.1765	0.1760
TPES/Population (toe per capita)	1.7014 e	2.9798	3.4645	3.5124	3.9163	4.0622
Oil Supply/GDP (toe per thousand 2000 US$)	0.0818 e	0.1548	0.1781	0.1285	0.0802	0.0735
Oil Supply/Population (toe per capita)	0.6166 e	1.8037	2.3326	1.9618	1.5004	1.4305
Elect. Cons./GDP (kWh per 2000 US$)	0.1938 e	0.2256	0.2411	0.2900	0.3194	0.3407
Elect. Cons./Population (kWh per capita)	1 460 e	2 629	3 157	4 426	5 975	6 632
Industry Cons.**/Industrial Production (2000=100)	159.45	204.21	161.47	142.44	104.86	112.32
Industry Oil Cons.**/Industrial Production (2000=100)	148.32	352.93	264.97	209.77	105.95	121.53

	2000	2001	2002	2003	2004	2005
Energy Production (Mtoe)	132.08	133.45	135.24	136.48	137.31	136.89
Net Imports (Mtoe)	132.79	134.72	136.08	137.31	140.27	143.30
Total Primary Energy Supply (Mtoe)	258.36	266.90	266.68	271.33	274.93	275.97
Net Oil Imports (Mtoe)	89.99	94.47	93.39	93.78	93.87	94.18
Oil Supply (Mtoe)	87.25	93.86	91.27	91.13	92.13	91.44
Electricity Consumption (TWh)*	440.89	450.81	451.26	468.79	480.23	483.23
GDP (billion 2000 US$ using exch. rates)	1 327.96	1 352.59	1 366.49	1 381.34	1 413.38	1 430.13
GDP (billion 2000 US$ using PPPs)	1 574.81	1 604.01	1 620.49	1 638.11	1 676.10	1 695.97
Population (millions)	60.71	61.12	61.53	61.93	62.32	62.70
Industrial Production Index (2000=100)	100.00	101.20	100.00	99.60	102.10	102.30
Energy Production/TPES	0.5112	0.5000	0.5071	0.5030	0.4994	0.4960
Net Oil Imports/GDP (toe per thousand 2000 US$)	0.0678	0.0698	0.0683	0.0679	0.0664	0.0659
TPES/GDP (toe per thousand 2000 US$)	0.1946	0.1973	0.1952	0.1964	0.1945	0.1930
TPES/GDP (toe per thousand 2000 US$ PPP)	0.1641	0.1664	0.1646	0.1656	0.1640	0.1627
TPES/Population (toe per capita)	4.2553	4.3668	4.3342	4.3812	4.4113	4.4013
Oil Supply/GDP (toe per thousand 2000 US$)	0.0657	0.0694	0.0668	0.0660	0.0652	0.0639
Oil Supply/Population (toe per capita)	1.4370	1.5356	1.4833	1.4715	1.4783	1.4583
Elect. Cons./GDP (kWh per 2000 US$)	0.3320	0.3333	0.3302	0.3394	0.3398	0.3379
Elect. Cons./Population (kWh per capita)	7 262	7 376	7 334	7 569	7 705	7 707
Industry Cons.**/Industrial Production (2000=100)	100.00	100.74	97.93	99.73	95.86	95.58
Industry Oil Cons.**/Industrial Production (2000=100)	100.00	103.91	97.63	98.91	98.12	97.67

* Electricity consumption equals domestic supply less distribution losses.
La consommation d'électricité représente l'approvisionnement intérieur diminué des pertes de distribution.

** Includes non-energy use in industry/transformation/energy sectors.
Comprend l'usage non-énergétique dans les secteurs de l'industrie/transformation/énergie.

France

Figure 1. TPES* in 1973

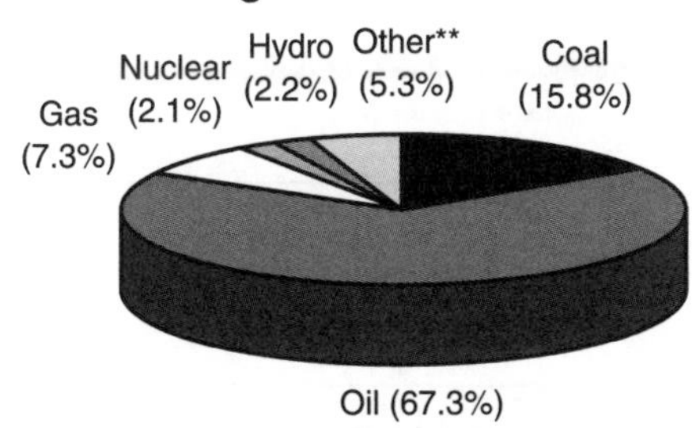

Figure 2. TPES* in 2005

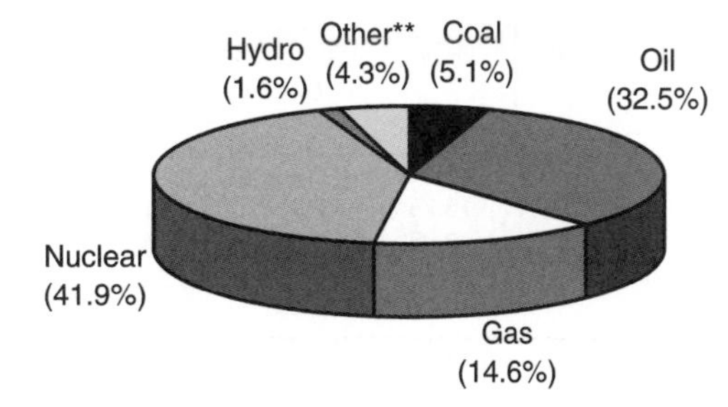

Figure 3. Final Consumption by Sector***

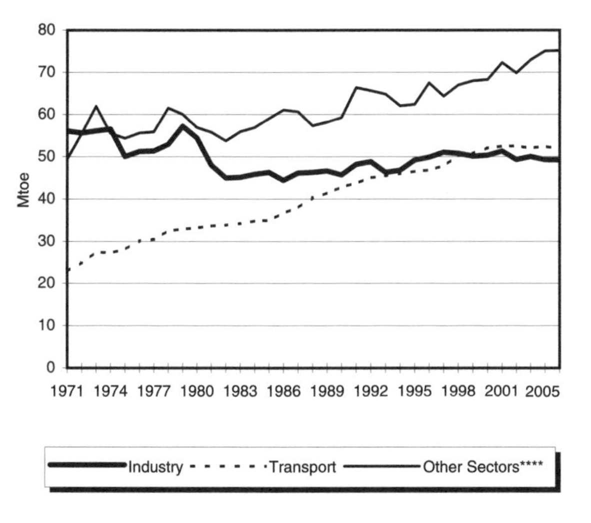

Figure 4. Breakdown of Sectorial Final Consumption by Source in 1973 and 2005***

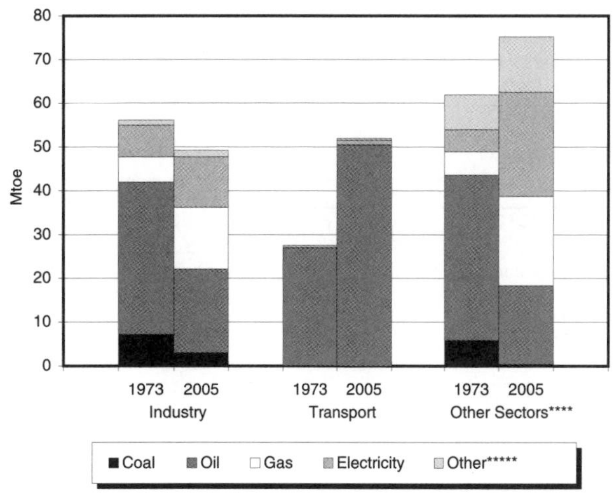

Figure 5. Electricity Generation by Fuel

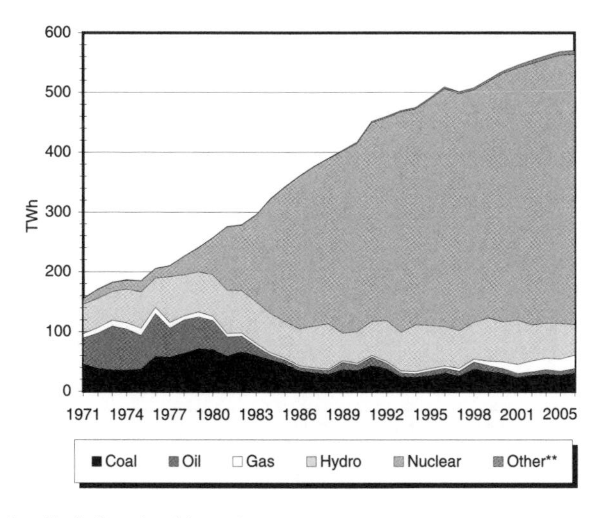

Figure 6. Electricity Consumption/GDP, TPES/GDP and Energy Production/TPES

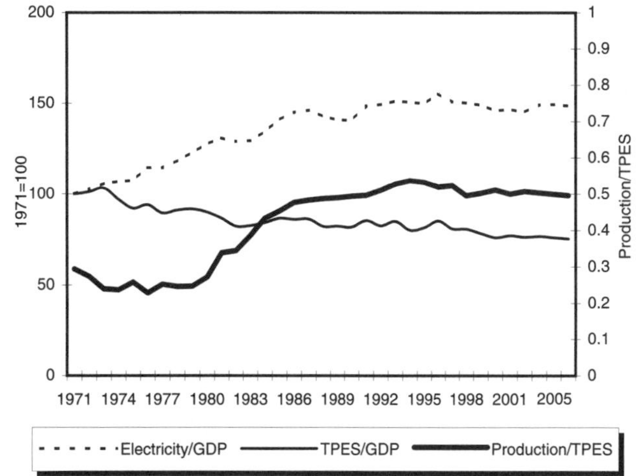

* Excluding electricity trade.

** Includes geothermal, solar, wind, combustible renewables & waste, etc.

*** Includes non-energy use.

**** Includes residential, commercial and public services, agriculture/forestry, fishing and non-specified.

***** Includes comb. renewables & waste, direct use of geothermal/solar thermal and heat produced in CHP/heat plants.

France : 2004

Million tonnes of oil equivalent / *Million de tonnes d'équivalent pétrole*

SUPPLY AND CONSUMPTION *APPROVISIONNEMENT ET DEMANDE*	Coal *Charbon*	Crude Oil *Pétrole brut*	Petroleum Products *Produits pétroliers*	Gas *Gaz*	Nuclear *Nucléaire*	Hydro *Hydro*	Geotherm. Solar etc. *Géotherm. solaire etc.*	Combust. Renew. & Waste *Comb. ren. & déchets*	Electricity *Electricité*	Heat *Chaleur*	Total *Total*
Production	0.54	1.53	-	1.11	116.81	5.14	0.25	11.93	-	-	137.31
Imports	13.75	85.10	33.11	39.92	-	-	-	-	0.57	-	172.44
Exports	-0.63	-0.06	-24.28	-1.26	-	-	-	-0.06	-5.88	-	-32.17
Intl. Marine Bunkers	-	-	-3.16	-	-	-	-	-	-	-	-3.16
Stock Changes	0.25	0.02	-0.12	0.37	-	-	-	-	-	-	0.52
TPES	**13.90**	**86.59**	**5.54**	**40.14**	**116.81**	**5.14**	**0.25**	**11.87**	**-5.32**	**-**	**274.93**
Transfers	-	0.20	-0.06	-	-	-	-	-	-	-	0.14
Statistical Differences	-0.57	0.65	-0.29	-0.04	-	-	-	0.01	-	-	-0.25
Electricity Plants	-5.98	-	-1.21	-0.15	-116.81	-5.14	-0.10	-0.63	46.77	-	-83.25
CHP Plants	-0.49	-	-0.19	-4.78	-	-	-	-1.03	2.13	3.97	-0.39
Heat Plants	-	-	-	-	-	-	-	-0.27	-	0.15	-0.12
Gas Works	-	-	-	-	-	-	-	-	-	-	-
Petroleum Refineries	-	-89.09	91.28	-	-	-	-	-	-	-	2.19
Coal Transformation	-2.81 e	-	-0.03	-	-	-	-	-	-	-	-2.84
Liquefaction Plants	-	-	-	-	-	-	-	-	-	-	-
Other Transformation	-	1.65	-1.75	-	-	-	-	-	-	-	-0.10
Own Use	-0.50	-	-4.81	-0.05	-	-	-	-	-4.76	-	-10.12
Distribution Losses	-	-	-	-0.65	-	-	-	-	-2.73	-	-3.38
TFC	**3.55**	**-**	**88.49**	**34.46**	**-**	**-**	**0.15**	**9.95**	**36.09**	**4.12**	**176.81**
INDUSTRY SECTOR	**3.14**	**-**	**6.72**	**12.15**	**-**	**-**	**-**	**1.48**	**11.75**	**-**	**35.24**
Iron and Steel	2.00 e	-	0.02	0.62	-	-	-	-	1.42	-	4.06
Chemical and Petrochem.	0.37	-	2.41	2.26	-	-	-	-	1.86	-	6.90
Non-Ferrous Metals	-	-	0.07	0.27	-	-	-	-	0.87	-	1.21
Non-Metallic Minerals	0.20	-	1.42	1.85	-	-	-	-	0.77	-	4.25
Transport Equipment	0.01	-	0.07	0.73	-	-	-	-	0.72	-	1.54
Machinery	0.03	-	0.19	0.93	-	-	-	-	1.19	-	2.35
Mining and Quarrying	-	-	0.10	0.06	-	-	-	-	0.15	-	0.31
Food and Tobacco	0.39	-	0.62	2.40	-	-	-	0.06	1.66	-	5.12
Paper, Pulp and Printing	0.13	-	0.18	1.24	-	-	-	0.58	1.15	-	3.28
Wood and Wood Products	-	-	0.02	-	-	-	-	0.84	0.19	-	1.05
Construction	..	-	1.12	0.19	-	-	-	-	0.14	-	1.45
Textile and Leather	-	-	0.07	1.24	-	-	-	-	0.24	-	1.56
Non-specified	0.02	-	0.41	0.37	-	-	-	-	1.38	-	2.18
TRANSPORT SECTOR	**-**	**-**	**50.58**	**0.04**	**-**	**-**	**-**	**0.37**	**1.07**	**-**	**52.06**
International Aviation	-	-	5.60	-	-	-	-	-	-	-	5.60
Domestic Aviation	-	-	1.46	-	-	-	-	-	-	-	1.46
Road	-	-	42.96	0.04	-	-	-	0.37	-	-	43.37
Rail	-	-	0.24	-	-	-	-	-	0.78	-	1.03
Pipeline Transport	-	-	-	-	-	-	-	-	-	-	-
Domestic Navigation	-	-	0.31	-	-	-	-	-	-	-	0.31
Non-specified	-	-	-	-	-	-	-	-	0.28	-	0.28
OTHER SECTORS	**0.41**	**-**	**18.39**	**20.56**	**-**	**-**	**0.15**	**8.10**	**23.27**	**4.12**	**74.99**
Residential	0.41	-	10.34	14.76	-	-	0.14	7.70	12.71	-	46.06
Comm. and Publ. Services	-	-	5.16	5.47	-	-	-	0.36	10.08	-	21.08
Agriculture/Forestry	-	-	2.36	0.33	-	-	0.01	0.04	0.27	-	3.01
Fishing	-	-	0.42	-	-	-	-	-	0.01	-	0.43
Non-specified	-	-	0.10	-	-	-	-	-	0.19	4.12	4.42
NON-ENERGY USE	**-**	**-**	**12.81**	**1.71**	**-**	**-**	**-**	**-**	**-**	**-**	**14.52**
in Industry/Transf./Energy	-	-	12.35	1.71	-	-	-	-	-	-	14.06
of which: Feedstocks	-	-	*8.62*	*1.71*	-	-	-	-	-	-	*10.33*
in Transport	-	-	0.39	-	-	-	-	-	-	-	0.39
in Other Sectors	-	-	0.07	-	-	-	-	-	-	-	0.07
Electricity Generated - TWh	***27.24***	**-**	***6.53***	***20.62***	***448.24***	***59.82***	***1.13***	***5.02***	**-**	**-**	***568.58***
Electricity Plants	*26.38*	-	*5.02*	*0.56*	*448.24*	*59.82*	*1.13*	*2.69*	-	-	*543.83*
CHP plants	*0.86*	-	*1.51*	*20.05*	-	-	-	*2.33*	-	-	*24.75*
Heat Generated - PJ	***15.38***	**-**	***28.29***	***102.11***	**-**	**-**	**-**	***26.93***	**-**	**-**	***172.71***
CHP plants	*15.38*	-	*28.29*	*102.11*	-	-	-	*20.67*	-	-	*166.46*
Heat Plants	-	-	-	-	-	-	-	*6.26*	-	-	*6.26*

France : 2005

Million tonnes of oil equivalent / *Million de tonnes d'équivalent pétrole*

SUPPLY AND CONSUMPTION / ***APPROVISIONNEMENT ET DEMANDE***	Coal / *Charbon*	Crude Oil / *Pétrole brut*	Petroleum Products / *Produits pétroliers*	Gas / *Gaz*	Nuclear / *Nucléaire*	Hydro / *Hydro*	Geotherm. Solar etc. / *Géotherm. solaire etc.*	Combust. Renew. & Waste / *Comb. ren. & déchets*	Electricity / *Electricité*	Heat / *Chaleur*	Total / *Total*
Production	0.38	1.31	-	0.83	117.67	4.45	0.28	11.97	-	-	136.89
Imports	14.12	84.14	37.93	41.61	-	-	-	-	0.69	-	178.49
Exports	-0.47	-0.05	-27.85	-0.90	-	-	-	-0.06	-5.88	-	-35.19
Intl. Marine Bunkers	-	-	-2.90	-	-	-	-	-	-	-	-2.90
Stock Changes	0.39	0.19	-1.34	-0.55	-	-	-	-	-	-	-1.32
TPES	**14.42**	**85.60**	**5.84**	**40.98**	**117.67**	**4.45**	**0.28**	**11.91**	**-5.19**	**-**	**275.97**
Transfers	-	0.06	0.04	-	-	-	-	-	-	-	0.11
Statistical Differences	-0.49	-0.29	0.60	0.00	-	-	-	-0.01	-	-	-0.18
Electricity Plants	-6.69	-	-1.45	-0.16	-117.67	-4.45	-0.13	-0.62	46.72	-	-84.45
CHP Plants	-0.55	-	-1.22	-5.30	-	-	-	-1.02	2.35	4.35	-1.39
Heat Plants	-	-	-	-	-	-	-	-0.27	-	0.15	-0.13
Gas Works	-	-	-	-	-	-	-	-	-	-	-
Petroleum Refineries	-	-86.99	89.07	-	-	-	-	-	-	-	2.08
Coal Transformation	-2.86 e	-	-0.04	-	-	-	-	-	-	-	-2.90
Liquefaction Plants	-	-	-	-	-	-	-	-	-	-	-
Other Transformation	-	1.62	-1.72	-	-	-	-	-	-	-	-0.10
Own Use	-0.45	-	-3.75	-0.16	-	-	-	-	-4.82	-	-9.18
Distribution Losses	-	-	-	-0.69	-	-	-	-	-2.74	-	-3.42
TFC	**3.38**	**-**	**87.37**	**34.68**	**-**	**-**	**0.15**	**9.99**	**36.34**	**4.49**	**176.40**
INDUSTRY SECTOR	**3.02**	**-**	**6.76**	**12.38**	**-**	**-**	**-**	**1.52**	**11.51**	**-**	**35.20**
Iron and Steel	1.89 e	-	0.01	0.61	-	-	-	-	1.35	-	3.86
Chemical and Petrochem.	0.40	-	2.66	2.62	-	-	-	-	2.05	-	7.73
Non-Ferrous Metals	0.01	-	0.07	0.29	-	-	-	-	0.84	-	1.21
Non-Metallic Minerals	0.18	-	1.31	1.91	-	-	-	-	0.75	-	4.16
Transport Equipment	0.01	-	0.05	0.73	-	-	-	-	0.71	-	1.49
Machinery	0.02	-	0.32	0.81	-	-	-	-	1.17	-	2.32
Mining and Quarrying	-	-	0.11	0.04	-	-	-	-	0.14	-	0.30
Food and Tobacco	0.36	-	0.48	2.21	-	-	-	0.06	1.68	-	4.79
Paper, Pulp and Printing	0.12	-	0.14	1.28	-	-	-	0.60	1.16	-	3.29
Wood and Wood Products	-	-	0.04	-	-	-	-	0.87	0.21	-	1.12
Construction	..	-	1.06	0.28	-	-	-	-	0.15	-	1.48
Textile and Leather	-	-	0.11	1.28	-	-	-	-	0.22	-	1.60
Non-specified	0.03	-	0.41	0.34	-	-	-	-	1.06	-	1.85
TRANSPORT SECTOR	**-**	**-**	**50.04**	**0.05**	**-**	**-**	**-**	**0.42**	**1.05**	**-**	**51.57**
International Aviation	-	-	5.67	-	-	-	-	-	-	-	5.67
Domestic Aviation	-	-	1.40	-	-	-	-	-	-	-	1.40
Road	-	-	42.44	0.05	-	-	-	0.42	-	-	42.91
Rail	-	-	0.22	-	-	-	-	-	0.76	-	0.98
Pipeline Transport	-	-	-	-	-	-	-	-	-	-	-
Domestic Navigation	-	-	0.31	-	-	-	-	-	-	-	0.31
Non-specified	-	-	-	-	-	-	-	-	0.29	-	0.29
OTHER SECTORS	**0.36**	**-**	**17.85**	**20.45**	**-**	**-**	**0.15**	**8.04**	**23.77**	**4.49**	**75.12**
Residential	0.36	-	10.11	14.45	-	-	0.14	7.65	12.88	-	45.59
Comm. and Publ. Services	-	-	4.95	5.70	-	-	-	0.35	10.44	-	21.44
Agriculture/Forestry	-	-	2.31	0.30	-	-	0.01	0.04	0.28	-	2.94
Fishing	-	-	0.41	-	-	-	-	-	0.01	-	0.42
Non-specified	-	-	0.08	-	-	-	-	-	0.16	4.49	4.73
NON-ENERGY USE	**-**	**-**	**12.71**	**1.80**	**-**	**-**	**-**	**-**	**-**	**-**	**14.51**
in Industry/Transf./Energy	-	-	12.25	1.80	-	-	-	-	-	-	14.05
of which: Feedstocks	-	-	*8.63*	*1.80*	-	-	-	-	-	-	*10.44*
in Transport	-	-	0.39	-	-	-	-	-	-	-	0.39
in Other Sectors	-	-	0.07	-	-	-	-	-	-	-	0.07
Electricity Generated - TWh	***30.64***	**-**	***7.23***	***22.96***	***451.53***	***51.70***	***1.51***	***5.08***	**-**	**-**	***570.65***
Electricity Plants	*29.67*	-	*5.56*	*0.62*	*451.53*	*51.70*	*1.51*	*2.72*	-	-	*543.31*
CHP plants	*0.97*	-	*1.67*	*22.34*	-	-	-	*2.36*	-	-	*27.34*
Heat Generated - PJ	***17.34***	**-**	***31.30***	***113.10***	**-**	**-**	**-**	***26.37***	**-**	**-**	***188.10***
CHP plants	*17.34*	-	*31.30*	*113.10*	-	-	-	*20.28*	-	-	*182.01*
Heat Plants	-	-	-	-	-	-	-	*6.10*	-	-	*6.10*

Germany / Allemagne
Key Indicators
Indicateurs principaux

	1960	1970	1973	1980	1990	1995
Energy Production (Mtoe)	125.26	174.69	171.65	185.63	186.16	145.03
Net Imports (Mtoe)	16.50	134.98	171.44	183.86	167.85	196.11
Total Primary Energy Supply (Mtoe)	142.65	304.45	337.88	360.39	356.22	342.40
Net Oil Imports (Mtoe)	29.09	135.30	161.22	149.34	122.70	132.55
Oil Supply (Mtoe)	31.08	137.92	161.88	147.07	126.47	135.64
Electricity Consumption (TWh)*	115.54	299.72	367.45	453.88	527.41	516.84
GDP (billion 2000 US$ using exch. rates)	597.23 e	921.64	1 038.75	1 225.93	1 543.20	1 720.46
GDP (billion 2000 US$ using PPPs)	660.44 e	1 019.19	1 148.69	1 355.69	1 706.54	1 902.56
Population (millions)	71.22 e	77.71	78.96	78.30	79.36	81.66
Industrial Production Index (2000=100)	35.70	62.60	69.70	75.20	90.70	87.40
Energy Production/TPES	0.8781	0.5738	0.5080	0.5151	0.5226	0.4236
Net Oil Imports/GDP (toe per thousand 2000 US$)	0.0487 e	0.1468	0.1552	0.1218	0.0795	0.0770
TPES/GDP (toe per thousand 2000 US$)	0.2389 e	0.3303	0.3253	0.2940	0.2308	0.1990
TPES/GDP (toe per thousand 2000 US$ PPP)	0.2160 e	0.2987	0.2941	0.2658	0.2087	0.1800
TPES/Population (toe per capita)	2.0030 e	3.9178	4.2794	4.6024	4.4884	4.1929
Oil Supply/GDP (toe per thousand 2000 US$)	0.0520 e	0.1497	0.1558	0.1200	0.0820	0.0788
Oil Supply/Population (toe per capita)	0.4365 e	1.7749	2.0503	1.8782	1.5935	1.6610
Elect. Cons./GDP (kWh per 2000 US$)	0.1935 e	0.3252	0.3537	0.3702	0.3418	0.3004
Elect. Cons./Population (kWh per capita)	1 622 e	3 857	4 654	5 796	6 646	6 329
Industry Cons. **/Industrial Production (2000=100)***	167.53	194.08	194.12	173.32	125.79	114.45
Industry Oil Cons./Industrial Production (2000=100)**	88.20	231.21	239.93	174.37	106.12	117.96

	2000	2001	2002	2003	2004	2005
Energy Production (Mtoe)	135.34	134.71	134.51	134.64	136.19	134.50
Net Imports (Mtoe)	206.14	217.23	209.82	213.81	215.76	214.47
Total Primary Energy Supply (Mtoe)	343.62	353.52	345.25	347.18	348.22	344.75
Net Oil Imports (Mtoe)	127.38	132.90	124.45	126.30	122.41	123.43
Oil Supply (Mtoe)	131.72	134.49	128.83	126.51	125.21	123.40
Electricity Consumption (TWh)*	549.18 e	564.23 e	556.09 e	569.39 e	579.98 e	586.41
GDP (billion 2000 US$ using exch. rates)	1 900.22	1 923.78	1 923.78	1 920.17	1 944.12	1 961.79
GDP (billion 2000 US$ using PPPs)	2 101.35	2 127.41	2 127.41	2 123.41	2 149.89	2 169.43
Population (millions)	82.19	82.34	82.48	82.52	82.50	82.46
Industrial Production Index (2000=100)	100.00	100.20	99.10	99.60	102.60	106.10
Energy Production/TPES	0.3939	0.3810	0.3896	0.3878	0.3911	0.3902
Net Oil Imports/GDP (toe per thousand 2000 US$)	0.0670	0.0691	0.0647	0.0658	0.0630	0.0629
TPES/GDP (toe per thousand 2000 US$)	0.1808	0.1838	0.1795	0.1808	0.1791	0.1757
TPES/GDP (toe per thousand 2000 US$ PPP)	0.1635	0.1662	0.1623	0.1635	0.1620	0.1589
TPES/Population (toe per capita)	4.1809	4.2934	4.1858	4.2073	4.2208	4.1806
Oil Supply/GDP (toe per thousand 2000 US$)	0.0693	0.0699	0.0670	0.0659	0.0644	0.0629
Oil Supply/Population (toe per capita)	1.6027	1.6334	1.5619	1.5331	1.5176	1.4964
Elect. Cons./GDP (kWh per 2000 US$)	0.2890 e	0.2933 e	0.2891 e	0.2965 e	0.2983 e	0.2989
Elect. Cons./Population (kWh per capita)	6 682 e	6 852 e	6 742 e	6 900 e	7 030 e	7 111
Industry Cons. **/Industrial Production (2000=100)***	100.00	98.81	99.17	106.02	103.98	100.16
Industry Oil Cons./Industrial Production (2000=100)**	100.00	97.78	98.81	96.48	94.67	89.75

* Electricity consumption equals domestic supply less distribution losses.
La consommation d'électricité représente l'approvisionnement intérieur diminué des pertes de distribution.

** Includes non-energy use in industry/transformation/energy sectors.
Comprend l'usage non-énergétique dans les secteurs de l'industrie/transformation/énergie.

*** From 1991 the industrial production index refers to unified Germany and has been linked to the series for western Germany.
A partir de 1991, l'indice de production se réfère à l'Allemagne unifiée et a été rattaché à la série de l'Allemagne occidentale.

Germany / Allemagne

Figure 1. TPES* in 1973

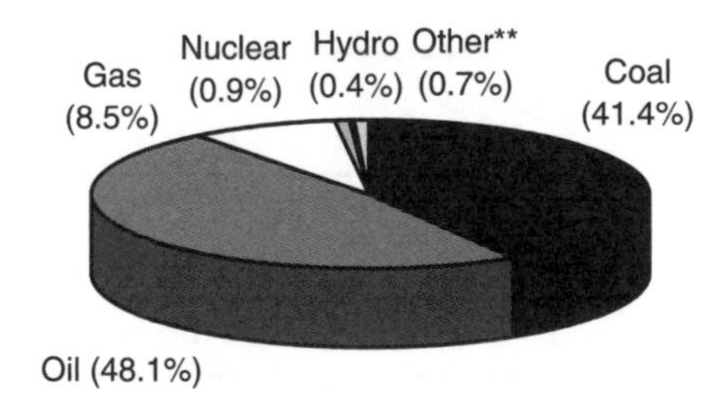

Figure 2. TPES* in 2005

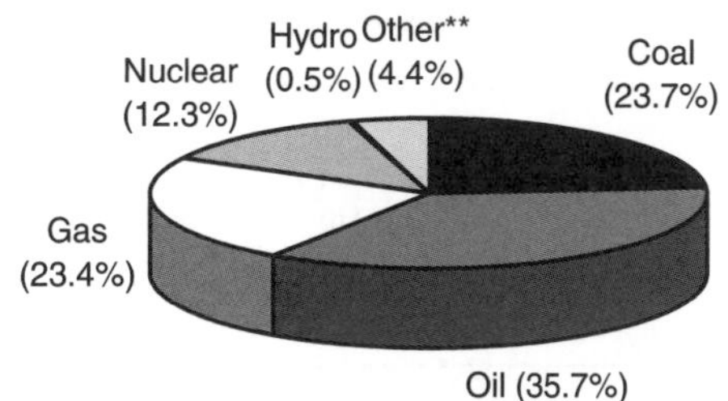

Figure 3. Final Consumption by Sector***

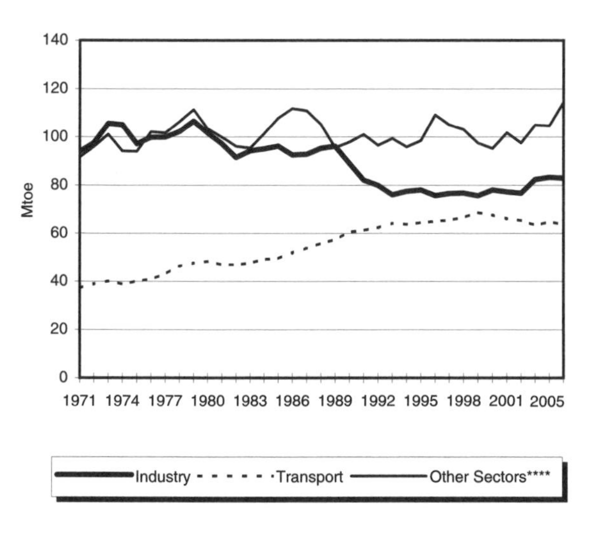

Figure 4. Breakdown of Sectorial Final Consumption by Source in 1973 and 2005***

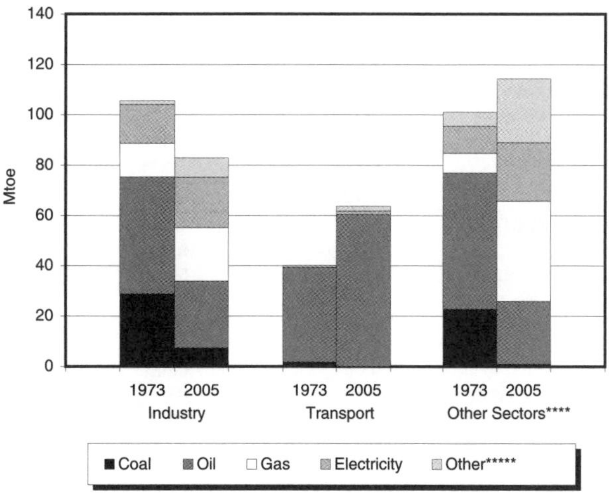

Figure 5. Electricity Generation by Fuel

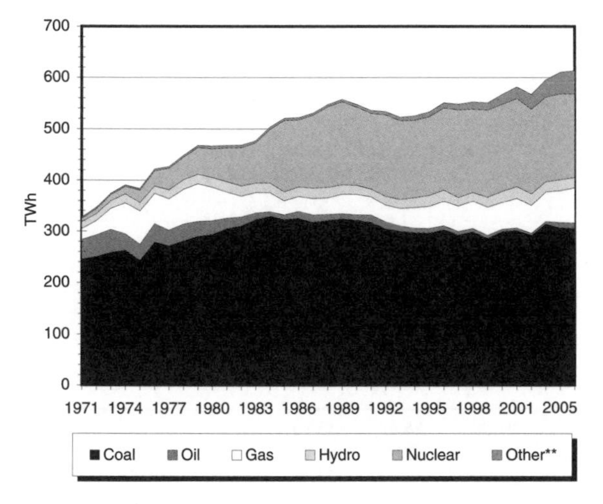

Figure 6. Electricity Consumption/GDP, TPES/GDP and Energy Production/TPES

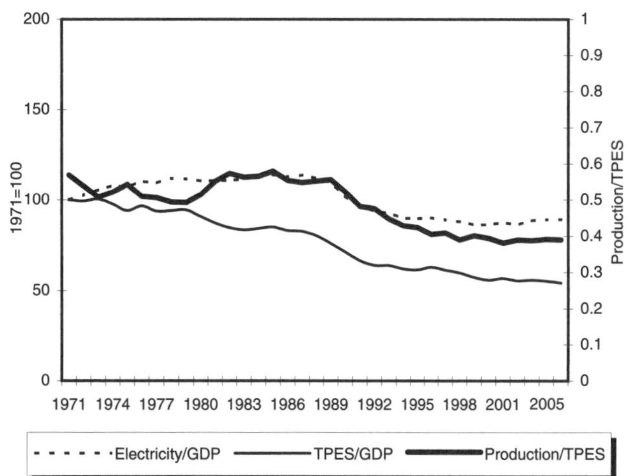

* Excluding electricity trade.

** Includes geothermal, solar, wind, combustible renewables & waste, etc.

*** Includes non-energy use.

**** Includes residential, commercial and public services, agriculture/forestry, fishing and non-specified.

***** Includes comb. renewables & waste, direct use of geothermal/solar thermal and heat produced in CHP/heat plants.

Germany / Allemagne : 2004

Million tonnes of oil equivalent / *Million de tonnes d'équivalent pétrole*

SUPPLY AND CONSUMPTION / *APPROVISIONNEMENT ET DEMANDE*	Coal / *Charbon*	Crude Oil / *Pétrole brut*	Petroleum Products / *Produits pétroliers*	Gas / *Gaz*	Nuclear / *Nucléaire*	Hydro / *Hydro*	Geotherm. Solar etc. / *Géotherm. solaire etc.*	Combust. Renew. & Waste / *Comb. ren. & déchets*	Electricity / *Electricité*	Heat / *Chaleur*	Total / *Total*
Production	58.33	4.42	-	14.73	43.54	1.81	2.61 e	10.75	-	-	136.19
Imports	28.27	112.46	35.30	72.85	-	-	-	-	4.14	-	253.02
Exports	-0.57	-1.13	-24.21	-6.97	-	-	-	-	-4.37	-0.00 e	-37.26
Intl. Marine Bunkers	-	-	-2.65	-	-	-	-	-	-	-	-2.65
Stock Changes	-0.21	-0.64	1.67	-1.90	-	-	-	-	-	-	-1.08
TPES	**85.83**	**115.11**	**10.10**	**78.71**	**43.54**	**1.81**	**2.61**	**10.75**	**-0.23**	**-0.00**	**348.22**
Transfers	-	3.17	-2.56	-	-	-	-	-	-	-	0.60
Statistical Differences	1.09	0.00	0.42	1.42	-	-	-	-	-	-	2.93
Electricity Plants	-62.76	-	-1.03	-3.85	-43.54	-1.81	-2.24 e	-1.19	45.35 e	-	-71.07
CHP Plants	-9.00	-	-1.16	-12.48	-	-	-	-3.67	7.11 e	15.48 e	-3.72
Heat Plants	-0.55	-	-0.22	-0.40	-	-	-0.02 e	-0.25	-	1.92	0.49
Gas Works	-	-	-0.02	0.02	-	-	-	-	-	-	-0.00
Petroleum Refineries	-	-124.17	124.27	-	-	-	-	-	-	-	0.10
Coal Transformation	-4.86 e	0.04	-1.16	-0.04	-	-	-	-	-	-	-6.02
Liquefaction Plants	-	-	-	-	-	-	-	-	-	-	-
Other Transformation	-	5.86	-6.12	-	-	-	-	-	-	-	-0.26
Own Use	-1.02	-	-6.93	-0.70 e	-	-	-	-0.09	-5.15 e	-	-13.89
Distribution Losses	-0.30	-	-	-0.23 e	-	-	-	-	-2.94 e	-1.36 e	-4.82
TFC	**8.43**	**-**	**115.59**	**62.45**	**-**	**-**	**0.35**	**5.56**	**44.15**	**16.04**	**252.56**
INDUSTRY SECTOR	**6.98**	**-**	**4.03**	**18.98**	**-**	**-**	**-**	**-**	**20.11**	**7.79**	**57.89**
Iron and Steel	4.09 e	-	0.05	2.32 e	-	-	-	-	2.07	-	8.53
Chemical and Petrochem.	0.31	-	0.03	4.94 e	-	-	-	-	4.24	-	9.52
Non-Ferrous Metals	0.08	-	0.13	0.84 e	-	-	-	-	1.63	-	2.68
Non-Metallic Minerals	1.51	-	1.07	2.58 e	-	-	-	-	1.31	-	6.47
Transport Equipment	0.11	-	0.17	0.99 e	-	-	-	-	1.67	-	2.93
Machinery	0.06	-	0.65	1.59 e	-	-	-	-	0.88	-	3.19
Mining and Quarrying	0.19	-	0.07	0.15 e	-	-	-	-	0.18	-	0.59
Food and Tobacco	0.24	-	0.61	2.24 e	-	-	-	-	1.29	-	4.37
Paper, Pulp and Printing	0.33	-	0.19	2.06 e	-	-	-	-	1.91	-	4.49
Wood and Wood Products	0.02	-	0.07	0.16 e	-	-	-	-	0.34	-	0.60
Construction	-	-	0.41	0.12 e	-	-	-	-	0.07	-	0.61
Textile and Leather	0.03	-	0.11	0.37 e	-	-	-	-	0.38	-	0.88
Non-specified	0.01	-	0.49	0.62 e	-	-	-	-	4.13	7.79 e	13.05
TRANSPORT SECTOR	**-**	**-**	**62.08**	**-**	**-**	**-**	**-**	**0.98**	**1.39**	**-**	**64.45**
International Aviation	-	-	6.40	-	-	-	-	-	-	-	6.40
Domestic Aviation	-	-	1.62	-	-	-	-	-	-	-	1.62
Road	-	-	53.26	-	-	-	-	0.98	-	-	54.23
Rail	-	-	0.50	-	-	-	-	-	1.39	-	1.89
Pipeline Transport	-	-	-	-	-	-	-	-	-	-	-
Domestic Navigation	-	-	0.24	-	-	-	-	-	-	-	0.24
Non-specified	-	-	0.07	-	-	-	-	-	-	-	0.07
OTHER SECTORS	**1.30**	**-**	**26.12**	**41.32**	**-**	**-**	**0.35**	**4.58**	**22.64**	**8.25**	**104.56**
Residential	0.67 e	-	17.67	28.37 e	-	-	0.33	4.58	12.07	-	63.71
Comm. and Publ. Services	0.58 e	-	6.64	7.52 e	-	-	0.01	-	9.88 e	-	24.64
Agriculture/Forestry	0.04 e	-	1.70	0.26 e	-	-	-	-	0.68 e	-	2.68
Fishing	-	-	-	-	-	-	-	-	-	-	-
Non-specified	0.01 e	-	0.11	5.16 e	-	-	-	-	-	8.25 e	13.53
NON-ENERGY USE	**0.15**	**-**	**23.36**	**2.15**	**-**	**-**	**-**	**-**	**-**	**-**	**25.67**
in Industry/Transf./Energy	0.15	-	23.00	2.15	-	-	-	-	-	-	25.30
of which: Feedstocks	-	-	*19.30*	*2.15*	-	-	-	-	-	-	*21.45*
in Transport	-	-	0.35	-	-	-	-	-	-	-	0.35
in Other Sectors	-	-	0.01	-	-	-	-	-	-	-	0.01
Electricity Generated - TWh	***306.64***	-	***10.14***	***62.97***	***167.07***	***21.08***	***26.07***	***16.03***	-	-	***609.99***
Electricity Plants	*281.50 e*	-	*6.64*	*20.39 e*	*167.07*	*21.08*	*26.07*	*4.56*	-	-	*527.30*
CHP plants	*25.13 e*	-	*3.50*	*42.58*	-	-	-	*11.47*	-	-	*82.69*
Heat Generated - PJ	***214.86***	-	***38.57***	***316.69***	-	-	***0.41***	***36.63***	-	***121.47***	***728.63***
CHP plants	*199.02 e*	-	*31.75*	*304.62*	-	-	-	*29.94 e*	-	*83.07*	*648.39*
Heat Plants	*15.85 e*	-	*6.82*	*12.07*	-	-	*0.41*	*6.69 e*	-	*38.40*	*80.24*

Germany / Allemagne : 2005

Million tonnes of oil equivalent / *Million de tonnes d'équivalent pétrole*

SUPPLY AND CONSUMPTION / ***APPROVISIONNEMENT ET DEMANDE***	Coal / *Charbon*	Crude Oil / *Pétrole brut*	Petroleum Products / *Produits pétroliers*	Gas / *Gaz*	Nuclear / *Nucléaire*	Hydro / *Hydro*	Geotherm. Solar etc. / *Géotherm. solaire etc.*	Combust. Renew. & Waste / *Comb. ren. & déchets*	Electricity / *Electricité*	Heat / *Chaleur*	Total / *Total*
Production	56.49	4.57	-	14.22	42.49	1.68	2.85 e	12.19	-	-	134.50
Imports	26.35	114.70	36.23	73.51	-	-	-	-	4.89	-	255.68
Exports	-0.63	-0.72	-26.77	-7.79	-	-	-	-	-5.28	-0.00 e	-41.21
Intl. Marine Bunkers	-	-	-2.48	-	-	-	-	-	-	-	-2.48
Stock Changes	-0.52	-0.40	-1.73	0.90	-	-	-	-	-	-	-1.74
TPES	**81.69**	**118.16**	**5.25**	**80.83**	**42.49**	**1.68**	**2.85**	**12.19**	**-0.39**	**-0.00**	**344.75**
Transfers	-	2.85	-2.24	-	-	-	-	-	-	-	0.61
Statistical Differences	0.11	0.02	-0.67	-0.71	-	-	-	-	-	-	-1.24
Electricity Plants	-60.36	-	-2.10	-4.50	-42.49	-1.68	-2.45 e	-0.00	45.36 e	-	-68.23
CHP Plants	-7.28	-	-1.70	-12.94	-	-	-	-5.10	7.37 e	15.70 e	-3.96
Heat Plants	-	-	-0.21	-0.40	-	-	-0.02 e	-0.25	-	14.82 e	13.94
Gas Works	-	-	-0.02	0.02	-	-	-	-	-	-	-0.00
Petroleum Refineries	-	-127.25	127.07	-	-	-	-	-	-	-	-0.17
Coal Transformation	-4.51 e	0.02	-1.04	-0.04	-	-	-	-	-	-	-5.57
Liquefaction Plants	-	-	-	-	-	-	-	-	-	-	-
Other Transformation	-	6.20	-6.47	-	-	-	-	-	-	-	-0.27
Own Use	-1.04	-	-6.08	-0.73	-	-	-	-0.08	-5.31	-	-13.24
Distribution Losses	-0.45	-	-	-0.23	-	-	-	-	-2.52	-2.38 e	-5.58
TFC	**8.16**	**-**	**111.79**	**61.28**	**-**	**-**	**0.38**	**6.76**	**44.51**	**28.14**	**261.01**
INDUSTRY SECTOR	**7.09**	**-**	**3.85**	**19.24**	**-**	**-**	**-**	**-**	**19.96**	**7.76**	**57.89**
Iron and Steel	4.05 e	-	0.05	2.36	-	-	-	-	2.32	-	8.78
Chemical and Petrochem.	0.40	-	0.09	5.16	-	-	-	-	4.71	-	10.36
Non-Ferrous Metals	0.25	-	0.13	0.84	-	-	-	-	1.56	-	2.77
Non-Metallic Minerals	1.42	-	0.90	2.58	-	-	-	-	1.05	-	5.96
Transport Equipment	0.03	-	0.17	0.99	-	-	-	-	1.74	-	2.93
Machinery	0.06	-	0.65	1.59	-	-	-	-	0.89	-	3.19
Mining and Quarrying	0.18	-	0.07	0.14	-	-	-	-	0.17	-	0.57
Food and Tobacco	0.28	-	0.61	2.21	-	-	-	-	1.45	-	4.54
Paper, Pulp and Printing	0.32	-	0.19	2.06	-	-	-	-	2.16	-	4.73
Wood and Wood Products	0.03	-	0.07	0.16	-	-	-	-	0.36	-	0.62
Construction	-	-	0.40	0.12	-	-	-	-	0.07	-	0.59
Textile and Leather	0.02	-	0.11	0.39	-	-	-	-	0.26	-	0.78
Non-specified	0.03	-	0.42	0.62	-	-	-	-	3.22	7.76 e	12.06
TRANSPORT SECTOR	**-**	**-**	**60.01**	**-**	**-**	**-**	**-**	**1.94**	**1.39**	**-**	**63.34**
International Aviation	-	-	6.89	-	-	-	-	-	-	-	6.89
Domestic Aviation	-	-	1.74	-	-	-	-	-	-	-	1.74
Road	-	-	50.51	-	-	-	-	1.94	-	-	52.45
Rail	-	-	0.48	-	-	-	-	-	1.39	-	1.87
Pipeline Transport	-	-	-	-	-	-	-	-	-	-	-
Domestic Navigation	-	-	0.33	-	-	-	-	-	-	-	0.33
Non-specified	-	-	0.07	-	-	-	-	-	-	-	0.07
OTHER SECTORS	**0.89**	**-**	**24.92**	**39.90**	**-**	**-**	**0.38**	**4.81**	**23.15**	**20.38**	**114.43**
Residential	0.47	-	16.85	29.02	-	-	0.37	4.81	12.19	-	63.72
Comm. and Publ. Services	0.39	-	6.33	7.31	-	-	0.01	-	10.24	-	24.28
Agriculture/Forestry	0.02	-	1.65	0.21	-	-	-	-	0.71	-	2.60
Fishing	-	-	-	-	-	-	-	-	-	-	-
Non-specified	0.00	-	0.09	3.35	-	-	-	-	-	20.38 e	23.82
NON-ENERGY USE	**0.18**	**-**	**23.02**	**2.15**	**-**	**-**	**-**	**-**	**-**	**-**	**25.35**
in Industry/Transf./Energy	0.18	-	22.65	2.15	-	-	-	-	-	-	24.98
of which: Feedstocks	-	-	*18.74*	*2.15*	-	-	-	-	-	-	*20.89*
in Transport	-	-	0.35	-	-	-	-	-	-	-	0.35
in Other Sectors	-	-	0.01	-	-	-	-	-	-	-	0.01
Electricity Generated - TWh	***305.45***	-	***10.58***	***69.40***	***163.06***	***19.58***	***28.51***	***16.59***	-	-	***613.16***
Electricity Plants	*286.84 e*	-	*7.09*	*22.36 e*	*163.06*	*19.58*	*28.51*	*0.02*	-	-	*527.45*
CHP plants	*18.61*	-	*3.50*	*47.04*	-	-	-	*16.57 e*	-	-	*85.72*
Heat Generated - PJ	***158.01***	-	***26.52***	***337.43***	-	-	***0.45***	***52.28***	-	***703.39***	***1278.07***
CHP plants	*158.01*	-	*25.74*	*322.54*	-	-	-	*45.58 e*	-	*105.41*	*657.27*
Heat Plants	-	-	*0.78*	*14.89*	-	-	*0.45*	*6.69 e*	-	*597.98*	*620.80*

Greece / Grèce
Key Indicators
Indicateurs principaux

	1960	1970	1973	1980	1990	1995
Energy Production (Mtoe)	0.32	1.69	2.33	3.70	9.20	9.30
Net Imports (Mtoe)	2.74	7.00	12.01	13.63	15.29	17.98
Total Primary Energy Supply (Mtoe)	2.53	8.09	12.35	15.70	22.18	23.48
Net Oil Imports (Mtoe)	2.64	6.69	11.56	13.19	14.31	16.98
Oil Supply (Mtoe)	2.09	6.09	9.61	11.64	12.81	13.66
Electricity Consumption (TWh)*	2.01	9.00	13.82	21.67	32.85	39.18
GDP (billion 2000 US$ using exch. rates)	33.09 e	68.99	88.59	108.14	115.79	123.19
GDP (billion 2000 US$ using PPPs)	51.83 e	108.05	138.75	169.37	181.36	192.95
Population (millions)	8.47 e	8.95	9.08	9.81	10.34	10.63
Industrial Production Index (2000=100)	..	39.00	56.60	75.60	83.20	81.70
Energy Production/TPES	0.1275	0.2086	0.1889	0.2355	0.4148	0.3959
Net Oil Imports/GDP (toe per thousand 2000 US$)	0.0798 e	0.0969	0.1305	0.1220	0.1235	0.1379
TPES/GDP (toe per thousand 2000 US$)	0.0764 e	0.1173	0.1395	0.1451	0.1916	0.1906
TPES/GDP (toe per thousand 2000 US$ PPP)	0.0488 e	0.0749	0.0890	0.0927	0.1223	0.1217
TPES/Population (toe per capita)	0.2984 e	0.9049	1.3602	1.5999	2.1458	2.2082
Oil Supply/GDP (toe per thousand 2000 US$)	0.0632 e	0.0883	0.1084	0.1076	0.1106	0.1109
Oil Supply/Population (toe per capita)	0.2469 e	0.6806	1.0576	1.1861	1.2392	1.2843
Elect. Cons./GDP (kWh per 2000 US$)	0.0609 e	0.1305	0.1560	0.2004	0.2837	0.3180
Elect. Cons./Population (kWh per capita)	238 e	1 006	1 522	2 209	3 178	3 684
Industry Cons.**/Industrial Production (2000=100)	..	120.42	119.90	112.77	107.15	106.06
Industry Oil Cons.**/Industrial Production (2000=100)	..	164.15	167.75	160.27	98.51	106.99

	2000	2001	2002	2003	2004	2005
Energy Production (Mtoe)	9.99	9.97	10.23	9.90	10.29	10.30
Net Imports (Mtoe)	21.72	22.08	23.00	22.29	24.41	23.13
Total Primary Energy Supply (Mtoe)	27.82	28.70	29.03	29.88	30.47	30.98
Net Oil Imports (Mtoe)	19.27	19.34	20.37	19.68	21.53	20.10
Oil Supply (Mtoe)	15.61	16.14	16.57	17.19	17.30	17.69
Electricity Consumption (TWh)*	49.56	51.26	53.53	55.64	56.97	58.20
GDP (billion 2000 US$ using exch. rates)	145.96	152.48	158.42	166.11	173.96	180.45
GDP (billion 2000 US$ using PPPs)	228.60	238.83	248.12	260.16	272.46	282.62
Population (millions)	10.92	10.95	10.99	11.02	11.06	11.10
Industrial Production Index (2000=100)	100.00	98.20	99.00	99.30	100.20	99.50
Energy Production/TPES	0.3590	0.3472	0.3524	0.3315	0.3377	0.3326
Net Oil Imports/GDP (toe per thousand 2000 US$)	0.1320	0.1268	0.1286	0.1185	0.1238	0.1114
TPES/GDP (toe per thousand 2000 US$)	0.1906	0.1882	0.1833	0.1799	0.1752	0.1717
TPES/GDP (toe per thousand 2000 US$ PPP)	0.1217	0.1202	0.1170	0.1148	0.1118	0.1096
TPES/Population (toe per capita)	2.5485	2.6214	2.6420	2.7102	2.7545	2.7898
Oil Supply/GDP (toe per thousand 2000 US$)	0.1070	0.1059	0.1046	0.1035	0.0995	0.0980
Oil Supply/Population (toe per capita)	1.4302	1.4741	1.5080	1.5597	1.5640	1.5933
Elect. Cons./GDP (kWh per 2000 US$)	0.3395	0.3362	0.3379	0.3350	0.3275	0.3225
Elect. Cons./Population (kWh per capita)	4 540	4 681	4 871	5 047	5 150	5 242
Industry Cons.**/Industrial Production (2000=100)	100.00	102.12	101.28	99.92	94.89	94.73
Industry Oil Cons.**/Industrial Production (2000=100)	100.00	101.77	105.13	105.00	95.68	94.45

* Electricity consumption equals domestic supply less distribution losses.
La consommation d'électricité représente l'approvisionnement intérieur diminué des pertes de distribution.

** Includes non-energy use in industry/transformation/energy sectors.
Comprend l'usage non-énergétique dans les secteurs de l'industrie/transformation/énergie.

Greece / Grèce

Figure 1. TPES* in 1973

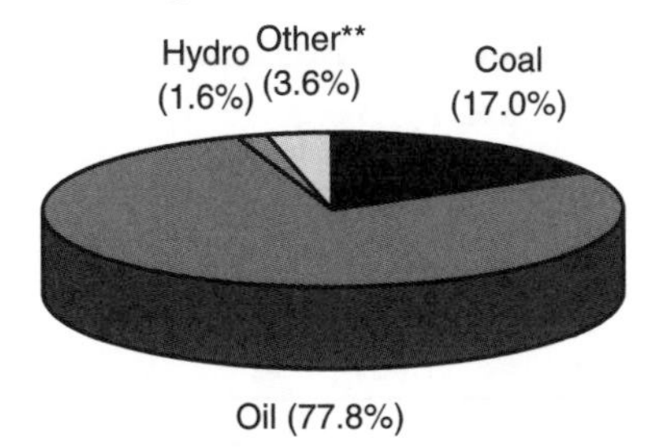

Figure 2. TPES* in 2005

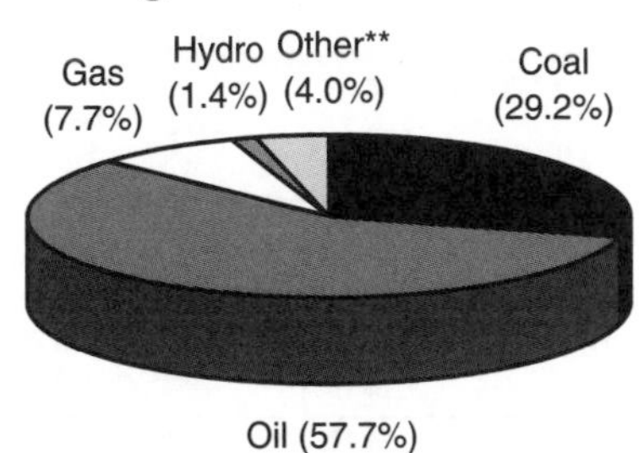

Figure 3. Final Consumption by Sector***

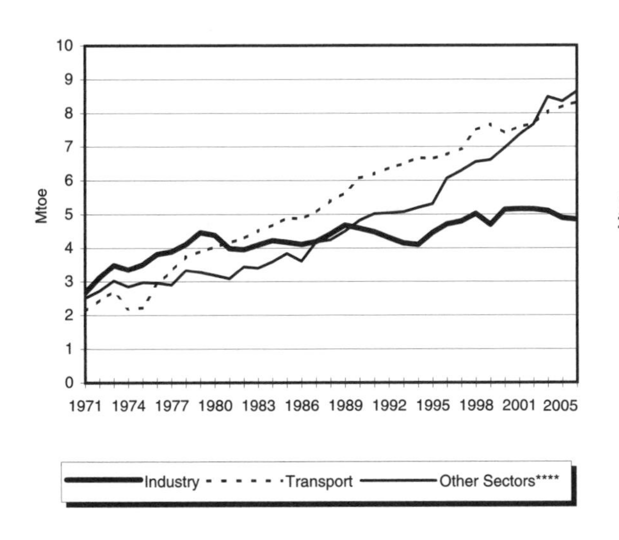

Figure 4. Breakdown of Sectorial Final Consumption by Source in 1973 and 2005***

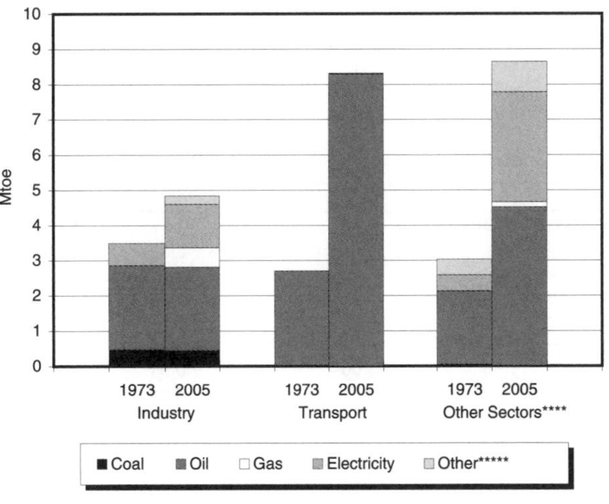

Figure 5. Electricity Generation by Fuel

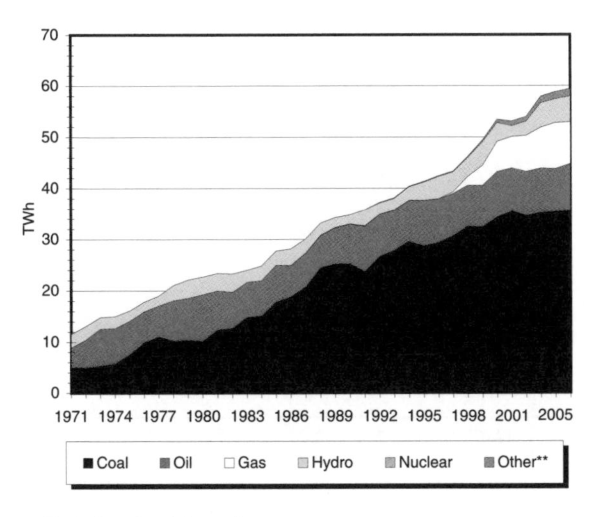

Figure 6. Electricity Consumption/GDP, TPES/GDP and Energy Production/TPES

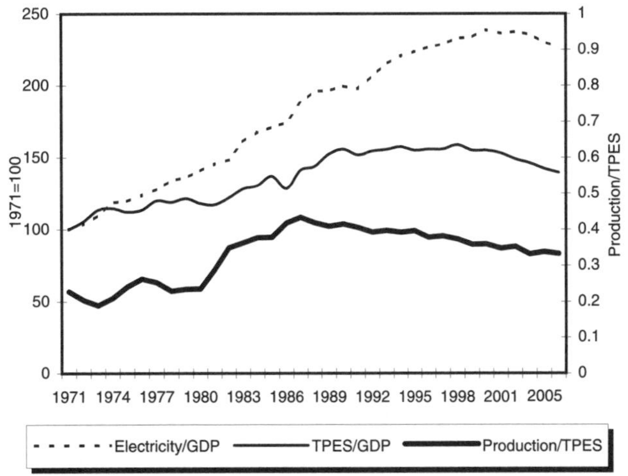

* Excluding electricity trade.

** Includes geothermal, solar, wind, combustible renewables & waste, etc.

*** Includes non-energy use.

**** Includes residential, commercial and public services, agriculture/forestry, fishing and non-specified.

***** Includes comb. renewables & waste, direct use of geothermal/solar thermal and heat produced in CHP/heat plants.

Greece / Grèce : 2004

Million tonnes of oil equivalent / *Million de tonnes d'équivalent pétrole*

SUPPLY AND CONSUMPTION / ***APPROVISIONNEMENT ET DEMANDE***	Coal / *Charbon*	Crude Oil / *Pétrole brut*	Petroleum Products / *Produits pétroliers*	Gas / *Gaz*	Nuclear / *Nucléaire*	Hydro / *Hydro*	Geotherm. Solar etc. / *Géotherm. solaire etc.*	Combust. Renew. & Waste / *Comb. ren. & déchets*	Electricity / *Electricité*	Heat / *Chaleur*	Total / *Total*
Production	8.55	0.12	-	0.03	-	0.40	0.21	0.99	-	-	10.29
Imports	0.50	21.44	5.88	2.17	-	-	-	-	0.42	-	30.41
Exports	-0.04	-0.81	-4.98	-	-	-	-	-	-0.17	-	-6.00
Intl. Marine Bunkers	-	-	-3.23	-	-	-	-	-	-	-	-3.23
Stock Changes	0.10	-1.03	-0.09	0.03	-	-	-	-	-	-	-1.00
TPES	**9.10**	**19.73**	**-2.43**	**2.23**	**-**	**0.40**	**0.21**	**0.99**	**0.24**	**-**	**30.47**
Transfers	-	1.15	-1.14	-	-	-	-	-	-	-	0.00
Statistical Differences	0.19	-0.11	0.04	0.00	-	-	-	-	-	-	0.12
Electricity Plants	-7.51	-	-1.81	-1.59	-	-0.40	-0.10	-0.03	4.55	-	-6.88
CHP Plants	-1.19	-	-0.13	-0.01	-	-	-	-0.04	0.51	0.04	-0.82
Heat Plants	-	-	-	-	-	-	-	-	-	-	-
Gas Works	-	-	-	-	-	-	-	-	-	-	-
Petroleum Refineries	-	-20.77	21.41	-	-	-	-	-	-	-	0.65
Coal Transformation	-0.04	-	-	-	-	-	-	-	-	-	-0.04
Liquefaction Plants	-	-	-	-	-	-	-	-	-	-	-
Other Transformation	-	-	-	-	-	-	-	-	-	-	-
Own Use	-	-	-1.02	-0.04	-	-	-	-	-0.58	-	-1.63
Distribution Losses	-	-	-	-0.01	-	-	-	-	-0.45	-	-0.45
TFC	**0.56**	**-**	**14.93**	**0.59**	**-**	**-**	**0.11**	**0.92**	**4.28**	**0.04**	**21.43**
INDUSTRY SECTOR	**0.55**	**-**	**1.72**	**0.37**	**-**	**-**	**0.00**	**0.21**	**1.20**	**-**	**4.06**
Iron and Steel	-	-	0.03	0.07	-	-	-	-	0.13	-	0.22
Chemical and Petrochem.	-	-	0.17	0.03	-	-	-	-	0.05	-	0.25
Non-Ferrous Metals	0.17	-	0.26	0.05	-	-	-	-	0.36	-	0.85
Non-Metallic Minerals	0.38	-	0.55	0.07	-	-	-	0.00	0.19	-	1.19
Transport Equipment	-	-	0.02	0.00	-	-	-	-	0.01	-	0.03
Machinery	0.00	-	0.01	0.00	-	-	-	-	0.05	-	0.06
Mining and Quarrying	-	-	0.07	-	-	-	-	-	0.03	-	0.09
Food and Tobacco	-	-	0.21	0.08	-	-	-	0.18	0.16	-	0.64
Paper, Pulp and Printing	-	-	0.06	0.03	-	-	-	-	0.05	-	0.14
Wood and Wood Products	-	-	0.00	0.00	-	-	-	0.02	0.02	-	0.05
Construction	-	-	0.16	-	-	-	-	-	0.00	-	0.16
Textile and Leather	-	-	0.06	0.03	-	-	-	-	0.08	-	0.17
Non-specified	-	-	0.12	0.01	-	-	0.00	-	0.07	-	0.20
TRANSPORT SECTOR	**-**	**-**	**8.11**	**0.01**	**-**	**-**	**-**	**-**	**0.02**	**-**	**8.14**
International Aviation	-	-	0.83	-	-	-	-	-	-	-	0.83
Domestic Aviation	-	-	0.42	-	-	-	-	-	-	-	0.42
Road	-	-	6.13	0.01	-	-	-	-	-	-	6.14
Rail	-	-	0.04	-	-	-	-	-	0.01	-	0.05
Pipeline Transport	-	-	-	0.00	-	-	-	-	-	-	0.00
Domestic Navigation	-	-	0.68	-	-	-	-	-	-	-	0.68
Non-specified	-	-	-	-	-	-	-	-	0.01	-	0.01
OTHER SECTORS	**0.01**	**-**	**4.34**	**0.08**	**-**	**-**	**0.11**	**0.71**	**3.05**	**0.04**	**8.35**
Residential	0.00	-	3.10	0.03	-	-	0.11	0.70	1.45	0.04	5.44
Comm. and Publ. Services	-	-	0.37	0.04	-	-	0.00	0.00	1.36	-	1.78
Agriculture/Forestry	-	-	0.87	-	-	-	0.00	0.01	0.24	-	1.12
Fishing	-	-	-	-	-	-	0.00	-	-	-	0.00
Non-specified	0.00	-	-	-	-	-	-	-	-	-	0.00
NON-ENERGY USE	**-**	**-**	**0.76**	**0.13**	**-**	**-**	**-**	**-**	**-**	**-**	**0.89**
in Industry/Transf./Energy	-	-	0.70	0.13	-	-	-	-	-	-	0.83
of which: Feedstocks	-	-	*0.25*	*0.13*	-	-	-	-	-	-	*0.38*
in Transport	-	-	0.06	-	-	-	-	-	-	-	0.06
in Other Sectors	-	-	0.00	-	-	-	-	-	-	-	0.00
Electricity Generated - TWh	***35.38***	-	***8.39***	***8.99***	-	***4.67***	***1.12***	***0.26***	-	-	***58.81***
Electricity Plants	*30.45*	-	*7.70*	*8.85*	-	*4.67*	*1.12*	*0.09*	-	-	*52.88*
CHP plants	*4.93*	-	*0.69*	*0.14*	-	-	-	*0.17*	-	-	*5.93*
Heat Generated - PJ	***1.81***	-	***0.01***	-	-	-	-	-	-	-	***1.82***
CHP plants	*1.81*	-	*0.01*	-	-	-	-	-	-	-	*1.82*
Heat Plants	-	-	-	-	-	-	-	-	-	-	-

Greece / Grèce : 2005

Million tonnes of oil equivalent / *Million de tonnes d'équivalent pétrole*

SUPPLY AND CONSUMPTION *APPROVISIONNEMENT ET DEMANDE*	Coal *Charbon*	Crude Oil *Pétrole brut*	Petroleum Products *Produits pétroliers*	Gas *Gaz*	Nuclear *Nucléaire*	Hydro *Hydro*	Geotherm. Solar etc. *Géotherm. solaire etc.*	Combust. Renew. & Waste *Comb. ren. & déchets*	Electricity *Electricité*	Heat *Chaleur*	Total *Total*
Production	8.54	0.09	-	0.02	-	0.43	0.21	1.01	-	-	10.30
Imports	0.40	20.05	6.05	2.33	-	-	-	-	0.48	-	29.32
Exports	-0.03	-0.92	-5.09	-	-	-	-	-	-0.16	-	-6.19
Intl. Marine Bunkers	-	-	-2.86	-	-	-	-	-	-	-	-2.86
Stock Changes	0.04	0.77	-0.41	0.00	-	-	-	-	-	-	0.41
TPES	**8.95**	**20.00**	**-2.31**	**2.35**	**-**	**0.43**	**0.21**	**1.01**	**0.33**	**-**	**30.98**
Transfers	-	1.16	-1.15	-	-	-	-	-	-	-	0.01
Statistical Differences	0.22	-0.12	0.12	0.00	-	-	-	-	-	-	0.21
Electricity Plants	-7.01	-	-1.97	-1.59	-	-0.43	-0.11	-0.02	4.41	-	-6.72
CHP Plants	-1.69	-	-0.10	-0.02	-	-	-	-0.03	0.70	0.05	-1.09
Heat Plants	-	-	-	-	-	-	-	-	-	-	-
Gas Works	-	-	-	-	-	-	-	-	-	-	-
Petroleum Refineries	-	-21.03	21.70	-	-	-	-	-	-	-	0.67
Coal Transformation	-0.03	-	-	-	-	-	-	-	-	-	-0.03
Liquefaction Plants	-	-	-	-	-	-	-	-	-	-	-
Other Transformation	-	-	-	-	-	-	-	-	-	-	-
Own Use	-	-	-1.13	-0.03	-	-	-	-	-0.58	-	-1.74
Distribution Losses	-	-	-	-0.01	-	-	-	-	-0.48	-	-0.49
TFC	**0.44**	**-**	**15.16**	**0.71**	**-**	**-**	**0.10**	**0.96**	**4.38**	**0.05**	**21.81**
INDUSTRY SECTOR	**0.44**	**-**	**1.80**	**0.43**	**-**	**-**	**0.00**	**0.24**	**1.24**	**-**	**4.15**
Iron and Steel	-	-	0.00	0.07	-	-	-	-	0.14	-	0.22
Chemical and Petrochem.	-	-	0.17	0.05	-	-	-	-	0.05	-	0.27
Non-Ferrous Metals	0.17	-	0.21	0.06	-	-	-	-	0.40	-	0.84
Non-Metallic Minerals	0.26	-	0.57	0.07	-	-	-	0.00	0.21	-	1.11
Transport Equipment	-	-	0.02	-	-	-	-	-	0.01	-	0.03
Machinery	0.00	-	0.01	0.00	-	-	-	-	0.05	-	0.06
Mining and Quarrying	-	-	0.07	-	-	-	-	-	0.02	-	0.09
Food and Tobacco	-	-	0.16	0.11	-	-	-	0.21	0.16	-	0.64
Paper, Pulp and Printing	-	-	0.05	0.03	-	-	-	-	0.05	-	0.13
Wood and Wood Products	-	-	0.00	0.00	-	-	-	0.03	0.02	-	0.05
Construction	-	-	0.17	-	-	-	-	-	0.00	-	0.17
Textile and Leather	-	-	0.06	0.02	-	-	-	-	0.07	-	0.14
Non-specified	-	-	0.32	0.01	-	-	0.00	-	0.07	-	0.40
TRANSPORT SECTOR	**-**	**-**	**8.22**	**0.01**	**-**	**-**	**-**	**-**	**0.02**	**-**	**8.25**
International Aviation	-	-	0.81	-	-	-	-	-	-	-	0.81
Domestic Aviation	-	-	0.42	-	-	-	-	-	-	-	0.42
Road	-	-	6.30	0.01	-	-	-	-	-	-	6.31
Rail	-	-	0.04	-	-	-	-	-	0.01	-	0.05
Pipeline Transport	-	-	-	0.00	-	-	-	-	-	-	0.00
Domestic Navigation	-	-	0.65	-	-	-	-	-	-	-	0.65
Non-specified	-	-	-	-	-	-	-	-	0.00	-	0.00
OTHER SECTORS	**0.01**	**-**	**4.50**	**0.15**	**-**	**-**	**0.10**	**0.72**	**3.12**	**0.05**	**8.64**
Residential	0.00	-	3.16	0.07	-	-	0.10	0.70	1.45	0.05	5.54
Comm. and Publ. Services	-	-	0.45	0.07	-	-	0.00	0.01	1.42	-	1.95
Agriculture/Forestry	0.00	-	0.89	-	-	-	0.00	0.01	0.25	-	1.16
Fishing	-	-	-	-	-	-	0.00	-	-	-	0.00
Non-specified	0.00	-	-	-	-	-	-	-	-	-	0.00
NON-ENERGY USE	**-**	**-**	**0.64**	**0.13**	**-**	**-**	**-**	**-**	**-**	**-**	**0.77**
in Industry/Transf./Energy	-	-	0.57	0.13	-	-	-	-	-	-	0.69
of which: Feedstocks	-	-	*0.25*	*0.13*	-	-	-	-	-	-	*0.38*
in Transport	-	-	0.07	-	-	-	-	-	-	-	0.07
in Other Sectors	-	-	0.00	-	-	-	-	-	-	-	0.00
Electricity Generated - TWh	***35.54***	**-**	***9.21***	***8.17***	**-**	***5.02***	***1.27***	***0.22***	**-**	**-**	***59.43***
Electricity Plants	*28.49*	-	*8.41*	*8.01*	-	*5.02*	*1.27*	*0.09*	-	-	*51.29*
CHP plants	*7.06*	-	*0.79*	*0.16*	-	-	-	*0.13*	-	-	*8.14*
Heat Generated - PJ	***2.03***	**-**	***0.02***	**-**	**-**	**-**	**-**	**-**	**-**	**-**	***2.05***
CHP plants	*2.03*	-	*0.02*	-	-	-	-	-	-	-	*2.05*
Heat Plants	-	-	-	-	-	-	-	-	-	-	-

Hungary / Hongrie
Key Indicators
Indicateurs principaux

	1960	1970	1973	1980	1990	1995
Energy Production (Mtoe)	..	11.77	12.70	14.49	14.33	13.45
Net Imports (Mtoe)	..	6.73	8.66	14.36	14.16	12.44
Total Primary Energy Supply (Mtoe)	..	17.94	21.33	28.49	28.56	25.70
Net Oil Imports (Mtoe)	..	4.27	6.48	8.33	6.43	5.32
Oil Supply (Mtoe)	..	6.05	8.21	10.93	8.51	7.50
Electricity Consumption (TWh)*	..	16.42	20.40	28.90	35.55	31.67
GDP (billion 2000 US$ using exch. rates)	13.33 e	25.10 e	30.96 e	39.65 e	44.41 e	39.40
GDP (billion 2000 US$ using PPPs)	35.03 e	65.96 e	81.35 e	104.21 e	116.70 e	103.54
Population (millions)	9.98 e	10.34	10.43	10.71	10.37	10.33
Industrial Production Index (2000=100)	..	..	..	69.30	67.60	59.40
Energy Production/TPES	..	0.6562	0.5952	0.5085	0.5016	0.5236
Net Oil Imports/GDP (toe per thousand 2000 US$)	..	0.1701 e	0.2093 e	0.2101 e	0.1449 e	0.1350
TPES/GDP (toe per thousand 2000 US$)	..	0.7147 e	0.6891 e	0.7186 e	0.6431 e	0.6522
TPES/GDP (toe per thousand 2000 US$ PPP)	..	0.2720 e	0.2622 e	0.2734 e	0.2447 e	0.2482
TPES/Population (toe per capita)	..	1.7354	2.0460	2.6613	2.7552	2.4877
Oil Supply/GDP (toe per thousand 2000 US$)	..	0.2410 e	0.2651 e	0.2757 e	0.1917 e	0.1903
Oil Supply/Population (toe per capita)	..	0.5852	0.7870	1.0211	0.8212	0.7259
Elect. Cons./GDP (kWh per 2000 US$)	..	0.6543 e	0.6590 e	0.7288 e	0.8005 e	0.8040
Elect. Cons./Population (kWh per capita)	..	1 589	1 957	2 699	3 430	3 067
Industry Cons.**/Industrial Production (2000=100)	..	..	..	298.20	237.71	178.99
Industry Oil Cons.**/Industrial Production (2000=100)	..	..	..	317.59	202.93	181.33

	2000	2001	2002	2003	2004	2005
Energy Production (Mtoe)	11.27	10.90	11.20	10.41	10.24	10.33
Net Imports (Mtoe)	13.86	13.78	14.68	16.35	16.01	17.58
Total Primary Energy Supply (Mtoe)	25.01	25.42	25.81	26.34	26.36	27.76
Net Oil Imports (Mtoe)	5.21	4.73	4.71	4.81	5.00	5.93
Oil Supply (Mtoe)	6.86	6.62	6.46	6.30	6.44	7.23
Electricity Consumption (TWh)*	33.79	34.91	36.01	36.84	37.20	38.04
GDP (billion 2000 US$ using exch. rates)	47.96	49.92	52.09	54.23	56.88	59.29
GDP (billion 2000 US$ using PPPs)	126.04	131.19	136.89	142.53	149.47	155.82
Population (millions)	10.21	10.19	10.16	10.13	10.11	10.09
Industrial Production Index (2000=100)	100.00	103.60	106.40	113.20	121.50	129.90
Energy Production/TPES	0.4507	0.4289	0.4339	0.3952	0.3883	0.3721
Net Oil Imports/GDP (toe per thousand 2000 US$)	0.1086	0.0948	0.0904	0.0887	0.0879	0.1000
TPES/GDP (toe per thousand 2000 US$)	0.5216	0.5092	0.4956	0.4857	0.4634	0.4682
TPES/GDP (toe per thousand 2000 US$ PPP)	0.1985	0.1938	0.1886	0.1848	0.1763	0.1782
TPES/Population (toe per capita)	2.4497	2.4952	2.5409	2.6003	2.6079	2.7523
Oil Supply/GDP (toe per thousand 2000 US$)	0.1431	0.1327	0.1241	0.1162	0.1133	0.1219
Oil Supply/Population (toe per capita)	0.6723	0.6501	0.6364	0.6223	0.6375	0.7165
Elect. Cons./GDP (kWh per 2000 US$)	0.7046	0.6993	0.6914	0.6794	0.6540	0.6416
Elect. Cons./Population (kWh per capita)	3 309	3 427	3 545	3 637	3 680	3 771
Industry Cons.**/Industrial Production (2000=100)	100.00	94.67	96.16	84.77	79.19	84.51
Industry Oil Cons.**/Industrial Production (2000=100)	100.00	80.30	93.54	78.98	84.33	107.82

* Electricity consumption equals domestic supply less distribution losses.
La consommation d'électricité représente l'approvisionnement intérieur diminué des pertes de distribution.

** Includes non-energy use in industry/transformation/energy sectors.
Comprend l'usage non-énergétique dans les secteurs de l'industrie/transformation/énergie.

Hungary / Hongrie

Figure 1. TPES* in 1973

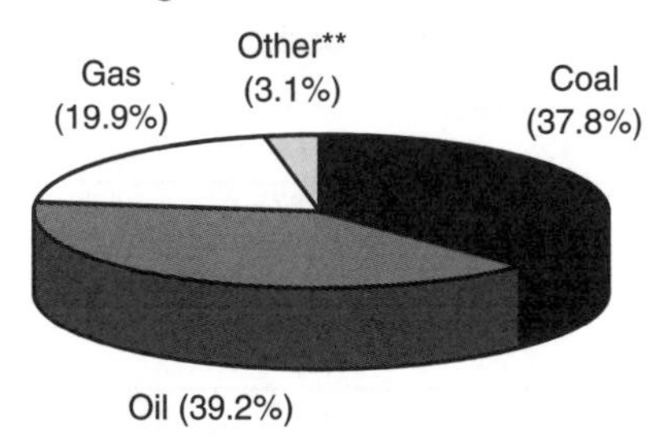

Figure 2. TPES* in 2005

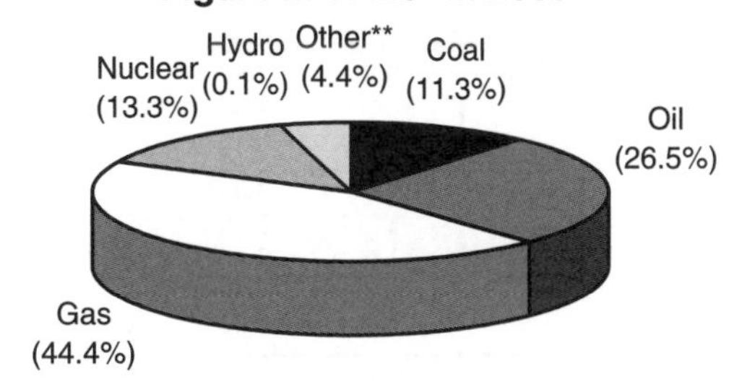

Figure 3. Final Consumption by Sector***

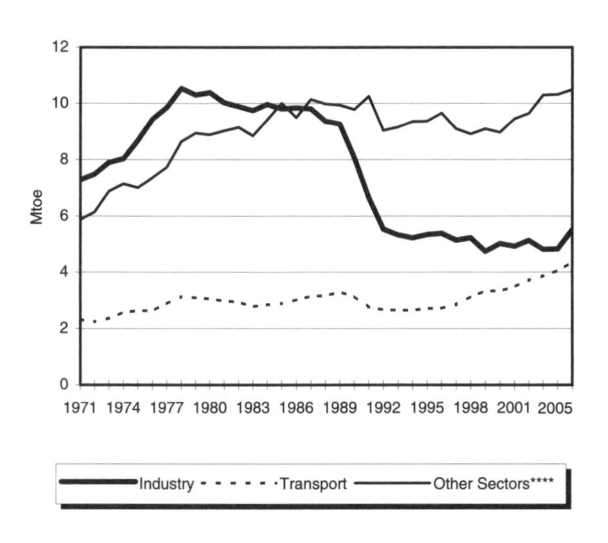

Figure 4. Breakdown of Sectorial Final Consumption by Source in 1973 and 2005***

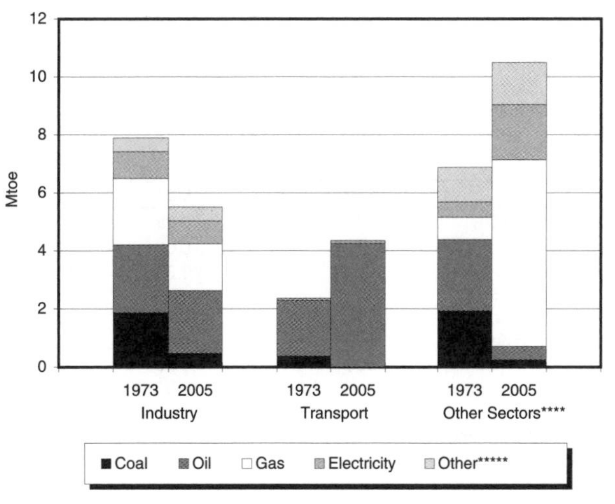

Figure 5. Electricity Generation by Fuel

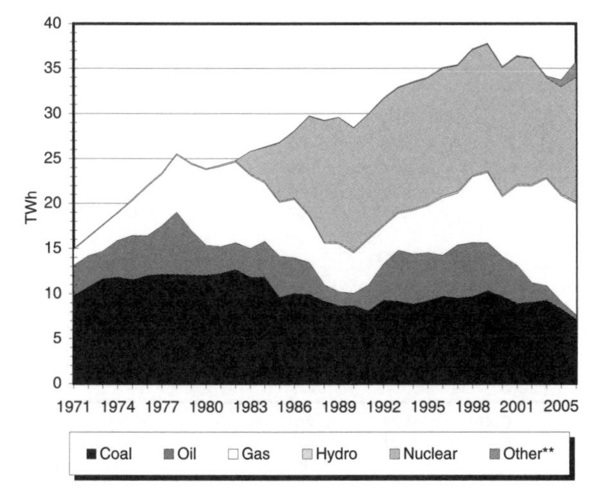

Figure 6. Electricity Consumption/GDP, TPES/GDP and Energy Production/TPES

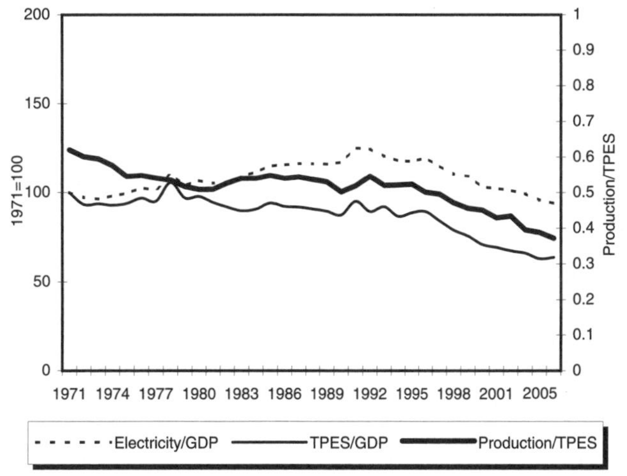

* Excluding electricity trade.

** Includes geothermal, solar, wind, combustible renewables & waste, etc.

*** Includes non-energy use.

**** Includes residential, commercial and public services, agriculture/forestry, fishing and non-specified.

***** Includes comb. renewables & waste, direct use of geothermal/solar thermal and heat produced in CHP/heat plants.

Hungary / Hongrie : 2004

Million tonnes of oil equivalent / *Million de tonnes d'équivalent pétrole*

SUPPLY AND CONSUMPTION / ***APPROVISIONNEMENT ET DEMANDE***	Coal / *Charbon*	Crude Oil / *Pétrole brut*	Petroleum Products / *Produits pétroliers*	Gas / *Gaz*	Nuclear / *Nucléaire*	Hydro / *Hydro*	Geotherm. Solar etc. / *Géotherm. solaire etc.*	Combust. Renew. & Waste / *Comb. ren. & déchets*	Electricity / *Electricité*	Heat / *Chaleur*	Total / *Total*
Production	2.18	1.59	-	2.37	3.12	0.02	0.09	0.87	-	-	10.24
Imports	1.21	5.70	2.12	9.28	-	-	-	-	0.91	-	19.21
Exports	-0.11	-0.15	-2.67	-	-	-	-	-	-0.26	-	-3.19
Intl. Marine Bunkers	-	-	-	-	-	-	-	-	-	-	-
Stock Changes	0.19	-0.15	0.01	0.07	-	-	-	-	-	-	0.11
TPES	**3.47**	**6.98**	**-0.54**	**11.71**	**3.12**	**0.02**	**0.09**	**0.87**	**0.64**	**-**	**26.36**
Transfers	-	0.37	-0.18	-	-	-	-	-	-	-	0.19
Statistical Differences	-0.03	-0.01	-	-0.08	-	-	-	-	-	-	-0.11
Electricity Plants	-2.21	-	-0.14	-1.09	-	-0.02	-0.00	-0.20	1.21	-	-2.44
CHP Plants	-0.27	-	-0.06	-1.75	-3.12	-	-	-0.04	1.69	0.98	-2.58
Heat Plants	-0.11	-	-0.01	-0.48	-	-	-0.01	-0.00	-	0.52	-0.09
Gas Works	-	-	-	-	-	-	-	-	-	-	-
Petroleum Refineries	-	-7.55	7.59	-	-	-	-	-	-	-	0.04
Coal Transformation	-0.15 e	-	-0.02	-0.06	-	-	-	-	-	-	-0.23
Liquefaction Plants	-	-	-	-	-	-	-	-	-	-	-
Other Transformation	-	0.23	-0.24	-	-	-	-	-	-	-	-0.01
Own Use	-0.00	-	-0.32	-0.15	-	-	-	-0.00	-0.46	-0.27 e	-1.21
Distribution Losses	-	-	-	-0.35	-	-	-	-	-0.34	-	-0.69
TFC	**0.70**	**0.01**	**6.07**	**7.75**	**-**	**-**	**0.08**	**0.63**	**2.74**	**1.22**	**19.21**
INDUSTRY SECTOR	**0.45**	**-**	**0.28**	**1.24**	**-**	**-**	**0.00**	**0.08**	**0.82**	**0.35**	**3.22**
Iron and Steel	0.35 e	-	0.00	0.07	-	-	-	-	0.05	0.02	0.49
Chemical and Petrochem.	-	-	0.03	0.15	-	-	-	0.00	0.18	0.16	0.53
Non-Ferrous Metals	0.00	-	-	0.11	-	-	-	-	0.09	0.06	0.26
Non-Metallic Minerals	0.09	-	0.17	0.27	-	-	0.00	0.03	0.08	0.01	0.65
Transport Equipment	0.00	-	0.02	0.05	-	-	0.00	-	0.06	0.02	0.16
Machinery	0.00	-	0.00	0.13	-	-	0.00	0.00	0.09	0.00	0.22
Mining and Quarrying	-	-	0.01	0.00	-	-	-	-	0.01	-	0.02
Food and Tobacco	0.01	-	0.03	0.30	-	-	-	0.02	0.12	0.03	0.50
Paper, Pulp and Printing	-	-	0.01	0.07	-	-	-	0.01	0.04	0.04	0.17
Wood and Wood Products	-	-	-	0.02	-	-	-	0.02	0.01	0.00	0.06
Construction	-	-	0.01	0.01	-	-	-	0.00	0.00	0.00	0.04
Textile and Leather	-	-	-	0.02	-	-	0.00	-	0.02	0.01	0.05
Non-specified	-	-	0.00	0.03	-	-	-	0.00	0.06	0.00	0.09
TRANSPORT SECTOR	**0.00**	**-**	**3.89**	**0.00**	**-**	**-**	**-**	**0.00**	**0.09**	**-**	**3.99**
International Aviation	-	-	0.23	-	-	-	-	-	-	-	0.23
Domestic Aviation	-	-	-	-	-	-	-	-	-	-	-
Road	-	-	3.59	0.00	-	-	-	-	-	-	3.60
Rail	0.00	-	0.07	-	-	-	-	0.00	0.09	-	0.17
Pipeline Transport	-	-	-	-	-	-	-	-	-	-	-
Domestic Navigation	-	-	0.00	-	-	-	-	-	-	-	0.00
Non-specified	-	-	-	-	-	-	-	-	-	-	-
OTHER SECTORS	**0.24**	**-**	**0.56**	**6.18**	**-**	**-**	**0.08**	**0.55**	**1.83**	**0.87**	**10.32**
Residential	0.23	-	0.24	3.57	-	-	0.00	0.48	0.95	0.67	6.14
Comm. and Publ. Services	0.01	-	0.04	2.40	-	-	0.00	0.06	0.78	0.20	3.49
Agriculture/Forestry	0.01	-	0.28	0.21	-	-	0.01	0.01	0.09	0.00	0.62
Fishing	-	-	-	-	-	-	-	-	-	-	-
Non-specified	-	-	-	-	-	-	0.07	-	-	-	0.07
NON-ENERGY USE	**-**	**0.01**	**1.34**	**0.32**	**-**	**-**	**-**	**-**	**-**	**-**	**1.67**
in Industry/Transf./Energy	-	0.01	1.28	0.32	-	-	-	-	-	-	1.61
of which: Feedstocks	-	*0.01*	*1.04*	*0.32*	-	-	-	-	-	-	*1.38*
in Transport	-	-	0.06	-	-	-	-	-	-	-	0.06
in Other Sectors	-	-	-	-	-	-	-	-	-	-	-
Electricity Generated - TWh	***8.34***	**-**	***0.77***	***11.72***	***11.92***	***0.21***	***0.01***	***0.75***	**-**	**-**	***33.71***
Electricity Plants	*7.87*	-	*0.53*	*4.77*	-	*0.21*	*0.01*	*0.67*	-	-	*14.06*
CHP plants	*0.47*	-	*0.24*	*6.95*	*11.92*	-	-	*0.08*	-	-	*19.65*
Heat Generated - PJ	***11.27***	**-**	***1.27***	***48.57***	***0.63***	**-**	***0.23***	***0.55***	**-**	**-**	***62.52***
CHP plants	*7.72*	-	*0.94*	*31.13*	*0.63*	-	-	*0.42* e	-	-	*40.84*
Heat Plants	*3.55*	-	*0.33*	*17.44*	-	-	*0.23*	*0.13*	-	-	*21.68*

Hungary / Hongrie : 2005

Million tonnes of oil equivalent / *Million de tonnes d'équivalent pétrole*

SUPPLY AND CONSUMPTION *APPROVISIONNEMENT ET DEMANDE*	Coal *Charbon*	Crude Oil *Pétrole brut*	Petroleum Products *Produits pétroliers*	Gas *Gaz*	Nuclear *Nucléaire*	Hydro *Hydro*	Geotherm. Solar etc. *Géotherm. solaire etc.*	Combust. Renew. & Waste *Comb. ren. & déchets*	Electricity *Electricité*	Heat *Chaleur*	Total *Total*
Production	1.75	1.41	-	2.33	3.62	0.02	0.09	1.11	-	-	10.33
Imports	1.46	6.68	2.56	9.80	-	-	-	-	1.34	-	21.84
Exports	-0.15	-0.36	-2.94	-	-	-	-	-	-0.81	-	-4.27
Intl. Marine Bunkers	-	-	-	-	-	-	-	-	-	-	-
Stock Changes	0.02	-0.05	-0.07	-0.04	-	-	-	-	-	-	-0.14
TPES	**3.07**	**7.68**	**-0.45**	**12.09**	**3.62**	**0.02**	**0.09**	**1.11**	**0.54**	**-**	**27.76**
Transfers	-	0.58	-0.34	-	-	-	-	-	-	-	0.24
Statistical Differences	-0.01	0.01	-	-	-	-	-	-	-	-	0.00
Electricity Plants	-1.78	-	-0.10	-1.04	-	-0.02	-0.00	-0.46	1.13	-	-2.26
CHP Plants	-0.23	-	-0.03	-1.95	-3.62	-	-	-0.08	1.94	1.00	-2.97
Heat Plants	-0.13	-	-0.01	-0.47	-	-	-0.01	-0.01	-	0.52	-0.11
Gas Works	-	-	-	-	-	-	-	-	-	-	-
Petroleum Refineries	-	-8.56	8.60	-	-	-	-	-	-	-	0.04
Coal Transformation	-0.17 e	-	-0.02	-0.05	-	-	-	-	-	-	-0.25
Liquefaction Plants	-	-	-	-	-	-	-	-	-	-	-
Other Transformation	-	0.37	-0.38	-	-	-	-	-	-	-	-0.01
Own Use	-0.00	-0.06	-0.42	-0.18	-	-	-	-0.00	-0.49	-0.21 e	-1.38
Distribution Losses	-0.02	-	-	-0.35	-	-	-	-	-0.34	-	-0.71
TFC	**0.72**	**0.01**	**6.84**	**8.05**	**-**	**-**	**0.08**	**0.57**	**2.78**	**1.31**	**20.36**
INDUSTRY SECTOR	**0.47**	**-**	**0.24**	**1.26**	**-**	**-**	**0.00**	**0.10**	**0.80**	**0.38**	**3.24**
Iron and Steel	0.34 e	-	-	0.07	-	-	-	-	0.07	0.03	0.51
Chemical and Petrochem.	-	-	0.04	0.20	-	-	-	-	0.18	0.18	0.60
Non-Ferrous Metals	-	-	0.00	0.10	-	-	-	-	0.08	0.06	0.24
Non-Metallic Minerals	0.12	-	0.12	0.26	-	-	0.00	0.05	0.08	0.01	0.63
Transport Equipment	0.00	-	0.00	0.06	-	-	0.00	-	0.06	0.01	0.14
Machinery	0.00	-	0.00	0.16	-	-	0.00	0.00	0.11	0.01	0.28
Mining and Quarrying	-	-	0.01	0.00	-	-	-	-	0.01	-	0.02
Food and Tobacco	0.01	-	0.02	0.26	-	-	-	0.03	0.11	0.02	0.45
Paper, Pulp and Printing	-	-	0.01	0.06	-	-	-	0.01	0.05	0.05	0.17
Wood and Wood Products	-	-	-	0.02	-	-	-	0.02	0.01	0.00	0.06
Construction	0.00	-	0.02	0.02	-	-	-	-	0.01	0.00	0.05
Textile and Leather	-	-	-	0.02	-	-	0.00	-	0.02	0.00	0.04
Non-specified	-	-	-	0.02	-	-	-	0.00	0.02	0.01	0.05
TRANSPORT SECTOR	**0.00**	**-**	**4.17**	**0.00**	**-**	**-**	**-**	**0.01**	**0.09**	**-**	**4.27**
International Aviation	-	-	0.22	-	-	-	-	-	-	-	0.22
Domestic Aviation	-	-	0.01	-	-	-	-	-	-	-	0.01
Road	-	-	3.87	0.00	-	-	-	0.01	-	-	3.87
Rail	0.00	-	0.06	-	-	-	-	0.00	0.09	-	0.16
Pipeline Transport	-	-	-	-	-	-	-	-	-	-	-
Domestic Navigation	-	-	0.00	-	-	-	-	-	-	-	0.00
Non-specified	-	-	-	-	-	-	-	-	-	-	-
OTHER SECTORS	**0.25**	**-**	**0.46**	**6.43**	**-**	**-**	**0.08**	**0.46**	**1.89**	**0.93**	**10.49**
Residential	0.24	-	0.18	3.93	-	-	0.00	0.40	0.96	0.70	6.41
Comm. and Publ. Services	0.00	-	0.04	2.28	-	-	0.00	0.05	0.85	0.23	3.46
Agriculture/Forestry	0.00	-	0.24	0.22	-	-	0.01	0.01	0.08	0.00	0.57
Fishing	-	-	-	-	-	-	-	-	-	-	-
Non-specified	-	-	-	-	-	-	0.06	-	-	-	0.06
NON-ENERGY USE	**-**	**0.01**	**1.98**	**0.36**	**-**	**-**	**-**	**-**	**-**	**-**	**2.35**
in Industry/Transf./Energy	-	0.01	1.90	0.36	-	-	-	-	-	-	2.27
of which: Feedstocks	-	*0.01*	*1.55*	*0.36*	-	-	-	-	-	-	*1.92*
in Transport	-	-	0.08	-	-	-	-	-	-	-	0.08
in Other Sectors	-	-	0.00	-	-	-	-	-	-	-	0.00
Electricity Generated - TWh	*7.15*	-	*0.46*	*12.38*	*13.83*	*0.20*	*0.01*	*1.73*	-	-	*35.76*
Electricity Plants	*6.63*	-	*0.39*	*4.41*	-	*0.20*	*0.01*	*1.56*	-	-	*13.19*
CHP plants	*0.52*	-	*0.07*	*7.97*	*13.83*	-	-	*0.17*	-	-	*22.56*
Heat Generated - PJ	*9.39*	-	*1.04*	*51.04*	*0.67*	-	*0.24*	*1.23*	-	-	*63.60*
CHP plants	*5.63*	-	*0.64*	*33.74*	*0.67*	-	-	*1.01*	-	-	*41.68*
Heat Plants	*3.76*	-	*0.40*	*17.30*	-	-	*0.24*	*0.22 e*	-	-	*21.92*

Iceland / Islande
Key Indicators
Indicateurs principaux

	1960	1970	1973	1980	1990	1995
Energy Production (Mtoe)	0.15	0.39	0.54	0.90	1.40	1.57
Net Imports (Mtoe)	0.41	0.54	0.70	0.60	0.80	0.81
Total Primary Energy Supply (Mtoe)	0.56	0.93	1.24	1.53	2.17	2.33
Net Oil Imports (Mtoe)	0.39	0.54	0.70	0.59	0.74	0.76
Oil Supply (Mtoe)	0.39	0.54	0.70	0.61	0.71	0.71
Electricity Consumption (TWh)*	0.46	1.32	2.10	2.89	4.12	4.65
GDP (billion 2000 US$ using exch. rates)	1.77 e	2.79	3.57	5.15	6.75	6.84
GDP (billion 2000 US$ using PPPs)	1.68 e	2.63	3.37	4.87	6.38	6.46
Population (millions)	0.18 e	0.20	0.21	0.23	0.26	0.27
Industrial Production Index (2000=100)	..	..	..	..	..	..
Energy Production/TPES	0.2712	0.4235	0.4365	0.5891	0.6448	0.6720
Net Oil Imports/GDP (toe per thousand 2000 US$)	0.2178 e	0.1939	0.1954	0.1138	0.1091	0.1105
TPES/GDP (toe per thousand 2000 US$)	0.3135 e	0.3348	0.3471	0.2979	0.3217	0.3405
TPES/GDP (toe per thousand 2000 US$ PPP)	0.3320 e	0.3545	0.3675	0.3155	0.3406	0.3606
TPES/Population (toe per capita)	3.1600 e	4.5724	5.8490	6.7312	8.5157	8.7235
Oil Supply/GDP (toe per thousand 2000 US$)	0.2178 e	0.1928	0.1954	0.1190	0.1048	0.1036
Oil Supply/Population (toe per capita)	2.1955 e	2.6331	3.2928	2.6890	2.7734	2.6551
Elect. Cons./GDP (kWh per 2000 US$)	0.2587 e	0.4749	0.5882	0.5616	0.6096	0.6803
Elect. Cons./Population (kWh per capita)	2 608 e	6 485	9 910	12 689	16 137	17 427
Industry Cons.**/Industrial Production (2000=100)	..	..	..	..	..	..
Industry Oil Cons.**/Industrial Production (2000=100)	..	..	..	..	..	..

	2000	2001	2002	2003	2004	2005
Energy Production (Mtoe)	2.31	2.45	2.46	2.46	2.52	2.64
Net Imports (Mtoe)	1.05	0.96	0.98	0.95	1.08	1.08
Total Primary Energy Supply (Mtoe)	3.24	3.36	3.40	3.39	3.50	3.63
Net Oil Imports (Mtoe)	0.95	0.86	0.88	0.86	0.98	0.98
Oil Supply (Mtoe)	0.84	0.82	0.84	0.84	0.88	0.89
Electricity Consumption (TWh)*	7.37	7.68	8.02	8.01	8.24	8.31
GDP (billion 2000 US$ using exch. rates)	8.64	8.95	8.93	9.17	9.87	10.61
GDP (billion 2000 US$ using PPPs)	8.16	8.46	8.43	8.66	9.32	10.02
Population (millions)	0.28	0.29	0.29	0.29	0.29	0.30
Industrial Production Index (2000=100)	..	..	..	..	..	..
Energy Production/TPES	0.7107	0.7289	0.7251	0.7256	0.7202	0.7270
Net Oil Imports/GDP (toe per thousand 2000 US$)	0.1100	0.0965	0.0987	0.0933	0.0993	0.0919
TPES/GDP (toe per thousand 2000 US$)	0.3754	0.3756	0.3804	0.3694	0.3544	0.3417
TPES/GDP (toe per thousand 2000 US$ PPP)	0.3975	0.3977	0.4027	0.3911	0.3753	0.3618
TPES/Population (toe per capita)	11.5450	11.7991	11.7897	11.7179	11.9376	12.2494
Oil Supply/GDP (toe per thousand 2000 US$)	0.0973	0.0915	0.0938	0.0915	0.0887	0.0839
Oil Supply/Population (toe per capita)	2.9929	2.8743	2.9071	2.9018	2.9891	3.0078
Elect. Cons./GDP (kWh per 2000 US$)	0.8527	0.8578	0.8986	0.8738	0.8350	0.7827
Elect. Cons./Population (kWh per capita)	26 221	26 947	27 851	27 716	28 126	28 057
Industry Cons.**/Industrial Production (2000=100)	..	..	..	..	..	..
Industry Oil Cons.**/Industrial Production (2000=100)	..	..	..	..	..	..

* Electricity consumption equals domestic supply less distribution losses.
La consommation d'électricité représente l'approvisionnement intérieur diminué des pertes de distribution.

** Includes non-energy use in industry/transformation/energy sectors.
Comprend l'usage non-énergétique dans les secteurs de l'industrie/transformation/énergie.

Iceland / Islande

Figure 1. TPES* in 1973

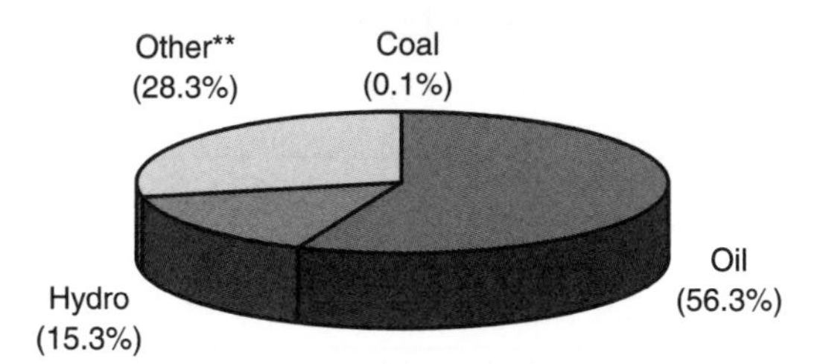

Figure 2. TPES* in 2005

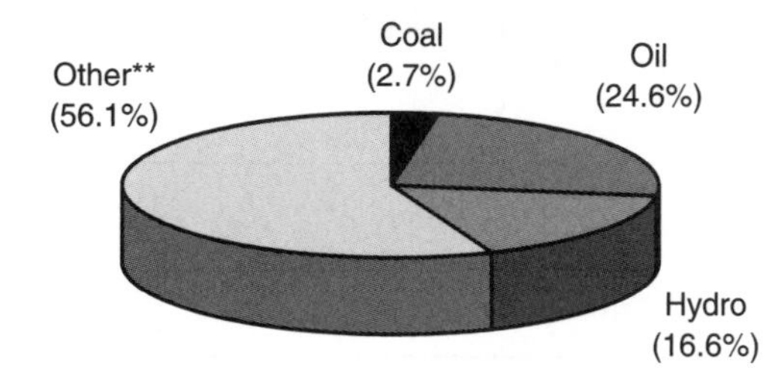

Figure 3. Final Consumption by Sector***

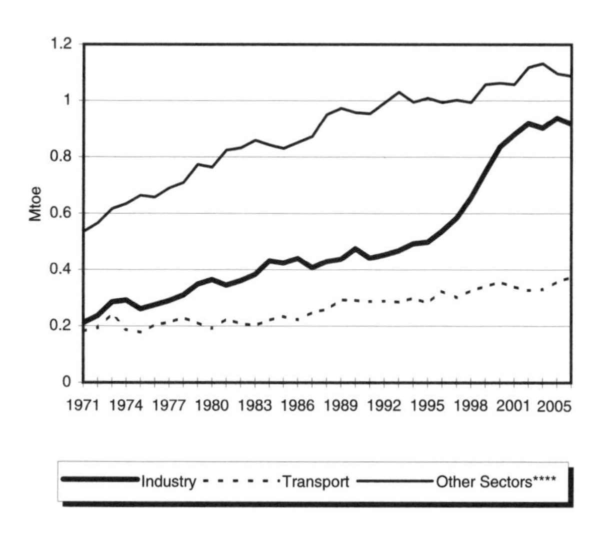

Figure 4. Breakdown of Sectorial Final Consumption by Source in 1973 and 2005***

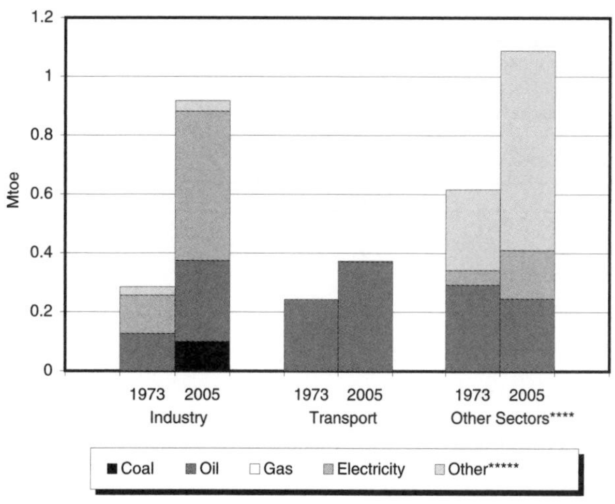

Figure 5. Electricity Generation by Fuel

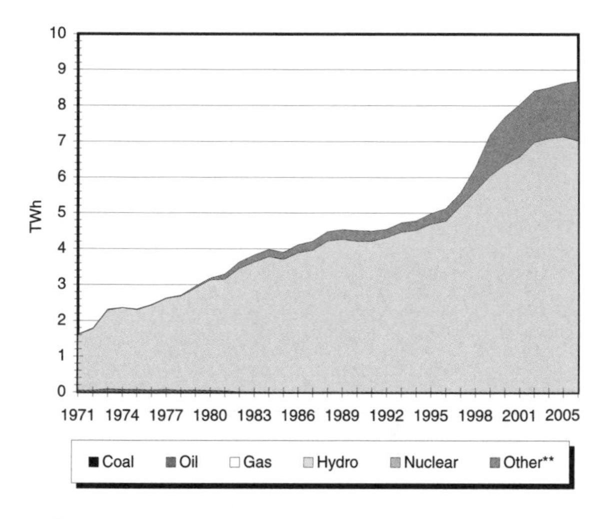

Figure 6. Electricity Consumption/GDP, TPES/GDP and Energy Production/TPES

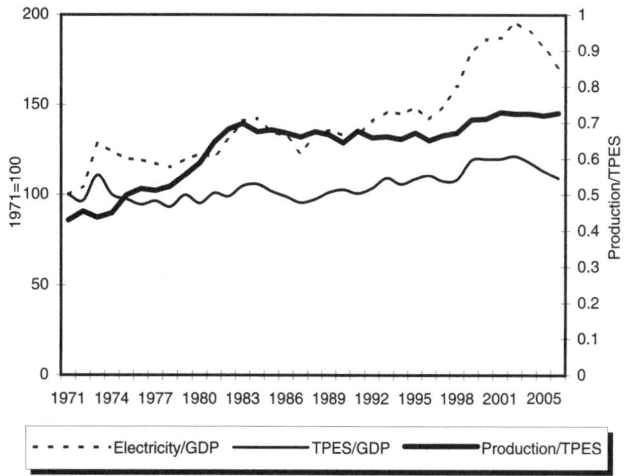

* Excluding electricity trade.

** Includes geothermal, solar, wind, combustible renewables & waste, etc.

*** Includes non-energy use.

**** Includes residential, commercial and public services, agriculture/forestry, fishing and non-specified.

***** Includes comb. renewables & waste, direct use of geothermal/solar thermal and heat produced in CHP/heat plants.

Iceland / Islande : 2004

Million tonnes of oil equivalent / *Million de tonnes d'équivalent pétrole*

SUPPLY AND CONSUMPTION / *APPROVISIONNEMENT ET DEMANDE*	Coal / *Charbon*	Crude Oil / *Pétrole brut*	Petroleum Products / *Produits pétroliers*	Gas / *Gaz*	Nuclear / *Nucléaire*	Hydro / *Hydro*	Geotherm. Solar etc. / *Géotherm. solaire etc.*	Combust. Renew. & Waste / *Comb. ren. & déchets*	Electricity / *Electricité*	Heat / *Chaleur*	Total / *Total*
Production	-	-	-	-	-	0.61	1.90	0.00	-	-	2.52
Imports	0.10	-	0.98	-	-	-	-	-	-	-	1.08
Exports	-	-	-	-	-	-	-	-	-	-	-
Intl. Marine Bunkers	-	-	-0.07	-	-	-	-	-	-	-	-0.07
Stock Changes	-	-	-0.03	-	-	-	-	-	-	-	-0.03
TPES	**0.10**	**-**	**0.88**	**-**	**-**	**0.61**	**1.90**	**0.00**	**-**	**-**	**3.50**
Transfers	-	-	-	-	-	-	-	-	-	-	-
Statistical Differences	-	-	-	-	-	-	-	-	-	-	-
Electricity Plants	-	-	-0.00	-	-	-0.61	-0.37	-0.00	0.65	-	-0.34
CHP Plants	-	-	-	-	-	-	-0.87	-	0.09	0.21	-0.56
Heat Plants	-	-	-	-	-	-	-0.02	-0.00	-0.02	0.03	-0.01
Gas Works	-	-	-	-	-	-	-	-	-	-	-
Petroleum Refineries	-	-	-	-	-	-	-	-	-	-	-
Coal Transformation	-	-	-	-	-	-	-	-	-	-	-
Liquefaction Plants	-	-	-	-	-	-	-	-	-	-	-
Other Transformation	-	-	-	-	-	-	-	-	-	-	-
Own Use	-	-	-	-	-	-	-	-	-0.02	-	-0.02
Distribution Losses	-	-	-	-	-	-	-0.11	-	-0.03	-0.03	-0.17
TFC	**0.10**	**-**	**0.87**	**-**	**-**	**-**	**0.53**	**-**	**0.67**	**0.21**	**2.39**
INDUSTRY SECTOR	**0.10**	**-**	**0.13**	**-**	**-**	**-**	**0.05**	**-**	**0.51**	**-**	**0.80**
Iron and Steel	0.09	-	-	-	-	-	-	-	0.09	-	0.18
Chemical and Petrochem.	-	-	-	-	-	-	-	-	0.00	-	0.00
Non-Ferrous Metals	-	-	0.01	-	-	-	-	-	0.36	-	0.37
Non-Metallic Minerals	0.01	-	-	-	-	-	-	-	0.00	-	0.02
Transport Equipment	-	-	-	-	-	-	-	-	0.00	-	0.00
Machinery	-	-	-	-	-	-	-	-	0.00	-	0.00
Mining and Quarrying	-	-	-	-	-	-	0.05	-	0.00	-	0.05
Food and Tobacco	-	-	0.05	-	-	-	0.00	-	0.04	-	0.09
Paper, Pulp and Printing	-	-	-	-	-	-	-	-	0.00	-	0.00
Wood and Wood Products	-	-	-	-	-	-	-	-	0.00	-	0.00
Construction	-	-	0.07	-	-	-	-	-	0.01	-	0.08
Textile and Leather	-	-	-	-	-	-	-	-	0.00	-	0.00
Non-specified	-	-	-	-	-	-	-	-	0.00	-	0.00
TRANSPORT SECTOR	**-**	**-**	**0.35**	**-**	**-**	**-**	**-**	**-**	**0.00**	**-**	**0.36**
International Aviation	-	-	0.12	-	-	-	-	-	-	-	0.12
Domestic Aviation	-	-	0.01	-	-	-	-	-	-	-	0.01
Road	-	-	0.22	-	-	-	-	-	-	-	0.22
Rail	-	-	-	-	-	-	-	-	-	-	-
Pipeline Transport	-	-	-	-	-	-	-	-	0.00	-	0.00
Domestic Navigation	-	-	0.01	-	-	-	-	-	-	-	0.01
Non-specified	-	-	-	-	-	-	-	-	-	-	-
OTHER SECTORS	**-**	**-**	**0.24**	**-**	**-**	**-**	**0.48**	**-**	**0.16**	**0.21**	**1.09**
Residential	-	-	0.01	-	-	-	0.38	-	0.06	0.18	0.62
Comm. and Publ. Services	-	-	-	-	-	-	0.05	-	0.08	0.01	0.14
Agriculture/Forestry	-	-	0.01	-	-	-	0.05	-	0.02	-	0.08
Fishing	-	-	0.23	-	-	-	-	-	0.00	-	0.23
Non-specified	-	-	-	-	-	-	-	-	0.01	0.02	0.02
NON-ENERGY USE	**-**	**-**	**0.15**	**-**	**-**	**-**	**-**	**-**	**-**	**-**	**0.15**
in Industry/Transf./Energy	-	-	0.14	-	-	-	-	-	-	-	0.14
of which: Feedstocks	-	-	-	-	-	-	-	-	-	-	-
in Transport	-	-	-	-	-	-	-	-	-	-	-
in Other Sectors	-	-	0.01	-	-	-	-	-	-	-	0.01
Electricity Generated - TWh	**-**	**-**	***0.00***	**-**	**-**	***7.13***	***1.48***	***0.00***	**-**	**-**	***8.62***
Electricity Plants	-	-	*0.00*	-	-	*7.13*	*0.43*	*0.00*	-	-	*7.57*
CHP plants	-	-	-	-	-	-	*1.06*	-	-	-	*1.06*
Heat Generated - PJ	**-**	**-**	**-**	**-**	**-**	**-**	***9.29***	***0.06***	***0.62***	**-**	***9.96***
CHP plants	-	-	-	-	-	-	*8.81*	-	-	-	*8.81*
Heat Plants	-	-	-	-	-	-	*0.48*	*0.06*	*0.62*	-	*1.15*

Iceland / Islande : 2005

Million tonnes of oil equivalent / *Million de tonnes d'équivalent pétrole*

SUPPLY AND CONSUMPTION / ***APPROVISIONNEMENT ET DEMANDE***	Coal / *Charbon*	Crude Oil / *Pétrole brut*	Petroleum Products / *Produits pétroliers*	Gas / *Gaz*	Nuclear / *Nucléaire*	Hydro / *Hydro*	Geotherm. Solar etc. / *Géotherm. solaire etc.*	Combust. Renew. & Waste / *Comb. ren. & déchets*	Electricity / *Electricité*	Heat / *Chaleur*	Total / *Total*
Production	-	-	-	-	-	0.60	2.03	0.00	-	-	2.64
Imports	0.10	-	0.98	-	-	-	-	-	-	-	1.08
Exports	-	-	-	-	-	-	-	-	-	-	-
Intl. Marine Bunkers	-	-	-0.07	-	-	-	-	-	-	-	-0.07
Stock Changes	-	-	-0.02	-	-	-	-	-	-	-	-0.02
TPES	**0.10**	**-**	**0.89**	**-**	**-**	**0.60**	**2.03**	**0.00**	**-**	**-**	**3.63**
Transfers	-	-	-	-	-	-	-	-	-	-	-
Statistical Differences	-	-	-	-	-	-	-	-	-	-	-
Electricity Plants	-	-	-0.00	-	-	-0.60	-0.44	-0.00	0.65	-	-0.40
CHP Plants	-	-	-	-	-	-	-0.98	-	0.10	0.19	-0.69
Heat Plants	-	-	-	-	-	-	-0.03	-0.00	-0.01	0.03	-0.02
Gas Works	-	-	-	-	-	-	-	-	-	-	-
Petroleum Refineries	-	-	-	-	-	-	-	-	-	-	-
Coal Transformation	-	-	-	-	-	-	-	-	-	-	-
Liquefaction Plants	-	-	-	-	-	-	-	-	-	-	-
Other Transformation	-	-	-	-	-	-	-	-	-	-	-
Own Use	-	-	-	-	-	-	-	-	-0.03	-	-0.03
Distribution Losses	-	-	-	-	-	-	-0.07	-	-0.03	-0.02	-0.13
TFC	**0.10**	**-**	**0.89**	**-**	**-**	**-**	**0.52**	**-**	**0.67**	**0.20**	**2.38**
INDUSTRY SECTOR	**0.10**	**-**	**0.12**	**-**	**-**	**-**	**0.04**	**-**	**0.51**	**-**	**0.77**
Iron and Steel	0.09	-	-	-	-	-	-	-	0.08	-	0.17
Chemical and Petrochem.	-	-	-	-	-	-	-	-	0.00	-	0.00
Non-Ferrous Metals	-	-	0.01	-	-	-	-	-	0.36	-	0.37
Non-Metallic Minerals	0.01	-	-	-	-	-	-	-	0.00	-	0.01
Transport Equipment	-	-	-	-	-	-	-	-	0.00	-	0.00
Machinery	-	-	-	-	-	-	-	-	0.00	-	0.00
Mining and Quarrying	-	-	-	-	-	-	0.03	-	0.00	-	0.03
Food and Tobacco	-	-	0.04	-	-	-	0.00	-	0.04	-	0.09
Paper, Pulp and Printing	-	-	-	-	-	-	-	-	0.00	-	0.00
Wood and Wood Products	-	-	-	-	-	-	-	-	0.00	-	0.00
Construction	-	-	0.07	-	-	-	-	-	0.01	-	0.08
Textile and Leather	-	-	-	-	-	-	-	-	0.00	-	0.00
Non-specified	-	-	-	-	-	-	-	-	0.00	-	0.00
TRANSPORT SECTOR	**-**	**-**	**0.37**	**-**	**-**	**-**	**-**	**-**	**0.00**	**-**	**0.37**
International Aviation	-	-	0.14	-	-	-	-	-	-	-	0.14
Domestic Aviation	-	-	0.01	-	-	-	-	-	-	-	0.01
Road	-	-	0.22	-	-	-	-	-	-	-	0.22
Rail	-	-	-	-	-	-	-	-	-	-	-
Pipeline Transport	-	-	-	-	-	-	-	-	0.00	-	0.00
Domestic Navigation	-	-	0.01	-	-	-	-	-	-	-	0.01
Non-specified	-	-	-	-	-	-	-	-	-	-	-
OTHER SECTORS	**-**	**-**	**0.24**	**-**	**-**	**-**	**0.48**	**-**	**0.16**	**0.20**	**1.08**
Residential	-	-	0.01	-	-	-	0.38	-	0.06	0.17	0.61
Comm. and Publ. Services	-	-	-	-	-	-	0.05	-	0.08	0.01	0.14
Agriculture/Forestry	-	-	0.01	-	-	-	0.05	-	0.02	-	0.08
Fishing	-	-	0.23	-	-	-	-	-	0.00	-	0.23
Non-specified	-	-	-	-	-	-	-	-	0.01	0.02	0.02
NON-ENERGY USE	**-**	**-**	**0.16**	**-**	**-**	**-**	**-**	**-**	**-**	**-**	**0.16**
in Industry/Transf./Energy	-	-	0.15	-	-	-	-	-	-	-	0.15
of which: Feedstocks	-	-	-	-	-	-	-	-	-	-	-
in Transport	-	-	-	-	-	-	-	-	-	-	-
in Other Sectors	-	-	0.01	-	-	-	-	-	-	-	0.01
Electricity Generated - TWh	***-***	***-***	***0.01***	***-***	***-***	***7.02***	***1.66***	***0.00***	***-***	***-***	***8.69***
Electricity Plants	*-*	*-*	*0.01*	*-*	*-*	*7.02*	*0.51*	*0.00*	*-*	*-*	*7.54*
CHP plants	*-*	*-*	*-*	*-*	*-*	*-*	*1.15*	*-*	*-*	*-*	*1.15*
Heat Generated - PJ	***-***	***-***	***-***	***-***	***-***	***-***	***8.67***	***0.06***	***0.57***	***-***	***9.29***
CHP plants	*-*	*-*	*-*	*-*	*-*	*-*	*8.07*	*-*	*-*	*-*	*8.07*
Heat Plants	*-*	*-*	*-*	*-*	*-*	*-*	*0.60*	*0.06*	*0.57*	*-*	*1.22*

Ireland / Irlande
Key Indicators
Indicateurs principaux

	1960	1970	1973	1980	1990	1995
Energy Production (Mtoe)	1.38	1.42	1.12	1.89	3.47	4.11
Net Imports (Mtoe)	2.59	5.09	5.99	6.69	7.12	7.77
Total Primary Energy Supply (Mtoe)	3.78	6.26	7.19	8.49	10.37	10.80
Net Oil Imports (Mtoe)	1.43	4.30	5.48	5.88	5.11	5.80
Oil Supply (Mtoe)	1.25	4.08	5.54	5.77	4.87	5.67
Electricity Consumption (TWh)*	1.97	5.18	6.61	9.79	13.24	16.33
GDP (billion 2000 US$ using exch. rates)	14.14 e	21.32	24.60	33.87	48.34	60.62
GDP (billion 2000 US$ using PPPs)	16.09 e	24.27	28.00	38.54	55.01	69.00
Population (millions)	2.83 e	2.95	3.07	3.40	3.51	3.60
Industrial Production Index (2000=100)	..	..	..	16.80	30.90	49.60
Energy Production/TPES	0.3655	0.2264	0.1558	0.2232	0.3345	0.3805
Net Oil Imports/GDP (toe per thousand 2000 US$)	0.1012 e	0.2017	0.2229	0.1736	0.1057	0.0956
TPES/GDP (toe per thousand 2000 US$)	0.2675 e	0.2935	0.2922	0.2506	0.2144	0.1782
TPES/GDP (toe per thousand 2000 US$ PPP)	0.2350 e	0.2578	0.2567	0.2201	0.1884	0.1566
TPES/Population (toe per capita)	1.3344 e	2.1211	2.3396	2.4950	2.9565	3.0004
Oil Supply/GDP (toe per thousand 2000 US$)	0.0881 e	0.1912	0.2254	0.1703	0.1008	0.0936
Oil Supply/Population (toe per capita)	0.4393 e	1.3817	1.8044	1.6961	1.3894	1.5752
Elect. Cons./GDP (kWh per 2000 US$)	0.1391 e	0.2428	0.2688	0.2891	0.2739	0.2694
Elect. Cons./Population (kWh per capita)	694 e	1 755	2 152	2 878	3 776	4 535
Industry Cons.**/Industrial Production (2000=100)	..	..	..	460.38	248.31	165.56
Industry Oil Cons.**/Industrial Production (2000=100)	..	..	..	735.94	209.20	166.01

	2000	2001	2002	2003	2004	2005
Energy Production (Mtoe)	2.18	1.80	1.57	1.86	1.89	1.66
Net Imports (Mtoe)	12.29	13.81	13.83	13.70	14.00	13.80
Total Primary Energy Supply (Mtoe)	14.28	15.26	15.55	15.00	15.15	15.29
Net Oil Imports (Mtoe)	8.11	9.01	8.98	8.71	8.99	8.64
Oil Supply (Mtoe)	8.05	8.69	8.70	8.49	8.82	8.57
Electricity Consumption (TWh)*	22.06	22.80	23.73	24.35	25.11	25.93
GDP (billion 2000 US$ using exch. rates)	96.33	101.96	108.11	112.75	117.61	124.11
GDP (billion 2000 US$ using PPPs)	109.64	116.05	123.05	128.33	133.86	141.26
Population (millions)	3.80	3.86	3.93	3.99	4.06	4.15
Industrial Production Index (2000=100)	100.00	110.00	117.90	123.50	123.80	127.60
Energy Production/TPES	0.1527	0.1181	0.1010	0.1242	0.1246	0.1087
Net Oil Imports/GDP (toe per thousand 2000 US$)	0.0842	0.0884	0.0830	0.0773	0.0764	0.0696
TPES/GDP (toe per thousand 2000 US$)	0.1483	0.1497	0.1438	0.1330	0.1288	0.1232
TPES/GDP (toe per thousand 2000 US$ PPP)	0.1303	0.1315	0.1264	0.1169	0.1132	0.1082
TPES/Population (toe per capita)	3.7583	3.9549	3.9609	3.7577	3.7327	3.6850
Oil Supply/GDP (toe per thousand 2000 US$)	0.0836	0.0852	0.0805	0.0753	0.0750	0.0690
Oil Supply/Population (toe per capita)	2.1192	2.2521	2.2157	2.1272	2.1730	2.0644
Elect. Cons./GDP (kWh per 2000 US$)	0.2290	0.2236	0.2195	0.2160	0.2135	0.2089
Elect. Cons./Population (kWh per capita)	5 804	5 908	6 045	6 101	6 186	6 249
Industry Cons.**/Industrial Production (2000=100)	100.00	92.98	83.91	68.98	67.66	70.54
Industry Oil Cons.**/Industrial Production (2000=100)	100.00	90.76	85.38	80.31	77.26	79.64

* Electricity consumption equals domestic supply less distribution losses.
La consommation d'électricité représente l'approvisionnement intérieur diminué des pertes de distribution.

** Includes non-energy use in industry/transformation/energy sectors.
Comprend l'usage non-énergétique dans les secteurs de l'industrie/transformation/énergie.

Ireland / Irlande

Figure 1. TPES* in 1973

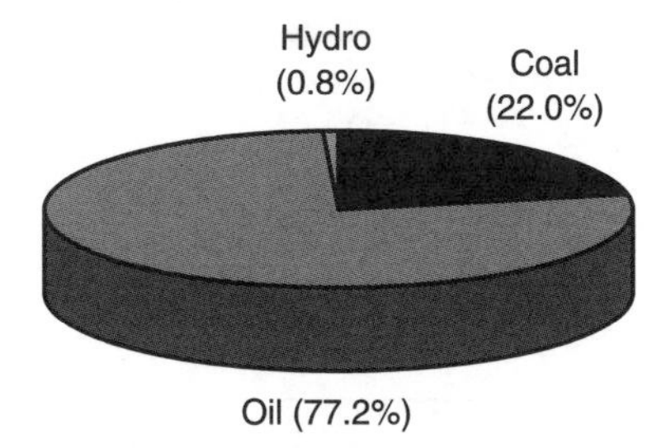

Figure 2. TPES* in 2005

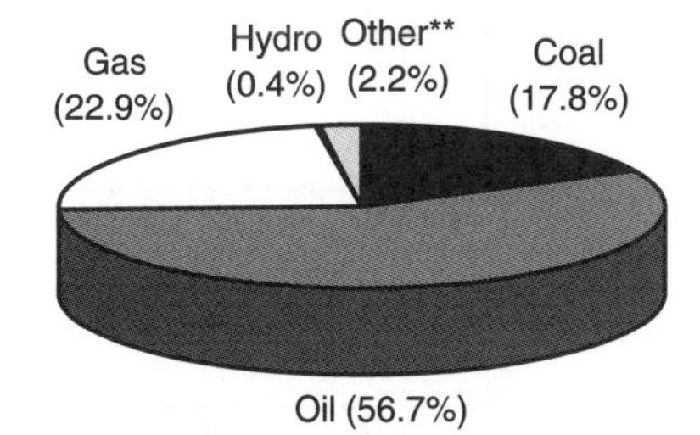

Figure 3. Final Consumption by Sector***

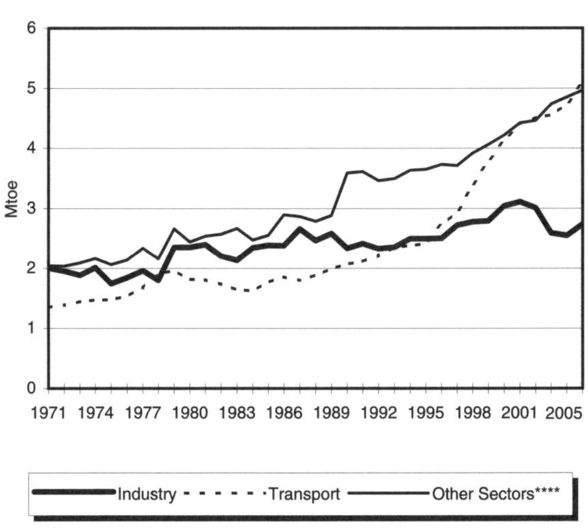

Figure 4. Breakdown of Sectorial Final Consumption by Source in 1973 and 2005***

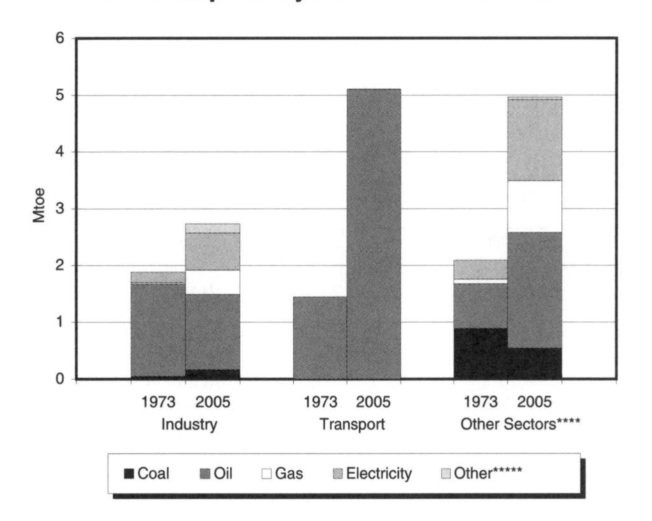

Figure 5. Electricity Generation by Fuel

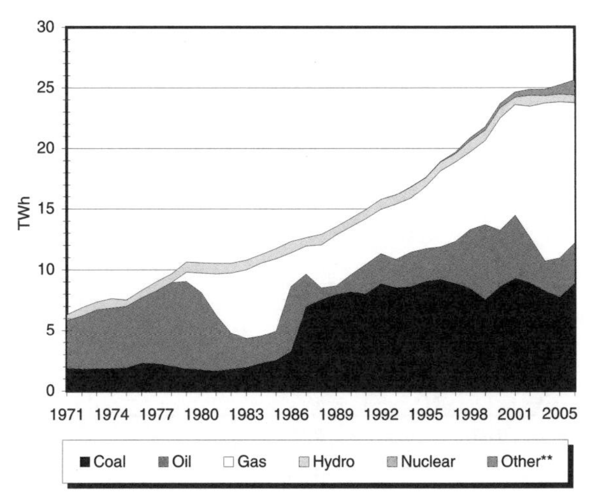

Figure 6. Electricity Consumption/GDP, TPES/GDP and Energy Production/TPES

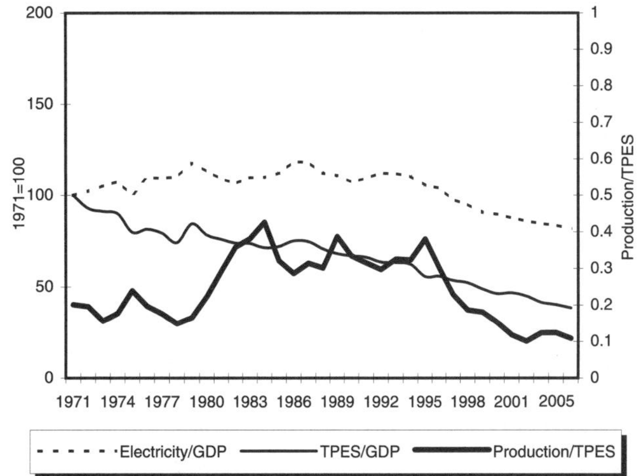

* Excluding electricity trade.

** Includes geothermal, solar, wind, combustible renewables & waste, etc.

*** Includes non-energy use.

**** Includes residential, commercial and public services, agriculture/forestry, fishing and non-specified.

***** Includes comb. renewables & waste, direct use of geothermal/solar thermal and heat produced in CHP/heat plants.

Ireland / Irlande : 2004

Million tonnes of oil equivalent / *Million de tonnes d'équivalent pétrole*

SUPPLY AND CONSUMPTION / ***APPROVISIONNEMENT ET DEMANDE***	Coal / *Charbon*	Crude Oil / *Pétrole brut*	Petroleum Products / *Produits pétroliers*	Gas / *Gaz*	Nuclear / *Nucléaire*	Hydro / *Hydro*	Geotherm. Solar etc. / *Géotherm. solaire etc.*	Combust. Renew. & Waste / *Comb. ren. & déchets*	Electricity / *Electricité*	Heat / *Chaleur*	Total / *Total*
Production	0.89	-	-	0.69	-	0.05	0.06	0.20	-	-	1.89
Imports	1.94	2.98	7.31	2.96	-	-	-	-	0.14	-	15.32
Exports	-0.02	-	-1.30	-	-	-	-	-	-	-	-1.32
Intl. Marine Bunkers	-	-	-0.15	-	-	-	-	-	-	-	-0.15
Stock Changes	-0.57	0.03	-0.05	-0.00	-	-	-	-	-	-	-0.59
TPES	**2.24**	**3.01**	**5.81**	**3.64**	**-**	**0.05**	**0.06**	**0.20**	**0.14**	**-**	**15.15**
Transfers	-	-	-0.00	-	-	-	-	-	-	-	-0.00
Statistical Differences	0.20	0.08	0.12	-0.01	-	-	-	-0.00	-0.01	-	0.37
Electricity Plants	-1.67	-	-0.77	-2.15	-	-0.05	-0.06	-0.02	2.11	-	-2.61
CHP Plants	-0.01	-	-0.01	-0.09	-	-	-	-0.00	0.06	-	-0.06
Heat Plants	-	-	-	-	-	-	-	-	-	-	-
Gas Works	-	-	-	-	-	-	-	-	-	-	-
Petroleum Refineries	-	-3.09	2.96	-	-	-	-	-	-	-	-0.13
Coal Transformation	-0.05	-	-0.01	-	-	-	-	-	-	-	-0.06
Liquefaction Plants	-	-	-	-	-	-	-	-	-	-	-
Other Transformation	-	-	-	-	-	-	-	-	-	-	-
Own Use	-0.04	-	-0.12	-	-	-	-	-	-0.13	-	-0.30
Distribution Losses	-	-	-	-0.06	-	-	-	-	-0.18	-	-0.24
TFC	**0.67**	**-**	**7.98**	**1.32**	**-**	**-**	**0.00**	**0.17**	**1.98**	**-**	**12.12**
INDUSTRY SECTOR	**0.15**	**-**	**1.05**	**0.43**	**-**	**-**	**-**	**0.13**	**0.59**	**-**	**2.35**
Iron and Steel	-	-	-	0.00	-	-	-	-	0.00	-	0.00
Chemical and Petrochem.	-	-	0.14	0.09	-	-	-	-	0.11	-	0.34
Non-Ferrous Metals	-	-	0.34	-	-	-	-	-	0.03	-	0.37
Non-Metallic Minerals	0.13	-	0.25	0.03	-	-	-	-	0.04	-	0.45
Transport Equipment	-	-	0.01	-	-	-	-	-	0.01	-	0.02
Machinery	-	-	0.05	-	-	-	-	-	0.11	-	0.16
Mining and Quarrying	-	-	0.03	0.03	-	-	-	-	0.04	-	0.10
Food and Tobacco	0.01	-	0.14	0.20	-	-	-	0.05	0.14	-	0.54
Paper, Pulp and Printing	-	-	0.01	-	-	-	-	-	0.02	-	0.03
Wood and Wood Products	-	-	0.01	-	-	-	-	0.08	0.03	-	0.12
Construction	-	-	-	-	-	-	-	-	0.01	-	0.01
Textile and Leather	0.01	-	0.02	-	-	-	-	-	0.01	-	0.04
Non-specified	-	-	0.06	0.09	-	-	-	-	0.04	-	0.18
TRANSPORT SECTOR	**-**	**-**	**4.70**	**-**	**-**	**-**	**-**	**-**	**0.00**	**-**	**4.71**
International Aviation	-	-	0.71	-	-	-	-	-	-	-	0.71
Domestic Aviation	-	-	0.04	-	-	-	-	-	-	-	0.04
Road	-	-	3.90	-	-	-	-	-	-	-	3.90
Rail	-	-	0.04	-	-	-	-	-	0.00	-	0.04
Pipeline Transport	-	-	-	-	-	-	-	-	-	-	-
Domestic Navigation	-	-	0.02	-	-	-	-	-	-	-	0.02
Non-specified	-	-	-	-	-	-	-	-	-	-	-
OTHER SECTORS	**0.52**	**-**	**1.94**	**0.89**	**-**	**-**	**0.00**	**0.05**	**1.39**	**-**	**4.78**
Residential	0.49	-	1.11	0.59	-	-	0.00	0.04	0.63	-	2.87
Comm. and Publ. Services	0.03	-	0.57	0.30	-	-	0.00	0.00	0.70	-	1.60
Agriculture/Forestry	-	-	0.26	-	-	-	-	-	0.05	-	0.31
Fishing	-	-	-	-	-	-	-	-	-	-	-
Non-specified	-	-	-	-	-	-	-	-	-	-	-
NON-ENERGY USE	**-**	**-**	**0.28**	**-**	**-**	**-**	**-**	**-**	**-**	**-**	**0.28**
in Industry/Transf./Energy	-	-	0.20	-	-	-	-	-	-	-	0.20
of which: Feedstocks	-	-	-	-	-	-	-	-	-	-	-
in Transport	-	-	0.02	-	-	-	-	-	-	-	0.02
in Other Sectors	-	-	0.07	-	-	-	-	-	-	-	0.07
Electricity Generated - TWh	***7.72***	**-**	***3.21***	***12.89***	**-**	***0.63***	***0.66***	***0.11***	**-**	**-**	***25.22***
Electricity Plants	*7.67*	-	*3.17*	*12.34*	-	*0.63*	*0.66*	*0.09*	-	-	*24.55*
CHP plants	*0.05*	-	*0.04*	*0.56*	-	-	-	*0.02*	-	-	*0.67*
Heat Generated - PJ	**-**	**-**	**-**	**-**	**-**	**-**	**-**	**-**	**-**	**-**	**-**
CHP plants	-	-	-	-	-	-	-	-	-	-	-
Heat Plants	-	-	-	-	-	-	-	-	-	-	-

Ireland / Irlande : 2005

Million tonnes of oil equivalent / *Million de tonnes d'équivalent pétrole*

SUPPLY AND CONSUMPTION / ***APPROVISIONNEMENT ET DEMANDE***	Coal / *Charbon*	Crude Oil / *Pétrole brut*	Petroleum Products / *Produits pétroliers*	Gas / *Gaz*	Nuclear / *Nucléaire*	Hydro / *Hydro*	Geotherm. Solar etc. / *Géotherm. solaire etc.*	Combust. Renew. & Waste / *Comb. ren. & déchets*	Electricity / *Electricité*	Heat / *Chaleur*	Total / *Total*
Production	0.81	-	-	0.46	-	0.05	0.10	0.24	-	-	1.66
Imports	1.99	3.35	6.73	3.01	-	-	-	-	0.18	-	15.25
Exports	-0.02	-	-1.44	-	-	-	-	-	-0.00	-	-1.46
Intl. Marine Bunkers	-	-	-0.11	-	-	-	-	-	-	-	-0.11
Stock Changes	-0.09	0.04	-0.01	-0.00	-	-	-	-	-	-	-0.06
TPES	**2.69**	**3.39**	**5.18**	**3.47**	**-**	**0.05**	**0.10**	**0.24**	**0.18**	**-**	**15.29**
Transfers	-	-	-0.01	-	-	-	-	-	-	-	-0.01
Statistical Differences	0.03	0.00	1.02	-0.02	-	-	-	-	0.07	-	1.09
Electricity Plants	-1.91	-	-0.77	-1.95	-	-0.05	-0.10	-0.02	2.15	-	-2.66
CHP Plants	-0.01	-	-0.01	-0.09	-	-	-	-0.00	0.05	-	-0.06
Heat Plants	-	-	-	-	-	-	-	-	-	-	-
Gas Works	-	-	-	-	-	-	-	-	-	-	-
Petroleum Refineries	-	-3.39	3.20	-	-	-	-	-	-	-	-0.19
Coal Transformation	-0.06	-	-0.01	-	-	-	-	-	-	-	-0.07
Liquefaction Plants	-	-	-	-	-	-	-	-	-	-	-
Other Transformation	-	-	-	-	-	-	-	-	-	-	-
Own Use	-0.02	-	-0.14	-	-	-	-	-	-0.17	-	-0.34
Distribution Losses	-	-	-	-0.07	-	-	-	-	-0.18	-	-0.25
TFC	**0.70**	**-**	**8.46**	**1.34**	**-**	**-**	**0.00**	**0.21**	**2.09**	**-**	**12.81**
INDUSTRY SECTOR	**0.16**	**-**	**1.06**	**0.43**	**-**	**-**	**-**	**0.16**	**0.66**	**-**	**2.47**
Iron and Steel	-	-	-	-	-	-	-	-	0.00	-	0.00
Chemical and Petrochem.	-	-	0.14	0.11	-	-	-	-	0.12	-	0.37
Non-Ferrous Metals	-	-	0.34	-	-	-	-	-	0.03	-	0.37
Non-Metallic Minerals	0.12	-	0.25	0.03	-	-	-	-	0.05	-	0.45
Transport Equipment	-	-	0.01	-	-	-	-	-	0.01	-	0.02
Machinery	0.01	-	0.05	-	-	-	-	-	0.12	-	0.18
Mining and Quarrying	-	-	0.03	0.02	-	-	-	-	0.04	-	0.08
Food and Tobacco	0.02	-	0.15	0.20	-	-	-	0.05	0.16	-	0.58
Paper, Pulp and Printing	-	-	0.01	-	-	-	-	-	0.03	-	0.03
Wood and Wood Products	-	-	0.01	-	-	-	-	0.11	0.03	-	0.15
Construction	-	-	-	-	-	-	-	-	0.01	-	0.01
Textile and Leather	0.01	-	0.03	-	-	-	-	-	0.02	-	0.05
Non-specified	-	-	0.06	0.07	-	-	-	-	0.05	-	0.18
TRANSPORT SECTOR	**-**	**-**	**5.10**	**-**	**-**	**-**	**-**	**0.00**	**0.01**	**-**	**5.10**
International Aviation	-	-	0.82	-	-	-	-	-	-	-	0.82
Domestic Aviation	-	-	0.05	-	-	-	-	-	-	-	0.05
Road	-	-	4.17	-	-	-	-	-	-	-	4.17
Rail	-	-	0.04	-	-	-	-	-	0.01	-	0.05
Pipeline Transport	-	-	-	-	-	-	-	-	-	-	-
Domestic Navigation	-	-	0.02	-	-	-	-	-	-	-	0.02
Non-specified	-	-	-	-	-	-	-	0.00	-	-	0.00
OTHER SECTORS	**0.54**	**-**	**1.99**	**0.91**	**-**	**-**	**0.00**	**0.05**	**1.43**	**-**	**4.92**
Residential	0.51	-	1.14	0.52	-	-	0.00	0.04	0.65	-	2.86
Comm. and Publ. Services	0.03	-	0.59	0.39	-	-	0.00	0.00	0.73	-	1.73
Agriculture/Forestry	-	-	0.27	-	-	-	-	-	0.06	-	0.33
Fishing	-	-	-	-	-	-	-	-	-	-	-
Non-specified	-	-	-	-	-	-	-	-	-	-	-
NON-ENERGY USE	**-**	**-**	**0.31**	**-**	**-**	**-**	**-**	**-**	**-**	**-**	**0.31**
in Industry/Transf./Energy	-	-	0.26	-	-	-	-	-	-	-	0.26
of which: Feedstocks	-	-	-	-	-	-	-	-	-	-	-
in Transport	-	-	0.00	-	-	-	-	-	-	-	0.00
in Other Sectors	-	-	0.04	-	-	-	-	-	-	-	0.04
Electricity Generated - TWh	*8.84*	-	*3.34*	*11.57*	-	*0.63*	*1.11*	*0.13*	-	-	*25.63*
Electricity Plants	*8.78*	-	*3.30*	*11.08*	-	*0.63*	*1.11*	*0.11*	-	-	*25.00*
CHP plants	*0.06*	-	*0.04*	*0.50*	-	-	-	*0.02*	-	-	*0.63*
Heat Generated - PJ	-	-	-	-	-	-	-	-	-	-	-
CHP plants	-	-	-	-	-	-	-	-	-	-	-
Heat Plants	-	-	-	-	-	-	-	-	-	-	-

Italy / Italie
Key Indicators
Indicateurs principaux

	1960	1970	1973	1980	1990	1995
Energy Production (Mtoe)	13.84	19.87	20.46	19.90	25.31	29.42
Net Imports (Mtoe)	30.87	100.18	116.44	116.77	127.19	134.17
Total Primary Energy Supply (Mtoe)	39.93	109.58	128.93	132.15	147.97	161.05
Net Oil Imports (Mtoe)	23.65	90.87	107.00	92.73	85.07	89.19
Oil Supply (Mtoe)	20.94	82.52	100.11	89.55	84.73	93.03
Electricity Consumption (TWh)*	48.95	111.57	134.56	175.22	235.10	261.36
GDP (billion 2000 US$ using exch. rates)	292.05 e	508.83	575.48	738.95	937.38	998.50
GDP (billion 2000 US$ using PPPs)	392.30 e	683.48	773.01	992.59	1 259.12	1 341.22
Population (millions)	49.94 e	53.82	54.75	56.43	56.72	56.84
Industrial Production Index (2000=100)	27.70	54.30	61.90	76.60	86.40	93.00
Energy Production/TPES	0.3466	0.1813	0.1587	0.1505	0.1711	0.1827
Net Oil Imports/GDP (toe per thousand 2000 US$)	0.0810 e	0.1786	0.1859	0.1255	0.0908	0.0893
TPES/GDP (toe per thousand 2000 US$)	0.1367 e	0.2154	0.2240	0.1788	0.1579	0.1613
TPES/GDP (toe per thousand 2000 US$ PPP)	0.1018 e	0.1603	0.1668	0.1331	0.1175	0.1201
TPES/Population (toe per capita)	0.7995 e	2.0361	2.3548	2.3417	2.6088	2.8331
Oil Supply/GDP (toe per thousand 2000 US$)	0.0717 e	0.1622	0.1740	0.1212	0.0904	0.0932
Oil Supply/Population (toe per capita)	0.4194 e	1.5332	1.8285	1.5868	1.4938	1.6365
Elect. Cons./GDP (kWh per 2000 US$)	0.1676 e	0.2193	0.2338	0.2371	0.2508	0.2618
Elect. Cons./Population (kWh per capita)	980 e	2 073	2 458	3 105	4 145	4 598
Industry Cons.**/Industrial Production (2000=100)	136.64	169.72	166.79	126.52	111.06	101.39
Industry Oil Cons.**/Industrial Production (2000=100)	210.30	370.53	352.81	215.25	141.06	114.65

	2000	2001	2002	2003	2004	2005
Energy Production (Mtoe)	28.17	26.85	27.45	27.59	28.15	27.63
Net Imports (Mtoe)	152.28	146.86	152.06	154.64	157.93	159.33
Total Primary Energy Supply (Mtoe)	173.12	173.49	173.68	180.68	182.80	185.19
Net Oil Imports (Mtoe)	87.81	83.82	85.49	83.97	81.29	78.25
Oil Supply (Mtoe)	88.45	87.21	87.63	86.87	83.77	81.78
Electricity Consumption (TWh)*	301.79	308.03	316.09	323.96	328.11	332.23
GDP (billion 2000 US$ using exch. rates)	1 097.34	1 117.05	1 120.87	1 121.28	1 133.23	1 132.83
GDP (billion 2000 US$ using PPPs)	1 473.99	1 500.45	1 505.59	1 506.14	1 522.19	1 521.65
Population (millions)	56.94	56.98	57.16	57.61	58.18	58.53
Industrial Production Index (2000=100)	100.00	99.00	97.40	96.90	96.30	95.50
Energy Production/TPES	0.1627	0.1548	0.1581	0.1527	0.1540	0.1492
Net Oil Imports/GDP (toe per thousand 2000 US$)	0.0800	0.0750	0.0763	0.0749	0.0717	0.0691
TPES/GDP (toe per thousand 2000 US$)	0.1578	0.1553	0.1550	0.1611	0.1613	0.1635
TPES/GDP (toe per thousand 2000 US$ PPP)	0.1175	0.1156	0.1154	0.1200	0.1201	0.1217
TPES/Population (toe per capita)	3.0403	3.0448	3.0386	3.1365	3.1422	3.1639
Oil Supply/GDP (toe per thousand 2000 US$)	0.0806	0.0781	0.0782	0.0775	0.0739	0.0722
Oil Supply/Population (toe per capita)	1.5534	1.5305	1.5332	1.5080	1.4399	1.3973
Elect. Cons./GDP (kWh per 2000 US$)	0.2750	0.2758	0.2820	0.2889	0.2895	0.2933
Elect. Cons./Population (kWh per capita)	5 300	5 406	5 530	5 624	5 640	5 676
Industry Cons.**/Industrial Production (2000=100)	100.00	102.16	103.76	107.64	110.12	109.75
Industry Oil Cons.**/Industrial Production (2000=100)	100.00	102.25	108.52	113.26	115.46	115.81

* Electricity consumption equals domestic supply less distribution losses.
La consommation d'électricité représente l'approvisionnement intérieur diminué des pertes de distribution.

** Includes non-energy use in industry/transformation/energy sectors.
Comprend l'usage non-énergétique dans les secteurs de l'industrie/transformation/énergie.

Italy / Italie

Figure 1. TPES* in 1973

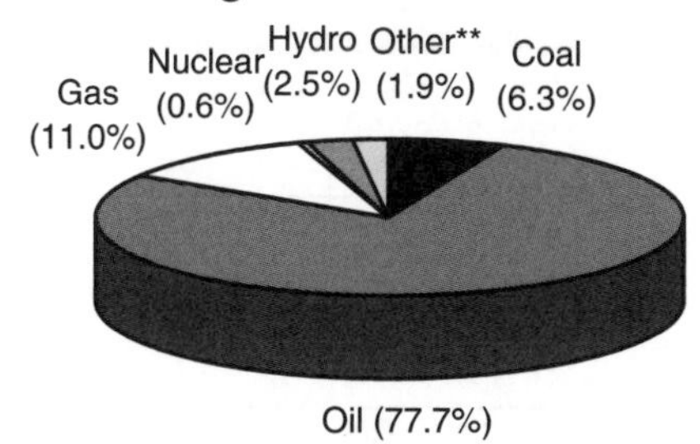

Figure 2. TPES* in 2005

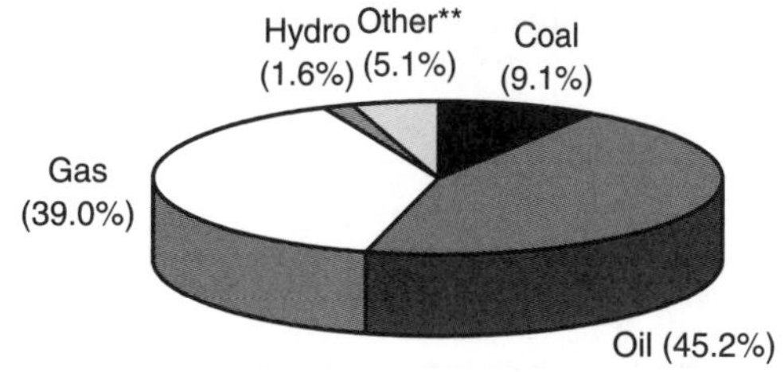

Figure 3. Final Consumption by Sector***

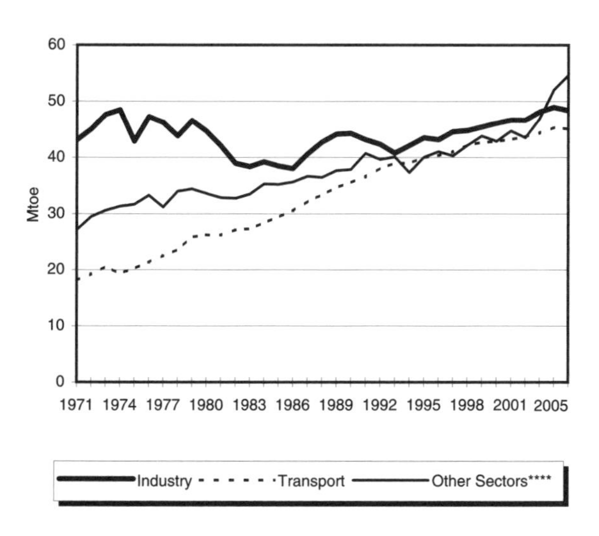

Figure 4. Breakdown of Sectorial Final Consumption by Source in 1973 and 2005***

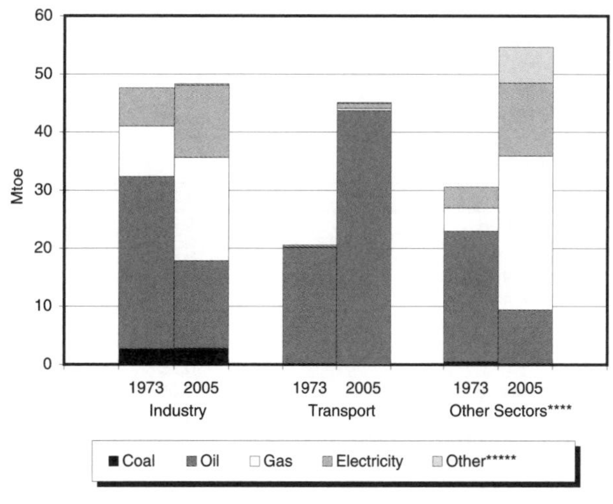

Figure 5. Electricity Generation by Fuel

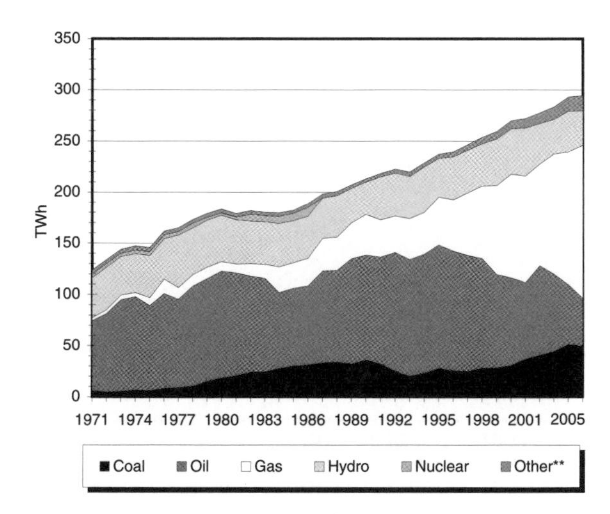

Figure 6. Electricity Consumption/GDP, TPES/GDP and Energy Production/TPES

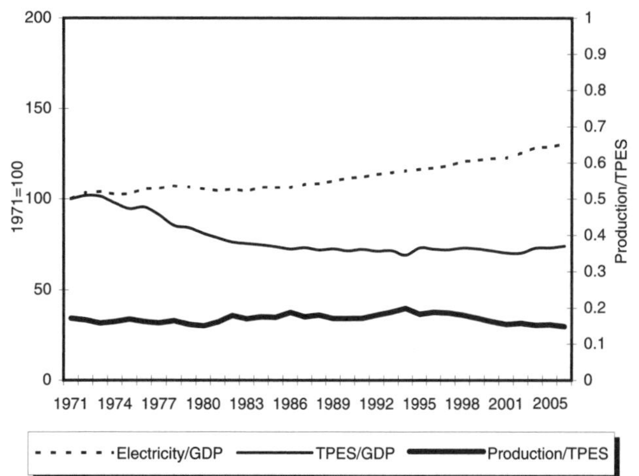

* Excluding electricity trade.

** Includes geothermal, solar, wind, combustible renewables & waste, etc.

*** Includes non-energy use.

**** Includes residential, commercial and public services, agriculture/forestry, fishing and non-specified.

***** Includes comb. renewables & waste, direct use of geothermal/solar thermal and heat produced in CHP/heat plants.

Italy / Italie : 2004

	Million tonnes of oil equivalent / *Million de tonnes d'équivalent pétrole*										
SUPPLY AND CONSUMPTION	Coal	Crude Oil	Petroleum Products	Gas	Nuclear	Hydro	Geotherm. Solar etc.	Combust. Renew. & Waste	Electricity	Heat	Total
APPROVISIONNEMENT ET DEMANDE	*Charbon*	*Pétrole brut*	*Produits pétroliers*	*Gaz*	*Nucléaire*	*Hydro*	*Géotherm. solaire etc.*	*Comb. ren. & déchets*	*Electricité*	*Chaleur*	*Total*
Production	0.06	5.62	-	10.61	-	3.41	5.07 e	3.39 e	-	-	28.15
Imports	16.95	93.29	14.23	55.60	-	-	-	0.65	3.99	-	184.70
Exports	-0.17	-1.41	-24.80	-0.32	-	-	-	-	-0.07	-	-26.78
Intl. Marine Bunkers	-	-	-3.37	-	-	-	-	-	-	-	-3.37
Stock Changes	-0.25	-0.12	0.35	0.11	-	-	-	-	-	-	0.09
TPES	**16.60**	**97.36**	**-13.60**	**66.00**	**-**	**3.41**	**5.07** e	**4.04**	**3.92**	**-**	**182.80**
Transfers	-	-	0.20	-	-	-	-	-	-	-	0.20
Statistical Differences	-0.00	-0.25	0.06	-0.00	-	-	-	-	-0.00	-	-0.20
Electricity Plants	-10.79	-	-8.81	-11.93	-	-3.41	-4.84 e	-1.03	18.05	-	-22.74
CHP Plants	-0.94	-	-2.84	-10.29	-	-	-	-1.07	7.15	4.53	-3.45
Heat Plants	-	-	-	-	-	-	-	-	-	-	-
Gas Works	-	-	-	-	-	-	-	-	-	-	-
Petroleum Refineries	-	-99.38	100.92	-	-	-	-	-	-	-	1.54
Coal Transformation	-1.74 e	-	-	-	-	-	-	-	-	-	-1.74
Liquefaction Plants	-	-	-	-	-	-	-	-	-	-	-
Other Transformation	-	2.27	-2.39	-	-	-	-	-0.09 e	-	-	-0.21
Own Use	-0.06	-	-5.31	-0.34	-	-	-	-	-1.91	-	-7.62
Distribution Losses	-	-	-	-0.47	-	-	-	-	-1.79	-	-2.26
TFC	**3.08**	**-**	**68.24**	**42.97**	**-**	**-**	**0.23**	**1.85**	**25.42**	**4.53**	**146.31**
INDUSTRY SECTOR	**2.93**	**-**	**6.67**	**17.20**	**-**	**-**	**-**	**0.28**	**12.40**	**-**	**39.48**
Iron and Steel	2.34 e	-	0.13	1.95	-	-	-	-	1.72	-	6.14
Chemical and Petrochem.	0.00	-	0.74	2.96	-	-	-	-	1.67	-	5.38
Non-Ferrous Metals	0.01	-	0.08	0.41	-	-	-	-	0.48	-	0.97
Non-Metallic Minerals	0.57	-	3.01	3.73	-	-	-	0.20	1.26	-	8.77
Transport Equipment	-	-	-	-	-	-	-	-	0.36	-	0.36
Machinery	-	-	0.75	2.34	-	-	-	-	1.98	-	5.07
Mining and Quarrying	-	-	0.05	0.03	-	-	-	-	0.09	-	0.17
Food and Tobacco	-	-	0.80	1.92	-	-	-	0.02	1.09	-	3.83
Paper, Pulp and Printing	-	-	0.23	1.69	-	-	-	-	0.93	-	2.85
Wood and Wood Products	-	-	-	-	-	-	-	-	0.37	-	0.37
Construction	-	-	0.07	-	-	-	-	-	0.14	-	0.20
Textile and Leather	-	-	0.37	1.28	-	-	-	-	0.84	-	2.49
Non-specified	0.01	-	0.45	0.89	-	-	-	0.06 e	1.46	-	2.87
TRANSPORT SECTOR	**-**	**-**	**43.53**	**0.36**	**-**	**-**	**-**	**0.25**	**0.83**	**-**	**44.97**
International Aviation	-	-	3.68	-	-	-	-	-	-	-	3.68
Domestic Aviation	-	-	0.16	-	-	-	-	-	-	-	0.16
Road	-	-	39.32	0.36	-	-	-	0.25	-	-	39.93
Rail	-	-	0.12	-	-	-	-	-	0.38	-	0.50
Pipeline Transport	-	-	-	-	-	-	-	-	0.04	-	0.04
Domestic Navigation	-	-	0.25	-	-	-	-	-	-	-	0.25
Non-specified	-	-	-	-	-	-	-	-	0.40	-	0.40
OTHER SECTORS	**0.01**	**-**	**9.22**	**24.43**	**-**	**-**	**0.23**	**1.31**	**12.19**	**4.53**	**51.91**
Residential	0.01	-	6.14	17.98	-	-	0.02	1.17	5.73	-	31.04
Comm. and Publ. Services	-	-	0.42	6.31	-	-	-	-	6.02	-	12.75
Agriculture/Forestry	-	-	2.40	0.14	-	-	-	0.14	0.44	-	3.12
Fishing	-	-	0.26	-	-	-	-	-	0.01	-	0.26
Non-specified	-	-	-	-	-	-	0.21	-	-	4.53	4.74
NON-ENERGY USE	**0.14**	**-**	**8.82**	**0.99**	**-**	**-**	**-**	**-**	**-**	**-**	**9.95**
in Industry/Transf./Energy	-	-	8.45	0.99	-	-	-	-	-	-	9.44
of which: Feedstocks	-	-	*4.71*	*0.99*	-	-	-	-	-	-	*5.70*
in Transport	-	-	0.37	-	-	-	-	-	-	-	0.37
in Other Sectors	0.14	-	-	-	-	-	-	-	-	-	0.14
Electricity Generated - TWh	***50.88***	***1.20***	***57.70***	***129.77***	-	***39.61***	***8.26 e***	***5.64***	-	-	***293.05***
Electricity Plants	*46.48*	*1.18*	*37.48*	*74.21*	-	*39.61*	*8.26 e*	*2.69*	-	-	*209.92*
CHP plants	*4.40*	*0.01*	*20.21*	*55.56*	-	-	-	*2.95*	-	-	*83.13*
Heat Generated - PJ	***4.59***	***0.11***	***61.68***	***112.88***	-	-	-	***10.32***	-	-	***189.58***
CHP plants	*4.59*	*0.11*	*61.68*	*112.88*	-	-	-	*10.32*	-	-	*189.58*
Heat Plants	-	-	-	-	-	-	-	-	-	-	-

Italy / Italie : 2005

Million tonnes of oil equivalent / *Million de tonnes d'équivalent pétrole*

SUPPLY AND CONSUMPTION *APPROVISIONNEMENT ET DEMANDE*	Coal *Charbon*	Crude Oil *Pétrole brut*	Petroleum Products *Produits pétroliers*	Gas *Gaz*	Nuclear *Nucléaire*	Hydro *Hydro*	Geotherm. Solar etc. *Géotherm. solaire etc.*	Combust. Renew. & Waste *Comb. ren. & déchets*	Electricity *Electricité*	Heat *Chaleur*	Total *Total*
Production	0.06	6.26	-	9.88	-	2.89	5.01	3.52	-	-	27.63
Imports	16.53	95.30	13.02	60.15	-	-	-	0.65	4.32	-	189.98
Exports	-0.16	-1.61	-28.47	-0.32	-	-	-	-	-0.10	-	-30.65
Intl. Marine Bunkers	-	-	-3.40	-	-	-	-	-	-	-	-3.40
Stock Changes	0.03	-0.09	0.76	0.93	-	-	-	-	-	-	1.63
TPES	**16.47**	**99.86**	**-18.08**	**70.63**	**-**	**2.89**	**5.01**	**4.17**	**4.23**	**-**	**185.19**
Transfers	-	-	0.07	-	-	-	-	-	-	-	0.07
Statistical Differences	-	-0.63	-0.19	-	-	-	-	-	-	-	-0.82
Electricity Plants	-10.48	-	-6.36	-12.78	-	-2.89	-4.78	-1.08	17.20	-	-21.18
CHP Plants	-0.98	-	-2.90	-12.31	-	-	-	-1.19	8.12	4.61	-4.64
Heat Plants	-	-	-	-	-	-	-	-	-	-	-
Gas Works	-	-	-	-	-	-	-	-	-	-	-
Petroleum Refineries	-	-101.31	103.33	-	-	-	-	-	-	-	2.02
Coal Transformation	-1.81 e	-	-	-	-	-	-	-	-	-	-1.81
Liquefaction Plants	-	-	-	-	-	-	-	-	-	-	-
Other Transformation	-	2.08	-2.19	-	-	-	-	-0.09	-	-	-0.21
Own Use	-0.27	-	-5.76	-0.34	-	-	-	-	-1.89	-	-8.27
Distribution Losses	-	-	-	-0.49	-	-	-	-	-1.77	-	-2.26
TFC	**2.92**	**-**	**67.92**	**44.71**	**-**	**-**	**0.23**	**1.81**	**25.88**	**4.61**	**148.07**
INDUSTRY SECTOR	**2.75**	**-**	**6.52**	**16.84**	**-**	**-**	**-**	**0.27**	**12.45**	**-**	**38.84**
Iron and Steel	2.14 e	-	0.11	1.95	-	-	-	-	1.75	-	5.96
Chemical and Petrochem.	0.01	-	0.70	2.83	-	-	-	-	1.64	-	5.17
Non-Ferrous Metals	0.01	-	0.07	0.40	-	-	-	-	0.48	-	0.97
Non-Metallic Minerals	0.59	-	3.14	3.67	-	-	-	0.20	1.26	-	8.87
Transport Equipment	-	-	-	-	-	-	-	-	0.36	-	0.36
Machinery	-	-	0.69	2.31	-	-	-	-	2.03	-	5.03
Mining and Quarrying	-	-	0.05	0.03	-	-	-	-	0.09	-	0.17
Food and Tobacco	-	-	0.76	1.80	-	-	-	0.01	1.12	-	3.69
Paper, Pulp and Printing	-	-	0.22	1.69	-	-	-	-	0.94	-	2.85
Wood and Wood Products	-	-	-	-	-	-	-	-	0.38	-	0.38
Construction	-	-	0.06	-	-	-	-	-	0.15	-	0.21
Textile and Leather	-	-	0.31	1.27	-	-	-	-	0.78	-	2.37
Non-specified	0.01	-	0.40	0.88	-	-	-	0.06	1.47	-	2.82
TRANSPORT SECTOR	**-**	**-**	**43.25**	**0.38**	**-**	**-**	**-**	**0.18**	**0.85**	**-**	**44.66**
International Aviation	-	-	3.84	-	-	-	-	-	-	-	3.84
Domestic Aviation	-	-	0.18	-	-	-	-	-	-	-	0.18
Road	-	-	38.87	0.38	-	-	-	0.18	-	-	39.43
Rail	-	-	0.10	-	-	-	-	-	0.39	-	0.49
Pipeline Transport	-	-	-	-	-	-	-	-	0.04	-	0.04
Domestic Navigation	-	-	0.25	-	-	-	-	-	-	-	0.25
Non-specified	-	-	-	-	-	-	-	-	0.42	-	0.42
OTHER SECTORS	**0.01**	**-**	**9.23**	**26.49**	**-**	**-**	**0.23**	**1.36**	**12.57**	**4.61**	**54.50**
Residential	0.01	-	6.14	18.78	-	-	0.02	1.21	5.76	-	31.92
Comm. and Publ. Services	-	-	0.43	7.54	-	-	-	-	6.35	-	14.33
Agriculture/Forestry	-	-	2.40	0.17	-	-	-	0.14	0.46	-	3.17
Fishing	-	-	0.26	-	-	-	-	-	0.01	-	0.26
Non-specified	-	-	-	-	-	-	0.21	-	-	4.61	4.82
NON-ENERGY USE	**0.16**	**-**	**8.92**	**0.99**	**-**	**-**	**-**	**-**	**-**	**-**	**10.08**
in Industry/Transf./Energy	-	-	8.51	0.99	-	-	-	-	-	-	9.51
of which: Feedstocks	-	-	*4.88*	*0.99*	-	-	-	-	-	-	*5.87*
in Transport	-	-	0.41	-	-	-	-	-	-	-	0.41
in Other Sectors	0.16	-	-	-	-	-	-	-	-	-	0.16
Electricity Generated - TWh	***49.42***	***0.02***	***47.10***	***149.26***	**-**	***33.61***	***8.82***	***6.15***	**-**	**-**	***294.38***
Electricity Plants	*45.11*	*0.01*	*27.86*	*81.68*	-	*33.61*	*8.82*	*2.87*	-	-	*199.95*
CHP plants	*4.31*	*0.02*	*19.24*	*67.58*	-	-	-	*3.28*	-	-	*94.43*
Heat Generated - PJ	***5.37***	***0.11***	***55.68***	***120.82***	**-**	**-**	**-**	***11.08***	**-**	**-**	***193.06***
CHP plants	*5.37*	*0.11*	*55.68*	*120.82*	-	-	-	*11.08*	-	-	*193.06*
Heat Plants	-	-	-	-	-	-	-	-	-	-	-

Japan / Japon
Key Indicators
Indicateurs principaux

	1960	1970	1973	1980	1990	1995
Energy Production (Mtoe)	46.98	39.34	29.50	43.28	75.21	98.57
Net Imports (Mtoe)	35.49	238.06	317.43	318.80	378.07	407.71
Total Primary Energy Supply (Mtoe)	80.92	257.21	323.62	346.53	444.47	499.10
Net Oil Imports (Mtoe)	29.40	201.46	273.75	251.71	263.14	275.03
Oil Supply (Mtoe)	27.73	184.86	252.18	235.68	255.01	269.01
Electricity Consumption (TWh)*	102.70	336.20	442.15	550.94	802.51	925.55
GDP (billion 2000 US$ using exch. rates)	667.96 e	1 805.00	2 213.40	2 793.09	4 111.27	4 430.76
GDP (billion 2000 US$ using PPPs)	464.61 e	1 255.51	1 539.58	1 942.80	2 859.69	3 081.92
Population (millions)	93.46 e	103.73	108.67	116.81	123.48	125.47
Industrial Production Index (2000=100)	12.60	44.70	56.60	66.80	98.50	95.50
Energy Production/TPES	0.5806	0.1530	0.0912	0.1249	0.1692	0.1975
Net Oil Imports/GDP (toe per thousand 2000 US$)	0.0440 e	0.1116	0.1237	0.0901	0.0640	0.0621
TPES/GDP (toe per thousand 2000 US$)	0.1211 e	0.1425	0.1462	0.1241	0.1081	0.1126
TPES/GDP (toe per thousand 2000 US$ PPP)	0.1742 e	0.2049	0.2102	0.1784	0.1554	0.1619
TPES/Population (toe per capita)	0.8659 e	2.4797	2.9781	2.9667	3.5996	3.9778
Oil Supply/GDP (toe per thousand 2000 US$)	0.0415 e	0.1024	0.1139	0.0844	0.0620	0.0607
Oil Supply/Population (toe per capita)	0.2967 e	1.7822	2.3207	2.0177	2.0653	2.1440
Elect. Cons./GDP (kWh per 2000 US$)	0.1538 e	0.1863	0.1998	0.1973	0.1952	0.2089
Elect. Cons./Population (kWh per capita)	1 099 e	3 241	4 069	4 717	6 499	7 377
Industry Cons.**/Industrial Production (2000=100)	206.19	183.89	179.68	129.26	101.12	105.33
Industry Oil Cons.**/Industrial Production (2000=100)	113.49	216.27	219.09	131.37	94.87	103.25

	2000	2001	2002	2003	2004	2005
Energy Production (Mtoe)	105.79	104.74	96.87	84.00	95.01	99.77
Net Imports (Mtoe)	430.74	415.85	426.16	435.75	441.36	438.98
Total Primary Energy Supply (Mtoe)	527.56	519.45	519.88	515.32	532.26	530.46
Net Oil Imports (Mtoe)	270.74	253.35	258.82	260.62	256.84	258.73
Oil Supply (Mtoe)	262.76	252.83	256.23	256.87	253.60	251.69
Electricity Consumption (TWh)*	1 013.90	997.36	1 011.92	1 001.42	1 031.47	1 051.90
GDP (billion 2000 US$ using exch. rates)	4 649.64	4 667.53	4 673.77	4 756.80	4 866.31	4 994.13
GDP (billion 2000 US$ using PPPs)	3 234.16	3 246.61	3 250.95	3 308.70	3 384.87	3 473.78
Population (millions)	126.84	127.15	127.44	127.71	127.75	127.76
Industrial Production Index (2000=100)	100.00	93.70	92.60	95.40	100.50	101.70
Energy Production/TPES	0.2005	0.2016	0.1863	0.1630	0.1785	0.1881
Net Oil Imports/GDP (toe per thousand 2000 US$)	0.0582	0.0543	0.0554	0.0548	0.0528	0.0518
TPES/GDP (toe per thousand 2000 US$)	0.1135	0.1113	0.1112	0.1083	0.1094	0.1062
TPES/GDP (toe per thousand 2000 US$ PPP)	0.1631	0.1600	0.1599	0.1557	0.1572	0.1527
TPES/Population (toe per capita)	4.1592	4.0855	4.0794	4.0351	4.1664	4.1520
Oil Supply/GDP (toe per thousand 2000 US$)	0.0565	0.0542	0.0548	0.0540	0.0521	0.0504
Oil Supply/Population (toe per capita)	2.0716	1.9885	2.0106	2.0113	1.9851	1.9700
Elect. Cons./GDP (kWh per 2000 US$)	0.2181	0.2137	0.2165	0.2105	0.2120	0.2106
Elect. Cons./Population (kWh per capita)	7 993	7 844	7 940	7 841	8 074	8 233
Industry Cons.**/Industrial Production (2000=100)	100.00	101.76	105.15	102.86	99.46	97.75
Industry Oil Cons.**/Industrial Production (2000=100)	100.00	101.46	104.12	101.32	97.81	94.68

* Electricity consumption equals domestic supply less distribution losses.
La consommation d'électricité représente l'approvisionnement intérieur diminué des pertes de distribution.

** Includes non-energy use in industry/transformation/energy sectors.
Comprend l'usage non-énergétique dans les secteurs de l'industrie/transformation/énergie.

Japan / Japon

Figure 1. TPES* in 1973

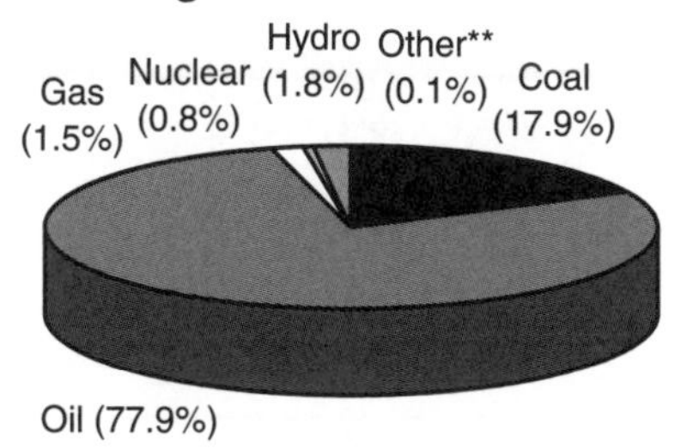

Figure 2. TPES* in 2005

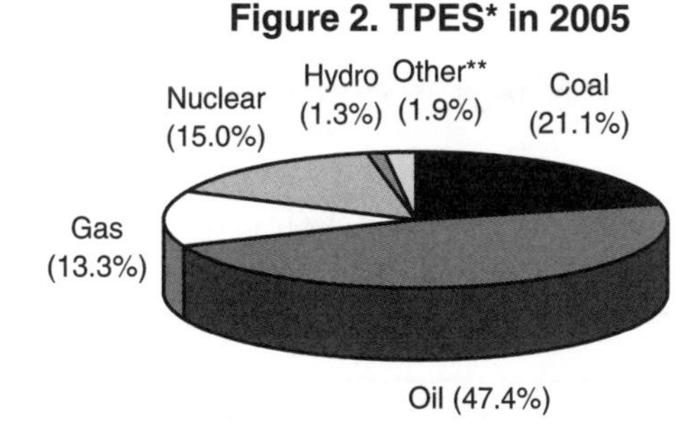

Figure 3. Final Consumption by Sector***

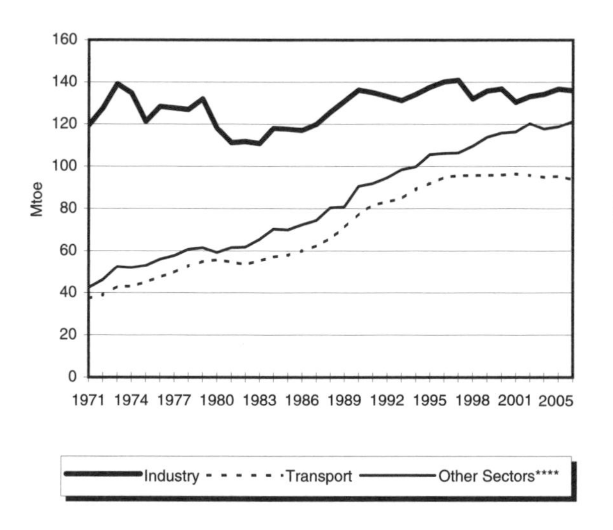

Figure 4. Breakdown of Sectorial Final Consumption by Source in 1973 and 2005***

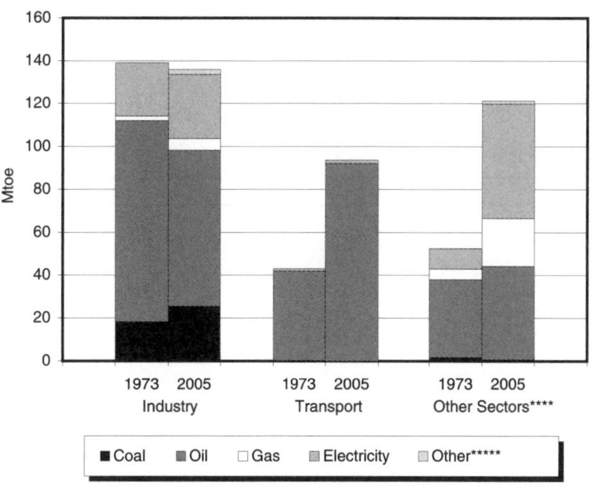

Figure 5. Electricity Generation by Fuel

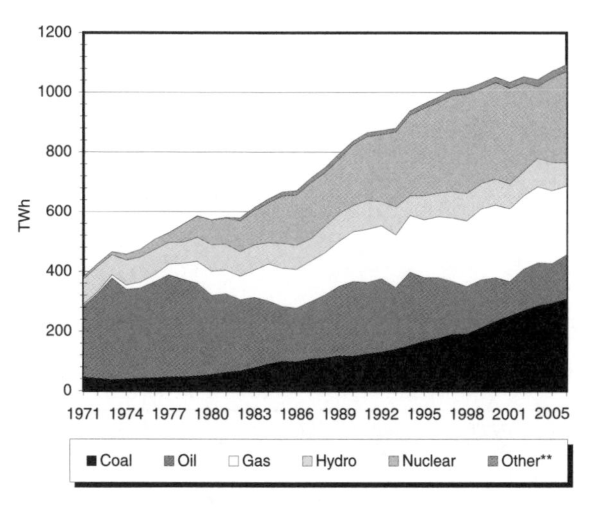

Figure 6. Electricity Consumption/GDP, TPES/GDP and Energy Production/TPES

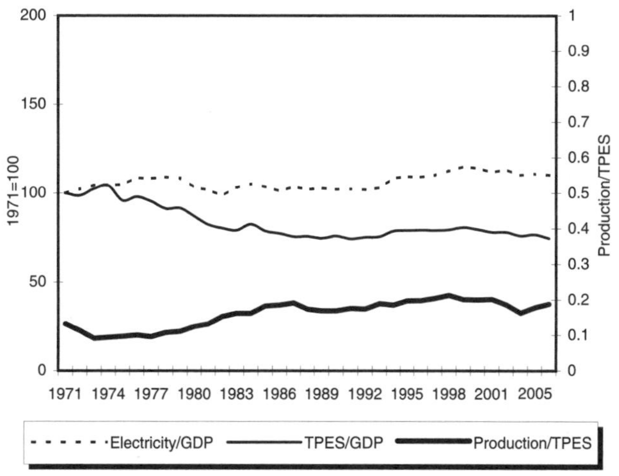

* Excluding electricity trade.

** Includes geothermal, solar, wind, combustible renewables & waste, etc.

*** Includes non-energy use.

**** Includes residential, commercial and public services, agriculture/forestry, fishing and non-specified.

***** Includes comb. renewables & waste, direct use of geothermal/solar thermal and heat produced in CHP/heat plants.

Japan / Japon : 2004

Million tonnes of oil equivalent / *Million de tonnes d'équivalent pétrole*

SUPPLY AND CONSUMPTION / ***APPROVISIONNEMENT ET DEMANDE***	Coal / *Charbon*	Crude Oil / *Pétrole brut*	Petroleum Products / *Produits pétroliers*	Gas / *Gaz*	Nuclear / *Nucléaire*	Hydro / *Hydro*	Geotherm. Solar etc. / *Géotherm. solaire etc.*	Combust. Renew. & Waste / *Comb. ren. & déchets*	Electricity / *Electricité*	Heat / *Chaleur*	Total / *Total*
Production	-	0.71	-	2.69	73.61	8.09	3.81	6.10 e	-	-	95.01
Imports	117.94	209.76	51.65	68.04	-	-	-	-	-	-	447.40
Exports	-1.46	-	-4.57	-	-	-	-	-	-	-	-6.04
Intl. Marine Bunkers	-	-	-5.21	-	-	-	-	-	-	-	-5.21
Stock Changes	0.01	0.70	0.56	-0.17	-	-	-	-	-	-	1.10
TPES	**116.48**	**211.18**	**42.43**	**70.56**	**73.61**	**8.09**	**3.81**	**6.10**	**-**	**-**	**532.26**
Transfers	-	-	-0.01	-	-	-	-	-	-	-	-0.01
Statistical Differences	-6.36	-0.91	-0.64	0.89	-	-	-	0.00	-0.03	-0.02	-7.07
Electricity Plants	-60.14	-5.83	-17.73	-46.68	-73.61	-8.09	-3.01	-3.57	92.13	-	-126.53
CHP Plants	-	-	-	-	-	-	-	-	-	-	-
Heat Plants	-0.01	-	-0.03	-0.34	-	-	-	-0.15	-0.10	0.61	-0.02
Gas Works	-0.06	-	-2.50	1.92	-	-	-	-	-	-	-0.64
Petroleum Refineries	-	-209.51	206.33	-	-	-	-	-	-	-	-3.18
Coal Transformation	-22.08 e	-	-0.79	-	-	-	-	-	-	-	-22.87
Liquefaction Plants	-	-	-	-	-	-	-	-	-	-	-
Other Transformation	-	6.51	-6.97	-	-	-	-	-0.02 e	-	-	-0.49
Own Use	-2.37	-0.00	-8.58	-0.87	-	-	-	-	-4.77	-	-16.60
Distribution Losses	-	-	-	-	-	-	-	-	-4.20	-	-4.20
TFC	**25.46**	**1.43**	**211.51**	**25.48**	**-**	**-**	**0.80**	**2.36**	**83.02**	**0.59**	**350.65**
INDUSTRY SECTOR	**24.46**	**0.03**	**33.12**	**4.73**	**-**	**-**	**-**	**2.33**	**30.12**	**-**	**94.78**
Iron and Steel	11.88 e	-	1.74	1.45	-	-	-	-	5.85	-	20.91
Chemical and Petrochem.	2.86	0.03	11.56	0.68	-	-	-	-	4.72	-	19.85
Non-Ferrous Metals	0.29	-	0.31	0.01	-	-	-	-	1.24	-	1.85
Non-Metallic Minerals	4.48	-	2.09	0.16	-	-	-	0.10	1.92	-	8.76
Transport Equipment	-	-	-	-	-	-	-	-	-	-	-
Machinery	0.27	-	0.90	1.01	-	-	-	0.00	6.33	-	8.51
Mining and Quarrying	0.02	-	0.25	0.05	-	-	-	-	0.08	-	0.40
Food and Tobacco	-	-	3.27	-	-	-	-	-	1.28	-	4.55
Paper, Pulp and Printing	1.50	-	1.80	0.25	-	-	-	2.22	2.96	-	8.74
Wood and Wood Products	-	-	-	-	-	-	-	-	-	-	-
Construction	0.00	-	3.57	-	-	-	-	-	0.12	-	3.70
Textile and Leather	-	-	-	-	-	-	-	-	-	-	-
Non-specified	3.16	-	7.63	1.10	-	-	-	-	5.62	-	17.51
TRANSPORT SECTOR	**-**	**-**	**92.98**	**-**	**-**	**-**	**-**	**-**	**1.61**	**-**	**94.59**
International Aviation	-	-	7.17	-	-	-	-	-	-	-	7.17
Domestic Aviation	-	-	3.61	-	-	-	-	-	-	-	3.61
Road	-	-	78.12	-	-	-	-	-	-	-	78.12
Rail	-	-	0.22	-	-	-	-	-	1.61	-	1.83
Pipeline Transport	-	-	-	-	-	-	-	-	-	-	-
Domestic Navigation	-	-	3.86	-	-	-	-	-	-	-	3.86
Non-specified	-	-	-	-	-	-	-	-	-	-	-
OTHER SECTORS	**0.59**	**-**	**44.92**	**20.40**	**-**	**-**	**0.80**	**0.03**	**51.29**	**0.59**	**118.63**
Residential	-	-	15.25	8.95	-	-	0.56	0.03	23.56	0.03	48.37
Comm. and Publ. Services	0.59	-	24.57	11.46	-	-	0.14	-	27.61	0.56	64.93
Agriculture/Forestry	-	-	3.23	-	-	-	0.09	-	0.13	-	3.45
Fishing	-	-	1.88	-	-	-	-	-	-	-	1.88
Non-specified	-	-	-	-	-	-	-	-	-	-	-
NON-ENERGY USE	**0.41**	**1.40**	**40.49**	**0.35**	**-**	**-**	**-**	**-**	**-**	**-**	**42.65**
in Industry/Transf./Energy	0.41	1.40	39.76	0.35	-	-	-	-	-	-	41.92
of which: Feedstocks	*0.37*	*1.40*	*30.38*	*0.35*	-	-	-	-	-	-	*32.50*
in Transport	-	-	0.73	-	-	-	-	-	-	-	0.73
in Other Sectors	-	-	-	-	-	-	-	-	-	-	-
Electricity Generated - TWh	***294.53***	***33.41***	***98.83***	***244.57***	***282.44***	***94.06***	***4.69***	***18.71***	***-***	***-***	***1071.25***
Electricity Plants	*294.53*	*33.41*	*98.83*	*244.57*	*282.44*	*94.06*	*4.69*	*18.71*	-	-	*1071.25*
CHP plants	-	-	-	-	-	-	-	-	-	-	-
Heat Generated - PJ	***0.45***	***-***	***1.20***	***13.85***	***-***	***-***	***-***	***6.15***	***3.99***	***-***	***25.63***
CHP plants	-	-	-	-	-	-	-	-	-	-	-
Heat Plants	*0.45*	-	*1.20*	*13.85*	-	-	-	*6.15*	*3.99*	-	*25.63*

Japan / Japon : 2005

Million tonnes of oil equivalent / *Million de tonnes d'équivalent pétrole*

SUPPLY AND CONSUMPTION *APPROVISIONNEMENT ET DEMANDE*	Coal *Charbon*	Crude Oil *Pétrole brut*	Petroleum Products *Produits pétroliers*	Gas *Gaz*	Nuclear *Nucléaire*	Hydro *Hydro*	Geotherm. Solar etc. *Géotherm. solaire etc.*	Combust. Renew. & Waste *Comb. ren. & déchets*	Electricity *Electricité*	Heat *Chaleur*	Total *Total*
Production	-	0.75	-	2.86	79.42	6.73	3.72	6.29 e	-	-	99.77
Imports	113.68	216.24	51.32	67.78	-	-	-	-	-	-	449.02
Exports	-1.21	-	-8.84	-	-	-	-	-	-	-	-10.04
Intl. Marine Bunkers	-	-	-5.86	-	-	-	-	-	-	-	-5.86
Stock Changes	-0.40	-0.70	-1.22	-0.10	-	-	-	-	-	-	-2.43
TPES	**112.07**	**216.30**	**35.40**	**70.54**	**79.42**	**6.73**	**3.72**	**6.29**	**-**	**-**	**530.46**
Transfers	-	-	-0.01	-	-	-	-	-	-	-	-0.01
Statistical Differences	0.81	0.98	-2.74	1.18	-	-	-	-0.00	-0.09	0.00	0.14
Electricity Plants	-62.99	-7.54	-18.67	-43.97	-79.42	-6.73	-2.92	-3.71	94.10	-	-131.85
CHP Plants	-	-	-	-	-	-	-	-	-	-	-
Heat Plants	-0.02	-	-0.03	-0.36	-	-	-	-0.15	-0.10	0.62	-0.03
Gas Works	-0.04	-	-2.26	1.69	-	-	-	-	-	-	-0.61
Petroleum Refineries	-	-215.10	212.37	-	-	-	-	-	-	-	-2.73
Coal Transformation	-21.44 e	-	-0.37	-	-	-	-	-	-	-	-21.81
Liquefaction Plants	-	-	-	-	-	-	-	-	-	-	-
Other Transformation	-	6.56	-7.03	-	-	-	-	-0.02 e	-	-	-0.49
Own Use	-2.33	-0.12	-9.38	-1.12	-	-	-	-	-4.94	-	-17.90
Distribution Losses	-	-	-	-	-	-	-	-	-4.34	-	-4.34
TFC	**26.06**	**1.08**	**207.28**	**27.96**	**-**	**-**	**0.79**	**2.42**	**84.63**	**0.62**	**350.85**
INDUSTRY SECTOR	**25.03**	**0.03**	**32.96**	**5.17**	**-**	**-**	**-**	**2.39**	**29.83**	**-**	**95.40**
Iron and Steel	11.95 e	-	1.83	1.57	-	-	-	-	5.87	-	21.22
Chemical and Petrochem.	3.63	0.03	11.94	0.76	-	-	-	-	4.60	-	20.95
Non-Ferrous Metals	0.28	-	0.31	0.02	-	-	-	-	1.29	-	1.90
Non-Metallic Minerals	4.03	-	1.88	0.20	-	-	-	0.09	1.97	-	8.18
Transport Equipment	-	-	-	-	-	-	-	-	-	-	-
Machinery	0.27	-	0.84	1.16	-	-	-	0.00	6.61	-	8.88
Mining and Quarrying	0.02	-	0.22	0.06	-	-	-	-	0.08	-	0.37
Food and Tobacco	-	-	2.86	-	-	-	-	-	1.29	-	4.15
Paper, Pulp and Printing	1.51	-	1.72	0.27	-	-	-	2.30	2.96	-	8.76
Wood and Wood Products	-	-	-	-	-	-	-	-	-	-	-
Construction	0.00	-	3.57	-	-	-	-	-	0.09	-	3.67
Textile and Leather	-	-	-	-	-	-	-	-	-	-	-
Non-specified	3.34	-	7.79	1.12	-	-	-	-	5.08	-	17.32
TRANSPORT SECTOR	**-**	**-**	**91.37**	**-**	**-**	**-**	**-**	**-**	**1.64**	**-**	**93.01**
International Aviation	-	-	7.27	-	-	-	-	-	-	-	7.27
Domestic Aviation	-	-	3.66	-	-	-	-	-	-	-	3.66
Road	-	-	76.32	-	-	-	-	-	-	-	76.32
Rail	-	-	0.22	-	-	-	-	-	1.64	-	1.86
Pipeline Transport	-	-	-	-	-	-	-	-	-	-	-
Domestic Navigation	-	-	3.91	-	-	-	-	-	-	-	3.91
Non-specified	-	-	-	-	-	-	-	-	-	-	-
OTHER SECTORS	**0.64**	**-**	**43.47**	**22.45**	**-**	**-**	**0.79**	**0.03**	**53.16**	**0.62**	**121.16**
Residential	-	-	16.03	9.36	-	-	0.56	0.03	28.73	0.03	54.74
Comm. and Publ. Services	0.64	-	22.71	13.08	-	-	0.14	-	24.34	0.59	61.50
Agriculture/Forestry	-	-	2.99	-	-	-	0.09	-	0.08	-	3.17
Fishing	-	-	1.74	-	-	-	-	-	-	-	1.74
Non-specified	-	-	-	-	-	-	-	-	-	-	-
NON-ENERGY USE	**0.40**	**1.05**	**39.48**	**0.35**	**-**	**-**	**-**	**-**	**-**	**-**	**41.28**
in Industry/Transf./Energy	0.40	1.05	38.75	0.35	-	-	-	-	-	-	40.55
of which: Feedstocks	*0.36*	*1.05*	*29.91*	*0.35*	-	-	-	-	-	-	*31.67*
in Transport	-	-	0.73	-	-	-	-	-	-	-	0.73
in Other Sectors	-	-	-	-	-	-	-	-	-	-	-
Electricity Generated - TWh	***309.33***	***41.69***	***104.30***	***231.38***	***304.76***	***78.21***	***4.98***	***19.54***	**-**	**-**	***1094.19***
Electricity Plants	*309.33*	*41.69*	*104.30*	*231.38*	*304.76*	*78.21*	*4.98*	*19.54*	-	-	*1094.19*
CHP plants	-	-	-	-	-	-	-	-	-	-	-
Heat Generated - PJ	***0.57***	**-**	***0.92***	***14.54***	**-**	**-**	**-**	***5.90***	***4.05***	**-**	***25.98***
CHP plants	-	-	-	-	-	-	-	-	-	-	-
Heat Plants	*0.57*	-	*0.92*	*14.54*	-	-	-	*5.90*	*4.05*	-	*25.98*

Korea / Corée
Key Indicators
Indicateurs principaux

	1960	1970	1973	1980	1990	1995
Energy Production (Mtoe)	..	..	6.76	9.27	22.62	21.15
Net Imports (Mtoe)	..	..	13.58	30.66	70.11	135.13
Total Primary Energy Supply (Mtoe)	..	..	21.64	41.37	93.39	147.93
Net Oil Imports (Mtoe)	..	..	13.25	27.18	51.68	98.71
Oil Supply (Mtoe)	..	..	13.40	26.81	50.03	94.31
Electricity Consumption (TWh)*	..	..	13.54 e	34.83 e	101.74	175.01
GDP (billion 2000 US$ using exch. rates)	27.75 e	61.05	77.34	122.81	283.56	413.01
GDP (billion 2000 US$ using PPPs)	41.67 e	91.67	116.14	184.41	425.79	620.16
Population (millions)	25.01 e	32.24	34.10	38.12	42.87	45.09
Industrial Production Index (2000=100)	..	..	..	14.30	43.10	64.90
Energy Production/TPES	..	..	0.3124	0.2241	0.2422	0.1430
Net Oil Imports/GDP (toe per thousand 2000 US$)	..	..	0.1713	0.2213	0.1823	0.2390
TPES/GDP (toe per thousand 2000 US$)	..	..	0.2798	0.3369	0.3293	0.3582
TPES/GDP (toe per thousand 2000 US$ PPP)	..	..	0.1863	0.2243	0.2193	0.2385
TPES/Population (toe per capita)	..	..	0.6346	1.0852	2.1784	3.2807
Oil Supply/GDP (toe per thousand 2000 US$)	..	..	0.1733	0.2183	0.1765	0.2283
Oil Supply/Population (toe per capita)	..	..	0.3930	0.7032	1.1672	2.0914
Elect. Cons./GDP (kWh per 2000 US$)	..	..	0.1751 e	0.2836 e	0.3588	0.4237
Elect. Cons./Population (kWh per capita)	..	..	397 e	914 e	2 373	3 881
Industry Cons.**/Industrial Production (2000=100)	..	..	..	151.86	98.83	117.65
Industry Oil Cons.**/Industrial Production (2000=100)	..	..	..	181.63	106.56	125.46

	2000	2001	2002	2003	2004	2005
Energy Production (Mtoe)	32.59	33.24	34.84	37.94	38.27	42.93
Net Imports (Mtoe)	165.48	164.33	172.41	177.96	184.02	176.26
Total Primary Energy Supply (Mtoe)	190.15	192.84	202.90	207.44	213.28	213.77
Net Oil Imports (Mtoe)	109.93	106.39	106.47	108.69	107.84	103.23
Oil Supply (Mtoe)	103.53	100.21	102.00	101.20	101.43	96.16
Electricity Consumption (TWh)*	247.45	265.24	317.98 e	334.16	355.37	375.66
GDP (billion 2000 US$ using exch. rates)	511.66	531.29	568.32	585.92	613.63	637.95
GDP (billion 2000 US$ using PPPs)	768.29	797.76	853.37	879.80	921.41	957.92
Population (millions)	47.01	47.35	47.62	47.85	48.08	48.29
Industrial Production Index (2000=100)	100.00	100.70	108.80	114.60	126.30	134.10
Energy Production/TPES	0.1714	0.1724	0.1717	0.1829	0.1794	0.2008
Net Oil Imports/GDP (toe per thousand 2000 US$)	0.2149	0.2003	0.1873	0.1855	0.1757	0.1618
TPES/GDP (toe per thousand 2000 US$)	0.3716	0.3630	0.3570	0.3540	0.3476	0.3351
TPES/GDP (toe per thousand 2000 US$ PPP)	0.2475	0.2417	0.2378	0.2358	0.2315	0.2232
TPES/Population (toe per capita)	4.0450	4.0723	4.2613	4.3353	4.4358	4.4265
Oil Supply/GDP (toe per thousand 2000 US$)	0.2023	0.1886	0.1795	0.1727	0.1653	0.1507
Oil Supply/Population (toe per capita)	2.2025	2.1162	2.1421	2.1150	2.1094	1.9912
Elect. Cons./GDP (kWh per 2000 US$)	0.4836	0.4992	0.5595 e	0.5703	0.5791	0.5889
Elect. Cons./Population (kWh per capita)	5 264	5 601	6 678 e	6 984	7 391	7 779
Industry Cons.**/Industrial Production (2000=100)	100.00	102.22	102.12	98.62	92.87	88.22
Industry Oil Cons.**/Industrial Production (2000=100)	100.00	97.67	91.15	88.52	82.13	79.11

* Electricity consumption equals domestic supply less distribution losses.
La consommation d'électricité représente l'approvisionnement intérieur diminué des pertes de distribution.

** Includes non-energy use in industry/transformation/energy sectors.
Comprend l'usage non-énergétique dans les secteurs de l'industrie/transformation/énergie.

Korea / Corée

Figure 1. TPES* in 1973

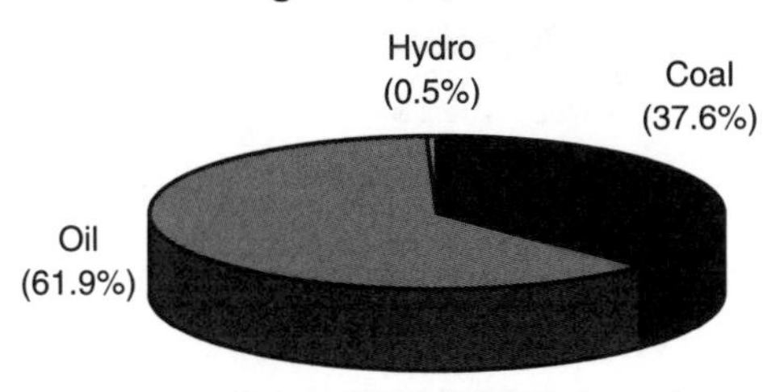

Figure 2. TPES* in 2005

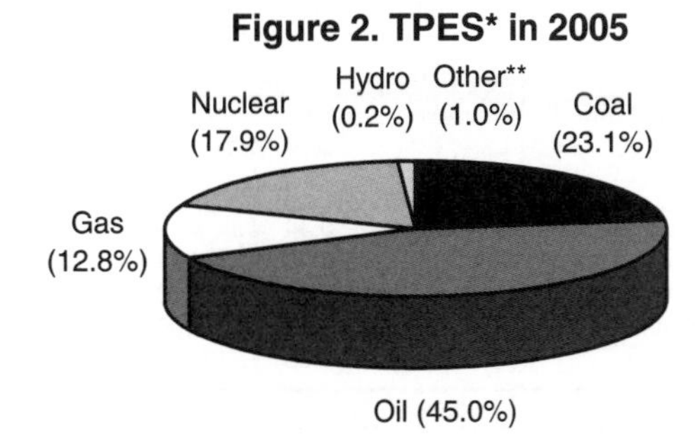

Figure 3. Final Consumption by Sector***

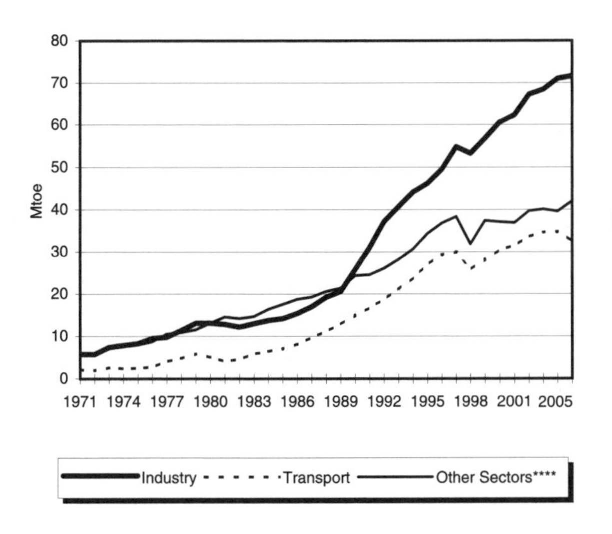

Figure 4. Breakdown of Sectorial Final Consumption by Source in 1973 and 2005***

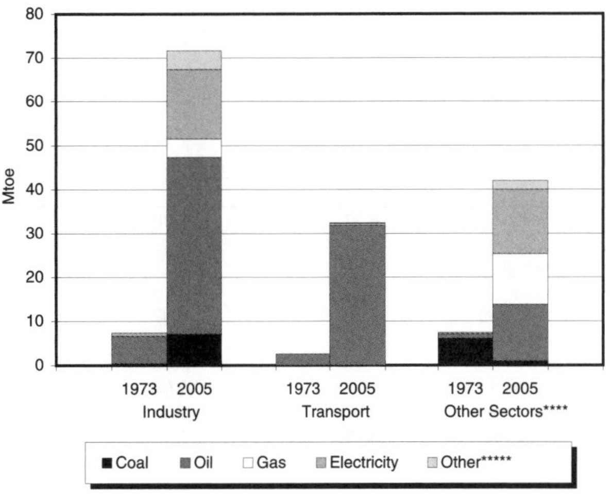

Figure 5. Electricity Generation by Fuel

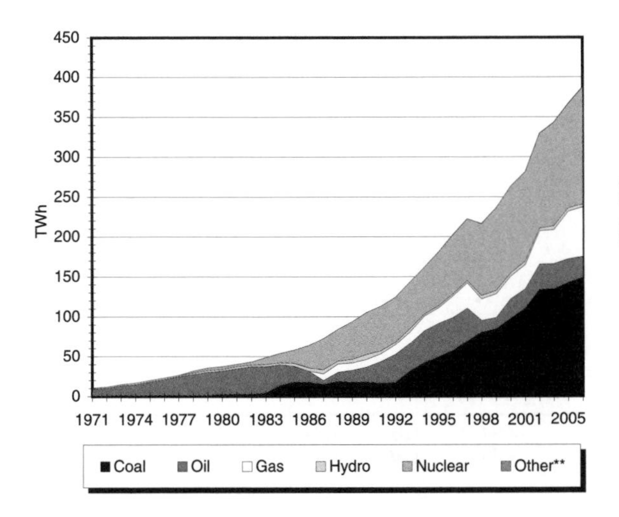

Figure 6. Electricity Consumption/GDP, TPES/GDP and Energy Production/TPES

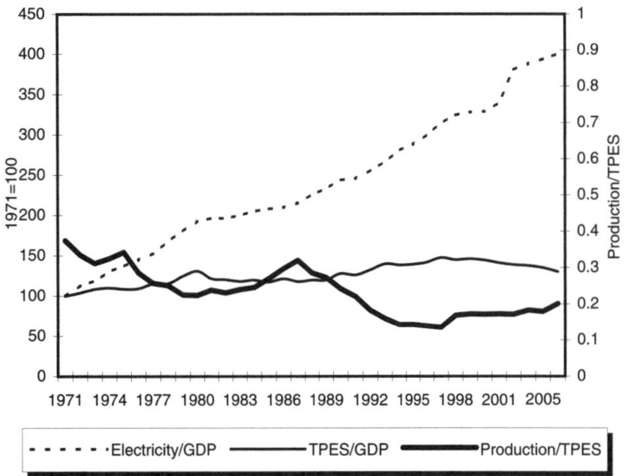

* Excluding electricity trade.

** Includes geothermal, solar, wind, combustible renewables & waste, etc.

*** Includes non-energy use.

**** Includes residential, commercial and public services, agriculture/forestry, fishing and non-specified.

***** Includes comb. renewables & waste, direct use of geothermal/solar thermal and heat produced in CHP/heat plants.

Korea / Corée : 2004

Million tonnes of oil equivalent / *Million de tonnes d'équivalent pétrole*

SUPPLY AND CONSUMPTION ***APPROVISIONNEMENT ET DEMANDE***	Coal *Charbon*	Crude Oil *Pétrole brut*	Petroleum Products *Produits pétroliers*	Gas *Gaz*	Nuclear *Nucléaire*	Hydro *Hydro*	Geotherm. Solar etc. *Géotherm. solaire etc.*	Combust. Renew. & Waste *Comb. ren. & déchets*	Electricity *Electricité*	Heat *Chaleur*	Total *Total*
Production	1.37	0.44	-	-	34.07	0.37	0.04 e	1.98	-	-	38.27
Imports	50.25	116.55	23.44	25.91	-	-	-	0.03	-	-	216.17
Exports	-	-0.01	-32.13	-	-	-	-	-	-	-	-32.14
Intl. Marine Bunkers	-	-	-6.96	-	-	-	-	-	-	-	-6.96
Stock Changes	-1.53	1.08	-0.97	-0.63	-	-	-	-	-	-	-2.05
TPES	**50.09**	**118.05**	**-16.62**	**25.28**	**34.07**	**0.37**	**0.04** e	**2.01**	**-**	**-**	**213.28**
Transfers	-	-0.41	0.42	-	-	-	-	-	-	-	0.02
Statistical Differences	0.14	-4.23	-0.60	0.38	-	-	-	-0.01	0.00 e	-	-4.32
Electricity Plants	-29.37	-0.47	-3.47	-7.39	-34.07	-0.37	-0.00 e	-0.06	28.40 e	-	-46.79
CHP Plants	-3.98	-	-0.83	-3.15	-	-	-	-0.15	3.13	4.06 e	-0.91
Heat Plants	-	-	-0.63	-0.06	-	-	-	-0.12	-	0.36 e	-0.44
Gas Works	-	-	-	-	-	-	-	-	-	-	-
Petroleum Refineries	-	-119.56	119.68	-	-	-	-	-	-	-	0.12
Coal Transformation	-7.74 e	-	-	-	-	-	-	-	-	-	-7.74
Liquefaction Plants	-	-	-	-	-	-	-	-	-	-	-
Other Transformation	-	6.62	-6.46	-	-	-	-	-	-	-	0.16
Own Use	-0.22	-	-4.70	-0.56	-	-	-	-	-1.37	..	-6.84
Distribution Losses	-	-	-	-	-	-	-	-	-1.10	-0.08	-1.18
TFC	**8.93**	**-**	**86.79**	**14.51**	**-**	**-**	**0.04**	**1.67**	**29.06**	**4.34**	**145.34**
INDUSTRY SECTOR	**8.27**	**-**	**7.90**	**3.94**	**-**	**-**	**0.00**	**1.35**	**15.25**	**2.89**	**39.59**
Iron and Steel	4.36 e	-	0.54	0.79	-	-	-	0.00	3.58	-	9.28
Chemical and Petrochem.	0.08	-	1.41	0.39	-	-	0.00	0.14	3.39	1.84	7.26
Non-Ferrous Metals	-	-	0.15	-	-	-	-	0.02	0.04	0.02	0.23
Non-Metallic Minerals	3.33	-	0.87	0.30	-	-	-	0.40	0.87	-	5.77
Transport Equipment	-	-	0.35	0.79	-	-	-	0.01	1.15	-	2.31
Machinery	-	-	0.46	-	-	-	-	0.01	2.99	0.07	3.53
Mining and Quarrying	-	-	0.05	-	-	-	-	0.00	0.11	-	0.16
Food and Tobacco	0.02	-	0.64	0.24	-	-	-	0.03	0.65	0.03	1.61
Paper, Pulp and Printing	0.05	-	1.00	0.06	-	-	-	0.22	0.88	0.20	2.40
Wood and Wood Products	-	-	0.06	0.03	-	-	-	0.03	0.13	-	0.25
Construction	-	-	0.56	0.00	-	-	-	-	-	-	0.56
Textile and Leather	0.08	-	1.13	0.38	-	-	-	0.01	1.28	0.72	3.59
Non-specified	0.35	-	0.67	0.95	-	-	0.00	0.48	0.18	0.01 e	2.63
TRANSPORT SECTOR	**-**	**-**	**33.80**	**0.23**	**-**	**-**	**-**	**0.00**	**0.21**	**-**	**34.25**
International Aviation	-	-	1.33	-	-	-	-	-	-	-	1.33
Domestic Aviation	-	-	2.22	-	-	-	-	-	-	-	2.22
Road	-	-	26.08	0.23	-	-	-	0.00	-	-	26.31
Rail	-	-	0.28	-	-	-	-	-	0.21	-	0.50
Pipeline Transport	-	-	0.00	-	-	-	-	-	-	-	0.00
Domestic Navigation	-	-	3.77	-	-	-	-	-	-	-	3.77
Non-specified	-	-	0.13	-	-	-	-	-	-	-	0.13
OTHER SECTORS	**0.66**	**-**	**13.12**	**10.34**	**-**	**-**	**0.04**	**0.32**	**13.60**	**1.45**	**39.53**
Residential	0.66	-	3.40	7.73	-	-	0.03	0.04	4.18	1.28	17.32
Comm. and Publ. Services	-	-	6.00	2.59	-	-	0.01	0.28	8.86	0.17	17.91
Agriculture/Forestry	-	-	1.50	0.02	-	-	-	-	0.42	-	1.95
Fishing	-	-	1.11	-	-	-	-	-	0.14	-	1.25
Non-specified	-	-	1.11	-	-	-	-	-	-	-	1.11
NON-ENERGY USE	**-**	**-**	**31.97**	**-**	**-**	**-**	**-**	**-**	**-**	**-**	**31.97**
in Industry/Transf./Energy	-	-	31.44	-	-	-	-	-	-	-	31.44
of which: Feedstocks	-	-	*28.82*	-	-	-	-	-	-	-	*28.82*
in Transport	-	-	0.50	-	-	-	-	-	-	-	0.50
in Other Sectors	-	-	0.03	-	-	-	-	-	-	-	0.03
Electricity Generated - TWh	***142.26***	***1.80***	***27.68***	***59.40***	***130.72***	***4.33***	***0.06***	***0.37***	**-**	**-**	***366.61***
Electricity Plants	*127.49*	*1.80*	*20.44*	*45.10*	*130.72*	*4.33*	*0.06 e*	*0.25 e*	-	-	*330.19*
CHP plants	*14.77*	-	*7.24*	*14.30*	-	-	-	*0.12*	-	-	*36.43*
Heat Generated - PJ	***34.57***	**-**	***101.05***	***42.94***	**-**	**-**	**-**	***6.75***	**-**	**-**	***185.31***
CHP plants	*34.57*	-	*92.36*	*40.70*	-	-	-	*2.55*	-	-	*170.17*
Heat Plants	-	-	*8.69*	*2.25*	-	-	-	*4.20*	-	-	*15.14*

Korea / Corée : 2005

Million tonnes of oil equivalent / *Million de tonnes d'équivalent pétrole*

SUPPLY AND CONSUMPTION	Coal	Crude Oil	Petroleum Products	Gas	Nuclear	Hydro	Geotherm. Solar etc.	Combust. Renew. & Waste	Electricity	Heat	Total
APPROVISIONNEMENT ET DEMANDE	*Charbon*	*Pétrole brut*	*Produits pétroliers*	*Gaz*	*Nucléaire*	*Hydro*	*Géotherm. solaire etc.*	*Comb. ren. & déchets*	*Electricité*	*Chaleur*	*Total*
Production	1.21	0.53	-	0.44	38.25	0.32	0.05	2.12	-	0.01	42.93
Imports	46.90	117.35	21.46	26.10	-	-	-	0.03	-	-	211.84
Exports	-	-0.00	-35.58	-	-	-	-	-	-	-	-35.58
Intl. Marine Bunkers	-	-	-9.90	-	-	-	-	-	-	-	-9.90
Stock Changes	1.36	0.94	1.37	0.82	-	-	-	-	-	-	4.48
TPES	**49.47**	**118.82**	**-22.66**	**27.37**	**38.25**	**0.32**	**0.05**	**2.14**	**-**	**0.01**	**213.77**
Transfers	-	-0.51	0.54	-	-	-	-	-	-	-	0.03
Statistical Differences	-0.25	0.36	-1.50	-0.07	-	-	-	-0.00	-	-	-1.47
Electricity Plants	-29.32	-0.69	-3.35	-7.88	-38.25	-0.32	-0.01	-0.04	30.39	-0.01 e	-49.49
CHP Plants	-3.75	-	-0.58	-3.07	-	-	-	-0.11	2.97	4.10 e	-0.45
Heat Plants	-	-	-0.64	-0.12	-	-	-	-0.19	-	0.51 e	-0.44
Gas Works	-	-	-	-	-	-	-	-	-	-	-
Petroleum Refineries	-	-123.98	123.88	-	-	-	-	-	-	-	-0.10
Coal Transformation	-8.07 e	-	-	-	-	-	-	-	-	-	-8.07
Liquefaction Plants	-	-	-	-	-	-	-	-	-	-	-
Other Transformation	-	6.01	-5.94	-	-	-	-	-	-	-	0.07
Own Use	-0.02	-	-4.78	-0.24	-	-	-	-	-1.47	..	-6.52
Distribution Losses	-	-	-	-	-	-	-	-	-1.18	-0.09 e	-1.27
TFC	**8.05**	**-**	**84.97**	**15.98**	**-**	**-**	**0.04**	**1.80**	**30.71**	**4.52**	**146.07**
INDUSTRY SECTOR	**7.10**	**-**	**7.47**	**4.17**	**-**	**-**	**0.00**	**1.47**	**15.82**	**2.87**	**38.89**
Iron and Steel	3.72	-	0.56	0.92	-	-	-	0.00	3.72	-	8.91
Chemical and Petrochem.	0.08	-	1.58	0.42	-	-	0.00	0.13	3.43	1.85	7.49
Non-Ferrous Metals	-	-	0.12	-	-	-	-	0.02	0.03	0.03	0.20
Non-Metallic Minerals	2.83	-	0.84	0.33	-	-	-	0.34	0.86	-	5.18
Transport Equipment	-	-	0.15	0.86	-	-	-	0.01	1.26	-	2.28
Machinery	-	-	0.44	-	-	-	-	0.01	3.35	0.07	3.88
Mining and Quarrying	-	-	0.06	-	-	-	-	-	0.11	-	0.17
Food and Tobacco	0.02	-	0.60	0.22	-	-	-	0.02	0.66	0.03	1.54
Paper, Pulp and Printing	0.02	-	0.89	0.07	-	-	-	0.30	0.87	0.17	2.33
Wood and Wood Products	-	-	0.05	0.01	-	-	-	0.07	0.13	-	0.26
Construction	-	-	0.60	0.00	-	-	-	-	-	-	0.60
Textile and Leather	0.09	-	0.92	0.35	-	-	-	0.02	1.21	0.70	3.28
Non-specified	0.34	-	0.68	1.00	-	-	0.00	0.53	0.18	0.02 e	2.76
TRANSPORT SECTOR	**-**	**-**	**31.33**	**0.32**	**-**	**-**	**-**	**0.01**	**0.18**	**-**	**31.84**
International Aviation	-	-	2.45	-	-	-	-	-	-	-	2.45
Domestic Aviation	-	-	1.25	-	-	-	-	-	-	-	1.25
Road	-	-	26.37	0.32	-	-	-	0.01	-	-	26.71
Rail	-	-	0.27	-	-	-	-	-	0.18	-	0.44
Pipeline Transport	-	-	0.00	-	-	-	-	-	-	-	0.00
Domestic Navigation	-	-	0.84	-	-	-	-	-	-	-	0.84
Non-specified	-	-	0.15	-	-	-	-	-	-	-	0.15
OTHER SECTORS	**0.95**	**-**	**12.76**	**11.49**	**-**	**-**	**0.04**	**0.32**	**14.71**	**1.65**	**41.92**
Residential	0.95	-	3.22	8.37	-	-	0.03	0.05	4.38	1.45	18.45
Comm. and Publ. Services	-	-	5.92	3.10	-	-	0.01	0.27	9.73	0.20	19.23
Agriculture/Forestry	-	-	1.43	0.02	-	-	-	-	0.45	-	1.91
Fishing	-	-	1.00	-	-	-	-	-	0.15	-	1.15
Non-specified	-	-	1.18	-	-	-	-	-	-	-	1.18
NON-ENERGY USE	**-**	**-**	**33.42**	**-**	**-**	**-**	**-**	**-**	**-**	**-**	**33.42**
in Industry/Transf./Energy	-	-	32.76	-	-	-	-	-	-	-	32.76
of which: Feedstocks	-	-	*30.75*	-	-	-	-	-	-	-	*30.75*
in Transport	-	-	0.60	-	-	-	-	-	-	-	0.60
in Other Sectors	-	-	0.06	-	-	-	-	-	-	-	0.06
Electricity Generated - TWh	***148.79***	***1.70***	***24.29***	***62.15***	***146.78***	***3.67***	***0.15***	***0.29***	***-***	***0.05***	***387.87***
Electricity Plants	*134.07*	*1.70*	*18.65*	*48.12*	*146.78*	*3.67*	*0.15*	*0.18*	-	*0.05*	*353.35*
CHP plants	*14.72*	-	*5.65*	*14.04*	-	-	-	*0.12*	-	-	*34.52*
Heat Generated - PJ	***35.23***	***-***	***100.66***	***48.12***	***-***	***-***	***-***	***9.00***	***-***	***0.50***	***193.50***
CHP plants	*35.23*	-	*90.37*	*43.42*	-	-	-	*2.53*	-	-	*171.54*
Heat Plants	-	-	*10.29*	*4.69*	-	-	-	*6.47*	-	*0.50 e*	*21.96*

Luxembourg
Key Indicators
Indicateurs principaux

	1960	1970	1973	1980	1990	1995
Energy Production (Mtoe)	-	0.01	-	0.03	0.03	0.05
Net Imports (Mtoe)	3.32	4.20	4.51	3.63	3.55	3.30
Total Primary Energy Supply (Mtoe)	3.31	4.15	4.50	3.64	3.57	3.38
Net Oil Imports (Mtoe)	0.23	1.34	1.67	1.12	1.65	1.80
Oil Supply (Mtoe)	0.23	1.34	1.67	1.12	1.64	1.83
Electricity Consumption (TWh)*	1.43	3.61	4.13	3.93	5.22	6.10
GDP (billion 2000 US$ using exch. rates)	4.19 e	5.93	7.02	7.65	12.40	15.05
GDP (billion 2000 US$ using PPPs)	4.61 e	6.51	7.71	8.40	13.62	16.53
Population (millions)	0.31 e	0.34	0.35	0.36	0.38	0.41
Industrial Production Index (2000=100)	43.50	55.20	63.80	55.40	79.50	81.30
Energy Production/TPES	0.0005	0.0020	0.0009	0.0081	0.0086	0.0138
Net Oil Imports/GDP (toe per thousand 2000 US$)	0.0555 e	0.2265	0.2381	0.1468	0.1332	0.1193
TPES/GDP (toe per thousand 2000 US$)	0.7892 e	0.6998	0.6414	0.4762	0.2880	0.2242
TPES/GDP (toe per thousand 2000 US$ PPP)	0.7186 e	0.6372	0.5841	0.4336	0.2622	0.2042
TPES/Population (toe per capita)	10.5389 e	12.2317	12.8344	10.0078	9.3494	8.2330
Oil Supply/GDP (toe per thousand 2000 US$)	0.0552 e	0.2259	0.2381	0.1465	0.1323	0.1214
Oil Supply/Population (toe per capita)	0.7374 e	3.9491	4.7639	3.0789	4.2951	4.4586
Elect. Cons./GDP (kWh per 2000 US$)	0.3406 e	0.6096	0.5886	0.5134	0.4209	0.4050
Elect. Cons./Population (kWh per capita)	4 548 e	10 655	11 778	10 789	13 662	14 871
Industry Cons.**/Industrial Production (2000=100)	298.44	347.35	338.02	312.24	175.50	132.23
Industry Oil Cons.**/Industrial Production (2000=100)	145.71	1 558.82	1 471.82	431.72	428.16	237.77

	2000	2001	2002	2003	2004	2005
Energy Production (Mtoe)	0.06	0.06	0.06	0.06	0.07	0.07
Net Imports (Mtoe)	3.68	3.75	4.00	4.21	4.59	4.68
Total Primary Energy Supply (Mtoe)	3.68	3.83	4.04	4.26	4.68	4.78
Net Oil Imports (Mtoe)	2.39	2.46	2.56	2.75	3.01	3.14
Oil Supply (Mtoe)	2.34	2.48	2.54	2.74	3.02	3.16
Electricity Consumption (TWh)*	6.76	6.72	6.92	7.17	7.45	7.29
GDP (billion 2000 US$ using exch. rates)	20.27	20.78	21.58	21.87	22.66	23.56
GDP (billion 2000 US$ using PPPs)	22.26	22.82	23.70	24.02	24.89	25.88
Population (millions)	0.44	0.44	0.45	0.45	0.45	0.46
Industrial Production Index (2000=100)	100.00	103.10	105.20	110.70	117.80	125.20
Energy Production/TPES	0.0154	0.0156	0.0140	0.0141	0.0155	0.0155
Net Oil Imports/GDP (toe per thousand 2000 US$)	0.1179	0.1181	0.1186	0.1257	0.1328	0.1334
TPES/GDP (toe per thousand 2000 US$)	0.1817	0.1845	0.1872	0.1949	0.2065	0.2027
TPES/GDP (toe per thousand 2000 US$ PPP)	0.1654	0.1680	0.1705	0.1775	0.1880	0.1846
TPES/Population (toe per capita)	8.3898	8.6749	9.0596	9.4715	10.3315	10.4516
Oil Supply/GDP (toe per thousand 2000 US$)	0.1154	0.1196	0.1178	0.1254	0.1334	0.1342
Oil Supply/Population (toe per capita)	5.3272	5.6205	5.7019	6.0932	6.6758	6.9190
Elect. Cons./GDP (kWh per 2000 US$)	0.3333	0.3231	0.3205	0.3279	0.3286	0.3096
Elect. Cons./Population (kWh per capita)	15 390	15 192	15 507	15 933	16 439	15 961
Industry Cons.**/Industrial Production (2000=100)	100.00	93.19	87.56	84.01	85.54	79.50
Industry Oil Cons.**/Industrial Production (2000=100)	100.00	89.88	66.06	66.08	67.15	95.45

* Electricity consumption equals domestic supply less distribution losses.
La consommation d'électricité représente l'approvisionnement intérieur diminué des pertes de distribution.

** Includes non-energy use in industry/transformation/energy sectors.
Comprend l'usage non-énergétique dans les secteurs de l'industrie/transformation/énergie.

Luxembourg

Figure 1. TPES* in 1973

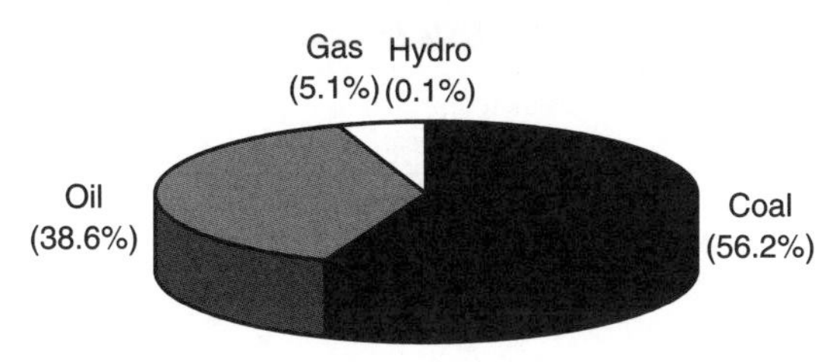

Figure 2. TPES* in 2005

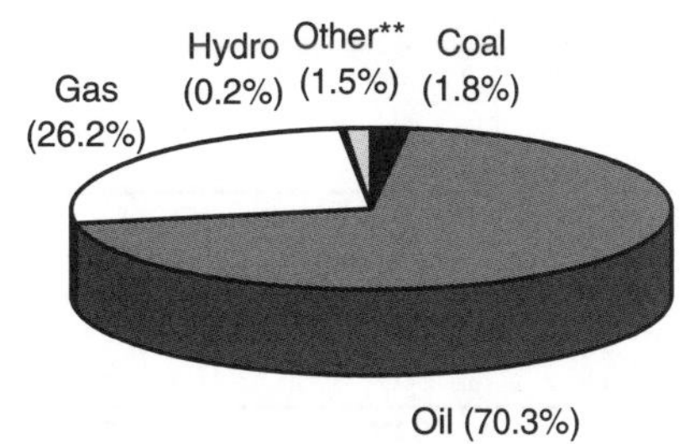

Figure 3. Final Consumption by Sector***

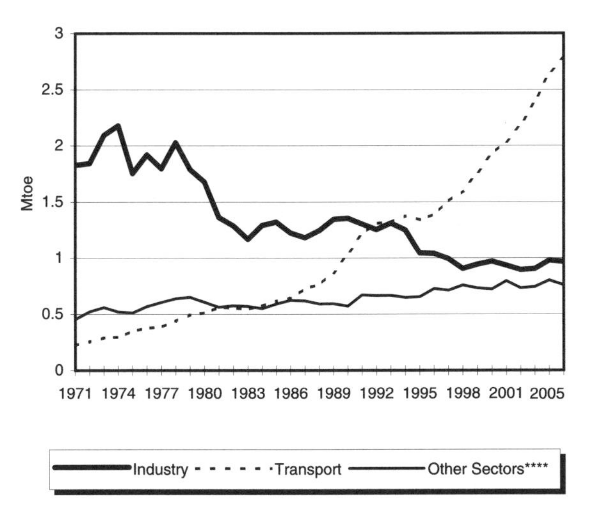

Figure 4. Breakdown of Sectorial Final Consumption by Source in 1973 and 2005***

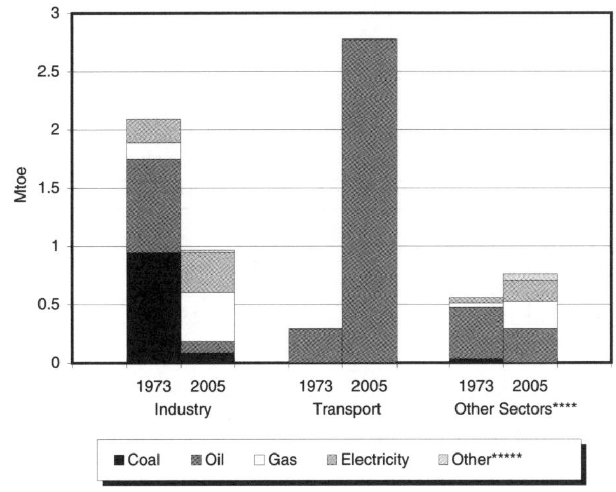

Figure 5. Electricity Generation by Fuel

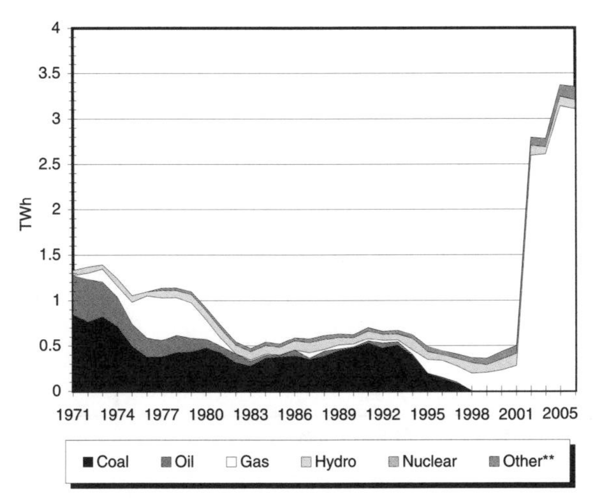

Figure 6. Electricity Consumption/GDP, TPES/GDP and Energy Production/TPES

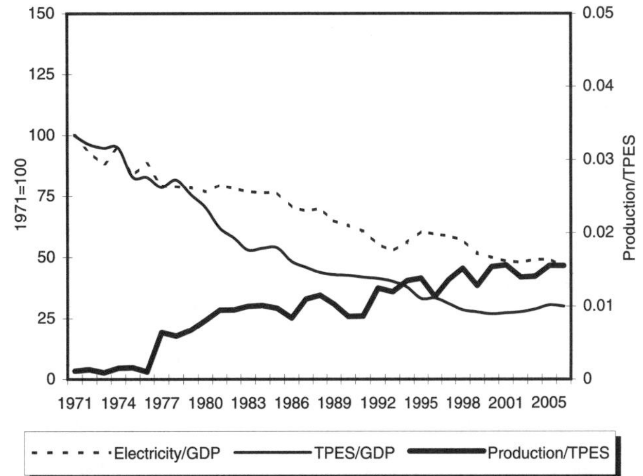

* Excluding electricity trade.

** Includes geothermal, solar, wind, combustible renewables & waste, etc.

*** Includes non-energy use.

**** Includes residential, commercial and public services, agriculture/forestry, fishing and non-specified.

***** Includes comb. renewables & waste, direct use of geothermal/solar thermal and heat produced in CHP/heat plants.

Luxembourg : 2004

Million tonnes of oil equivalent / *Million de tonnes d'équivalent pétrole*

SUPPLY AND CONSUMPTION / *APPROVISIONNEMENT ET DEMANDE*	Coal / *Charbon*	Crude Oil / *Pétrole brut*	Petroleum Products / *Produits pétroliers*	Gas / *Gaz*	Nuclear / *Nucléaire*	Hydro / *Hydro*	Geotherm. Solar etc. / *Géotherm. solaire etc.*	Combust. Renew. & Waste / *Comb. ren. & déchets*	Electricity / *Electricité*	Heat / *Chaleur*	Total / *Total*
Production	-	-	-	-	-	0.01	0.00	0.06	-	-	0.07
Imports	0.09	-	3.03	1.20	-	-	-	-	0.56	-	4.88
Exports	-	-	-0.02	-	-	-	-	-	-0.27	-	-0.28
Intl. Marine Bunkers	-	-	-	-	-	-	-	-	-	-	-
Stock Changes	-	-	0.01	-	-	-	-	-	-	-	0.01
TPES	**0.09**	**-**	**3.02**	**1.20**	**-**	**0.01**	**0.00**	**0.06**	**0.29**	**-**	**4.68**
Transfers	-	-	-	-	-	-	-	-	-	-	-
Statistical Differences	-	-	0.01	-	-	-	-	-	0.00	-	0.01
Electricity Plants	-	-	-	-0.43	-	-0.01	-0.00	-0.04	0.25	-	-0.23
CHP Plants	-	-	-	-0.09	-	-	-	-0.00	0.04	0.05	-0.01
Heat Plants	-	-	-	-	-	-	-	-	-	-	-
Gas Works	-	-	-	-	-	-	-	-	-	-	-
Petroleum Refineries	-	-	-	-	-	-	-	-	-	-	-
Coal Transformation	-	-	-	-	-	-	-	-	-	-	-
Liquefaction Plants	-	-	-	-	-	-	-	-	-	-	-
Other Transformation	-	-	-	-	-	-	-	-	-	-	-
Own Use	-	-	-	-	-	-	-	-	-0.03	-	-0.03
Distribution Losses	-	-	-	-	-	-	-	-	-0.00	-	-0.00
TFC	**0.09**	**-**	**3.03**	**0.68**	**-**	**-**	**0.00**	**0.02**	**0.55**	**0.05**	**4.42**
INDUSTRY SECTOR	**0.09**	**-**	**0.06**	**0.43**	**-**	**-**	**-**	**-**	**0.36**	**0.03**	**0.97**
Iron and Steel	0.03	-	0.00	0.18	-	-	-	-	0.16	-	0.38
Chemical and Petrochem.	-	-	0.00	-	-	-	-	-	-	0.03	0.03
Non-Ferrous Metals	-	-	-	-	-	-	-	-	-	-	-
Non-Metallic Minerals	0.07	-	0.01	-	-	-	-	-	-	-	0.07
Transport Equipment	-	-	-	-	-	-	-	-	-	-	-
Machinery	-	-	-	-	-	-	-	-	-	-	-
Mining and Quarrying	-	-	0.00	-	-	-	-	-	-	-	0.00
Food and Tobacco	-	-	0.01	-	-	-	-	-	-	-	0.01
Paper, Pulp and Printing	-	-	-	-	-	-	-	-	-	-	-
Wood and Wood Products	-	-	-	-	-	-	-	-	-	-	-
Construction	-	-	0.02	-	-	-	-	-	-	-	0.02
Textile and Leather	-	-	-	-	-	-	-	-	-	-	-
Non-specified	-	-	0.02	0.24	-	-	-	-	0.20	-	0.46
TRANSPORT SECTOR	**-**	**-**	**2.63**	**-**	**-**	**-**	**-**	**0.00**	**0.01**	**-**	**2.64**
International Aviation	-	-	0.44	-	-	-	-	-	-	-	0.44
Domestic Aviation	-	-	-	-	-	-	-	-	-	-	-
Road	-	-	2.18	-	-	-	-	0.00	-	-	2.18
Rail	-	-	0.00	-	-	-	-	-	0.01	-	0.01
Pipeline Transport	-	-	-	-	-	-	-	-	-	-	-
Domestic Navigation	-	-	-	-	-	-	-	-	-	-	-
Non-specified	-	-	0.01	-	-	-	-	-	-	-	0.01
OTHER SECTORS	**0.00**	**-**	**0.33**	**0.25**	**-**	**-**	**0.00**	**0.02**	**0.18**	**0.03**	**0.80**
Residential	0.00	-	0.31	0.25	-	-	0.00	0.02	0.06	0.03	0.67
Comm. and Publ. Services	-	-	-	-	-	-	-	-	0.11	-	0.11
Agriculture/Forestry	-	-	0.01	-	-	-	-	-	0.01	-	0.02
Fishing	-	-	-	-	-	-	-	-	-	-	-
Non-specified	-	-	0.00	-	-	-	-	-	-	-	0.00
NON-ENERGY USE	**-**	**-**	**0.01**	**-**	**-**	**-**	**-**	**-**	**-**	**-**	**0.01**
in Industry/Transf./Energy	-	-	0.01	-	-	-	-	-	-	-	0.01
of which: Feedstocks	-	-	-	-	-	-	-	-	-	-	-
in Transport	-	-	0.00	-	-	-	-	-	-	-	0.00
in Other Sectors	-	-	-	-	-	-	-	-	-	-	-
Electricity Generated - TWh	-	-	-	***3.14***	-	***0.11***	***0.05***	***0.08***	-	-	***3.37***
Electricity Plants	-	-	-	*2.72*	-	*0.11*	*0.05*	*0.06*	-	-	*2.93*
CHP plants	-	-	-	*0.42*	-	-	-	*0.02*	-	-	*0.44*
Heat Generated - PJ	-	-	-	***2.05***	-	-	-	***0.10***	-	-	***2.15***
CHP plants	-	-	-	*2.05*	-	-	-	*0.10*	-	-	*2.15*
Heat Plants	-	-	-	-	-	-	-	-	-	-	-

Luxembourg : 2005

Million tonnes of oil equivalent / *Million de tonnes d'équivalent pétrole*

SUPPLY AND CONSUMPTION *APPROVISIONNEMENT ET DEMANDE*	Coal *Charbon*	Crude Oil *Pétrole brut*	Petroleum Products *Produits pétroliers*	Gas *Gaz*	Nuclear *Nucléaire*	Hydro *Hydro*	Geotherm. Solar etc. *Géotherm. solaire etc.*	Combust. Renew. & Waste *Comb. ren. & déchets*	Electricity *Electricité*	Heat *Chaleur*	Total *Total*
Production	-	-	-	-	-	0.01	0.01	0.06	-	-	0.07
Imports	0.08	-	3.16	1.18	-	-	-	-	0.55	-	4.97
Exports	-	-	-0.02	-	-	-	-	-	-0.27	-	-0.28
Intl. Marine Bunkers	-	-	-	-	-	-	-	-	-	-	-
Stock Changes	-	-	0.02	-	-	-	-	-	-	-	0.02
TPES	**0.08**	**-**	**3.16**	**1.18**	**-**	**0.01**	**0.01**	**0.06**	**0.28**	**-**	**4.78**
Transfers	-	-	-	-	-	-	-	-	-	-	-
Statistical Differences	-	-	-	-	-	-	-	-	-	-	-
Electricity Plants	-	-	-	-0.42	-	-0.01	-0.01	-0.04	0.25	-	-0.22
CHP Plants	-	-	-	-0.10	-	-	-	-0.01	0.04	0.06	-0.01
Heat Plants	-	-	-	-	-	-	-	-	-	-	-
Gas Works	-	-	-	-	-	-	-	-	-	-	-
Petroleum Refineries	-	-	-	-	-	-	-	-	-	-	-
Coal Transformation	-	-	-	-	-	-	-	-	-	-	-
Liquefaction Plants	-	-	-	-	-	-	-	-	-	-	-
Other Transformation	-	-	-	-	-	-	-	-	-	-	-
Own Use	-	-	-	-	-	-	-	-	-0.03	-	-0.03
Distribution Losses	-	-	-	-	-	-	-	-	-0.01	-	-0.01
TFC	**0.08**	**-**	**3.16**	**0.65**	**-**	**-**	**0.00**	**0.02**	**0.53**	**0.06**	**4.50**
INDUSTRY SECTOR	**0.08**	**-**	**0.09**	**0.42**	**-**	**-**	**-**	**-**	**0.34**	**0.02**	**0.95**
Iron and Steel	0.02	-	0.00	0.17	-	-	-	-	0.15	-	0.34
Chemical and Petrochem.	-	-	0.00	-	-	-	-	-	-	0.02	0.03
Non-Ferrous Metals	-	-	-	-	-	-	-	-	-	-	-
Non-Metallic Minerals	0.06	-	0.01	-	-	-	-	-	-	-	0.06
Transport Equipment	-	-	-	-	-	-	-	-	-	-	-
Machinery	-	-	-	-	-	-	-	-	-	-	-
Mining and Quarrying	-	-	0.01	-	-	-	-	-	-	-	0.01
Food and Tobacco	-	-	0.01	-	-	-	-	-	-	-	0.01
Paper, Pulp and Printing	-	-	-	-	-	-	-	-	-	-	-
Wood and Wood Products	-	-	-	-	-	-	-	-	-	-	-
Construction	-	-	0.02	-	-	-	-	-	-	-	0.02
Textile and Leather	-	-	-	-	-	-	-	-	-	-	-
Non-specified	-	-	0.04	0.25	-	-	-	-	0.20	-	0.48
TRANSPORT SECTOR	**-**	**-**	**2.77**	**-**	**-**	**-**	**-**	**0.00**	**0.01**	**-**	**2.78**
International Aviation	-	-	0.45	-	-	-	-	-	-	-	0.45
Domestic Aviation	-	-	-	-	-	-	-	-	-	-	-
Road	-	-	2.31	-	-	-	-	0.00	-	-	2.31
Rail	-	-	0.00	-	-	-	-	-	0.01	-	0.01
Pipeline Transport	-	-	-	-	-	-	-	-	-	-	-
Domestic Navigation	-	-	-	-	-	-	-	-	-	-	-
Non-specified	-	-	0.01	-	-	-	-	-	-	-	0.01
OTHER SECTORS	**0.00**	**-**	**0.29**	**0.24**	**-**	**-**	**0.00**	**0.02**	**0.18**	**0.04**	**0.76**
Residential	0.00	-	0.27	0.24	-	-	0.00	0.02	0.06	0.04	0.62
Comm. and Publ. Services	-	-	-	-	-	-	-	-	0.11	-	0.11
Agriculture/Forestry	-	-	0.02	-	-	-	-	-	0.01	0.00	0.02
Fishing	-	-	-	-	-	-	-	-	-	-	-
Non-specified	-	-	0.01	-	-	-	-	-	-	-	0.01
NON-ENERGY USE	**-**	**-**	**0.02**	**-**	**-**	**-**	**-**	**-**	**-**	**-**	**0.02**
in Industry/Transf./Energy	-	-	0.02	-	-	-	-	-	-	-	0.02
of which: Feedstocks	-	-	-	-	-	-	-	-	-	-	-
in Transport	-	-	0.00	-	-	-	-	-	-	-	0.00
in Other Sectors	-	-	-	-	-	-	-	-	-	-	-
Electricity Generated - TWh	**-**	**-**	**-**	***3.11***	**-**	***0.10***	***0.07***	***0.08***	**-**	**-**	***3.35***
Electricity Plants	-	-	-	*2.69*	-	*0.10*	*0.07*	*0.05*	-	-	*2.91*
CHP plants	-	-	-	*0.42*	-	-	-	*0.03*	-	-	*0.45*
Heat Generated - PJ	**-**	**-**	**-**	***2.39***	**-**	**-**	**-**	***0.16***	**-**	**-**	***2.54***
CHP plants	-	-	-	*2.39*	-	-	-	*0.16*	-	-	*2.54*
Heat Plants	-	-	-	-	-	-	-	-	-	-	-

Mexico / Mexique
Key Indicators
Indicateurs principaux

	1960	1970	1973	1980	1990	1995
Energy Production (Mtoe)	..	..	47.29	147.62	194.78	202.33
Net Imports (Mtoe)	..	..	5.97	- 49.35	- 69.48	- 69.15
Total Primary Energy Supply (Mtoe)	..	..	53.20	97.13	124.34	132.65
Net Oil Imports (Mtoe)	..	..	5.72	- 47.58	- 69.96	- 71.06
Oil Supply (Mtoe)	..	..	33.10	66.47	83.34	84.73
Electricity Consumption (TWh)*	..	..	32.80	60.11	107.77	134.94
GDP (billion 2000 US$ using exch. rates)	94.97 e	182.13	223.14	345.12	412.80	445.34
GDP (billion 2000 US$ using PPPs)	146.70 e	281.34	344.69	533.12	637.66	687.92
Population (millions)	34.61 e	48.26	53.27	65.70	81.25	90.16
Industrial Production Index (2000=100)	..	..	..	56.60	67.30	70.40
Energy Production/TPES	..	..	0.8890	1.5198	1.5665	1.5252
Net Oil Imports/GDP (toe per thousand 2000 US$)	..	..	0.0256	- 0.1379	- 0.1695	- 0.1596
TPES/GDP (toe per thousand 2000 US$)	..	..	0.2384	0.2814	0.3012	0.2979
TPES/GDP (toe per thousand 2000 US$ PPP)	..	..	0.1543	0.1822	0.1950	0.1928
TPES/Population (toe per capita)	..	..	0.9986	1.4785	1.5303	1.4713
Oil Supply/GDP (toe per thousand 2000 US$)	..	..	0.1483	0.1926	0.2019	0.1903
Oil Supply/Population (toe per capita)	..	..	0.6214	1.0117	1.0257	0.9397
Elect. Cons./GDP (kWh per 2000 US$)	..	..	0.1470	0.1742	0.2611	0.3030
Elect. Cons./Population (kWh per capita)	..	..	616	915	1 326	1 497
Industry Cons.**/Industrial Production (2000=100)	..	..	..	123.52	141.25	133.73
Industry Oil Cons.**/Industrial Production (2000=100)	..	..	..	114.02	166.14	131.87

	2000	2001	2002	2003	2004	2005
Energy Production (Mtoe)	226.09	230.24	229.87	242.31	253.60	259.20
Net Imports (Mtoe)	- 72.77	- 76.87	- 72.69	- 82.61	- 86.15	- 81.27
Total Primary Energy Supply (Mtoe)	150.32	152.09	155.46	159.76	165.22	176.53
Net Oil Imports (Mtoe)	- 76.71	- 81.78	- 81.73	- 94.40	- 97.77	- 92.21
Oil Supply (Mtoe)	91.83	92.61	92.34	91.71	96.12	103.84
Electricity Consumption (TWh)*	175.81	178.86	183.50	183.49	187.62	195.73
GDP (billion 2000 US$ using exch. rates)	580.79	580.60	585.08	593.22	617.90	636.16
GDP (billion 2000 US$ using PPPs)	897.16	896.87	903.79	916.36	954.49	982.69
Population (millions)	98.66	100.05	101.40	102.71	104.00	105.30
Industrial Production Index (2000=100)	100.00	96.50	96.40	96.30	100.30	101.90
Energy Production/TPES	1.5040	1.5139	1.4787	1.5167	1.5349	1.4683
Net Oil Imports/GDP (toe per thousand 2000 US$)	- 0.1321	- 0.1409	- 0.1397	- 0.1591	- 0.1582	- 0.1450
TPES/GDP (toe per thousand 2000 US$)	0.2588	0.2620	0.2657	0.2693	0.2674	0.2775
TPES/GDP (toe per thousand 2000 US$ PPP)	0.1676	0.1696	0.1720	0.1743	0.1731	0.1796
TPES/Population (toe per capita)	1.5237	1.5201	1.5331	1.5555	1.5887	1.6765
Oil Supply/GDP (toe per thousand 2000 US$)	0.1581	0.1595	0.1578	0.1546	0.1556	0.1632
Oil Supply/Population (toe per capita)	0.9308	0.9257	0.9106	0.8930	0.9243	0.9862
Elect. Cons./GDP (kWh per 2000 US$)	0.3027	0.3081	0.3136	0.3093	0.3036	0.3077
Elect. Cons./Population (kWh per capita)	1 782	1 788	1 810	1 787	1 804	1 859
Industry Cons.**/Industrial Production (2000=100)	100.00	95.89	96.30	92.60	92.24	90.57
Industry Oil Cons.**/Industrial Production (2000=100)	100.00	100.93	92.71	88.91	88.33	85.35

* Electricity consumption equals domestic supply less distribution losses.
La consommation d'électricité représente l'approvisionnement intérieur diminué des pertes de distribution.

** Includes non-energy use in industry/transformation/energy sectors.
Comprend l'usage non-énergétique dans les secteurs de l'industrie/transformation/énergie.

Mexico / Mexique

Figure 1. TPES* in 1973

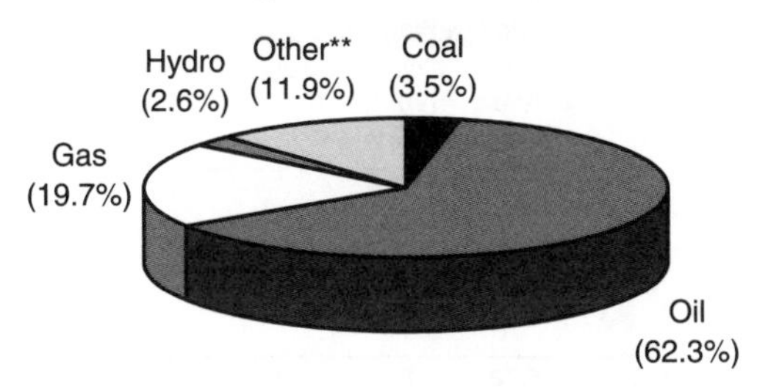

Figure 2. TPES* in 2005

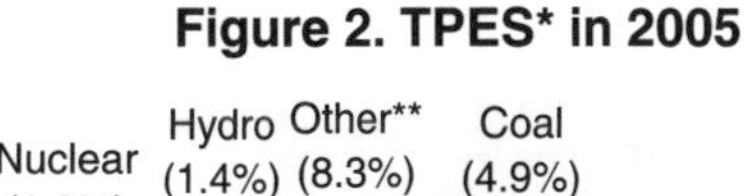

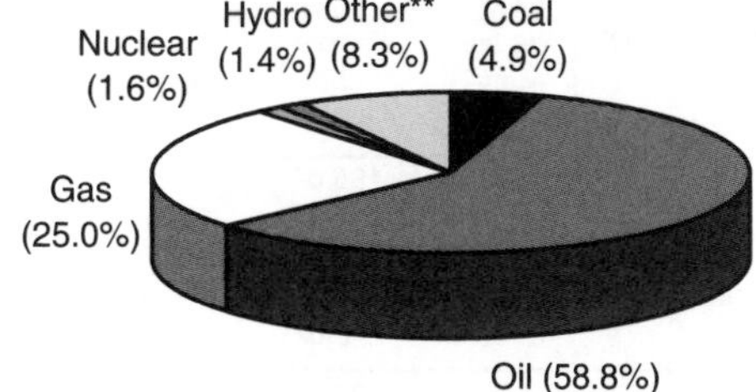

Figure 3. Final Consumption by Sector***

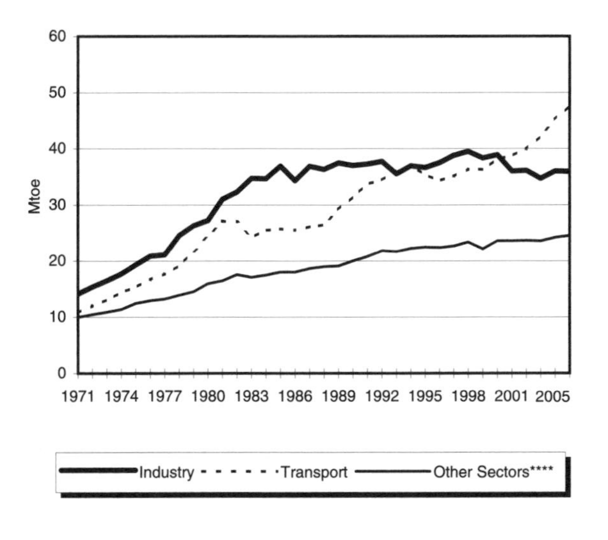

Figure 4. Breakdown of Sectorial Final Consumption by Source in 1973 and 2005***

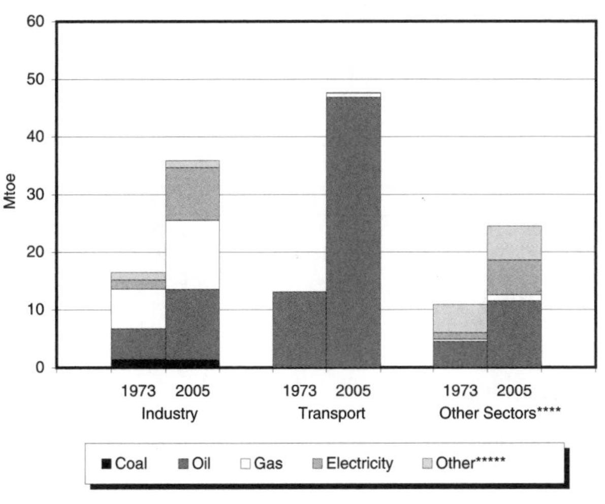

Figure 5. Electricity Generation by Fuel

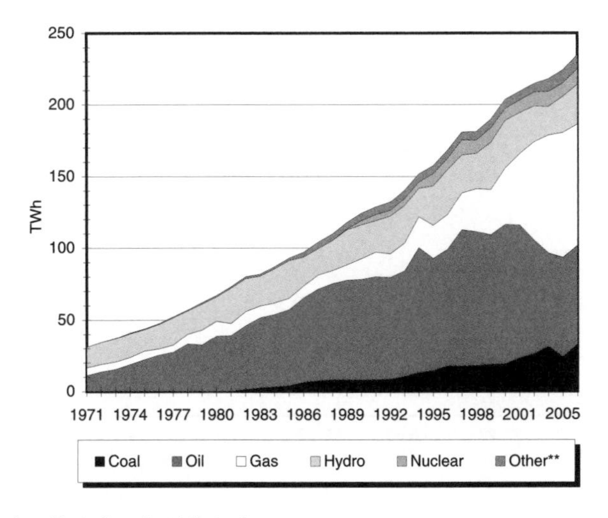

Figure 6. Electricity Consumption/GDP, TPES/GDP and Energy Production/TPES

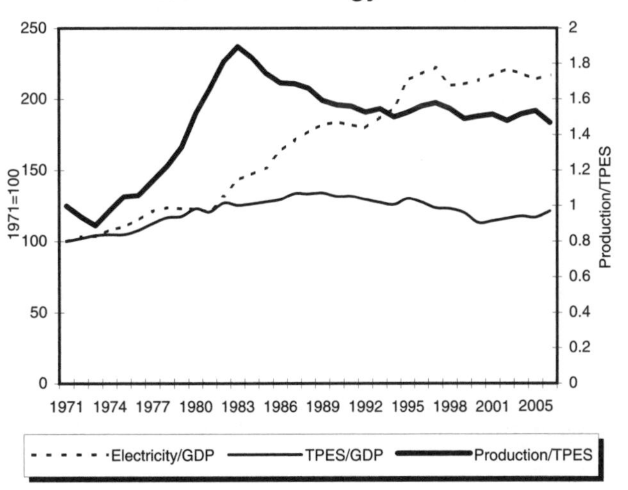

* Excluding electricity trade.

** Includes geothermal, solar, wind, combustible renewables & waste, etc.

*** Includes non-energy use.

**** Includes residential, commercial and public services, agriculture/forestry, fishing and non-specified.

***** Includes comb. renewables & waste, direct use of geothermal/solar thermal and heat produced in CHP/heat plants.

Mexico / Mexique : 2004

Million tonnes of oil equivalent / *Million de tonnes d'équivalent pétrole*

SUPPLY AND CONSUMPTION *APPROVISIONNEMENT ET DEMANDE*	Coal *Charbon*	Crude Oil *Pétrole brut*	Petroleum Products *Produits pétroliers*	Gas *Gaz*	Nuclear *Nucléaire*	Hydro *Hydro*	Geotherm. Solar etc. *Géotherm. solaire etc.*	Combust. Renew. & Waste *Comb. ren. & déchets*	Electricity *Electricité*	Heat *Chaleur*	Total *Total*
Production	4.75	195.02	-	35.49 e	2.40	2.17	5.73	8.05	-	-	253.60
Imports	2.36	0.30	13.16	9.35 e	-	-	-	-	0.00	-	25.17
Exports	-0.00	-107.17	-4.06	-	-	-	-	-	-0.09	-	-111.32
Intl. Marine Bunkers	-	-	-0.78	-	-	-	-	-	-	-	-0.78
Stock Changes	0.02	-0.52	0.17	-1.13 e	-	-	-	-	-	-	-1.45
TPES	**7.13**	**87.64**	**8.48**	**43.70**	**2.40**	**2.17**	**5.73**	**8.05**	**-0.08**	**-**	**165.22**
Transfers	-	-12.86	14.08	-	-	-	-	-	-	-	1.22
Statistical Differences	-	-	-2.34	-2.17	-	-	-	-	-	-	-4.51
Electricity Plants	-5.53	-	-15.92	-18.52	-2.40	-2.17	-5.66	-1.11	19.27	-	-32.03
CHP Plants	-	-	-	-	-	-	-	-	-	-	-
Heat Plants	-	-	-	-	-	-	-	-	-	-	-
Gas Works	-	-	-	-	-	-	-	-	-	-	-
Petroleum Refineries	-	-74.78	70.31	-	-	-	-	-	-	-	-4.47
Coal Transformation	-0.30 e	-	-	-	-	-	-	-	-	-	-0.30
Liquefaction Plants	-	-	-	-	-	-	-	-	-	-	-
Other Transformation	-	-	-	-	-	-	-	-	-	-	-
Own Use	-0.02	-	-6.32	-8.89	-	-	-	-	-1.51	-	-16.75
Distribution Losses	-	-	-	-	-	-	-	-	-3.05	-	-3.05
TFC	**1.28**	**-**	**68.29**	**14.13**	**-**	**-**	**0.07**	**6.94**	**14.62**	**-**	**105.33**
INDUSTRY SECTOR	**1.28**	**-**	**5.89**	**10.23**	**-**	**-**	**-**	**1.02**	**8.75**	**-**	**27.17**
Iron and Steel	1.07 e	-	0.36	3.00	-	-	-	-	0.67	-	5.10
Chemical and Petrochem.	-	-	0.44	2.79	-	-	-	-	0.49	-	3.72
Non-Ferrous Metals	-	-	0.00	0.03	-	-	-	-	0.07	-	0.10
Non-Metallic Minerals	0.08	-	0.13	0.80	-	-	-	-	0.49	-	1.49
Transport Equipment	-	-	-	0.05	-	-	-	-	0.15	-	0.20
Machinery	-	-	0.01	-	-	-	-	-	-	-	0.01
Mining and Quarrying	0.13	-	0.35	0.70	-	-	-	-	0.49	-	1.67
Food and Tobacco	-	-	0.93	0.25	-	-	-	1.02	0.16	-	2.35
Paper, Pulp and Printing	-	-	0.34	0.35	-	-	-	-	0.24	-	0.93
Wood and Wood Products	-	-	-	-	-	-	-	-	-	-	-
Construction	-	-	0.16	-	-	-	-	-	0.04	-	0.19
Textile and Leather	-	-	-	-	-	-	-	-	..	-	-
Non-specified	-	-	3.17	2.27	-	-	-	-	5.97	-	11.41
TRANSPORT SECTOR	**-**	**-**	**44.45**	**0.60**	**-**	**-**	**-**	**-**	**0.10**	**-**	**45.15**
International Aviation	-	-	2.57	-	-	-	-	-	-	-	2.57
Domestic Aviation	-	-	0.02	-	-	-	-	-	-	-	0.02
Road	-	-	40.48	0.02	-	-	-	-	-	-	40.50
Rail	-	-	0.59	-	-	-	-	-	0.10	-	0.69
Pipeline Transport	-	-	-	0.58	-	-	-	-	-	-	0.58
Domestic Navigation	-	-	0.78	-	-	-	-	-	-	-	0.78
Non-specified	-	-	0.01	-	-	-	-	-	-	-	0.01
OTHER SECTORS	**-**	**-**	**11.37**	**1.06**	**-**	**-**	**0.07**	**5.92**	**5.77**	**-**	**24.18**
Residential	-	-	7.50	0.86	-	-	-	5.92	3.52	-	17.79
Comm. and Publ. Services	-	-	1.60	0.20	-	-	0.07	-	1.66	-	3.52
Agriculture/Forestry	-	-	2.27	-	-	-	-	-	0.60	-	2.87
Fishing	-	-	-	-	-	-	-	-	-	-	-
Non-specified	-	-	-	-	-	-	-	-	-	-	-
NON-ENERGY USE	**-**	**-**	**6.59**	**2.24**	**-**	**-**	**-**	**-**	**-**	**-**	**8.83**
in Industry/Transf./Energy	-	-	6.59	2.24	-	-	-	-	-	-	8.83
of which: Feedstocks	*-*	*-*	*5.55*	*2.24*	*-*	*-*	*-*	*-*	*-*	*-*	*7.79*
in Transport	-	-	-	-	-	-	-	-	-	-	-
in Other Sectors	-	-	-	-	-	-	-	-	-	-	-
Electricity Generated - TWh	***23.90***	***-***	***69.60***	***87.05***	***9.19***	***25.21***	***6.63***	***2.52***	***-***	***-***	***224.08***
Electricity Plants	*23.90*	*-*	*69.60*	*87.05*	*9.19*	*25.21*	*6.63*	*2.52*	*-*	*-*	*224.08*
CHP plants	*-*	*-*	*-*	*-*	*-*	*-*	*-*	*-*	*-*	*-*	*-*
Heat Generated - PJ	***-***	***-***	***-***	***-***	***-***	***-***	***-***	***-***	***-***	***-***	***-***
CHP plants	*-*	*-*	*-*	*-*	*-*	*-*	*-*	*-*	*-*	*-*	*-*
Heat Plants	*-*	*-*	*-*	*-*	*-*	*-*	*-*	*-*	*-*	*-*	*-*

Mexico / Mexique : 2005

Million tonnes of oil equivalent / *Million de tonnes d'équivalent pétrole*

SUPPLY AND CONSUMPTION *APPROVISIONNEMENT ET DEMANDE*	Coal *Charbon*	Crude Oil *Pétrole brut*	Petroleum Products *Produits pétroliers*	Gas *Gaz*	Nuclear *Nucléaire*	Hydro *Hydro*	Geotherm. Solar etc. *Géotherm. solaire etc.*	Combust. Renew. & Waste *Comb. ren. & déchets*	Electricity *Electricité*	Heat *Chaleur*	Total *Total*
Production	5.16	197.29	-	36.89	2.82	2.38	6.35	8.31	-	-	259.20
Imports	3.77	0.38	16.82	7.49	-	-	-	-	0.01	-	28.47
Exports	-0.00	-105.48	-3.94	-0.21	-	-	-	-	-0.11	-	-109.74
Intl. Marine Bunkers	-	-	-0.89	-	-	-	-	-	-	-	-0.89
Stock Changes	-0.19	-0.08	-0.26	0.02	-	-	-	-	-	-	-0.51
TPES	**8.74**	**92.12**	**11.73**	**44.19**	**2.82**	**2.38**	**6.35**	**8.31**	**-0.10**	**-**	**176.53**
Transfers	-	-12.35	13.52	-	-	-	-	-	-	-	1.17
Statistical Differences	-	-	-3.83	-1.26	-	-	-	-	-	-	-5.09
Electricity Plants	-7.12	-	-15.62	-17.96	-2.82	-2.38	-6.28	-1.15	20.20	-	-33.13
CHP Plants	-	-	-	-	-	-	-	-	-	-	-
Heat Plants	-	-	-	-	-	-	-	-	-	-	-
Gas Works	-	-	-	-	-	-	-	-	-	-	-
Petroleum Refineries	-	-79.76	71.30	-	-	-	-	-	-	-	-8.46
Coal Transformation	-0.31 e	-	-	-	-	-	-	-	-	-	-0.31
Liquefaction Plants	-	-	-	-	-	-	-	-	-	-	-
Other Transformation	-	-	-	-	-	-	-	-	-	-	-
Own Use	-0.02	-	-6.55	-11.19	-	-	-	-	-1.58	-	-19.34
Distribution Losses	-	-	-	-	-	-	-	-	-3.26	-	-3.26
TFC	**1.28**	**-**	**70.56**	**13.78**	**-**	**-**	**0.07**	**7.16**	**15.25**	**-**	**108.11**
INDUSTRY SECTOR	**1.28**	**-**	**5.80**	**10.00**	**-**	**-**	**-**	**1.26**	**9.12**	**-**	**27.47**
Iron and Steel	1.06 e	-	0.30	3.01	-	-	-	-	0.70	-	5.07
Chemical and Petrochem.	-	-	0.48	2.65	-	-	-	-	0.51	-	3.64
Non-Ferrous Metals	-	-	0.00	0.03	-	-	-	-	0.08	-	0.11
Non-Metallic Minerals	0.09	-	0.87	0.83	-	-	-	-	0.51	-	2.30
Transport Equipment	-	-	-	0.05	-	-	-	-	0.16	-	0.21
Machinery	-	-	0.01	-	-	-	-	-	-	-	0.01
Mining and Quarrying	0.13	-	0.33	0.71	-	-	-	-	0.51	-	1.68
Food and Tobacco	-	-	0.60	0.25	-	-	-	1.26	0.16	-	2.27
Paper, Pulp and Printing	-	-	0.29	0.36	-	-	-	-	0.25	-	0.90
Wood and Wood Products	-	-	-	-	-	-	-	-	-	-	-
Construction	-	-	0.18	-	-	-	-	-	0.04	-	0.22
Textile and Leather	-	-	-	-	-	-	-	-	-	-	-
Non-specified	-	-	2.73	2.09	-	-	-	-	6.22	-	11.05
TRANSPORT SECTOR	**-**	**-**	**46.84**	**0.73**	**-**	**-**	**-**	**-**	**0.10**	**-**	**47.67**
International Aviation	-	-	2.66	-	-	-	-	-	-	-	2.66
Domestic Aviation	-	-	0.02	-	-	-	-	-	-	-	0.02
Road	-	-	42.69	0.02	-	-	-	-	-	-	42.71
Rail	-	-	0.62	-	-	-	-	-	0.10	-	0.72
Pipeline Transport	-	-	-	0.71	-	-	-	-	-	-	0.71
Domestic Navigation	-	-	0.85	-	-	-	-	-	-	-	0.85
Non-specified	-	-	-	-	-	-	-	-	-	-	-
OTHER SECTORS	**-**	**-**	**11.47**	**1.06**	**-**	**-**	**0.07**	**5.90**	**6.02**	**-**	**24.53**
Residential	-	-	7.40	0.86	-	-	-	5.90	3.67	-	17.83
Comm. and Publ. Services	-	-	1.60	0.20	-	-	0.07	-	1.73	-	3.61
Agriculture/Forestry	-	-	2.46	-	-	-	-	-	0.63	-	3.09
Fishing	-	-	-	-	-	-	-	-	-	-	-
Non-specified	-	-	-	-	-	-	-	-	-	-	-
NON-ENERGY USE	**-**	**-**	**6.45**	**2.00**	**-**	**-**	**-**	**-**	**-**	**-**	**8.45**
in Industry/Transf./Energy	-	-	6.45	2.00	-	-	-	-	-	-	8.45
of which: Feedstocks	-	-	*5.44*	*2.00*	-	-	-	-	-	-	*7.44*
in Transport	-	-	-	-	-	-	-	-	-	-	-
in Other Sectors	-	-	-	-	-	-	-	-	-	-	-
Electricity Generated - TWh	***32.93***	**-**	***68.73***	***84.75***	***10.81***	***27.73***	***7.35***	***2.60***	**-**	**-**	***234.90***
Electricity Plants	*32.93*	-	*68.73*	*84.75*	*10.81*	*27.73*	*7.35*	*2.60*	-	-	*234.90*
CHP plants	-	-	-	-	-	-	-	-	-	-	-
Heat Generated - PJ	**-**	**-**	**-**	**-**	**-**	**-**	**-**	**-**	**-**	**-**	**-**
CHP plants	-	-	-	-	-	-	-	-	-	-	-
Heat Plants	-	-	-	-	-	-	-	-	-	-	-

Netherlands / Pays-Bas
Key Indicators
Indicateurs principaux

	1960	1970	1973	1980	1990	1995
Energy Production (Mtoe)	10.20	28.87	56.76	71.82	60.54	66.23
Net Imports (Mtoe)	13.58	30.35	17.64	3.12	17.32	15.25
Total Primary Energy Supply (Mtoe)	21.15	49.26	62.44	64.98	66.75	72.49
Net Oil Imports (Mtoe)	12.01	37.05	41.46	37.90	30.86	31.60
Oil Supply (Mtoe)	10.94	29.07	30.91	29.48	24.35	26.00
Electricity Consumption (TWh)*	15.55	38.44	48.55	61.75	78.02	88.99
GDP (billion 2000 US$ using exch. rates)	104.50 e	171.22	192.61	228.29	284.85	315.81
GDP (billion 2000 US$ using PPPs)	122.64 e	200.95	226.06	267.93	334.31	370.64
Population (millions)	11.48 e	13.03	13.44	14.15	14.95	15.46
Industrial Production Index (2000=100)	29.20	59.20	70.70	78.90	83.90	90.90
Energy Production/TPES	0.4824	0.5860	0.9090	1.1052	0.9070	0.9137
Net Oil Imports/GDP (toe per thousand 2000 US$)	0.1149 e	0.2164	0.2152	0.1660	0.1083	0.1000
TPES/GDP (toe per thousand 2000 US$)	0.2024 e	0.2877	0.3242	0.2847	0.2343	0.2295
TPES/GDP (toe per thousand 2000 US$ PPP)	0.1724 e	0.2452	0.2762	0.2425	0.1997	0.1956
TPES/Population (toe per capita)	1.8419 e	3.7803	4.6468	4.5932	4.4658	4.6887
Oil Supply/GDP (toe per thousand 2000 US$)	0.1047 e	0.1698	0.1605	0.1291	0.0855	0.0823
Oil Supply/Population (toe per capita)	0.9530 e	2.2304	2.2999	2.0834	1.6288	1.6816
Elect. Cons./GDP (kWh per 2000 US$)	0.1488 e	0.2245	0.2520	0.2705	0.2739	0.2818
Elect. Cons./Population (kWh per capita)	1 354 e	2 950	3 613	4 365	5 220	5 756
Industry Cons.**/Industrial Production (2000=100)	82.21	109.83	130.99	115.99	110.23	98.93
Industry Oil Cons.**/Industrial Production (2000=100)	119.21	145.72	160.44	131.06	106.11	88.81

	2000	2001	2002	2003	2004	2005
Energy Production (Mtoe)	57.19	60.97	60.43	58.44	67.66	61.90
Net Imports (Mtoe)	34.53	31.67	31.81	35.84	29.92	37.86
Total Primary Energy Supply (Mtoe)	75.86	77.99	78.68	80.97	82.17	81.85
Net Oil Imports (Mtoe)	41.86	41.83	40.49	41.29	44.53	48.34
Oil Supply (Mtoe)	28.60	29.57	29.85	31.53	31.96	32.88
Electricity Consumption (TWh)*	104.46	106.86	108.23	109.47	112.66	114.04
GDP (billion 2000 US$ using exch. rates)	385.08	392.49	392.79	394.11	401.81	407.95
GDP (billion 2000 US$ using PPPs)	451.93	460.64	460.99	462.54	471.57	478.78
Population (millions)	15.92	16.04	16.15	16.22	16.28	16.32
Industrial Production Index (2000=100)	100.00	100.60	101.50	100.10	102.60	101.40
Energy Production/TPES	0.7539	0.7818	0.7680	0.7218	0.8234	0.7563
Net Oil Imports/GDP (toe per thousand 2000 US$)	0.1087	0.1066	0.1031	0.1048	0.1108	0.1185
TPES/GDP (toe per thousand 2000 US$)	0.1970	0.1987	0.2003	0.2054	0.2045	0.2006
TPES/GDP (toe per thousand 2000 US$ PPP)	0.1679	0.1693	0.1707	0.1751	0.1743	0.1710
TPES/Population (toe per capita)	4.7646	4.8610	4.8730	4.9909	5.0487	5.0165
Oil Supply/GDP (toe per thousand 2000 US$)	0.0743	0.0753	0.0760	0.0800	0.0795	0.0806
Oil Supply/Population (toe per capita)	1.7962	1.8434	1.8484	1.9434	1.9633	2.0154
Elect. Cons./GDP (kWh per 2000 US$)	0.2713	0.2723	0.2756	0.2778	0.2804	0.2795
Elect. Cons./Population (kWh per capita)	6 561	6 661	6 703	6 748	6 922	6 989
Industry Cons.**/Industrial Production (2000=100)	100.00	98.97	97.67	107.26	107.13	115.64
Industry Oil Cons.**/Industrial Production (2000=100)	100.00	104.71	102.29	119.54	117.08	133.69

* Electricity consumption equals domestic supply less distribution losses.
La consommation d'électricité représente l'approvisionnement intérieur diminué des pertes de distribution.

** Includes non-energy use in industry/transformation/energy sectors.
Comprend l'usage non-énergétique dans les secteurs de l'industrie/transformation/énergie.

Netherlands / Pays-Bas

Figure 1. TPES* in 1973

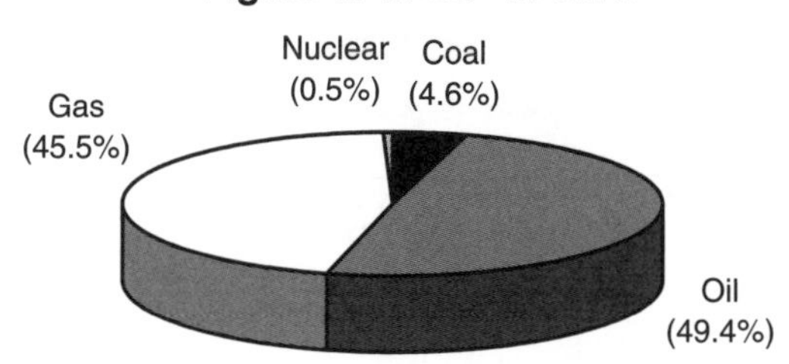

Figure 2. TPES* in 2005

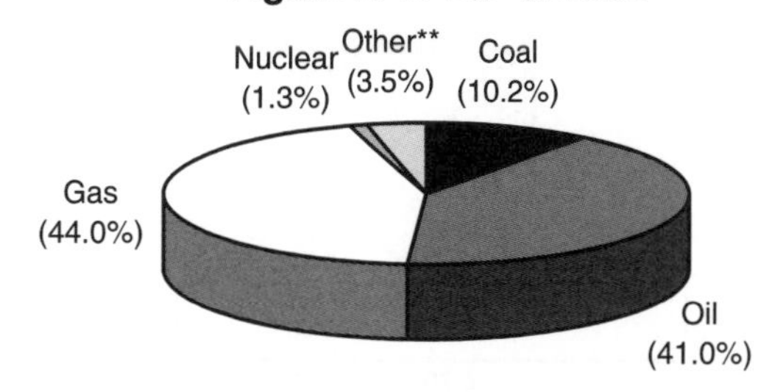

Figure 3. Final Consumption by Sector***

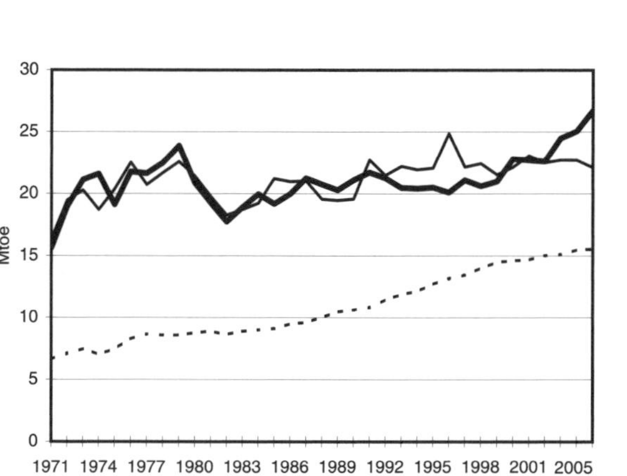

Figure 4. Breakdown of Sectorial Final Consumption by Source in 1973 and 2005***

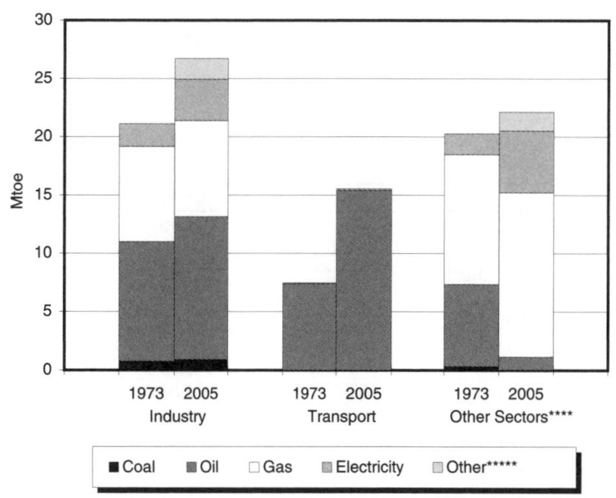

Figure 5. Electricity Generation by Fuel

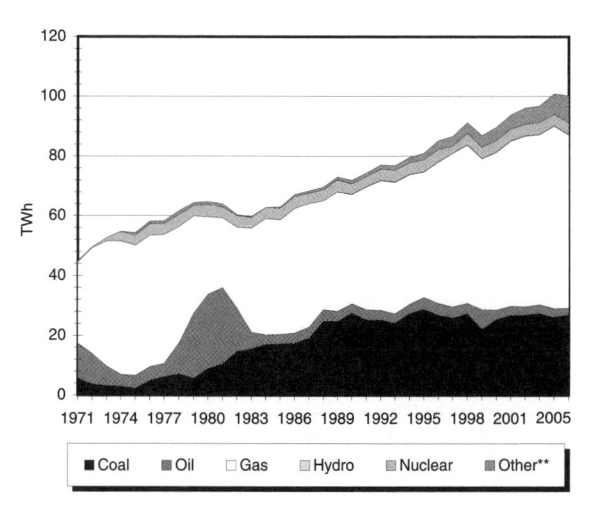

Figure 6. Electricity Consumption/GDP, TPES/GDP and Energy Production/TPES

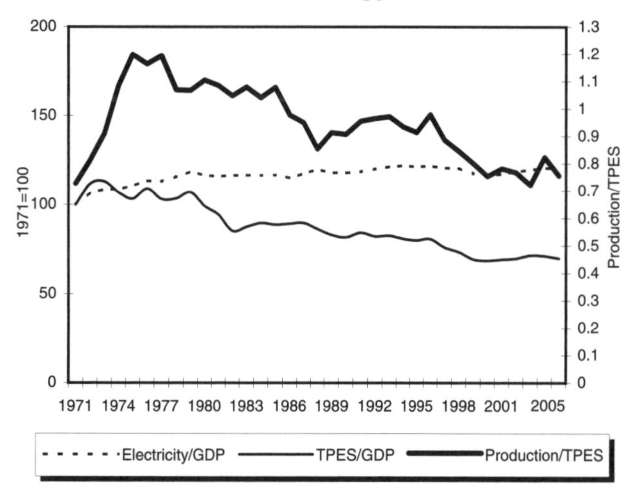

* Excluding electricity trade.

** Includes geothermal, solar, wind, combustible renewables & waste, etc.

*** Includes non-energy use.

**** Includes residential, commercial and public services, agriculture/forestry, fishing and non-specified.

***** Includes comb. renewables & waste, direct use of geothermal/solar thermal and heat produced in CHP/heat plants.

Netherlands / Pays-Bas : 2004

Million tonnes of oil equivalent / *Million de tonnes d'équivalent pétrole*

SUPPLY AND CONSUMPTION / *APPROVISIONNEMENT ET DEMANDE*	Coal / *Charbon*	Crude Oil / *Pétrole brut*	Petroleum Products / *Produits pétroliers*	Gas / *Gaz*	Nuclear / *Nucléaire*	Hydro / *Hydro*	Geotherm. Solar etc. / *Géotherm. solaire etc.*	Combust. Renew. & Waste / *Comb. ren. & déchets*	Electricity / *Electricité*	Heat / *Chaleur*	Total / *Total*
Production	-	2.97	-	61.57	1.00	0.01	0.20	1.92	-	-	67.66
Imports	14.57	61.84	56.83	13.50	-	-	-	0.28	1.84	-	148.87
Exports	-5.99	-1.23	-72.91	-38.35	-	-	-	-0.02	-0.45	-	-118.94
Intl. Marine Bunkers	-	-	-14.69	-	-	-	-	-	-	-	-14.69
Stock Changes	0.12	0.00	-0.86	0.02	-	-	-	-	-	-	-0.72
TPES	**8.70**	**63.58**	**-31.63**	**36.73**	**1.00**	**0.01**	**0.20**	**2.19**	**1.39**	**-**	**82.17**
Transfers	-	22.84	-23.73	-	-	-	-	-	-	-	-0.89
Statistical Differences	-0.12	-	-	-	-	-	-	-	-	-	-0.12
Electricity Plants	-	-	-	-	-1.00	-0.01	-0.18	-1.00	0.77	-	-1.41
CHP Plants	-5.94	-	-0.63	-12.09	-	-	-	-0.61	7.89	2.89	-8.49
Heat Plants	-	-	-	-	-	-	-	-0.18	-	0.12	-0.06
Gas Works	-	-	-	-	-	-	-	-	-	-	-
Petroleum Refineries	-	-86.42	87.13	-	-	-	-	-	-	-	0.71
Coal Transformation	-1.48 e	-	-	-	-	-	-	-	-	-	-1.48
Liquefaction Plants	-	-	-	-	-	-	-	-	-	-	-
Other Transformation	-	-	-	-	-	-	-	-0.00	-	-	-0.00
Own Use	-0.19	-	-3.96	-1.39	-	-	-	-	-0.82	-	-6.36
Distribution Losses	-	-	-	-	-	-	-	-	-0.37	-0.45	-0.82
TFC	**0.98**	**-**	**27.19**	**23.26**	**-**	**-**	**0.02**	**0.39**	**8.87**	**2.56**	**63.25**
INDUSTRY SECTOR	**0.65**	**-**	**1.65**	**5.99**	**-**	**-**	**-**	**0.12**	**3.56**	**1.43**	**13.40**
Iron and Steel	0.60 e	-	0.00	0.27	-	-	-	-	0.23	-	1.11
Chemical and Petrochem.	-	-	1.37	2.18	-	-	-	0.00	1.04	1.12	5.71
Non-Ferrous Metals	-	-	-	0.10	-	-	-	-	0.54	-	0.64
Non-Metallic Minerals	0.04	-	0.02	0.56	-	-	-	-	0.12	-	0.73
Transport Equipment	-	-	0.01	0.07	-	-	-	-	0.05	-	0.13
Machinery	-	-	0.08	0.33	-	-	-	-	0.29	-	0.70
Mining and Quarrying	0.00	-	0.04	0.12	-	-	-	-	0.05	-	0.21
Food and Tobacco	0.01	-	0.01	1.47	-	-	-	0.02	0.56	0.15	2.23
Paper, Pulp and Printing	-	-	-	0.49	-	-	-	0.00	0.32	0.16	0.97
Wood and Wood Products	-	-	0.00	0.02	-	-	-	-	0.02	-	0.03
Construction	-	-	0.11	0.09	-	-	-	-	0.04	-	0.25
Textile and Leather	-	-	-	0.10	-	-	-	-	0.04	-	0.15
Non-specified	-	-	0.01	0.20	-	-	-	0.09	0.24	-	0.54
TRANSPORT SECTOR	**-**	**-**	**15.28**	**-**	**-**	**-**	**-**	**-**	**0.14**	**-**	**15.42**
International Aviation	-	-	3.63	-	-	-	-	-	-	-	3.63
Domestic Aviation	-	-	0.06	-	-	-	-	-	-	-	0.06
Road	-	-	11.25	-	-	-	-	-	-	-	11.25
Rail	-	-	0.05	-	-	-	-	-	0.14	-	0.19
Pipeline Transport	-	-	-	-	-	-	-	-	-	-	-
Domestic Navigation	-	-	0.29	-	-	-	-	-	-	-	0.29
Non-specified	-	-	-	-	-	-	-	-	-	-	-
OTHER SECTORS	**0.03**	**-**	**0.88**	**15.11**	**-**	**-**	**0.02**	**0.27**	**5.17**	**1.12**	**22.60**
Residential	0.00	-	0.07	7.90	-	-	0.02	0.23	2.02	0.20	10.44
Comm. and Publ. Services	0.03	-	0.31	4.38	-	-	-	0.04	2.80	0.73	8.29
Agriculture/Forestry	-	-	0.50	2.84	-	-	-	-	0.35	0.19	3.88
Fishing	-	-	-	-	-	-	-	-	-	-	-
Non-specified	-	-	-	-	-	-	-	-	-	-	-
NON-ENERGY USE	**0.29**	**-**	**9.38**	**2.16**	**-**	**-**	**-**	**-**	**-**	**-**	**11.83**
in Industry/Transf./Energy	0.29	-	9.20	2.16	-	-	-	-	-	-	11.65
of which: Feedstocks	*0.10*	-	*7.84*	*2.16*	-	-	-	-	-	-	*10.09*
in Transport	-	-	0.07	-	-	-	-	-	-	-	0.07
in Other Sectors	-	-	0.11	-	-	-	-	-	-	-	0.11
Electricity Generated - TWh	***26.24***	-	***2.82***	***61.01***	***3.82***	***0.10***	***2.10***	***4.68***	-	-	***100.77***
Electricity Plants	-	-	-	-	*3.82*	*0.10*	*2.10*	*2.95*	-	-	*8.97*
CHP plants	*26.24*	-	*2.82*	*61.01*	-	-	-	*1.73*	-	-	*91.80*
Heat Generated - PJ	***4.94***	-	***2.24***	***110.59***	-	-	-	***8.15***	-	-	***125.92***
CHP plants	*4.94*	-	*2.24*	*110.59*	-	-	-	*3.05*	-	-	*120.81*
Heat Plants	-	-	-	-	-	-	-	*5.11*	-	-	*5.11*

Netherlands / Pays-Bas : 2005

Million tonnes of oil equivalent / *Million de tonnes d'équivalent pétrole*

SUPPLY AND CONSUMPTION	Coal	Crude Oil	Petroleum Products	Gas	Nuclear	Hydro	Geotherm. Solar etc.	Combust. Renew. & Waste	Electricity	Heat	Total
APPROVISIONNEMENT ET DEMANDE	*Charbon*	*Pétrole brut*	*Produits pétroliers*	*Gaz*	*Nucléaire*	*Hydro*	*Géotherm. solaire etc.*	*Comb. ren. & déchets*	*Electricité*	*Chaleur*	*Total*
Production	-	2.34	-	56.25	1.04	0.01	0.22	2.04	-	-	61.90
Imports	13.02	63.25	64.28	16.44	-	-	-	0.62	2.04	-	159.64
Exports	-4.70	-1.16	-78.03	-37.37	-	-	-	-0.04	-0.46	-	-121.77
Intl. Marine Bunkers	-	-	-16.89	-	-	-	-	-	-	-	-16.89
Stock Changes	-0.13	-0.25	-0.66	-0.00	-	-	-	-	-	-	-1.03
TPES	**8.19**	**64.18**	**-31.30**	**35.31**	**1.04**	**0.01**	**0.22**	**2.62**	**1.57**	**-**	**81.85**
Transfers	-	23.06	-23.96	-	-	-	-	-	-	-	-0.90
Statistical Differences	-	-	-0.10	-	-	-	-	-	-	-	-0.10
Electricity Plants	-3.35	-	-	-3.21	-1.04	-0.01	-0.20	-1.30	3.65	-0.28	-5.74
CHP Plants	-2.24	-	-0.58	-8.06	-	-	-	-0.75	4.97	3.70	-2.96
Heat Plants	-	-	-	-0.26	-	-	-	-0.17	-	0.38	-0.06
Gas Works	-	-	-	-	-	-	-	-	-	-	-
Petroleum Refineries	-	-87.24	88.59	-	-	-	-	-	-	-	1.35
Coal Transformation	-1.48 e	-	-	-	-	-	-	-	-	-	-1.48
Liquefaction Plants	-	-	-	-	-	-	-	-	-	-	-
Other Transformation	-	-	-	-	-	-	-	-0.00	-	-	-0.00
Own Use	-0.19	-	-3.88	-1.48	-	-	-	-	-0.82	-0.21	-6.58
Distribution Losses	-	-	-	-	-	-	-	-	-0.38	-0.61	-1.00
TFC	**0.93**	**-**	**28.76**	**22.29**	**-**	**-**	**0.02**	**0.39**	**8.99**	**2.98**	**64.37**
INDUSTRY SECTOR	**0.62**	**-**	**2.05**	**5.75**	**-**	**-**	**-**	**0.12**	**3.58**	**1.68**	**13.79**
Iron and Steel	0.57 e	-	0.00	0.29	-	-	-	-	0.23	0.00	1.10
Chemical and Petrochem.	-	-	1.32	2.05	-	-	-	0.00	1.06	0.98	5.41
Non-Ferrous Metals	-	-	-	0.10	-	-	-	-	0.54	0.04	0.68
Non-Metallic Minerals	0.03	-	0.02	0.55	-	-	-	-	0.12	0.03	0.76
Transport Equipment	-	-	0.00	0.06	-	-	-	-	0.05	0.00	0.12
Machinery	-	-	0.55	0.33	-	-	-	-	0.29	0.02	1.19
Mining and Quarrying	0.00	-	0.02	0.11	-	-	-	-	0.05	0.17	0.36
Food and Tobacco	0.01	-	0.02	1.41	-	-	-	0.02	0.57	0.18	2.21
Paper, Pulp and Printing	-	-	-	0.47	-	-	-	0.00	0.32	0.19	0.98
Wood and Wood Products	-	-	0.00	0.02	-	-	-	-	0.02	0.04	0.08
Construction	-	-	0.11	0.09	-	-	-	-	0.04	-	0.24
Textile and Leather	0.00	-	-	0.08	-	-	-	-	0.04	0.00	0.12
Non-specified	-	-	0.01	0.19	-	-	-	0.10	0.24	0.01	0.55
TRANSPORT SECTOR	**-**	**-**	**15.31**	**-**	**-**	**-**	**-**	**-**	**0.14**	**-**	**15.45**
International Aviation	-	-	3.73	-	-	-	-	-	-	-	3.73
Domestic Aviation	-	-	0.08	-	-	-	-	-	-	-	0.08
Road	-	-	11.26	-	-	-	-	-	-	-	11.26
Rail	-	-	0.03	-	-	-	-	-	0.14	-	0.17
Pipeline Transport	-	-	-	-	-	-	-	-	-	-	-
Domestic Navigation	-	-	0.21	-	-	-	-	-	-	-	0.21
Non-specified	-	-	0.00	-	-	-	-	-	0.00	-	0.00
OTHER SECTORS	**0.03**	**-**	**0.96**	**14.09**	**-**	**-**	**0.02**	**0.27**	**5.27**	**1.30**	**21.95**
Residential	0.00	-	0.08	7.52	-	-	0.02	0.23	2.08	0.41	10.34
Comm. and Publ. Services	0.03	-	0.39	3.57	-	-	-	0.04	2.69	0.84	7.56
Agriculture/Forestry	-	-	0.49	3.00	-	-	-	-	0.50	0.06	4.04
Fishing	-	-	-	-	-	-	-	-	-	-	-
Non-specified	-	-	-	-	-	-	-	-	-	-	-
NON-ENERGY USE	**0.28**	**-**	**10.44**	**2.46**	**-**	**-**	**-**	**-**	**-**	**-**	**13.17**
in Industry/Transf./Energy	0.28	-	10.20	2.46	-	-	-	-	-	-	12.93
of which: Feedstocks	*0.09*	-	*8.60*	*2.46*	-	-	-	-	-	-	*11.15*
in Transport	-	-	0.09	-	-	-	-	-	-	-	0.09
in Other Sectors	-	-	0.15	-	-	-	-	-	-	-	0.15
Electricity Generated - TWh	***26.93***	**-**	***2.26***	***57.86***	***4.00***	***0.09***	***2.36***	***6.73***	**-**	**-**	***100.22***
Electricity Plants	*16.14*	-	-	*15.61*	*4.00*	*0.09*	*2.36*	*4.26*	-	-	*42.46*
CHP plants	*10.79*	-	*2.26*	*42.24*	-	-	-	*2.47*	-	-	*57.76*
Heat Generated - PJ	***18.40***	**-**	***7.64***	***135.98***	**-**	**-**	**-**	***8.85***	**-**	**-**	***170.86***
CHP plants	*18.40*	-	*7.64*	*125.31*	-	-	-	*3.76*	-	-	*155.11*
Heat Plants	-	-	-	*10.66*	-	-	-	*5.09*	-	-	*15.76*

New Zealand / Nouvelle-Zélande
Key Indicators
Indicateurs principaux

	1960	1970	1973	1980	1990	1995
Energy Production (Mtoe)	2.49	3.40	4.05	5.47	12.01	12.99
Net Imports (Mtoe)	1.82	4.18	4.58	4.22	2.11	3.03
Total Primary Energy Supply (Mtoe)	4.12	7.23	8.27	9.20	13.76	15.83
Net Oil Imports (Mtoe)	1.83	4.19	4.60	4.27	2.33	4.02
Oil Supply (Mtoe)	1.66	3.87	4.42	4.22	3.96	5.68
Electricity Consumption (TWh)*	5.83	12.01	16.36	19.75	28.61	31.32
GDP (billion 2000 US$ using exch. rates)	19.41 e	27.79	32.68	33.07	39.83	46.42
GDP (billion 2000 US$ using PPPs)	29.55 e	42.30	49.74	50.33	60.63	70.66
Population (millions)	2.38 e	2.82	2.97	3.14	3.36	3.68
Industrial Production Index (2000=100)	..	..	..	..	83.10	94.90
Energy Production/TPES	0.6033	0.4703	0.4896	0.5950	0.8728	0.8211
Net Oil Imports/GDP (toe per thousand 2000 US$)	0.0941 e	0.1507	0.1408	0.1291	0.0585	0.0865
TPES/GDP (toe per thousand 2000 US$)	0.2123 e	0.2601	0.2531	0.2781	0.3454	0.3409
TPES/GDP (toe per thousand 2000 US$ PPP)	0.1395 e	0.1709	0.1662	0.1827	0.2269	0.2240
TPES/Population (toe per capita)	1.7342 e	2.5625	2.7834	2.9248	4.0922	4.3052
Oil Supply/GDP (toe per thousand 2000 US$)	0.0857 e	0.1394	0.1354	0.1276	0.0995	0.1223
Oil Supply/Population (toe per capita)	0.7002 e	1.3735	1.4890	1.3420	1.1787	1.5440
Elect. Cons./GDP (kWh per 2000 US$)	0.3002 e	0.4321	0.5008	0.5972	0.7184	0.6747
Elect. Cons./Population (kWh per capita)	2 452 e	4 257	5 508	6 281	8 511	8 520
Industry Cons.**/Industrial Production (2000=100)	..	..	..	..	85.04	91.54
Industry Oil Cons.**/Industrial Production (2000=100)	..	..	..	..	114.24	111.97

	2000	2001	2002	2003	2004	2005
Energy Production (Mtoe)	14.86	14.72	14.37	12.97	12.74	12.20
Net Imports (Mtoe)	3.38	3.30	3.62	4.13	5.27	4.92
Total Primary Energy Supply (Mtoe)	17.95	18.07	17.60	17.13	17.43	16.91
Net Oil Imports (Mtoe)	4.50	4.61	5.04	5.73	6.20	6.05
Oil Supply (Mtoe)	6.31	6.27	6.40	6.74	7.03	6.82
Electricity Consumption (TWh)*	35.02	34.54	35.71	36.94	40.01	39.92
GDP (billion 2000 US$ using exch. rates)	52.67	54.75	57.30	59.34	61.53	62.70
GDP (billion 2000 US$ using PPPs)	80.18	83.34	87.23	90.34	93.67	95.45
Population (millions)	3.86	3.89	3.94	4.01	4.06	4.10
Industrial Production Index (2000=100)	100.00	99.60	105.80	108.20	111.60	108.70
Energy Production/TPES	0.8276	0.8145	0.8162	0.7571	0.7312	0.7216
Net Oil Imports/GDP (toe per thousand 2000 US$)	0.0855	0.0842	0.0879	0.0966	0.1007	0.0965
TPES/GDP (toe per thousand 2000 US$)	0.3409	0.3301	0.3072	0.2887	0.2832	0.2697
TPES/GDP (toe per thousand 2000 US$ PPP)	0.2239	0.2169	0.2018	0.1896	0.1861	0.1771
TPES/Population (toe per capita)	4.6514	4.6509	4.4658	4.2720	4.2895	4.1231
Oil Supply/GDP (toe per thousand 2000 US$)	0.1197	0.1144	0.1117	0.1136	0.1143	0.1088
Oil Supply/Population (toe per capita)	1.6340	1.6125	1.6239	1.6805	1.7309	1.6628
Elect. Cons./GDP (kWh per 2000 US$)	0.6648	0.6308	0.6232	0.6224	0.6502	0.6366
Elect. Cons./Population (kWh per capita)	9 071	8 887	9 059	9 212	9 846	9 734
Industry Cons.**/Industrial Production (2000=100)	100.00	94.97	92.45	76.58	77.48	69.27
Industry Oil Cons.**/Industrial Production (2000=100)	100.00	89.87	88.27	87.02	97.85	97.23

* Electricity consumption equals domestic supply less distribution losses.
La consommation d'électricité représente l'approvisionnement intérieur diminué des pertes de distribution.

** Includes non-energy use in industry/transformation/energy sectors.
Comprend l'usage non-énergétique dans les secteurs de l'industrie/transformation/énergie.

New Zealand / Nouvelle-Zélande

Figure 1. TPES* in 1973

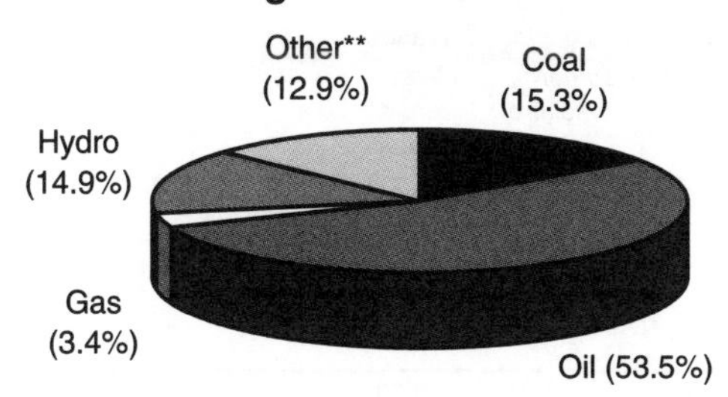

Figure 2. TPES* in 2005

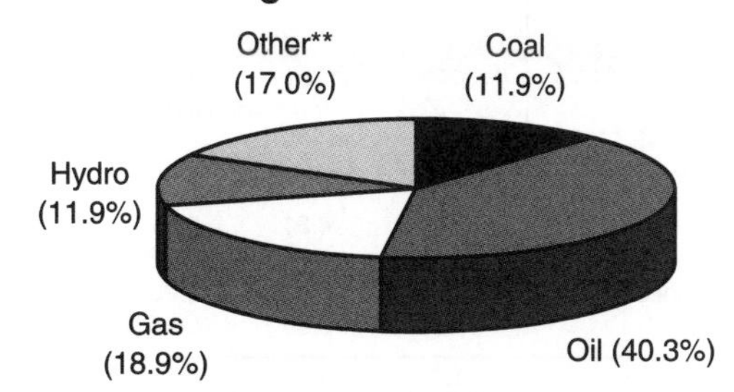

Figure 3. Final Consumption by Sector***

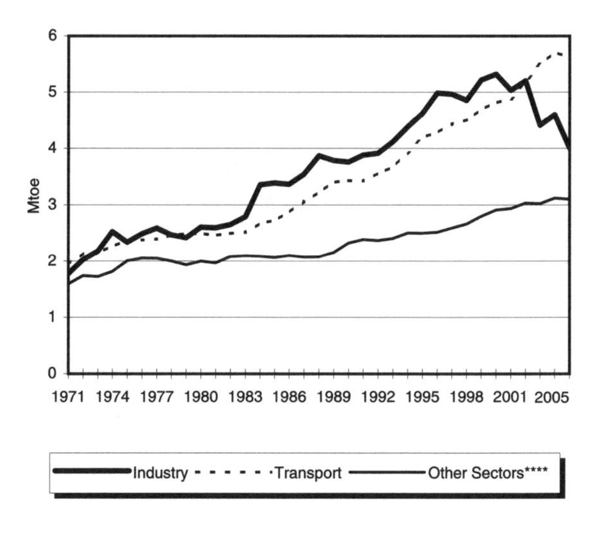

Figure 4. Breakdown of Sectorial Final Consumption by Source in 1973 and 2005***

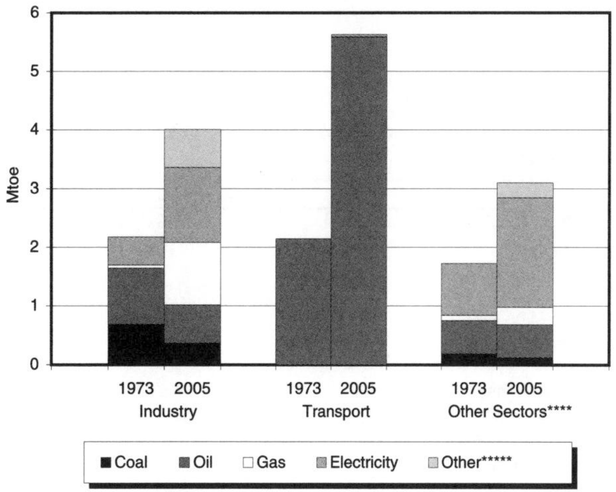

Figure 5. Electricity Generation by Fuel

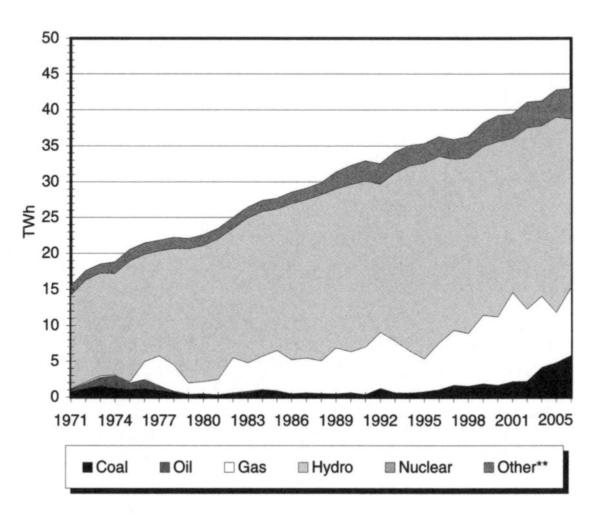

Figure 6. Electricity Consumption/GDP, TPES/GDP and Energy Production/TPES

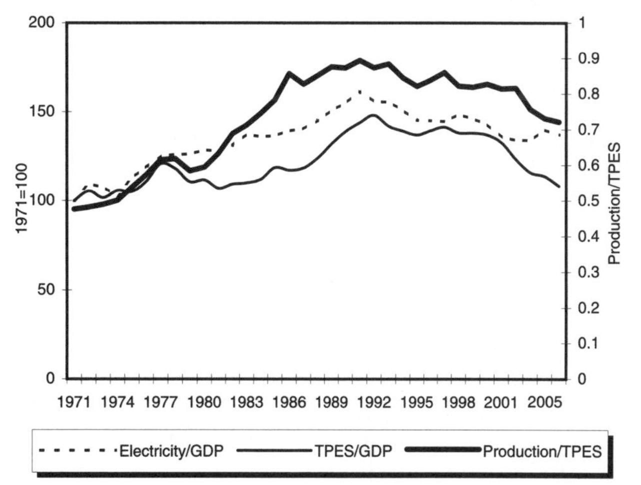

* Excluding electricity trade.
** Includes geothermal, solar, wind, combustible renewables & waste, etc.
*** Includes non-energy use.
**** Includes residential, commercial and public services, agriculture/forestry, fishing and non-specified.
***** Includes comb. renewables & waste, direct use of geothermal/solar thermal and heat produced in CHP/heat plants.

New Zealand / Nouvelle-Zélande : 2004

Million tonnes of oil equivalent / *Million de tonnes d'équivalent pétrole*

SUPPLY AND CONSUMPTION / *APPROVISIONNEMENT ET DEMANDE*	Coal / *Charbon*	Crude Oil / *Pétrole brut*	Petroleum Products / *Produits pétroliers*	Gas / *Gaz*	Nuclear / *Nucléaire*	Hydro / *Hydro*	Geotherm. Solar etc. / *Géotherm. solaire etc.*	Combust. Renew. & Waste / *Comb. ren. & déchets*	Electricity / *Electricité*	Heat / *Chaleur*	Total / *Total*
Production	3.01	1.15	-	3.45	-	2.34	1.94	0.83	-	0.02	12.74
Imports	0.45	4.81	2.21	-	-	-	-	-	-	-	7.47
Exports	-1.38	-0.74	-0.08	-	-	-	-	-	-	-	-2.20
Intl. Marine Bunkers	-	-	-0.23	-	-	-	-	-	-	-	-0.23
Stock Changes	-0.27	0.06	-0.15	-0.00	-	-	-	-	-	-	-0.36
TPES	**1.81**	**5.28**	**1.76**	**3.45**	**-**	**2.34**	**1.94**	**0.83**	**-**	**0.02**	**17.43**
Transfers	-	-0.18	0.19	-	-	-	-	-	-	-	0.00
Statistical Differences	0.08	0.12	-0.15	-0.01	-	-	-	-	-0.07	-	-0.02
Electricity Plants	-0.96	-	-0.01	-1.19	-	-2.34	-1.55	-0.03	3.54	-0.02	-2.55
CHP Plants	-0.37	-	-	-0.11	-	-	-0.01	-0.15	0.14	-	-0.51
Heat Plants	-	-	-	-	-	-	-	-	-	-	-
Gas Works	-	-	-	-	-	-	-	-	-	-	-
Petroleum Refineries	-	-5.21	5.33	-	-	-	-	-	-	-	0.12
Coal Transformation	-0.05	-	-	-	-	-	-	-	-	-	-0.05
Liquefaction Plants	-	-	-	-	-	-	-	-	-	-	-
Other Transformation	-	-	-	-	-	-	-	-	-	-	-
Own Use	-	-	-0.32	-0.12	-	-	-	-	-0.15	-	-0.59
Distribution Losses	-	-	-	-0.02	-	-	-0.14	-	-0.24	-	-0.40
TFC	**0.52**	**-**	**6.80**	**2.00**	**-**	**-**	**0.23**	**0.65**	**3.23**	**-**	**13.43**
INDUSTRY SECTOR	**0.34**	**-**	**0.38**	**0.57**	**-**	**-**	**0.13**	**0.50**	**1.30**	**-**	**3.22**
Iron and Steel	-	-	-	-	-	-	-	-	0.11	-	0.11
Chemical and Petrochem.	-	-	-	-	-	-	-	-	0.02	-	0.02
Non-Ferrous Metals	-	-	-	-	-	-	-	-	0.45	-	0.45
Non-Metallic Minerals	-	-	-	-	-	-	-	-	0.02	-	0.02
Transport Equipment	-	-	-	-	-	-	-	-	0.01	-	0.01
Machinery	-	-	-	-	-	-	-	-	0.03	-	0.03
Mining and Quarrying	-	-	0.07	-	-	-	-	-	0.02	-	0.10
Food and Tobacco	-	-	0.00	-	-	-	-	-	0.21	-	0.22
Paper, Pulp and Printing	-	-	-	-	-	-	0.13	-	0.19	-	0.32
Wood and Wood Products	-	-	-	-	-	-	-	0.50	0.16	-	0.66
Construction	-	-	0.06	-	-	-	-	-	0.02	-	0.08
Textile and Leather	-	-	-	-	-	-	-	-	0.01	-	0.01
Non-specified	0.34	-	0.24	0.57	-	-	-	-	0.04	-	1.19
TRANSPORT SECTOR	**-**	**-**	**5.66**	**0.00**	**-**	**-**	**-**	**-**	**0.04**	**-**	**5.71**
International Aviation	-	-	0.87	-	-	-	-	-	-	-	0.87
Domestic Aviation	-	-	0.43	-	-	-	-	-	-	-	0.43
Road	-	-	4.26	0.00	-	-	-	-	-	-	4.27
Rail	-	-	-	-	-	-	-	-	0.01	-	0.01
Pipeline Transport	-	-	-	-	-	-	-	-	-	-	-
Domestic Navigation	-	-	-	-	-	-	-	-	-	-	-
Non-specified	-	-	0.10	-	-	-	-	-	0.03	-	0.13
OTHER SECTORS	**0.18**	**-**	**0.47**	**0.34**	**-**	**-**	**0.10**	**0.15**	**1.89**	**-**	**3.12**
Residential	0.02	-	0.05	0.14	-	-	0.01	0.15	1.10	-	1.47
Comm. and Publ. Services	0.15	-	0.13	0.19	-	-	0.09	0.00	0.67	-	1.23
Agriculture/Forestry	0.01	-	0.17	-	-	-	-	-	0.12	-	0.30
Fishing	-	-	0.11	-	-	-	-	-	0.00	-	0.12
Non-specified	-	-	-	-	-	-	-	-	-	-	-
NON-ENERGY USE	**-**	**-**	**0.29**	**1.09**	**-**	**-**	**-**	**-**	**-**	**-**	**1.38**
in Industry/Transf./Energy	-	-	0.29	1.09	-	-	-	-	-	-	1.38
of which: Feedstocks	-	-	-	*1.09*	-	-	-	-	-	-	*1.09*
in Transport	-	-	-	-	-	-	-	-	-	-	-
in Other Sectors	-	-	-	-	-	-	-	-	-	-	-
Electricity Generated - TWh	***4.76***	-	***0.02***	***7.05***	-	***27.20***	***3.11***	***0.55***	-	***0.09***	***42.79***
Electricity Plants	*4.08*	-	*0.02*	*6.59*	-	*27.20*	*3.09*	*0.10*	-	*0.09*	*41.16*
CHP plants	*0.68*	-	-	*0.46*	-	-	*0.03*	*0.46*	-	-	*1.63*
Heat Generated - PJ	-	-	-	-	-	-	-	-	-	***1.00***	***1.00***
CHP plants	-	-	-	-	-	-	-	-	-	-	-
Heat Plants	-	-	-	-	-	-	-	-	-	*1.00*	*1.00*

New Zealand / Nouvelle-Zélande : 2005

Million tonnes of oil equivalent / *Million de tonnes d'équivalent pétrole*

SUPPLY AND CONSUMPTION / ***APPROVISIONNEMENT ET DEMANDE***	Coal / *Charbon*	Crude Oil / *Pétrole brut*	Petroleum Products / *Produits pétroliers*	Gas / *Gaz*	Nuclear / *Nucléaire*	Hydro / *Hydro*	Geotherm. Solar etc. / *Géotherm. solaire etc.*	Combust. Renew. & Waste / *Comb. ren. & déchets*	Electricity / *Electricité*	Heat / *Chaleur*	Total / *Total*
Production	3.06	1.06	-	3.19	-	2.02	1.99	0.87	-	0.01	12.20
Imports	0.56	4.83	2.02	-	-	-	-	-	-	-	7.41
Exports	-1.68	-0.62	-0.18	-	-	-	-	-	-	-	-2.48
Intl. Marine Bunkers	-	-	-0.23	-	-	-	-	-	-	-	-0.23
Stock Changes	0.07	-0.16	0.10	0.00	-	-	-	-	-	-	0.02
TPES	**2.00**	**5.10**	**1.71**	**3.19**	**-**	**2.02**	**1.99**	**0.87**	**-**	**0.01**	**16.91**
Transfers	-	-0.17	0.18	-	-	-	-	-	-	-	0.01
Statistical Differences	0.10	0.25	-0.21	0.02	-	-	-	-	-0.08	-	0.08
Electricity Plants	-1.21	-	-0.00	-1.56	-	-2.02	-1.60	-0.02	3.54	-0.01	-2.89
CHP Plants	-0.33	-	-	-0.14	-	-	-0.02	-0.18	0.16	-	-0.50
Heat Plants	-	-	-	-	-	-	-	-	-	-	-
Gas Works	-	-	-	-	-	-	-	-	-	-	-
Petroleum Refineries	-	-5.19	5.46	-	-	-	-	-	-	-	0.27
Coal Transformation	-0.08	-	-	-	-	-	-	-	-	-	-0.08
Liquefaction Plants	-	-	-	-	-	-	-	-	-	-	-
Other Transformation	-	-	-	-	-	-	-	-	-	-	-
Own Use	-	-	-0.34	-0.13	-	-	-	-	-0.17	-	-0.63
Distribution Losses	-	-	-	-0.02	-	-	-0.14	-	-0.26	-	-0.42
TFC	**0.49**	**-**	**6.79**	**1.37**	**-**	**-**	**0.24**	**0.66**	**3.19**	**-**	**12.74**
INDUSTRY SECTOR	**0.36**	**-**	**0.37**	**0.63**	**-**	**-**	**0.14**	**0.51**	**1.28**	**-**	**3.30**
Iron and Steel	-	-	-	-	-	-	-	-	0.11	-	0.11
Chemical and Petrochem.	-	-	-	-	-	-	-	-	0.02	-	0.02
Non-Ferrous Metals	-	-	-	-	-	-	-	-	0.45	-	0.45
Non-Metallic Minerals	-	-	-	-	-	-	-	-	0.02	-	0.02
Transport Equipment	-	-	-	-	-	-	-	-	0.01	-	0.01
Machinery	-	-	-	-	-	-	-	-	0.03	-	0.03
Mining and Quarrying	-	-	0.07	-	-	-	-	-	0.02	-	0.09
Food and Tobacco	-	-	0.00	-	-	-	-	-	0.22	-	0.22
Paper, Pulp and Printing	-	-	-	-	-	-	0.14	-	0.17	-	0.31
Wood and Wood Products	-	-	-	-	-	-	-	0.51	0.16	-	0.67
Construction	-	-	0.07	-	-	-	-	-	0.02	-	0.09
Textile and Leather	-	-	-	-	-	-	-	-	0.01	-	0.01
Non-specified	0.36	-	0.23	0.63	-	-	-	-	0.04	-	1.26
TRANSPORT SECTOR	**-**	**-**	**5.58**	**0.00**	**-**	**-**	**-**	**-**	**0.04**	**-**	**5.63**
International Aviation	-	-	0.83	-	-	-	-	-	-	-	0.83
Domestic Aviation	-	-	0.37	-	-	-	-	-	-	-	0.37
Road	-	-	4.26	0.00	-	-	-	-	-	-	4.27
Rail	-	-	-	-	-	-	-	-	0.01	-	0.01
Pipeline Transport	-	-	-	-	-	-	-	-	-	-	-
Domestic Navigation	-	-	-	-	-	-	-	-	-	-	-
Non-specified	-	-	0.12	-	-	-	-	-	0.03	-	0.15
OTHER SECTORS	**0.12**	**-**	**0.56**	**0.30**	**-**	**-**	**0.10**	**0.15**	**1.87**	**-**	**3.10**
Residential	0.02	-	0.05	0.14	-	-	0.01	0.15	1.08	-	1.45
Comm. and Publ. Services	0.08	-	0.20	0.16	-	-	0.09	0.00	0.67	-	1.20
Agriculture/Forestry	0.03	-	0.18	-	-	-	-	-	0.11	-	0.32
Fishing	-	-	0.12	-	-	-	-	-	0.00	-	0.13
Non-specified	-	-	-	-	-	-	-	-	-	-	-
NON-ENERGY USE	**-**	**-**	**0.28**	**0.43**	**-**	**-**	**-**	**-**	**-**	**-**	**0.71**
in Industry/Transf./Energy	-	-	0.28	0.43	-	-	-	-	-	-	0.71
of which: Feedstocks	-	-	-	*0.43*	-	-	-	-	-	-	*0.43*
in Transport	-	-	-	-	-	-	-	-	-	-	-
in Other Sectors	-	-	-	-	-	-	-	-	-	-	-
Electricity Generated - TWh	***5.82***	**-**	***0.00***	***9.47***	**-**	***23.47***	***3.47***	***0.68***	**-**	***0.05***	***42.96***
Electricity Plants	*5.21*	-	*0.00*	*8.87*	-	*23.47*	*3.44*	*0.09*	-	*0.05*	*41.13*
CHP plants	*0.61*	-	-	*0.60*	-	-	*0.03*	*0.59*	-	-	*1.83*
Heat Generated - PJ	**-**	**-**	**-**	**-**	**-**	**-**	**-**	**-**	**-**	***0.51***	***0.51***
CHP plants	-	-	-	-	-	-	-	-	-	-	-
Heat Plants	-	-	-	-	-	-	-	-	-	*0.51*	*0.51*

Norway / Norvège
Key Indicators
Indicateurs principaux

	1960	1970	1973	1980	1990	1995
Energy Production (Mtoe)	2.97	5.29	8.08	55.31	120.32	186.53
Net Imports (Mtoe)	4.28	9.18	6.79	- 35.98	- 96.49	- 161.42
Total Primary Energy Supply (Mtoe)	6.97	13.56	14.63	18.65	21.51	23.88
Net Oil Imports (Mtoe)	3.73	8.45	6.65	- 14.83	- 73.63	- 136.92
Oil Supply (Mtoe)	3.48	7.58	7.90	9.04	8.57	8.37
Electricity Consumption (TWh)*	27.51	52.15	61.56	76.51	99.06	106.92
GDP (billion 2000 US$ using exch. rates)	38.14 e	57.47	66.30	91.05	115.80	139.85
GDP (billion 2000 US$ using PPPs)	37.24 e	56.13	64.75	88.92	113.08	136.58
Population (millions)	3.58 e	3.88	3.96	4.09	4.24	4.36
Industrial Production Index (2000=100)	16.20	27.40	32.30	46.20	71.50	90.30
Energy Production/TPES	0.4259	0.3904	0.5518	2.9650	5.5937	7.8104
Net Oil Imports/GDP (toe per thousand 2000 US$)	0.0979 e	0.1471	0.1003	- 0.1629	- 0.6359	- 0.9790
TPES/GDP (toe per thousand 2000 US$)	0.1827 e	0.2359	0.2207	0.2049	0.1858	0.1708
TPES/GDP (toe per thousand 2000 US$ PPP)	0.1870 e	0.2416	0.2260	0.2098	0.1902	0.1749
TPES/Population (toe per capita)	1.9441 e	3.4976	3.6955	4.5651	5.0720	5.4800
Oil Supply/GDP (toe per thousand 2000 US$)	0.0914 e	0.1318	0.1192	0.0993	0.0740	0.0599
Oil Supply/Population (toe per capita)	0.9724 e	1.9544	1.9959	2.2131	2.0210	1.9216
Elect. Cons./GDP (kWh per 2000 US$)	0.7213 e	0.9073	0.9284	0.8402	0.8554	0.7645
Elect. Cons./Population (kWh per capita)	7 677 e	13 450	15 544	18 724	23 357	24 535
Industry Cons.**/Industrial Production (2000=100)	215.73	254.55	238.54	192.65	122.16	99.83
Industry Oil Cons.**/Industrial Production (2000=100)	291.54	430.77	379.44	316.55	159.07	120.52

	2000	2001	2002	2003	2004	2005
Energy Production (Mtoe)	229.05	226.45	235.22	235.50	238.60	233.70
Net Imports (Mtoe)	- 202.05	- 201.25	- 209.12	- 206.71	- 210.21	- 200.44
Total Primary Energy Supply (Mtoe)	25.81	26.48	25.10	27.14	28.27	32.12
Net Oil Imports (Mtoe)	- 158.84	- 157.99	- 152.59	- 145.41	- 144.89	- 127.92
Oil Supply (Mtoe)	9.41	8.07	8.42	9.89	10.58	14.17
Electricity Consumption (TWh)*	112.25 e	115.51	111.73	105.91	111.19	116.22
GDP (billion 2000 US$ using exch. rates)	166.91	171.46	173.35	175.31	180.71	184.79
GDP (billion 2000 US$ using PPPs)	162.99	167.44	169.29	171.20	176.47	180.46
Population (millions)	4.49	4.51	4.54	4.57	4.59	4.62
Industrial Production Index (2000=100)	100.00	98.70	99.50	95.50	97.40	96.90
Energy Production/TPES	8.8748	8.5532	9.3711	8.6757	8.4405	7.2749
Net Oil Imports/GDP (toe per thousand 2000 US$)	- 0.9517	- 0.9214	- 0.8802	- 0.8295	- 0.8018	- 0.6922
TPES/GDP (toe per thousand 2000 US$)	0.1546	0.1544	0.1448	0.1548	0.1564	0.1738
TPES/GDP (toe per thousand 2000 US$ PPP)	0.1583	0.1581	0.1483	0.1586	0.1602	0.1780
TPES/Population (toe per capita)	5.7469	5.8665	5.5299	5.9462	6.1573	6.9504
Oil Supply/GDP (toe per thousand 2000 US$)	0.0564	0.0471	0.0486	0.0564	0.0585	0.0767
Oil Supply/Population (toe per capita)	2.0956	1.7885	1.8549	2.1669	2.3038	3.0647
Elect. Cons./GDP (kWh per 2000 US$)	0.6725 e	0.6737	0.6445	0.6041	0.6153	0.6289
Elect. Cons./Population (kWh per capita)	24 994 e	25 595	24 616	23 201	24 219	25 145
Industry Cons.**/Industrial Production (2000=100)	100.00	103.54	95.29	104.45	103.92	102.91
Industry Oil Cons.**/Industrial Production (2000=100)	100.00	114.36	111.80	132.16	115.50	113.55

* Electricity consumption equals domestic supply less distribution losses.
La consommation d'électricité représente l'approvisionnement intérieur diminué des pertes de distribution.

** Includes non-energy use in industry/transformation/energy sectors.
Comprend l'usage non-énergétique dans les secteurs de l'industrie/transformation/énergie.

Norway / Norvège

Figure 1. TPES* in 1973

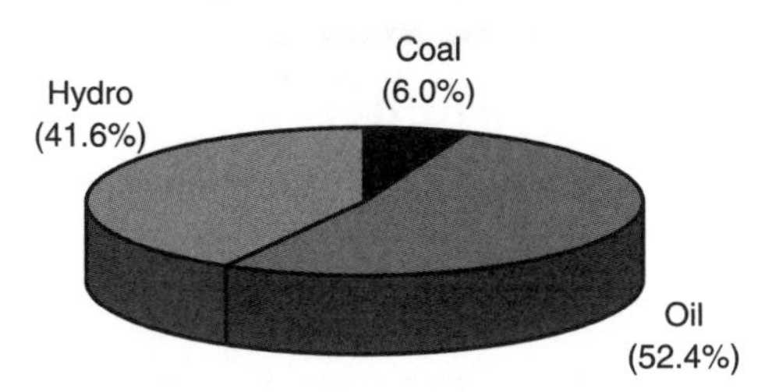

Figure 2. TPES* in 2005

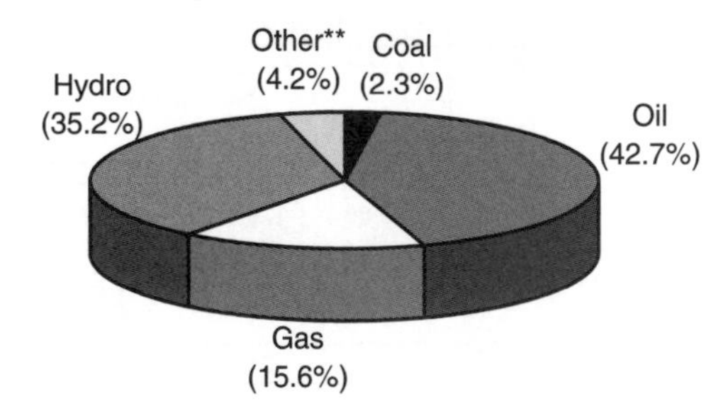

Figure 3. Final Consumption by Sector***

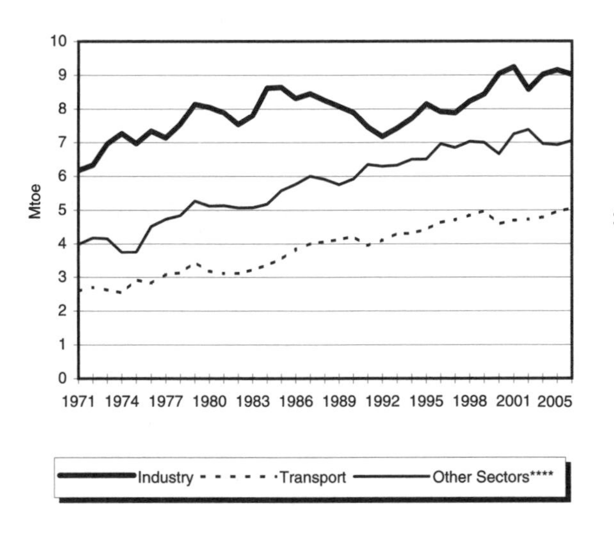

Figure 4. Breakdown of Sectorial Final Consumption by Source in 1973 and 2005***

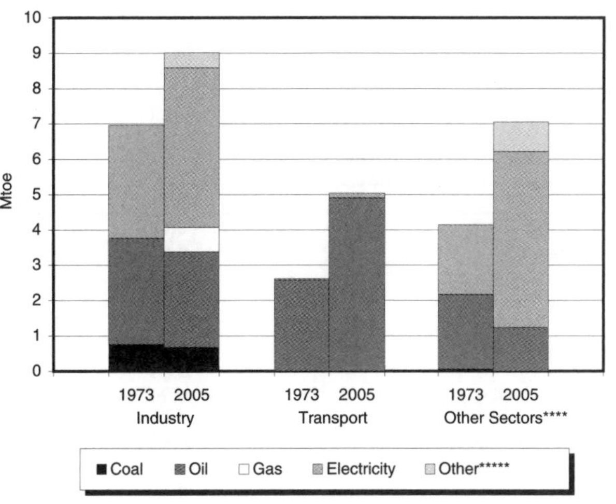

Figure 5. Electricity Generation by Fuel

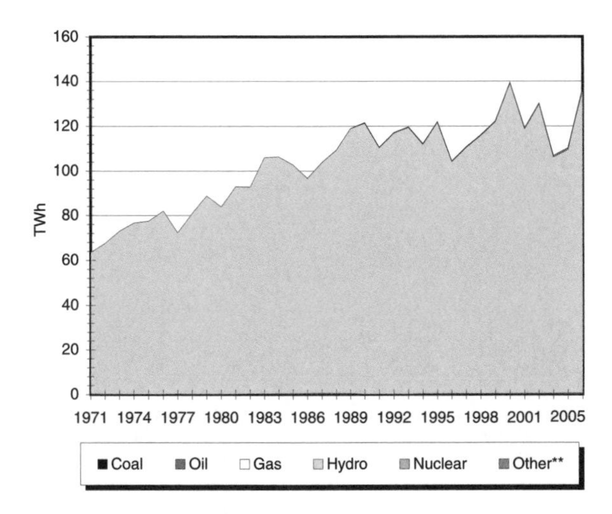

Figure 6. Electricity Consumption/GDP, TPES/GDP and Energy Production/TPES

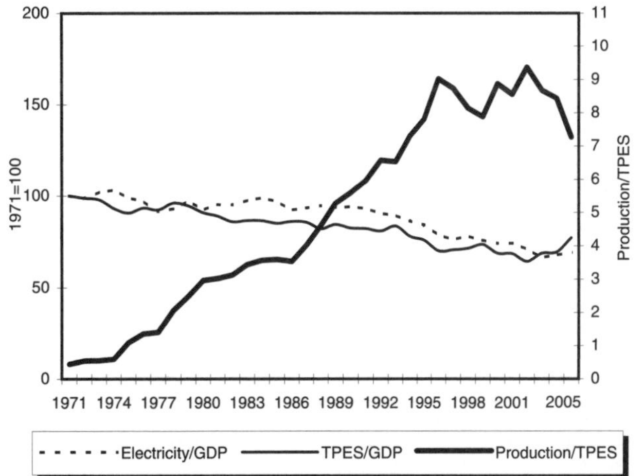

* Excluding electricity trade.

** Includes geothermal, solar, wind, combustible renewables & waste, etc.

*** Includes non-energy use.

**** Includes residential, commercial and public services, agriculture/forestry, fishing and non-specified.

***** Includes comb. renewables & waste, direct use of geothermal/solar thermal and heat produced in CHP/heat plants.

Norway / Norvège : 2004

Million tonnes of oil equivalent / *Million de tonnes d'équivalent pétrole*

SUPPLY AND CONSUMPTION / *APPROVISIONNEMENT ET DEMANDE*	Coal / *Charbon*	Crude Oil / *Pétrole brut*	Petroleum Products / *Produits pétroliers*	Gas / *Gaz*	Nuclear / *Nucléaire*	Hydro / *Hydro*	Geotherm. Solar etc. / *Géotherm. solaire etc.*	Combust. Renew. & Waste / *Comb. ren. & déchets*	Electricity / *Electricité*	Heat / *Chaleur*	Total / *Total*
Production	1.95	155.58	-	70.40	-	9.36	0.02	1.26	-	0.03	238.60
Imports	0.83	0.55	3.90	-	-	-	-	0.03	1.32	-	6.62
Exports	-1.84	-134.75	-14.59	-65.32	-	-	-	-0.00	-0.33	-	-216.83
Intl. Marine Bunkers	-	-	-0.52	-	-	-	-	-	-	-	-0.52
Stock Changes	-0.01	0.30	0.11	-	-	-	-	c	-	-	0.40
TPES	**0.93**	**21.68**	**-11.10**	**5.07**	**-**	**9.36**	**0.02**	**1.29**	**0.99**	**0.03**	**28.27**
Transfers	-	-6.39	6.99	-	-	-	-	-	-	-	0.60
Statistical Differences	-0.02	-0.66	-1.00	-0.79	-	-	-	0.00	-	-	-2.47
Electricity Plants	-0.01	-	-0.00	-0.05	-	-9.36	-0.02	-0.04	9.46	-0.04 e	-0.06
CHP Plants	-0.02	-	-	-0.00	-	-	-	-0.10	0.01	0.09	-0.01
Heat Plants	-0.00	-	-0.02	-0.00	-	-	-	-0.11	-0.05	0.18 e	-0.02
Gas Works	-	-	-	-	-	-	-	-	-	-	-
Petroleum Refineries	-	-14.66	14.65	-	-	-	-	-	-	-	-0.01
Coal Transformation	-0.07 e	-	-	-	-	-	-	-	-	-	-0.07
Liquefaction Plants	-	-	-	-	-	-	-	-	-	-	-
Other Transformation	-	0.03	-0.03	-	-	-	-	-	-	-	-0.00
Own Use	-	-	-0.57	-3.43	-	-	-	-	-0.19	-0.01	-4.19
Distribution Losses	-0.01	-	-	-	-	-	-	-0.01	-0.94	-0.04	-1.01
TFC	**0.79**	**-**	**8.91**	**0.80**	**-**	**-**	**-**	**1.03**	**9.28**	**0.20**	**21.02**
INDUSTRY SECTOR	**0.79**	**-**	**0.83**	**0.19**	**-**	**-**	**-**	**0.38**	**4.41**	**0.02**	**6.62**
Iron and Steel	0.45 e	-	0.01	0.00	-	-	-	0.01	0.59	0.00	1.06
Chemical and Petrochem.	0.18	-	0.14	0.13	-	-	-	0.00	0.61	0.01	1.07
Non-Ferrous Metals	-	-	0.04	0.03	-	-	-	-	1.93	-	2.00
Non-Metallic Minerals	0.16	-	0.14	0.00	-	-	-	0.02	0.07	0.00	0.39
Transport Equipment	-	-	0.01	-	-	-	-	-	0.06	0.00	0.08
Machinery	-	-	0.03	0.00	-	-	-	0.00	0.10	0.00	0.13
Mining and Quarrying	-	-	0.05	0.00	-	-	-	-	0.04	0.00	0.09
Food and Tobacco	-	-	0.11	0.02	-	-	-	0.00	0.25	0.01	0.39
Paper, Pulp and Printing	-	-	0.15	0.01	-	-	-	0.28	0.58	0.00	1.01
Wood and Wood Products	-	-	0.01	-	-	-	-	0.08	0.08	0.00	0.17
Construction	-	-	0.12	-	-	-	-	0.00	0.05	-	0.17
Textile and Leather	-	-	0.01	0.00	-	-	-	-	0.01	-	0.02
Non-specified	-	-	0.01	0.00	-	-	-	0.00	0.03	0.00	0.04
TRANSPORT SECTOR	**-**	**-**	**4.82**	**0.01**	**-**	**-**	**-**	**-**	**0.13**	**-**	**4.95**
International Aviation	-	-	0.25	-	-	-	-	-	-	-	0.25
Domestic Aviation	-	-	0.38	-	-	-	-	-	-	-	0.38
Road	-	-	3.35	0.00	-	-	-	c	-	-	3.35
Rail	-	-	0.02	-	-	-	-	-	0.04	-	0.06
Pipeline Transport	-	-	-	-	-	-	-	-	-	-	-
Domestic Navigation	-	-	0.83	-	-	-	-	-	-	-	0.83
Non-specified	-	-	-	0.01	-	-	-	-	0.08	-	0.09
OTHER SECTORS	**0.00**	**-**	**1.34**	**0.01**	**-**	**-**	**-**	**0.65**	**4.74**	**0.17**	**6.92**
Residential	0.00	-	0.30	0.00	-	-	-	0.63	2.79	0.04	3.76
Comm. and Publ. Services	-	-	0.41	0.01	-	-	-	0.02	1.78	0.14	2.35
Agriculture/Forestry	-	-	0.14	0.01	-	-	-	0.00	0.17	0.00	0.31
Fishing	-	-	0.47	-	-	-	-	-	0.01	-	0.48
Non-specified	-	-	0.02	-	-	-	-	-	-	-	0.02
NON-ENERGY USE	**-**	**-**	**1.93**	**0.59**	**-**	**-**	**-**	**-**	**-**	**-**	**2.52**
in Industry/Transf./Energy	-	-	1.93	0.59	-	-	-	-	-	-	2.52
of which: Feedstocks	-	-	*1.28*	*0.59*	-	-	-	-	-	-	*1.87*
in Transport	-	-	-	-	-	-	-	-	-	-	-
in Other Sectors	-	-	-	-	-	-	-	-	-	-	-
Electricity Generated - TWh	***0.11***	-	***0.03***	***0.37***	-	***108.86***	***0.29***	***0.45***	-	***0.08***	***110.19***
Electricity Plants	*0.06*	-	*0.03*	*0.37*	-	*108.86*	*0.29*	*0.34*	-	*0.08*	*110.03*
CHP plants	*0.04*	-	-	-	-	-	-	*0.11*	-	-	*0.16*
Heat Generated - PJ	***0.55***	-	***0.83***	***0.22***	-	-	***0.42***	***6.99***	***1.94***	***1.33***	***12.28***
CHP plants	*0.54*	-	-	*0.01*	-	-	-	*3.27*	*1.20*	-	*5.02*
Heat Plants	*0.01*	-	*0.83*	*0.21*	-	-	*0.42 e*	*3.71*	*0.74*	*1.33 e*	*7.25*

Norway / Norvège : 2005

Million tonnes of oil equivalent / *Million de tonnes d'équivalent pétrole*

SUPPLY AND CONSUMPTION *APPROVISIONNEMENT ET DEMANDE*	Coal *Charbon*	Crude Oil *Pétrole brut*	Petroleum Products *Produits pétroliers*	Gas *Gaz*	Nuclear *Nucléaire*	Hydro *Hydro*	Geotherm. Solar etc. *Géotherm. solaire etc.*	Combust. Renew. & Waste *Comb. ren. & déchets*	Electricity *Electricité*	Heat *Chaleur*	Total *Total*
Production	0.99	143.42	-	76.26	-	11.68	0.04	1.29	-	0.03	233.70
Imports	0.71	0.81	3.86	-	-	-	-	0.02	0.31	-	5.71
Exports	-1.12	-117.13	-15.46	-71.10	-	-	-	-0.00	-1.35	-	-206.15
Intl. Marine Bunkers	-	-	-0.70	-	-	-	-	-	-	-	-0.70
Stock Changes	0.20	-0.44	-0.20	-	-	-	-	c	-	-	-0.44
TPES	**0.78**	**26.66**	**-12.50**	**5.16**	**-**	**11.68**	**0.04**	**1.31**	**-1.04**	**0.03**	**32.12**
Transfers	-	-7.42	8.08	-	-	-	-	-	-	-	0.66
Statistical Differences	0.00	-3.23	-2.20	-0.18	-	-	-	-0.00	-	-	-5.61
Electricity Plants	-0.01 e	-	-0.00	-0.05	-	-11.68	-0.04	-0.03	11.80	-0.05 e	-0.06
CHP Plants	-0.02	-	-	-0.00	-	-	-	-0.09	0.01	0.09	-0.01
Heat Plants	-0.00 e	-	-0.01	-0.01	-	-	-	-0.12	-0.06	0.19 e	-0.01
Gas Works	-	-	-	-	-	-	-	-	-	-	-
Petroleum Refineries	-	-16.06	16.07	-	-	-	-	-	-	-	0.00
Coal Transformation	-0.07 e	-	-	-	-	-	-	-	-	-	-0.07
Liquefaction Plants	-	-	-	-	-	-	-	-	-	-	-
Other Transformation	-	0.04	-0.05	-	-	-	-	-	-	-	-0.00
Own Use	-	-	-0.59	-4.18	-	-	-	-	-0.24	-0.01	-5.02
Distribution Losses	-0.01	-	-	-	-	-	-	-0.01	-0.85	-0.04	-0.91
TFC	**0.67**	**-**	**8.79**	**0.75**	**-**	**-**	**-**	**1.06**	**9.62**	**0.21**	**21.10**
INDUSTRY SECTOR	**0.67**	**-**	**0.76**	**0.18**	**-**	**-**	**-**	**0.40**	**4.51**	**0.03**	**6.56**
Iron and Steel	0.37 e	-	0.01	0.00	-	-	-	0.00	0.54	0.00	0.93
Chemical and Petrochem.	0.16	-	0.12	0.10	-	-	-	0.01	0.62	0.01	1.02
Non-Ferrous Metals	-	-	0.04	0.04	-	-	-	-	2.07	0.00	2.14
Non-Metallic Minerals	0.14	-	0.13	0.00	-	-	-	0.03	0.08	0.00	0.39
Transport Equipment	-	-	0.01	0.00	-	-	-	-	0.06	0.00	0.08
Machinery	-	-	0.03	0.00	-	-	-	0.00	0.11	0.00	0.14
Mining and Quarrying	-	-	0.05	0.00	-	-	-	-	0.04	-	0.09
Food and Tobacco	-	-	0.09	0.02	-	-	-	0.00	0.24	0.01	0.36
Paper, Pulp and Printing	-	-	0.13	0.01	-	-	-	0.28	0.58	0.00	0.99
Wood and Wood Products	-	-	0.01	-	-	-	-	0.08	0.08	0.00	0.17
Construction	-	-	0.13	0.00	-	-	-	0.00	0.06	-	0.19
Textile and Leather	-	-	0.01	0.00	-	-	-	-	0.02	-	0.02
Non-specified	-	-	0.01	0.00	-	-	-	0.00	0.02	0.00	0.03
TRANSPORT SECTOR	**-**	**-**	**4.89**	**0.01**	**-**	**-**	**-**	**-**	**0.13**	**-**	**5.04**
International Aviation	-	-	0.28	-	-	-	-	-	-	-	0.28
Domestic Aviation	-	-	0.38	-	-	-	-	-	-	-	0.38
Road	-	-	3.37	0.00	-	-	-	c	-	-	3.38
Rail	-	-	0.01	-	-	-	-	-	0.04	-	0.06
Pipeline Transport	-	-	-	-	-	-	-	-	-	-	-
Domestic Navigation	-	-	0.85	-	-	-	-	-	-	-	0.85
Non-specified	-	-	-	0.01	-	-	-	-	0.09	-	0.10
OTHER SECTORS	**0.00**	**-**	**1.20**	**0.03**	**-**	**-**	**-**	**0.66**	**4.98**	**0.18**	**7.05**
Residential	0.00	-	0.24	0.01	-	-	-	0.63	2.88	0.04	3.80
Comm. and Publ. Services	-	-	0.37	0.01	-	-	-	0.02	1.92	0.15	2.47
Agriculture/Forestry	-	-	0.13	0.02	-	-	-	0.00	0.17	0.00	0.32
Fishing	-	-	0.43	-	-	-	-	-	0.01	-	0.45
Non-specified	-	-	0.02	-	-	-	-	-	-	-	0.02
NON-ENERGY USE	**-**	**-**	**1.94**	**0.52**	**-**	**-**	**-**	**-**	**-**	**-**	**2.46**
in Industry/Transf./Energy	-	-	1.94	0.52	-	-	-	-	-	-	2.46
of which: Feedstocks	-	-	*1.28*	*0.52*	-	-	-	-	-	-	*1.80*
in Transport	-	-	-	-	-	-	-	-	-	-	-
in Other Sectors	-	-	-	-	-	-	-	-	-	-	-
Electricity Generated - TWh	***0.13***	**-**	***0.01***	***0.36***	**-**	***135.80***	***0.56***	***0.39***	**-**	***0.10***	***137.33***
Electricity Plants	*0.09*	-	*0.01*	*0.36*	-	*135.80*	*0.56*	*0.31*	-	*0.10*	*137.21*
CHP plants	*0.04*	-	-	-	-	-	-	*0.08*	-	-	*0.12*
Heat Generated - PJ	***0.52***	**-**	***0.45***	***0.32***	**-**	**-**	***0.55***	***7.21***	***2.26***	***1.58***	***12.88***
CHP plants	*0.50*	-	-	*0.01*	-	-	-	*3.13*	*1.39*	-	*5.02*
Heat Plants	*0.03*	-	*0.45*	*0.31*	-	-	*0.55 e*	*4.08*	*0.88*	*1.58 e*	*7.85*

Poland / Pologne
Key Indicators
Indicateurs principaux

	1960	1970	1973	1980	1990	1995
Energy Production (Mtoe)	64.81	95.76	107.40	122.22	99.37	99.36
Net Imports (Mtoe)	- 10.78	- 11.79	- 13.15	1.55	2.12	- 0.17
Total Primary Energy Supply (Mtoe)	54.19	83.51	93.08	123.03	99.88	99.74
Net Oil Imports (Mtoe)	2.02	7.81	11.78	17.76	14.35	15.47
Oil Supply (Mtoe)	2.10	7.91	10.89	16.89	13.27	15.89
Electricity Consumption (TWh)*	26.81	59.02	75.55	109.44	124.71	118.14
GDP (billion 2000 US$ using exch. rates)	54.78 e	83.69 e	102.92 e	119.10 e	118.29	131.72
GDP (billion 2000 US$ using PPPs)	130.79 e	199.82 e	245.72 e	284.37 e	282.42	314.49
Population (millions)	29.56 e	32.53	33.37	35.58	38.12	38.59
Industrial Production Index (2000=100)	..	..	..	..	61.00	69.70
Energy Production/TPES	1.1958	1.1467	1.1539	0.9934	0.9949	0.9962
Net Oil Imports/GDP (toe per thousand 2000 US$)	0.0369 e	0.0934 e	0.1145 e	0.1491 e	0.1213	0.1175
TPES/GDP (toe per thousand 2000 US$)	0.9893 e	0.9978 e	0.9044 e	1.0330 e	0.8444	0.7572
TPES/GDP (toe per thousand 2000 US$ PPP)	0.4144 e	0.4179 e	0.3788 e	0.4327 e	0.3537	0.3172
TPES/Population (toe per capita)	1.8333 e	2.5675	2.7893	3.4582	2.6202	2.5848
Oil Supply/GDP (toe per thousand 2000 US$)	0.0384 e	0.0946 e	0.1058 e	0.1418 e	0.1122	0.1207
Oil Supply/Population (toe per capita)	0.0711 e	0.2433	0.3262	0.4748	0.3480	0.4119
Elect. Cons./GDP (kWh per 2000 US$)	0.4894 e	0.7052 e	0.7340 e	0.9189 e	1.0543	0.8969
Elect. Cons./Population (kWh per capita)	907 e	1 815	2 264	3 076	3 272	3 061
Industry Cons.**/Industrial Production (2000=100)	..	..	..	..	209.06	166.40
Industry Oil Cons.**/Industrial Production (2000=100)	..	..	..	..	126.85	100.42

	2000	2001	2002	2003	2004	2005
Energy Production (Mtoe)	79.59	80.29	80.20	79.86	78.83	78.63
Net Imports (Mtoe)	9.61	9.43	10.20	12.17	13.57	16.68
Total Primary Energy Supply (Mtoe)	89.43	90.04	89.17	91.45	91.79	92.97
Net Oil Imports (Mtoe)	19.87	19.13	19.73	20.26	21.22	22.16
Oil Supply (Mtoe)	19.46	19.99	20.10	20.23	21.71	22.14
Electricity Consumption (TWh)*	124.58	124.69	122.66	127.01	130.44	131.19
GDP (billion 2000 US$ using exch. rates)	171.33	173.25	175.68	182.43	192.03	198.26
GDP (billion 2000 US$ using PPPs)	409.07	413.65	419.45	435.56	458.50	473.37
Population (millions)	38.26	38.25	38.23	38.20	38.18	38.16
Industrial Production Index (2000=100)	100.00	100.40	101.80	110.70	124.80	129.90
Energy Production/TPES	0.8900	0.8917	0.8994	0.8732	0.8588	0.8458
Net Oil Imports/GDP (toe per thousand 2000 US$)	0.1160	0.1104	0.1123	0.1111	0.1105	0.1118
TPES/GDP (toe per thousand 2000 US$)	0.5220	0.5197	0.5076	0.5013	0.4780	0.4689
TPES/GDP (toe per thousand 2000 US$ PPP)	0.2186	0.2177	0.2126	0.2100	0.2002	0.1964
TPES/Population (toe per capita)	2.3376	2.3539	2.3323	2.3943	2.4040	2.4362
Oil Supply/GDP (toe per thousand 2000 US$)	0.1136	0.1154	0.1144	0.1109	0.1131	0.1117
Oil Supply/Population (toe per capita)	0.5088	0.5226	0.5256	0.5296	0.5687	0.5802
Elect. Cons./GDP (kWh per 2000 US$)	0.7271	0.7197	0.6982	0.6962	0.6792	0.6617
Elect. Cons./Population (kWh per capita)	3 256	3 260	3 208	3 325	3 416	3 438
Industry Cons.**/Industrial Production (2000=100)	100.00	90.76	85.85	83.11	76.60	70.87
Industry Oil Cons.**/Industrial Production (2000=100)	100.00	86.30	92.24	86.00	78.54	74.92

* Electricity consumption equals domestic supply less distribution losses.
La consommation d'électricité représente l'approvisionnement intérieur diminué des pertes de distribution.

** Includes non-energy use in industry/transformation/energy sectors.
Comprend l'usage non-énergétique dans les secteurs de l'industrie/transformation/énergie.

Poland / Pologne

Figure 1. TPES* in 1973

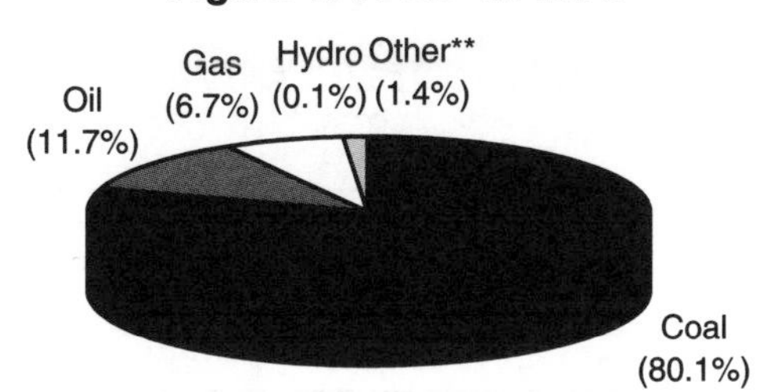

Figure 2. TPES* in 2005

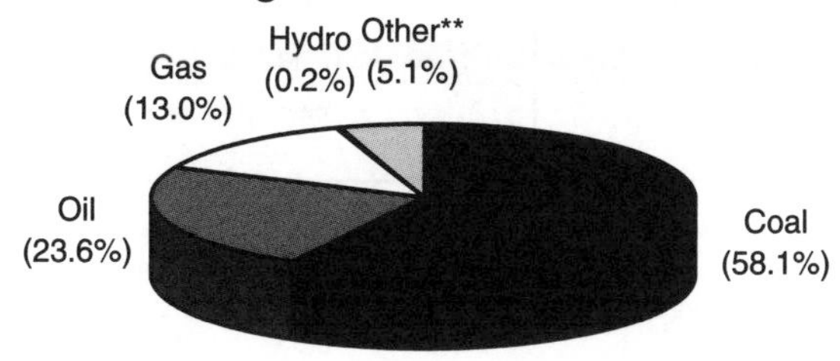

Figure 3. Final Consumption by Sector***

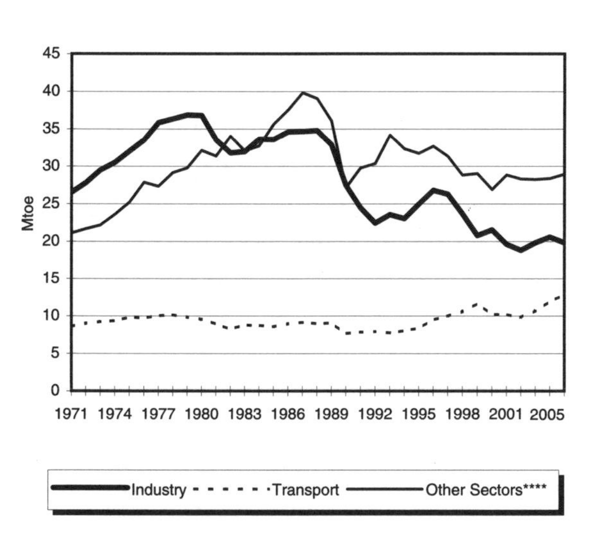

Figure 4. Breakdown of Sectorial Final Consumption by Source in 1973 and 2005***

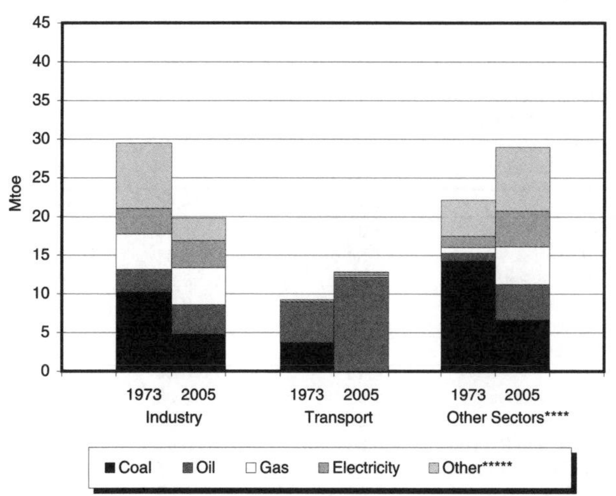

Figure 5. Electricity Generation by Fuel

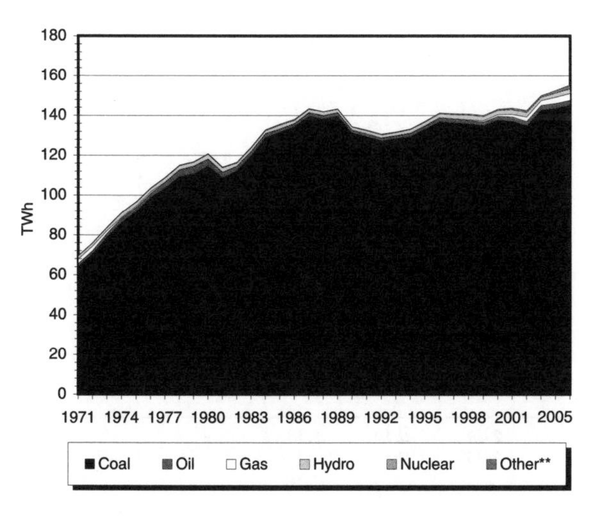

Figure 6. Electricity Consumption/GDP, TPES/GDP and Energy Production/TPES

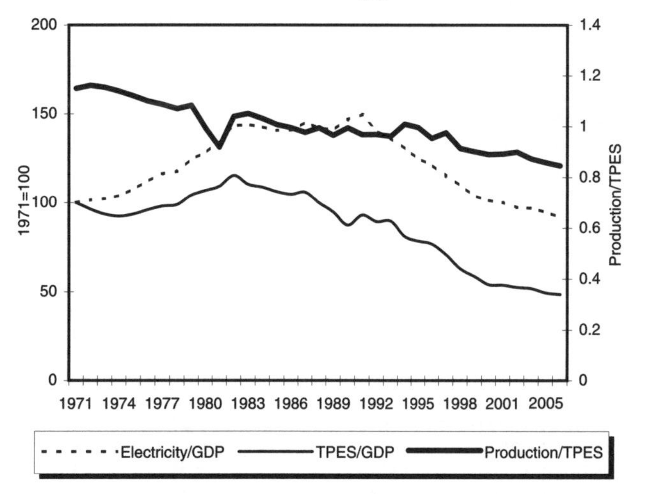

* Excluding electricity trade.

** Includes geothermal, solar, wind, combustible renewables & waste, etc.

*** Includes non-energy use.

**** Includes residential, commercial and public services, agriculture/forestry, fishing and non-specified.

***** Includes comb. renewables & waste, direct use of geothermal/solar thermal and heat produced in CHP/heat plants.

Poland / Pologne : 2004

Million tonnes of oil equivalent / *Million de tonnes d'équivalent pétrole*

SUPPLY AND CONSUMPTION *APPROVISIONNEMENT ET DEMANDE*	Coal *Charbon*	Crude Oil *Pétrole brut*	Petroleum Products *Produits pétroliers*	Gas *Gaz*	Nuclear *Nucléaire*	Hydro *Hydro*	Geotherm. Solar etc. *Géotherm. solaire etc.*	Combust. Renew. & Waste *Comb. ren. & déchets*	Electricity *Electricité*	Heat *Chaleur*	Total *Total*
Production	69.18	0.92	-	3.93	-	0.18	0.02	4.60	-	-	78.83
Imports	1.64	17.95	5.66	8.15	-	-	-	-	0.46	-	33.86
Exports	-16.61	-0.14	-2.25	-0.04	-	-	-	-	-1.26	-	-20.29
Intl. Marine Bunkers	-	-	-0.25	-	-	-	-	-	-	-	-0.25
Stock Changes	-0.02	0.00	-0.18	-0.17	-	-	-	-	-	-	-0.36
TPES	**54.19**	**18.73**	**2.98**	**11.88**	**-**	**0.18**	**0.02**	**4.60**	**-0.80**	**-**	**91.79**
Transfers	-	0.06	-0.00	-	-	-	-	-	-	-	0.05
Statistical Differences	0.40	0.05	-0.35	-0.10	-	-	-	-	-	0.19	0.20
Electricity Plants	-	-	-	-	-	-0.18	-0.01	-	0.19	-	-
CHP Plants	-36.46	-	-0.57	-0.97	-	-	-	-0.30	12.93	5.24	-20.13
Heat Plants	-3.23	-	-0.07	-0.31	-	-	-	-0.04	-	3.02	-0.62
Gas Works	-	-	-0.00	0.00	-	-	-	-	-	-	-0.00
Petroleum Refineries	-	-19.00	19.14	-	-	-	-	-	-	-	0.15
Coal Transformation	-1.84 e	-	-	-0.01	-	-	-	-0.00	-	-	-1.85
Liquefaction Plants	-	-	-	-	-	-	-	-	-	-	-
Other Transformation	-	0.16	-0.17	-	-	-	-	-	-	-	-0.01
Own Use	-1.63	-0.00	-1.01	-0.79	-	-	-	-0.01	-2.47	-1.29	-7.20
Distribution Losses	-0.04	-	-	-0.20	-	-	-	-	-1.24	-	-1.48
TFC	**11.40**	**-**	**19.95**	**9.50**	**-**	**-**	**0.01**	**4.25**	**8.61**	**7.16**	**60.89**
INDUSTRY SECTOR	**5.35**	**-**	**1.85**	**2.70**	**-**	**-**	**-**	**1.14**	**3.65**	**1.89**	**16.58**
Iron and Steel	1.64 e	-	0.01	0.47	-	-	-	0.04	0.62	0.22	2.99
Chemical and Petrochem.	0.74	-	0.87	0.18	-	-	-	0.21	0.75	1.07	3.82
Non-Ferrous Metals	0.16	-	0.02	0.15	-	-	-	0.04	0.31	0.04	0.73
Non-Metallic Minerals	0.92	-	0.29	0.91	-	-	-	0.05	0.30	0.04	2.50
Transport Equipment	0.05	-	0.02	0.08	-	-	-	0.00	0.15	0.10	0.40
Machinery	0.13	-	0.04	0.20	-	-	-	0.00	0.29	0.11	0.78
Mining and Quarrying	0.01	-	0.06	0.02	-	-	-	0.00	0.11	0.08	0.30
Food and Tobacco	0.89	-	0.27	0.39	-	-	-	0.01	0.37	0.06	1.99
Paper, Pulp and Printing	0.33	-	0.05	0.06	-	-	-	0.46	0.25	0.06	1.22
Wood and Wood Products	0.15	-	0.07	0.07	-	-	-	0.26	0.14	0.01	0.69
Construction	0.01	-	0.09	0.02	-	-	-	0.00	0.04	0.02	0.18
Textile and Leather	0.09	-	0.02	0.05	-	-	-	0.00	0.10	0.05	0.31
Non-specified	0.22	-	0.05	0.08	-	-	-	0.07	0.22	0.05	0.68
TRANSPORT SECTOR	**-**	**-**	**11.17**	**0.18**	**-**	**-**	**-**	**0.01**	**0.40**	**-**	**11.75**
International Aviation	-	-	0.30	-	-	-	-	-	-	-	0.30
Domestic Aviation	-	-	-	-	-	-	-	-	-	-	-
Road	-	-	10.70	-	-	-	-	0.01	-	-	10.71
Rail	-	-	0.17	-	-	-	-	-	0.37	-	0.53
Pipeline Transport	-	-	0.00	0.18	-	-	-	-	0.03	-	0.21
Domestic Navigation	-	-	0.00	-	-	-	-	-	-	-	0.00
Non-specified	-	-	-	-	-	-	-	-	-	-	-
OTHER SECTORS	**5.94**	**-**	**4.65**	**4.71**	**-**	**-**	**0.01**	**3.10**	**4.57**	**5.27**	**28.24**
Residential	4.41	-	1.19	3.02	-	-	0.01	2.47	2.19	4.58	17.87
Comm. and Publ. Services	0.68	-	0.64	1.66	-	-	0.00	0.16	2.25	0.66	6.04
Agriculture/Forestry	0.85	-	2.81	0.03	-	-	-	0.47	0.13	0.02	4.32
Fishing	-	-	0.00	-	-	-	-	-	0.00	0.00	0.01
Non-specified	-	-	-	-	-	-	-	-	-	-	-
NON-ENERGY USE	**0.11**	**-**	**2.29**	**1.91**	**-**	**-**	**-**	**-**	**-**	**-**	**4.31**
in Industry/Transf./Energy	0.11	-	1.98	1.91	-	-	-	-	-	-	3.99
of which: Feedstocks	-	-	*0.91*	*1.91*	-	-	-	-	-	-	*2.82*
in Transport	-	-	0.19	-	-	-	-	-	-	-	0.19
in Other Sectors	-	-	0.13	-	-	-	-	-	-	-	0.13
Electricity Generated - TWh	***143.49***	-	***2.51***	***3.14***	-	***2.08***	***0.14***	***1.18***	-	-	***152.55***
Electricity Plants	-	-	-	-	-	*2.08*	*0.14*	-	-	-	*2.22*
CHP plants	*143.49*	-	*2.51*	*3.14*	-	-	-	*1.18*	-	-	*150.33*
Heat Generated - PJ	***314.07***	-	***6.21***	***21.49***	-	-	-	***4.11***	-	-	***345.89***
CHP plants	*201.77*	-	*3.65*	*11.00*	-	-	-	*2.86*	-	-	*219.27*
Heat Plants	*112.31*	-	*2.56*	*10.50*	-	-	-	*1.25*	-	-	*126.61*

Poland / Pologne : 2005

Million tonnes of oil equivalent / *Million de tonnes d'équivalent pétrole*

SUPPLY AND CONSUMPTION *APPROVISIONNEMENT ET DEMANDE*	Coal *Charbon*	Crude Oil *Pétrole brut*	Petroleum Products *Produits pétroliers*	Gas *Gaz*	Nuclear *Nucléaire*	Hydro *Hydro*	Geotherm. Solar etc. *Géotherm. solaire etc.*	Combust. Renew. & Waste *Comb. ren. & déchets*	Electricity *Electricité*	Heat *Chaleur*	Total *Total*
Production	68.86	0.89	-	3.88	-	0.19	0.02	4.80	-	-	78.63
Imports	2.15	18.53	6.65	8.56	-	-	-	-	0.43	-	36.33
Exports	-15.14	-0.21	-2.81	-0.04	-	-	-	-0.06	-1.39	-	-19.65
Intl. Marine Bunkers	-	-	-0.32	-	-	-	-	-	-	-	-0.32
Stock Changes	-1.26	-0.36	-0.22	-0.18	-	-	-	0.00	-	-	-2.02
TPES	**54.61**	**18.85**	**3.29**	**12.23**	**-**	**0.19**	**0.02**	**4.74**	**-0.96**	**-**	**92.97**
Transfers	-	0.08	-0.04	-	-	-	-	-	-	-	0.04
Statistical Differences	-0.90	-0.03	0.04	0.02	-	-	-	-0.00	-	0.19	-0.68
Electricity Plants	-	-	-	-	-	-0.19	-0.01	-	0.20	-	-
CHP Plants	-36.54	-	-0.53	-1.07	-	-	-	-0.55	13.16	5.25	-20.26
Heat Plants	-3.09	-	-0.05	-0.29	-	-	-	-0.04	-	2.88	-0.60
Gas Works	-	-	-0.00	0.00	-	-	-	-	-	-	-0.00
Petroleum Refineries	-	-19.18	19.09	-	-	-	-	-	-	-	-0.09
Coal Transformation	-1.31 e	-	-	-0.01	-	-	-	-0.00	-	-	-1.32
Liquefaction Plants	-	-	-	-	-	-	-	-	-	-	-
Other Transformation	-	0.28	-0.30	-	-	-	-	-	-	-	-0.02
Own Use	-1.41	-	-0.97	-0.76	-	-	-	-0.01	-2.61	-1.27	-7.04
Distribution Losses	-0.03	-	-	-0.15	-	-	-	-	-1.25	-	-1.44
TFC	**11.33**	**-**	**20.53**	**9.97**	**-**	**-**	**0.01**	**4.14**	**8.54**	**7.05**	**61.56**
INDUSTRY SECTOR	**4.66**	**-**	**1.71**	**2.78**	**-**	**-**	**-**	**1.07**	**3.55**	**1.84**	**15.62**
Iron and Steel	1.14 e	-	0.00	0.48	-	-	-	0.02	0.51	0.16	2.31
Chemical and Petrochem.	0.77	-	0.68	0.19	-	-	-	0.17	0.71	1.06	3.59
Non-Ferrous Metals	0.13	-	0.01	0.15	-	-	-	0.02	0.30	0.07	0.70
Non-Metallic Minerals	0.84	-	0.35	0.93	-	-	-	0.08	0.30	0.04	2.54
Transport Equipment	0.04	-	0.03	0.09	-	-	-	0.00	0.17	0.10	0.43
Machinery	0.12	-	0.04	0.19	-	-	-	0.00	0.30	0.11	0.77
Mining and Quarrying	0.01	-	0.06	0.02	-	-	-	0.00	0.11	0.08	0.29
Food and Tobacco	0.88	-	0.24	0.42	-	-	-	0.01	0.38	0.06	1.99
Paper, Pulp and Printing	0.32	-	0.05	0.05	-	-	-	0.45	0.27	0.06	1.20
Wood and Wood Products	0.14	-	0.06	0.09	-	-	-	0.27	0.14	0.00	0.70
Construction	0.01	-	0.10	0.03	-	-	-	0.00	0.04	0.02	0.20
Textile and Leather	0.07	-	0.02	0.05	-	-	-	0.00	0.09	0.04	0.27
Non-specified	0.19	-	0.04	0.08	-	-	-	0.05	0.23	0.04	0.63
TRANSPORT SECTOR	**-**	**-**	**11.96**	**0.24**	**-**	**-**	**-**	**0.05**	**0.38**	**-**	**12.62**
International Aviation	-	-	0.34	-	-	-	-	-	-	-	0.34
Domestic Aviation	-	-	-	-	-	-	-	-	-	-	-
Road	-	-	11.46	-	-	-	-	0.05	-	-	11.51
Rail	-	-	0.16	-	-	-	-	-	0.34	-	0.51
Pipeline Transport	-	-	0.00	0.24	-	-	-	-	0.04	-	0.27
Domestic Navigation	-	-	0.00	-	-	-	-	-	-	-	0.00
Non-specified	-	-	-	-	-	-	-	-	-	-	-
OTHER SECTORS	**6.58**	**-**	**4.47**	**4.93**	**-**	**-**	**0.01**	**3.02**	**4.60**	**5.21**	**28.82**
Residential	4.98	-	1.09	3.23	-	-	0.01	2.40	2.16	4.54	18.40
Comm. and Publ. Services	0.67	-	0.48	1.68	-	-	0.00	0.16	2.32	0.66	5.96
Agriculture/Forestry	0.93	-	2.90	0.03	-	-	-	0.45	0.13	0.02	4.46
Fishing	-	-	0.00	-	-	-	-	-	0.00	0.00	0.00
Non-specified	-	-	-	-	-	-	-	-	-	-	-
NON-ENERGY USE	**0.09**	**-**	**2.39**	**2.02**	**-**	**-**	**-**	**-**	**-**	**-**	**4.49**
in Industry/Transf./Energy	0.09	-	2.08	2.02	-	-	-	-	-	-	4.19
of which: Feedstocks	-	-	*0.87*	*2.02*	-	-	-	-	-	-	*2.89*
in Transport	-	-	0.18	-	-	-	-	-	-	-	0.18
in Other Sectors	-	-	0.12	-	-	-	-	-	-	-	0.12
Electricity Generated - TWh	***145.17***	**-**	***2.39***	***3.57***	**-**	***2.20***	***0.14***	***1.90***	**-**	**-**	***155.36***
Electricity Plants	-	-	-	-	-	*2.20*	*0.14*	-	-	-	*2.34*
CHP plants	*145.17*	-	*2.39*	*3.57*	-	-	-	*1.90*	-	-	*153.02*
Heat Generated - PJ	***308.30***	**-**	***5.16***	***21.58***	**-**	**-**	**-**	***5.67***	**-**	**-**	***340.72***
CHP plants	*200.61*	-	*3.41*	*11.65*	-	-	-	*4.31*	-	-	*219.98*
Heat Plants	*107.69*	-	*1.76*	*9.94*	-	-	-	*1.36*	-	-	*120.74*

Portugal
Key Indicators
Indicateurs principaux

	1960	1970	1973	1980	1990	1995
Energy Production (Mtoe)	1.27	1.41	1.40	1.48	3.39	3.32
Net Imports (Mtoe)	2.01	5.26	6.49	9.95	15.43	18.16
Total Primary Energy Supply (Mtoe)	3.00	5.99	7.23	10.29	17.75	20.71
Net Oil Imports (Mtoe)	1.77	4.74	6.22	9.45	12.43	14.27
Oil Supply (Mtoe)	1.48	4.04	5.45	8.30	11.71	13.71
Electricity Consumption (TWh)*	2.84	6.63	8.59	15.22	25.38	30.85
GDP (billion 2000 US$ using exch. rates)	20.90 e	38.72	49.60	61.53	84.74	92.21
GDP (billion 2000 US$ using PPPs)	34.86 e	64.61	82.75	102.66	141.37	153.84
Population (millions)	9.23 e	8.81	8.72	9.86	10.00	10.03
Industrial Production Index (2000=100)	18.00	29.10	39.70	54.70	87.20	84.70
Energy Production/TPES	0.4215	0.2351	0.1938	0.1439	0.1912	0.1603
Net Oil Imports/GDP (toe per thousand 2000 US$)	0.0847 e	0.1225	0.1254	0.1535	0.1467	0.1548
TPES/GDP (toe per thousand 2000 US$)	0.1438 e	0.1546	0.1458	0.1672	0.2094	0.2246
TPES/GDP (toe per thousand 2000 US$ PPP)	0.0862 e	0.0927	0.0874	0.1002	0.1255	0.1346
TPES/Population (toe per capita)	0.3257 e	0.6800	0.8292	1.0435	1.7755	2.0644
Oil Supply/GDP (toe per thousand 2000 US$)	0.0707 e	0.1042	0.1100	0.1349	0.1382	0.1487
Oil Supply/Population (toe per capita)	0.1601 e	0.4583	0.6257	0.8416	1.1714	1.3667
Elect. Cons./GDP (kWh per 2000 US$)	0.1357 e	0.1712	0.1732	0.2474	0.2995	0.3346
Elect. Cons./Population (kWh per capita)	307 e	753	985	1 543	2 539	3 076
Industry Cons.**/Industrial Production (2000=100)	70.43	89.62	79.04	81.85	90.89	95.58
Industry Oil Cons.**/Industrial Production (2000=100)	43.23	95.23	96.10	101.59	96.04	100.11

	2000	2001	2002	2003	2004	2005
Energy Production (Mtoe)	3.85	4.10	3.64	4.34	3.90	3.58
Net Imports (Mtoe)	22.11	22.03	22.65	22.52	22.79	24.55
Total Primary Energy Supply (Mtoe)	25.29	25.43	26.46	25.78	26.55	27.17
Net Oil Imports (Mtoe)	16.08	16.80	16.29	16.37	15.72	16.85
Oil Supply (Mtoe)	15.53	15.87	16.45	15.28	15.42	15.90
Electricity Consumption (TWh)*	41.05	42.69	44.50	45.77	47.53	49.19
GDP (billion 2000 US$ using exch. rates)	112.65	114.92	115.80	114.50	115.86	116.32
GDP (billion 2000 US$ using PPPs)	187.94	191.73	193.19	191.03	193.30	194.07
Population (millions)	10.23	10.29	10.37	10.44	10.50	10.55
Industrial Production Index (2000=100)	100.00	103.10	102.70	102.60	100.00	100.30
Energy Production/TPES	0.1521	0.1611	0.1377	0.1683	0.1469	0.1319
Net Oil Imports/GDP (toe per thousand 2000 US$)	0.1427	0.1462	0.1407	0.1429	0.1357	0.1449
TPES/GDP (toe per thousand 2000 US$)	0.2245	0.2213	0.2285	0.2251	0.2291	0.2335
TPES/GDP (toe per thousand 2000 US$ PPP)	0.1346	0.1326	0.1369	0.1349	0.1373	0.1400
TPES/Population (toe per capita)	2.4731	2.4708	2.5518	2.4689	2.5280	2.5753
Oil Supply/GDP (toe per thousand 2000 US$)	0.1378	0.1381	0.1420	0.1335	0.1330	0.1367
Oil Supply/Population (toe per capita)	1.5182	1.5417	1.5863	1.4636	1.4678	1.5071
Elect. Cons./GDP (kWh per 2000 US$)	0.3644	0.3715	0.3843	0.3997	0.4102	0.4229
Elect. Cons./Population (kWh per capita)	4 014	4 148	4 292	4 383	4 526	4 663
Industry Cons.**/Industrial Production (2000=100)	100.00	94.28	95.33	92.84	95.67	94.48
Industry Oil Cons.**/Industrial Production (2000=100)	100.00	92.79	90.36	85.17	87.50	84.75

* Electricity consumption equals domestic supply less distribution losses.
La consommation d'électricité représente l'approvisionnement intérieur diminué des pertes de distribution.

** Includes non-energy use in industry/transformation/energy sectors.
Comprend l'usage non-énergétique dans les secteurs de l'industrie/transformation/énergie.

Portugal

Figure 1. TPES* in 1973

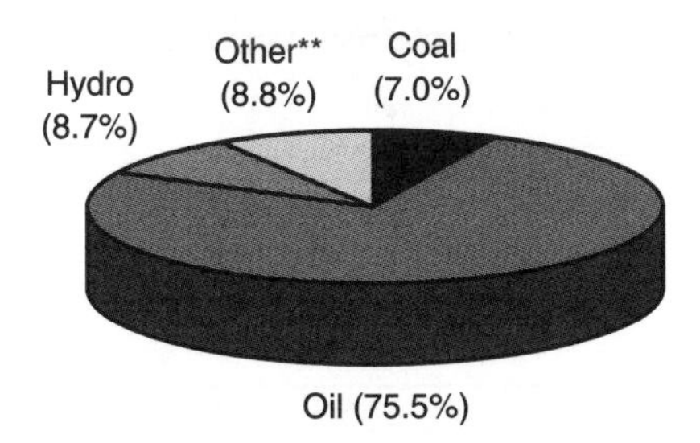

Figure 2. TPES* in 2005

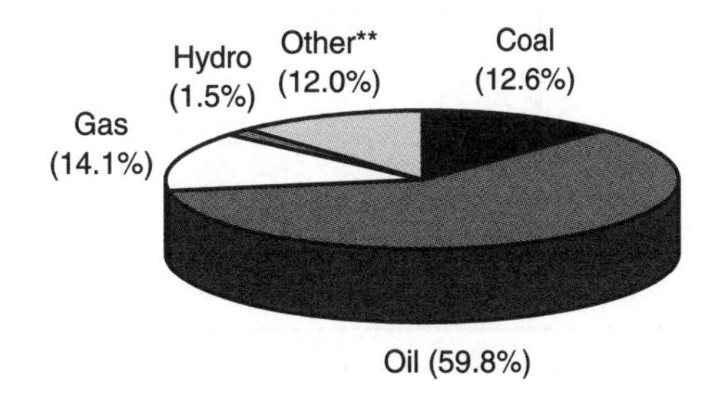

Figure 3. Final Consumption by Sector***

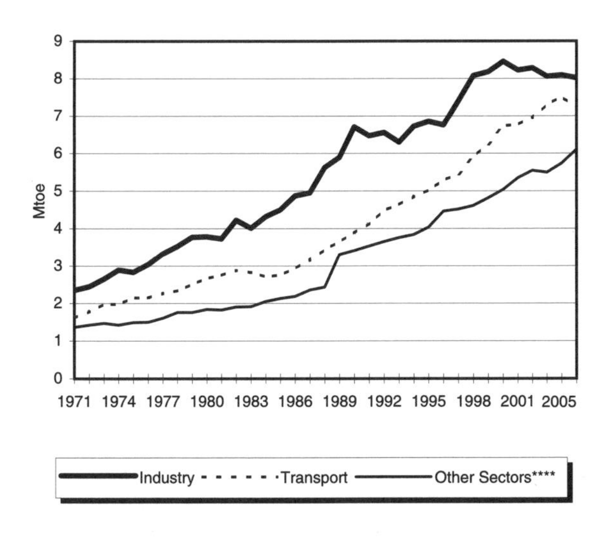

Figure 4. Breakdown of Sectorial Final Consumption by Source in 1973 and 2005***

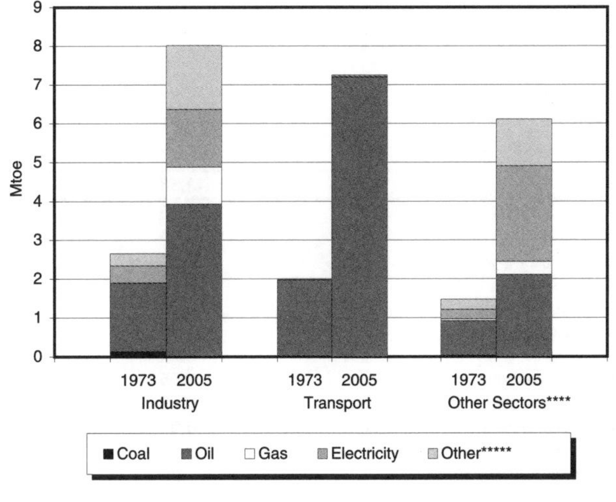

Figure 5. Electricity Generation by Fuel

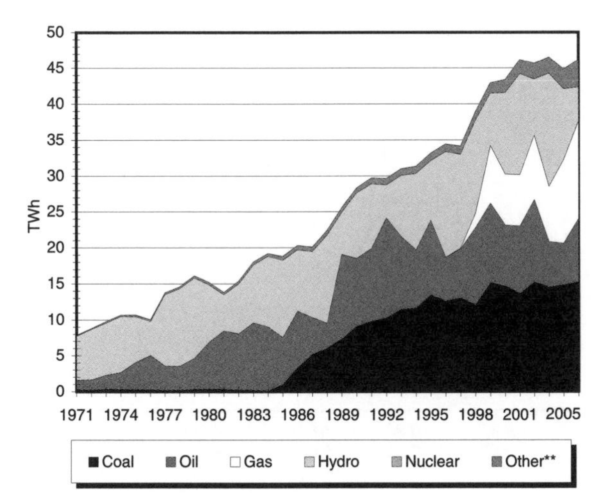

Figure 6. Electricity Consumption/GDP, TPES/GDP and Energy Production/TPES

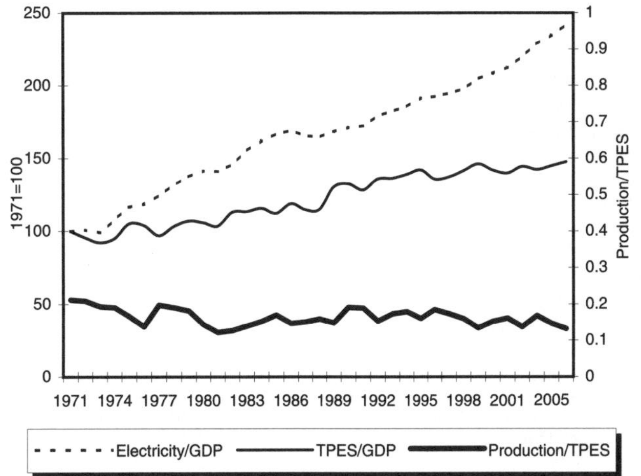

* Excluding electricity trade.

** Includes geothermal, solar, wind, combustible renewables & waste, etc.

*** Includes non-energy use.

**** Includes residential, commercial and public services, agriculture/forestry, fishing and non-specified.

***** Includes comb. renewables & waste, direct use of geothermal/solar thermal and heat produced in CHP/heat plants.

Portugal : 2004

Million tonnes of oil equivalent / *Million de tonnes d'équivalent pétrole*

SUPPLY AND CONSUMPTION *APPROVISIONNEMENT ET DEMANDE*	Coal *Charbon*	Crude Oil *Pétrole brut*	Petroleum Products *Produits pétroliers*	Gas *Gaz*	Nuclear *Nucléaire*	Hydro *Hydro*	Geotherm. Solar etc. *Géotherm. solaire etc.*	Combust. Renew. & Waste *Comb. ren. & déchets*	Electricity *Electricité*	Heat *Chaleur*	Total *Total*
Production	-	-	-	-	-	0.85	0.17	2.88	-	-	3.90
Imports	3.21	13.47	4.29	3.30	-	-	-	-	0.74	-	25.01
Exports	-	-	-2.03	-	-	-	-	-	-0.18	-	-2.22
Intl. Marine Bunkers	-	-	-0.66	-	-	-	-	-	-	-	-0.66
Stock Changes	0.16	-0.10	0.45	-0.00	-	-	-	-	-	-	0.51
TPES	**3.37**	**13.37**	**2.04**	**3.30**	**-**	**0.85**	**0.17**	**2.88**	**0.56**	**-**	**26.55**
Transfers	-	0.27	-0.23	-	-	-	-	-	-	-	0.03
Statistical Differences	-0.06	0.02	-0.12	0.00	-	-	-	-	-	-	-0.17
Electricity Plants	-3.23	-	-0.70	-1.56	-	-0.85	-0.15	-0.22	3.39	-	-3.32
CHP Plants	-	-	-0.55	-0.43	-	-	-	-0.18	0.46	0.26	-0.43
Heat Plants	-	-	-	-	-	-	-	-	-	-	-
Gas Works	-	-	-	-	-	-	-	-	-	-	-
Petroleum Refineries	-	-13.65	13.67	-	-	-	-	-	-	-	0.02
Coal Transformation	-	-	-	-	-	-	-	-	-	-	-
Liquefaction Plants	-	-	-	-	-	-	-	-	-	-	-
Other Transformation	-	-	-	-	-	-	-	-	-	-	-
Own Use	-	-	-0.74	-0.02	-	-	-	-	-0.22	-	-0.98
Distribution Losses	-	-	-	-0.02	-	-	-	-	-0.35	-	-0.37
TFC	**0.09**	**-**	**13.37**	**1.28**	**-**	**-**	**0.02**	**2.48**	**3.84**	**0.26**	**21.34**
INDUSTRY SECTOR	**0.09**	**-**	**1.70**	**0.95**	**-**	**-**	**-**	**1.32**	**1.47**	**0.24**	**5.76**
Iron and Steel	-	-	0.02	0.03	-	-	-	-	0.10	-	0.15
Chemical and Petrochem.	0.01	-	0.25	0.06	-	-	-	0.03	0.22	0.10	0.68
Non-Ferrous Metals	-	-	0.00	0.01	-	-	-	0.01	0.01	-	0.03
Non-Metallic Minerals	0.07	-	0.66	0.51	-	-	-	0.34	0.20	0.00	1.78
Transport Equipment	-	-	0.00	0.03	-	-	-	-	0.04	-	0.07
Machinery	-	-	0.04	0.02	-	-	-	0.00	0.10	0.00	0.16
Mining and Quarrying	-	-	0.05	0.01	-	-	-	-	0.04	0.02	0.12
Food and Tobacco	-	-	0.19	0.07	-	-	-	0.09	0.15	0.02	0.51
Paper, Pulp and Printing	-	-	0.06	0.03	-	-	-	0.76	0.20	0.04	1.10
Wood and Wood Products	-	-	0.02	0.01	-	-	-	0.04	0.05	0.01	0.13
Construction	-	-	0.29	0.01	-	-	-	-	0.06	-	0.36
Textile and Leather	-	-	0.10	0.15	-	-	-	0.05	0.16	0.04	0.51
Non-specified	-	-	0.01	0.02	-	-	-	0.00	0.13	-	0.16
TRANSPORT SECTOR	**-**	**-**	**7.40**	**0.01**	**-**	**-**	**-**	**-**	**0.04**	**-**	**7.45**
International Aviation	-	-	0.72	-	-	-	-	-	-	-	0.72
Domestic Aviation	-	-	0.16	-	-	-	-	-	-	-	0.16
Road	-	-	6.48	0.01	-	-	-	-	-	-	6.48
Rail	-	-	0.03	-	-	-	-	-	0.04	-	0.07
Pipeline Transport	-	-	-	-	-	-	-	-	-	-	-
Domestic Navigation	-	-	0.03	-	-	-	-	-	-	-	0.03
Non-specified	-	-	-	0.00	-	-	-	-	-	-	0.00
OTHER SECTORS	**-**	**-**	**1.83**	**0.32**	**-**	**-**	**0.02**	**1.16**	**2.33**	**0.02**	**5.68**
Residential	-	-	0.79	0.18	-	-	0.01	1.16	1.07	0.01	3.22
Comm. and Publ. Services	-	-	0.53	0.14	-	-	0.01	-	1.18	0.01	1.87
Agriculture/Forestry	-	-	0.45	0.00	-	-	-	-	0.08	0.00	0.53
Fishing	-	-	0.06	-	-	-	-	-	0.00	-	0.06
Non-specified	-	-	-	-	-	-	-	-	-	-	-
NON-ENERGY USE	**-**	**-**	**2.44**	**-**	**-**	**-**	**-**	**-**	**-**	**-**	**2.44**
in Industry/Transf./Energy	-	-	2.33	-	-	-	-	-	-	-	2.33
of which: Feedstocks	-	-	*1.73*	-	-	-	-	-	-	-	*1.73*
in Transport	-	-	0.05	-	-	-	-	-	-	-	0.05
in Other Sectors	-	-	0.05	-	-	-	-	-	-	-	0.05
Electricity Generated - TWh	***14.86***	**-**	***5.70***	***11.69***	**-**	***9.87***	***0.90***	***1.81***	**-**	**-**	***44.83***
Electricity Plants	*14.86*	-	*3.17*	*10.04*	-	*9.87*	*0.90*	*0.60*	-	-	*39.44*
CHP plants	-	-	*2.53*	*1.65*	-	-	-	*1.21*	-	-	*5.39*
Heat Generated - PJ	**-**	**-**	***3.52***	***7.27***	**-**	**-**	**-**	**-**	**-**	**-**	***10.79***
CHP plants	-	-	*3.52*	*7.27*	-	-	-	-	-	-	*10.79*
Heat Plants	-	-	-	-	-	-	-	-	-	-	-

Portugal : 2005

Million tonnes of oil equivalent / *Million de tonnes d'équivalent pétrole*

SUPPLY AND CONSUMPTION *APPROVISIONNEMENT ET DEMANDE*	Coal *Charbon*	Crude Oil *Pétrole brut*	Petroleum Products *Produits pétroliers*	Gas *Gaz*	Nuclear *Nucléaire*	Hydro *Hydro*	Geotherm. Solar etc. *Géotherm. solaire etc.*	Combust. Renew. & Waste *Comb. ren. & déchets*	Electricity *Electricité*	Heat *Chaleur*	Total *Total*
Production	-	-	-	-	-	0.41	0.24	2.94	-	-	3.58
Imports	3.22	13.76	5.50	3.89	-	-	-	-	0.83	-	27.20
Exports	-	-	-2.41	-	-	-	-	-	-0.24	-	-2.65
Intl. Marine Bunkers	-	-	-0.58	-	-	-	-	-	-	-	-0.58
Stock Changes	0.12	-0.05	-0.32	-0.14	-	-	-	-	-	-	-0.39
TPES	**3.35**	**13.71**	**2.19**	**3.75**	**-**	**0.41**	**0.24**	**2.94**	**0.59**	**-**	**27.17**
Transfers	-	0.28	-0.24	-	-	-	-	-	-	-	0.04
Statistical Differences	-0.01	-0.07	0.02	0.00	-	-	-	-	-	-	-0.06
Electricity Plants	-3.32	-	-1.36	-1.80	-	-0.41	-0.22	-0.25	3.47	-	-3.88
CHP Plants	-	-	-0.55	-0.51	-	-	-	-0.18	0.50	0.33	-0.41
Heat Plants	-	-	-	-	-	-	-	-	-	-	-
Gas Works	-	-	-	-	-	-	-	-	-	-	-
Petroleum Refineries	-	-13.92	13.95	-	-	-	-	-	-	-	0.04
Coal Transformation	-	-	-	-	-	-	-	-	-	-	-
Liquefaction Plants	-	-	-	-	-	-	-	-	-	-	-
Other Transformation	-	-	-	-	-	-	-	-	-	-	-
Own Use	-	-	-0.79	-0.08	-	-	-	-	-0.21	-	-1.08
Distribution Losses	-	-	-0.01	-0.06	-	-	-	-	-0.36	-	-0.43
TFC	**0.02**	**-**	**13.21**	**1.31**	**-**	**-**	**0.02**	**2.50**	**3.98**	**0.33**	**21.38**
INDUSTRY SECTOR	**0.02**	**-**	**1.58**	**0.96**	**-**	**-**	**-**	**1.34**	**1.48**	**0.31**	**5.68**
Iron and Steel	-	-	0.04	0.04	-	-	-	-	0.11	-	0.19
Chemical and Petrochem.	0.02	-	0.14	0.06	-	-	-	0.04	0.22	0.11	0.58
Non-Ferrous Metals	-	-	-	0.01	-	-	-	0.01	0.01	-	0.02
Non-Metallic Minerals	-	-	0.73	0.52	-	-	-	0.35	0.20	0.01	1.80
Transport Equipment	-	-	0.00	0.03	-	-	-	-	0.04	-	0.07
Machinery	-	-	0.04	0.02	-	-	-	0.00	0.10	0.00	0.16
Mining and Quarrying	-	-	0.05	0.01	-	-	-	-	0.04	0.02	0.13
Food and Tobacco	-	-	0.17	0.07	-	-	-	0.09	0.15	0.04	0.51
Paper, Pulp and Printing	-	-	0.08	0.04	-	-	-	0.77	0.21	0.08	1.18
Wood and Wood Products	-	-	0.02	0.01	-	-	-	0.04	0.06	0.01	0.14
Construction	-	-	0.27	0.01	-	-	-	-	0.06	-	0.33
Textile and Leather	-	-	0.04	0.13	-	-	-	0.05	0.15	0.04	0.42
Non-specified	-	-	0.00	0.02	-	-	-	0.00	0.12	-	0.14
TRANSPORT SECTOR	**-**	**-**	**7.14**	**0.01**	**-**	**-**	**-**	**-**	**0.04**	**-**	**7.20**
International Aviation	-	-	0.74	-	-	-	-	-	-	-	0.74
Domestic Aviation	-	-	0.17	-	-	-	-	-	-	-	0.17
Road	-	-	6.18	0.01	-	-	-	-	-	-	6.19
Rail	-	-	0.03	-	-	-	-	-	0.04	-	0.07
Pipeline Transport	-	-	-	-	-	-	-	-	-	-	-
Domestic Navigation	-	-	0.03	-	-	-	-	-	-	-	0.03
Non-specified	-	-	-	0.00	-	-	-	-	-	-	0.00
OTHER SECTORS	**-**	**-**	**2.01**	**0.34**	**-**	**-**	**0.02**	**1.16**	**2.47**	**0.01**	**6.02**
Residential	-	-	0.70	0.20	-	-	0.01	1.16	1.14	0.01	3.22
Comm. and Publ. Services	-	-	0.82	0.14	-	-	0.01	-	1.24	0.01	2.21
Agriculture/Forestry	-	-	0.43	0.00	-	-	-	-	0.09	0.00	0.52
Fishing	-	-	0.06	0.00	-	-	-	-	0.00	-	0.06
Non-specified	-	-	-	-	-	-	-	-	-	-	-
NON-ENERGY USE	**-**	**-**	**2.48**	**-**	**-**	**-**	**-**	**-**	**-**	**-**	**2.48**
in Industry/Transf./Energy	-	-	2.34	-	-	-	-	-	-	-	2.34
of which: Feedstocks	-	-	*1.69*	-	-	-	-	-	-	-	*1.69*
in Transport	-	-	0.05	-	-	-	-	-	-	-	0.05
in Other Sectors	-	-	0.09	-	-	-	-	-	-	-	0.09
Electricity Generated - TWh	***15.23***	**-**	***8.79***	***13.61***	**-**	***4.73***	***1.85***	***1.99***	**-**	**-**	***46.19***
Electricity Plants	*15.23*	-	*6.22*	*11.64*	-	*4.73*	*1.85*	*0.69*	-	-	*40.36*
CHP plants	-	-	*2.57*	*1.96*	-	-	-	*1.29*	-	-	*5.82*
Heat Generated - PJ	**-**	**-**	***5.02***	***8.70***	**-**	**-**	**-**	**-**	**-**	**-**	***13.71***
CHP plants	-	-	*5.02*	*8.70*	-	-	-	-	-	-	*13.71*
Heat Plants	-	-	-	-	-	-	-	-	-	-	-

Slovak Republic / République slovaque
Key Indicators
Indicateurs principaux

	1960	1970	1973	1980	1990	1995
Energy Production (Mtoe)	..	..	2.57	3.43	5.28	5.04
Net Imports (Mtoe)	..	..	12.94	17.29	16.40	12.26
Total Primary Energy Supply (Mtoe)	..	..	15.50	20.93	21.32	17.83
Net Oil Imports (Mtoe)	..	..	5.25	7.45	4.50	3.49
Oil Supply (Mtoe)	..	..	5.37	7.47	4.49	3.41
Electricity Consumption (TWh)*	..	..	14.05	21.71	29.37 e	26.41 e
GDP (billion 2000 US$ using exch. rates)	9.23 e	12.32 e	13.61 e	16.15 e	18.70 e	17.07
GDP (billion 2000 US$ using PPPs)	26.44 e	35.29 e	38.99 e	46.25 e	53.56 e	48.89
Population (millions)	3.99	4.53	4.64	4.98	5.30	5.36
Industrial Production Index (2000=100)	..	..	..	..	107.90	86.10
Energy Production/TPES	..	..	0.1661	0.1641	0.2479	0.2829
Net Oil Imports/GDP (toe per thousand 2000 US$)	..	..	0.3859 e	0.4611 e	0.2408 e	0.2043
TPES/GDP (toe per thousand 2000 US$)	..	..	1.1387 e	1.2961 e	1.1400 e	1.0445
TPES/GDP (toe per thousand 2000 US$ PPP)	..	..	0.3975 e	0.4524 e	0.3979 e	0.3646
TPES/Population (toe per capita)	..	..	3.3393	4.1985	4.0232	3.3241
Oil Supply/GDP (toe per thousand 2000 US$)	..	..	0.3944 e	0.4625 e	0.2402 e	0.2000
Oil Supply/Population (toe per capita)	..	..	1.1567	1.4981	0.8477	0.6366
Elect. Cons./GDP (kWh per 2000 US$)	..	..	1.0320 e	1.3444 e	1.5707 e	1.5476 e
Elect. Cons./Population (kWh per capita)	..	..	3 027	4 355	5 543 e	4 925 e
Industry Cons.**/Industrial Production (2000=100)	..	..	..	..	152.51	110.44
Industry Oil Cons.**/Industrial Production (2000=100)	..	..	..	..	179.59	75.45

	2000	2001	2002	2003	2004	2005
Energy Production (Mtoe)	6.33	6.68	6.82	6.59	6.45	6.61
Net Imports (Mtoe)	11.50	11.54	11.99	12.00	12.41	12.31
Total Primary Energy Supply (Mtoe)	17.74	18.58	18.74	18.63	18.33	18.83
Net Oil Imports (Mtoe)	2.60	2.74	3.19	3.05	3.15	3.15
Oil Supply (Mtoe)	2.82	2.99	3.45	3.19	3.21	3.46
Electricity Consumption (TWh)*	26.71 e	27.04	27.16	26.98	27.39	26.50
GDP (billion 2000 US$ using exch. rates)	20.45	21.11	21.98	22.89	24.13	25.61
GDP (billion 2000 US$ using PPPs)	58.58	60.47	62.96	65.57	69.13	73.36
Population (millions)	5.40	5.40	5.38	5.38	5.38	5.39
Industrial Production Index (2000=100)	100.00	106.90	113.70	119.50	124.20	129.00
Energy Production/TPES	0.3566	0.3597	0.3640	0.3538	0.3519	0.3510
Net Oil Imports/GDP (toe per thousand 2000 US$)	0.1273	0.1299	0.1449	0.1332	0.1304	0.1229
TPES/GDP (toe per thousand 2000 US$)	0.8675	0.8805	0.8528	0.8139	0.7597	0.7354
TPES/GDP (toe per thousand 2000 US$ PPP)	0.3028	0.3073	0.2977	0.2841	0.2652	0.2567
TPES/Population (toe per capita)	3.2842	3.4395	3.4842	3.4627	3.4063	3.4957
Oil Supply/GDP (toe per thousand 2000 US$)	0.1377	0.1415	0.1568	0.1392	0.1332	0.1351
Oil Supply/Population (toe per capita)	0.5213	0.5526	0.6405	0.5922	0.5971	0.6421
Elect. Cons./GDP (kWh per 2000 US$)	1.3060 e	1.2812	1.2360	1.1789	1.1350	1.0350
Elect. Cons./Population (kWh per capita)	4 945 e	5 005	5 050	5 016	5 089	4 920
Industry Cons.**/Industrial Production (2000=100)	100.00	95.78	93.41	89.68	83.31	80.92
Industry Oil Cons.**/Industrial Production (2000=100)	100.00	74.12	75.30	68.65	63.11	57.82

* Electricity consumption equals domestic supply less distribution losses.
La consommation d'électricité représente l'approvisionnement intérieur diminué des pertes de distribution.

** Includes non-energy use in industry/transformation/energy sectors.
Comprend l'usage non-énergétique dans les secteurs de l'industrie/transformation/énergie.

Slovak Republic / République slovaque

Figure 1. TPES* in 1973

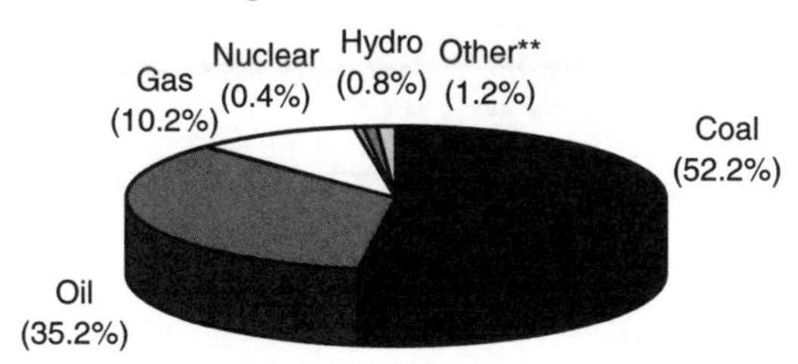

Figure 2. TPES* in 2005

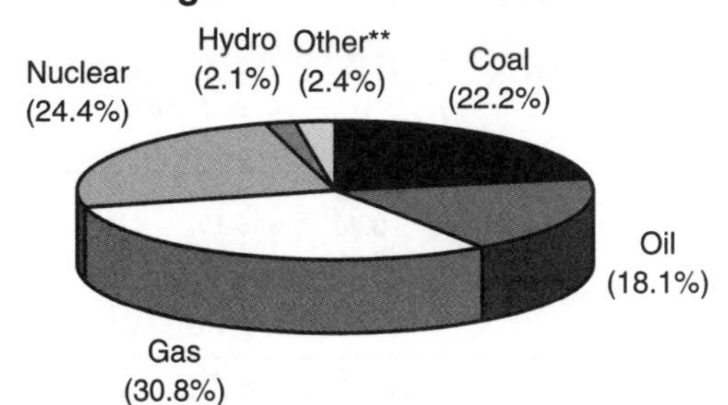

Figure 3. Final Consumption by Sector***

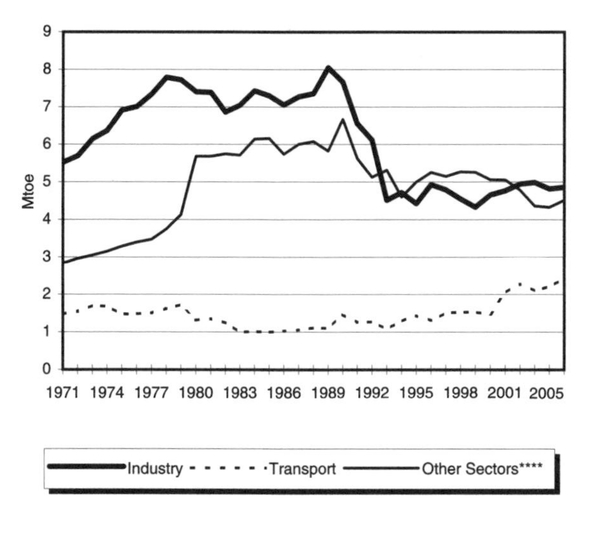

Figure 4. Breakdown of Sectorial Final Consumption by Source in 1973 and 2005***

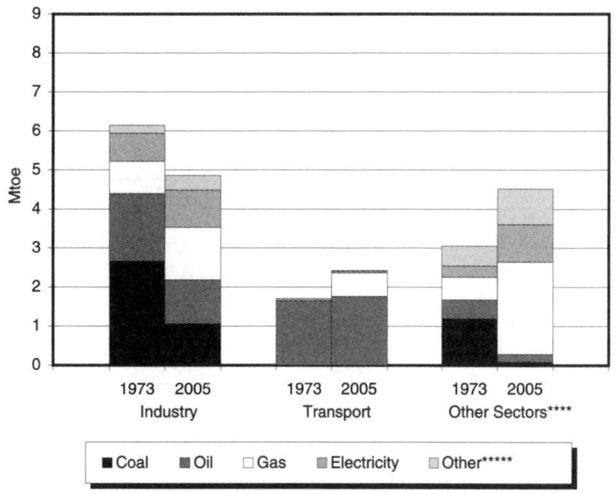

Figure 5. Electricity Generation by Fuel

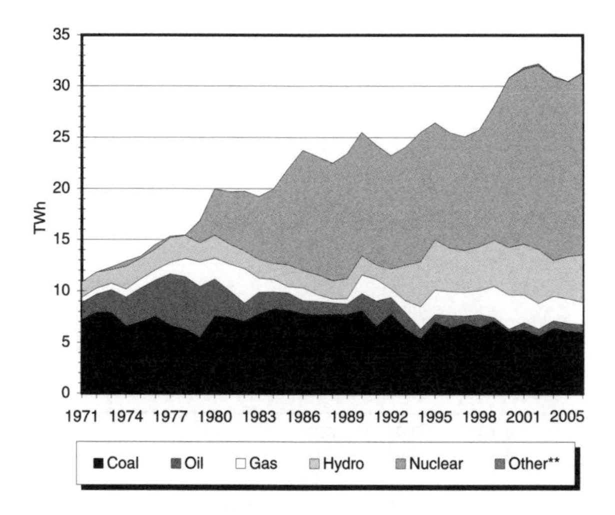

Figure 6. Electricity Consumption/GDP, TPES/GDP and Energy Production/TPES

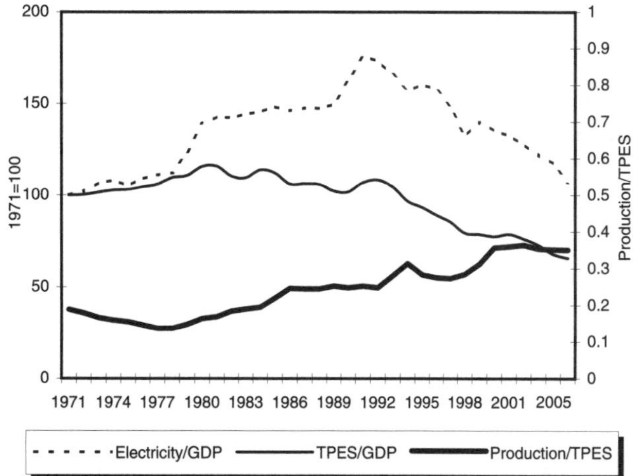

* Excluding electricity trade.

** Includes geothermal, solar, wind, combustible renewables & waste, etc.

*** Includes non-energy use.

**** Includes residential, commercial and public services, agriculture/forestry, fishing and non-specified.

***** Includes comb. renewables & waste, direct use of geothermal/solar thermal and heat produced in CHP/heat plants.

Slovak Republic / République slovaque : 2004

Million tonnes of oil equivalent / *Million de tonnes d'équivalent pétrole*

SUPPLY AND CONSUMPTION / ***APPROVISIONNEMENT ET DEMANDE***	Coal / *Charbon*	Crude Oil / *Pétrole brut*	Petroleum Products / *Produits pétroliers*	Gas / *Gaz*	Nuclear / *Nucléaire*	Hydro / *Hydro*	Geotherm. Solar etc. / *Géotherm. solaire etc.*	Combust. Renew. & Waste / *Comb. ren. & déchets*	Electricity / *Electricité*	Heat / *Chaleur*	Total / *Total*
Production	0.82	0.22	-	0.14	4.49	0.35	0.01 e	0.42 e	-	0.00	6.45
Imports	3.80	6.10	1.11	5.68	-	-	-	-	0.75	-	17.43
Exports	-0.04	-0.18	-3.88	-0.00	-	-	-	-0.02	-0.91	-	-5.03
Intl. Marine Bunkers	-	-	-	-	-	-	-	-	-	-	-
Stock Changes	-0.05	-0.18	0.03	-0.32	-	-	-	0.00	-	-	-0.53
TPES	**4.52**	**5.96**	**-2.74**	**5.50**	**4.49**	**0.35**	**0.01**	**0.41**	**-0.16**	**0.00**	**18.33**
Transfers	-	0.16	-0.16	-	-	-	-	-	-	-	0.00
Statistical Differences	0.03	0.23	-0.13	-	-	-	-	-0.00	-	-	0.13
Electricity Plants	-0.31	-	-0.00	-	-	-0.35	-0.00	-0.00	0.43	-	-0.23
CHP Plants	-1.51	-	-0.10	-0.72	-4.49	-	-	-0.03	2.19	0.67	-3.99
Heat Plants	-0.02	-	-0.00	-0.67	-	-	-0.01 e	-0.04	-0.00	0.62 e	-0.13
Gas Works	-	-	-	-	-	-	-	-	-	-	-
Petroleum Refineries	-	-6.73	6.86	-0.13	-	-	-	-	-	-	0.01
Coal Transformation	-0.96 e	-	-	-	-	-	-	-	-	-	-0.96
Liquefaction Plants	-	-	-	-	-	-	-	-	-	-	-
Other Transformation	-	0.38	-0.28	-	-	-	-	-	-	-	0.10
Own Use	-0.37	-	-0.49	-0.20	-	-	-	-0.00	-0.28	-0.12	-1.46
Distribution Losses	-0.03	-	-	-0.12	-	-	-	-0.00	-0.11	-0.16	-0.43
TFC	**1.34**	**-**	**2.95**	**3.66**	**-**	**-**	**0.00**	**0.34**	**2.07**	**1.00**	**11.36**
INDUSTRY SECTOR	**1.07**	**-**	**0.30**	**0.85**	**-**	**-**	**-**	**0.29**	**0.92**	**0.10**	**3.54**
Iron and Steel	0.80 e	-	0.01	0.14	-	-	-	0.00	0.22	-	1.18
Chemical and Petrochem.	0.01	-	0.19	0.07	-	-	-	0.02	0.12	0.05	0.46
Non-Ferrous Metals	0.01	-	-	0.03	-	-	-	-	0.20	-	0.24
Non-Metallic Minerals	0.12	-	0.06	0.16	-	-	-	0.00	0.07	0.01	0.41
Transport Equipment	0.00	-	-	0.05	-	-	-	0.00	0.02	-	0.07
Machinery	0.00	-	0.00	0.06	-	-	-	0.01	0.07	-	0.14
Mining and Quarrying	0.00	-	0.00	0.03	-	-	-	-	0.01	-	0.04
Food and Tobacco	0.00	-	0.00	0.13	-	-	-	0.00	0.04	0.02	0.20
Paper, Pulp and Printing	0.08	-	0.01	0.06	-	-	-	0.23	0.09	0.02	0.49
Wood and Wood Products	-	-	0.00	0.01	-	-	-	0.02	0.02	-	0.05
Construction	-	-	0.01	0.01	-	-	-	0.00	0.01	0.00	0.03
Textile and Leather	0.00	-	0.00	0.06	-	-	-	-	0.02	-	0.08
Non-specified	0.05	-	0.01	0.03	-	-	-	0.01	0.04	-	0.14
TRANSPORT SECTOR	**-**	**-**	**1.55**	**0.60**	**-**	**-**	**-**	**0.00**	**0.06**	**-**	**2.21**
International Aviation	-	-	0.03	-	-	-	-	-	-	-	0.03
Domestic Aviation	-	-	0.00	-	-	-	-	-	-	-	0.00
Road	-	-	1.52	-	-	-	-	0.00	-	-	1.52
Rail	-	-	-	-	-	-	-	-	0.05	-	0.05
Pipeline Transport	-	-	-	0.59	-	-	-	-	-	-	0.59
Domestic Navigation	-	-	-	-	-	-	-	-	-	-	-
Non-specified	-	-	-	0.01	-	-	-	-	0.01	-	0.01
OTHER SECTORS	**0.23**	**-**	**0.16**	**1.85**	**-**	**-**	**0.00**	**0.04**	**1.08**	**0.90**	**4.27**
Residential	0.10	-	0.01	1.49	-	-	-	0.03	0.41	0.62	2.67
Comm. and Publ. Services	0.13	-	0.07	0.32	-	-	0.00	0.01	0.63	0.28	1.44
Agriculture/Forestry	0.00	-	0.08	0.03	-	-	0.00	0.00	0.04	0.00	0.16
Fishing	-	-	-	-	-	-	-	-	-	-	-
Non-specified	-	-	-	-	-	-	-	-	-	-	-
NON-ENERGY USE	**0.04**	**-**	**0.94**	**0.36**	**-**	**-**	**-**	**-**	**-**	**-**	**1.33**
in Industry/Transf./Energy	0.04	-	0.88	0.36	-	-	-	-	-	-	1.27
of which: Feedstocks	-	-	*0.75*	*0.36*	-	-	-	-	-	-	*1.11*
in Transport	-	-	-	-	-	-	-	-	-	-	-
in Other Sectors	-	-	0.06	-	-	-	-	-	-	-	0.06
Electricity Generated - TWh	***6.14***	**-**	***0.74***	***2.42***	***17.03***	***4.10***	***0.01***	***0.04***	**-**	**-**	***30.46***
Electricity Plants	*0.86*	-	*0.00*	-	-	*4.10*	*0.01*	*0.00*	-	-	*4.97*
CHP plants	*5.28*	-	*0.74*	*2.42*	*17.03*	-	-	*0.03*	-	-	*25.49*
Heat Generated - PJ	***11.37***	**-**	***0.52***	***37.98***	***2.27***	**-**	***0.18***	***1.52***	***0.00***	***0.01***	***53.86***
CHP plants	*10.71*	-	*0.35*	*14.27*	*2.27*	-	-	*0.25*	-	-	*27.86*
Heat Plants	*0.66*	-	*0.17*	*23.71*	-	-	*0.18*	*1.27*	*0.00*	*0.01 e*	*26.00*

Slovak Republic / République slovaque : 2005

Million tonnes of oil equivalent / *Million de tonnes d'équivalent pétrole*

SUPPLY AND CONSUMPTION ***APPROVISIONNEMENT ET DEMANDE***	Coal *Charbon*	Crude Oil *Pétrole brut*	Petroleum Products *Produits pétroliers*	Gas *Gaz*	Nuclear *Nucléaire*	Hydro *Hydro*	Geotherm. Solar etc. *Géotherm. solaire etc.*	Combust. Renew. & Waste *Comb. ren. & déchets*	Electricity *Electricité*	Heat *Chaleur*	Total *Total*
Production	0.64	0.26	-	0.13	4.67	0.40	0.01	0.50	-	0.00	6.61
Imports	3.90	5.48	1.36	6.04	-	-	-	0.01	0.69	-	17.47
Exports	-0.15	-0.14	-3.55	-0.31	-	-	-	-0.05	-0.97	-	-5.17
Intl. Marine Bunkers	-	-	-	-	-	-	-	-	-	-	-
Stock Changes	-0.14	0.09	-0.04	0.02	-	-	-	-0.01	-	-	-0.08
TPES	**4.24**	**5.69**	**-2.23**	**5.88**	**4.67**	**0.40**	**0.01**	**0.45**	**-0.28**	**0.00**	**18.83**
Transfers	-	0.26	-0.25	-	-	-	-	-	-	-	0.01
Statistical Differences	-0.02	-0.00	-	0.02	-	-	-	-	-	-	0.00
Electricity Plants	-0.23	-	-0.00	-	-	-0.40	-0.00	-0.00	0.46	-	-0.18
CHP Plants	-1.51	-	-0.10	-0.64	-4.67	-	-	-0.04	2.23	0.62	-4.09
Heat Plants	-0.01	-	-0.00	-0.63	-	-	-0.01	-0.06	-0.00	0.63	-0.09
Gas Works	-	-	-	-	-	-	-	-	-	-	-
Petroleum Refineries	-	-6.30	6.47	-0.14	-	-	-	-	-	-	0.02
Coal Transformation	-0.91 e	-	-	-	-	-	-	-	-	-	-0.91
Liquefaction Plants	-	-	-	-	-	-	-	-	-	-	-
Other Transformation	-	0.36	-0.25	-	-	-	-	-	-	-	0.11
Own Use	-0.38	-	-0.56	-0.17	-	-	-	-0.00	-0.31	-0.16	-1.59
Distribution Losses	-0.04	-	-	-0.00	-	-	-	-	-0.15	-0.14	-0.33
TFC	**1.14**	**-**	**3.08**	**4.31**	**-**	**-**	**0.00**	**0.34**	**1.97**	**0.95**	**11.79**
INDUSTRY SECTOR	**1.02**	**-**	**0.31**	**0.97**	**-**	**-**	**-**	**0.29**	**0.95**	**0.08**	**3.63**
Iron and Steel	0.73 e	-	0.00	0.15	-	-	-	0.00	0.20	-	1.08
Chemical and Petrochem.	0.01	-	0.21	0.07	-	-	-	0.01	0.15	0.04	0.50
Non-Ferrous Metals	0.01	-	-	0.03	-	-	-	-	0.20	-	0.24
Non-Metallic Minerals	0.13	-	0.06	0.24	-	-	-	-	0.07	0.00	0.49
Transport Equipment	0.00	-	-	0.05	-	-	-	-	0.02	0.00	0.08
Machinery	0.00	-	0.00	0.08	-	-	-	0.01	0.07	-	0.15
Mining and Quarrying	0.00	-	0.00	0.03	-	-	-	0.00	0.01	0.00	0.04
Food and Tobacco	0.00	-	0.00	0.16	-	-	-	0.00	0.05	0.00	0.21
Paper, Pulp and Printing	0.08	-	0.00	0.06	-	-	-	0.24	0.09	0.02	0.49
Wood and Wood Products	-	-	-	0.01	-	-	-	0.02	0.01	-	0.05
Construction	-	-	0.01	0.02	-	-	-	0.00	0.01	0.00	0.04
Textile and Leather	0.00	-	0.00	0.04	-	-	-	-	0.02	0.01	0.07
Non-specified	0.05	-	0.01	0.05	-	-	-	0.01	0.06	-	0.19
TRANSPORT SECTOR	**-**	**-**	**1.76**	**0.60**	**-**	**-**	**-**	**0.01**	**0.05**	**-**	**2.42**
International Aviation	-	-	0.04	-	-	-	-	-	-	-	0.04
Domestic Aviation	-	-	0.01	-	-	-	-	-	-	-	0.01
Road	-	-	1.70	-	-	-	-	0.01	-	-	1.71
Rail	-	-	-	-	-	-	-	-	0.04	-	0.04
Pipeline Transport	-	-	-	0.59	-	-	-	-	-	-	0.59
Domestic Navigation	-	-	-	-	-	-	-	-	-	-	-
Non-specified	-	-	0.00	0.01	-	-	-	-	0.01	-	0.02
OTHER SECTORS	**0.08**	**-**	**0.14**	**2.36**	**-**	**-**	**0.00**	**0.04**	**0.97**	**0.87**	**4.46**
Residential	0.05	-	0.01	1.42	-	-	-	0.04	0.40	0.63	2.54
Comm. and Publ. Services	0.03	-	0.05	0.90	-	-	0.00	0.00	0.53	0.24	1.75
Agriculture/Forestry	0.00	-	0.08	0.04	-	-	0.00	0.00	0.03	0.00	0.17
Fishing	-	-	-	-	-	-	-	-	-	-	-
Non-specified	-	-	-	-	-	-	-	-	-	-	-
NON-ENERGY USE	**0.04**	**-**	**0.87**	**0.39**	**-**	**-**	**-**	**-**	**-**	**-**	**1.29**
in Industry/Transf./Energy	0.04	-	0.81	0.39	-	-	-	-	-	-	1.23
of which: Feedstocks	*-*	*-*	*0.63*	*0.39*	*-*	*-*	*-*	*-*	*-*	*-*	*1.02*
in Transport	-	-	0.00	-	-	-	-	-	-	-	0.00
in Other Sectors	-	-	0.06	-	-	-	-	-	-	-	0.06
Electricity Generated - TWh	***6.00***	***-***	***0.74***	***2.18***	***17.73***	***4.64***	***0.01***	***0.06***	***-***	***-***	***31.35***
Electricity Plants	*0.71*	*-*	*0.01*	*-*	*-*	*4.64*	*0.01*	*0.00*	*-*	*-*	*5.37*
CHP plants	*5.29*	*-*	*0.73*	*2.18*	*17.73*	*-*	*-*	*0.06*	*-*	*-*	*25.99*
Heat Generated - PJ	***10.94***	***-***	***0.26***	***36.59***	***2.23***	***-***	***0.19***	***2.34***	***0.00***	***0.01***	***52.55***
CHP plants	*10.56*	*-*	*0.20*	*12.91*	*2.23*	*-*	*-*	*0.25*	*-*	*-*	*26.15*
Heat Plants	*0.37*	*-*	*0.06*	*23.67*	*-*	*-*	*0.19*	*2.09*	*0.00*	*0.01*	*26.39*

Spain / Espagne
Key Indicators
Indicateurs principaux

	1960	1970	1973	1980	1990	1995
Energy Production (Mtoe)	9.84	9.68	11.35	15.77	34.58	31.51
Net Imports (Mtoe)	6.62	30.39	43.86	55.37	60.29	76.10
Total Primary Energy Supply (Mtoe)	16.16	38.35	52.39	68.58	91.07	102.82
Net Oil Imports (Mtoe)	6.41	28.82	40.95	49.95	49.56	59.55
Oil Supply (Mtoe)	6.00	26.72	38.38	50.66	46.46	55.51
Electricity Consumption (TWh)*	15.07	47.88	65.56	99.14	137.46	155.61
GDP (billion 2000 US$ using exch. rates)	113.17 e	231.11	281.94	329.98	440.64	474.85
GDP (billion 2000 US$ using PPPs)	165.47 e	337.91	412.23	482.48	644.28	694.30
Population (millions)	30.40 e	34.02	34.96	37.67	39.01	39.39
Industrial Production Index (2000=100)	..	41.30	56.90	67.10	80.90	83.90
Energy Production/TPES	0.6091	0.2525	0.2166	0.2300	0.3797	0.3065
Net Oil Imports/GDP (toe per thousand 2000 US$)	0.0567 e	0.1247	0.1452	0.1514	0.1125	0.1254
TPES/GDP (toe per thousand 2000 US$)	0.1428 e	0.1660	0.1858	0.2078	0.2067	0.2165
TPES/GDP (toe per thousand 2000 US$ PPP)	0.0976 e	0.1135	0.1271	0.1421	0.1414	0.1481
TPES/Population (toe per capita)	0.5315 e	1.1274	1.4986	1.8205	2.3344	2.6104
Oil Supply/GDP (toe per thousand 2000 US$)	0.0530 e	0.1156	0.1361	0.1535	0.1054	0.1169
Oil Supply/Population (toe per capita)	0.1972 e	0.7854	1.0980	1.3448	1.1907	1.4092
Elect. Cons./GDP (kWh per 2000 US$)	0.1332 e	0.2072	0.2325	0.3004	0.3120	0.3277
Elect. Cons./Population (kWh per capita)	496 e	1 407	1 875	2 632	3 524	3 951
Industry Cons.**/Industrial Production (2000=100)	..	114.16	107.39	103.69	91.29	97.75
Industry Oil Cons.**/Industrial Production (2000=100)	..	173.84	163.62	165.05	94.59	115.18

	2000	2001	2002	2003	2004	2005
Energy Production (Mtoe)	31.68	33.50	31.80	32.99	32.67	30.28
Net Imports (Mtoe)	100.24	100.62	108.72	109.71	115.96	124.68
Total Primary Energy Supply (Mtoe)	124.69	127.86	131.62	136.09	142.34	145.20
Net Oil Imports (Mtoe)	71.58	73.30	74.98	75.71	77.47	80.16
Oil Supply (Mtoe)	64.85	67.10	67.27	69.04	70.77	71.28
Electricity Consumption (TWh)*	209.65	221.51	231.05	239.46	252.91	266.77
GDP (billion 2000 US$ using exch. rates)	580.67	601.86	618.13	636.96	657.62	680.84
GDP (billion 2000 US$ using PPPs)	849.03	880.00	903.80	931.32	961.53	995.48
Population (millions)	40.26	40.72	41.31	42.01	42.69	43.40
Industrial Production Index (2000=100)	100.00	98.50	98.70	100.00	101.60	102.30
Energy Production/TPES	0.2540	0.2620	0.2416	0.2424	0.2295	0.2086
Net Oil Imports/GDP (toe per thousand 2000 US$)	0.1233	0.1218	0.1213	0.1189	0.1178	0.1177
TPES/GDP (toe per thousand 2000 US$)	0.2147	0.2124	0.2129	0.2137	0.2164	0.2133
TPES/GDP (toe per thousand 2000 US$ PPP)	0.1469	0.1453	0.1456	0.1461	0.1480	0.1459
TPES/Population (toe per capita)	3.0969	3.1398	3.1859	3.2399	3.3341	3.3457
Oil Supply/GDP (toe per thousand 2000 US$)	0.1117	0.1115	0.1088	0.1084	0.1076	0.1047
Oil Supply/Population (toe per capita)	1.6106	1.6479	1.6283	1.6437	1.6577	1.6425
Elect. Cons./GDP (kWh per 2000 US$)	0.3610	0.3680	0.3738	0.3759	0.3846	0.3918
Elect. Cons./Population (kWh per capita)	5 207	5 440	5 592	5 701	5 924	6 147
Industry Cons.**/Industrial Production (2000=100)	100.00	107.32	107.75	111.82	110.40	111.07
Industry Oil Cons.**/Industrial Production (2000=100)	100.00	104.87	102.50	101.88	93.59	88.74

* Electricity consumption equals domestic supply less distribution losses.
La consommation d'électricité représente l'approvisionnement intérieur diminué des pertes de distribution.

** Includes non-energy use in industry/transformation/energy sectors.
Comprend l'usage non-énergétique dans les secteurs de l'industrie/transformation/énergie.

Spain / Espagne

Figure 1. TPES* in 1973

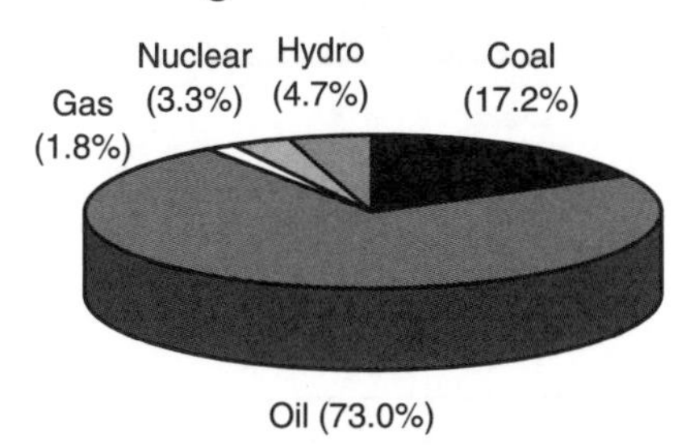

Figure 2. TPES* in 2005

Other** (4.8%)
Hydro (1.2%)
Nuclear (10.3%)
Coal (14.1%)
Gas (20.5%)
Oil (49.1%)

Figure 3. Final Consumption by Sector***

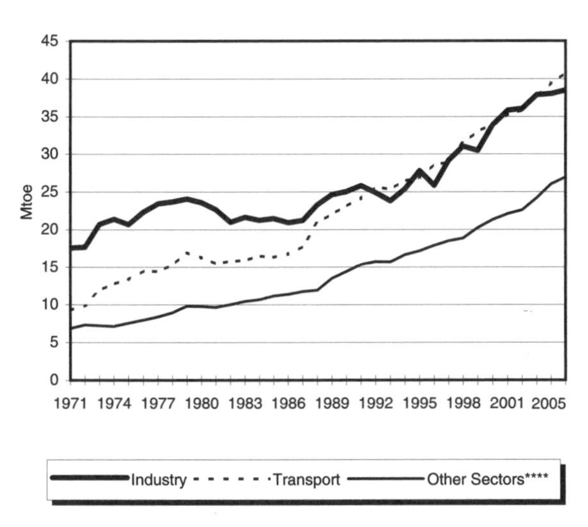

Figure 4. Breakdown of Sectorial Final Consumption by Source in 1973 and 2005***

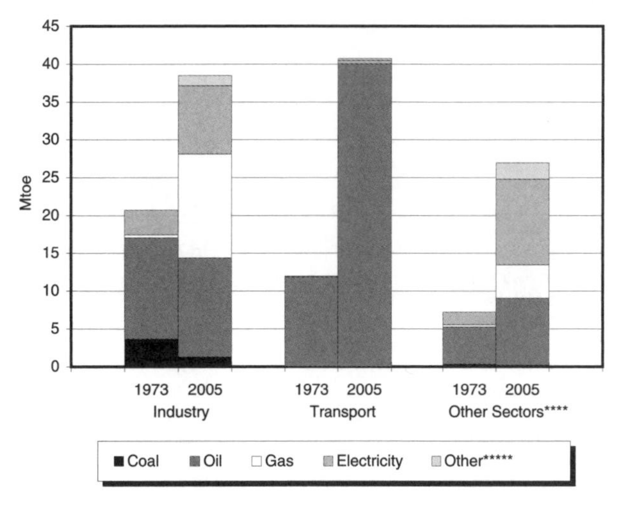

Figure 5. Electricity Generation by Fuel

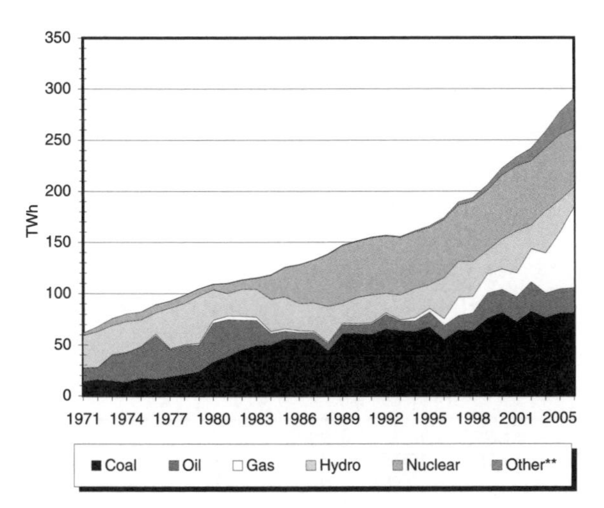

Figure 6. Electricity Consumption/GDP, TPES/GDP and Energy Production/TPES

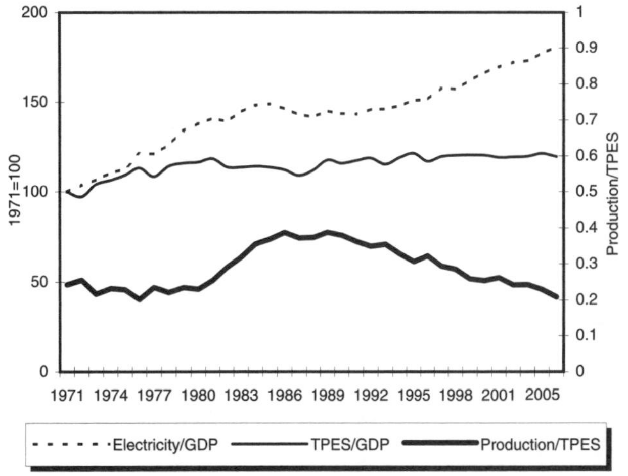

* Excluding electricity trade.

** Includes geothermal, solar, wind, combustible renewables & waste, etc.

*** Includes non-energy use.

**** Includes residential, commercial and public services, agriculture/forestry, fishing and non-specified.

***** Includes comb. renewables & waste, direct use of geothermal/solar thermal and heat produced in CHP/heat plants.

Spain / Espagne : 2004

Million tonnes of oil equivalent / *Million de tonnes d'équivalent pétrole*

SUPPLY AND CONSUMPTION ***APPROVISIONNEMENT ET DEMANDE***	Coal *Charbon*	Crude Oil *Pétrole brut*	Petroleum Products *Produits pétroliers*	Gas *Gaz*	Nuclear *Nucléaire*	Hydro *Hydro*	Geotherm. Solar etc. *Géotherm. solaire etc.*	Combust. Renew. & Waste *Comb. ren. & déchets*	Electricity *Electricité*	Heat *Chaleur*	Total *Total*
Production	6.45	0.26	-	0.31	16.58	2.71	1.42	4.94 e	-	-	32.67
Imports	14.85	60.58	25.06	24.61	-	-	-	-	0.70	..	125.80
Exports	-0.71	-	-8.17	-	-	-	-	-	-0.96	..	-9.84
Intl. Marine Bunkers	-	-	-7.19	-	-	-	-	-	-	-	-7.19
Stock Changes	0.42	0.18	0.06	0.25	-	-	-	-	-	-	0.90
TPES	**21.02**	**61.02**	**9.75**	**25.16**	**16.58**	**2.71**	**1.42**	**4.94**	**-0.26**	**-**	**142.34**
Transfers	-	0.13	-0.16	-	-	-	-	-	-	-	-0.04
Statistical Differences	-0.21	-	0.39	-0.50	-	-	-	-	-	-	-0.33
Electricity Plants	-17.90 e	-	-3.86	-5.00	-16.58	-2.71	-1.36	-0.95	20.70	-	-27.65
CHP Plants	-0.08 e	-	-1.01	-2.70	-	-	-	-0.31	3.13	..	-0.97
Heat Plants	-	-	-	-	-	-	-	-	-	-	-
Gas Works	-	-	-0.06	0.04	-	-	-	-	-	-	-0.03
Petroleum Refineries	-	-61.20	60.86	-	-	-	-	-	-	-	-0.34
Coal Transformation	-0.91 e	-	-	-	-	-	-	-	-	-	-0.91
Liquefaction Plants	-	-	-	-	-	-	-	-	-	-	-
Other Transformation	-	0.07	-0.07	-	-	-	-	-	-	-	-0.00
Own Use	-0.27	-	-4.37	-	-	-	-0.00	-0.00	-1.66	..	-6.32
Distribution Losses	-0.03	-	-	-0.16	-	-	-	-	-2.07	..	-2.26
TFC	**1.61**	**0.01**	**61.46**	**16.85**	**-**	**-**	**0.06**	**3.68**	**19.84**	**-**	**103.50**
INDUSTRY SECTOR	**1.44**	**0.01**	**5.71**	**12.34**	**-**	**-**	**0.00**	**1.36**	**8.73**	**-**	**29.60**
Iron and Steel	1.00 e	-	0.44	1.54	-	-	-	0.00	1.48	..	4.47
Chemical and Petrochem.	0.26	0.01	0.66	2.36	-	-	-	0.01	1.13	..	4.44
Non-Ferrous Metals	0.00	-	0.12	0.41	-	-	0.00	-	1.00	..	1.52
Non-Metallic Minerals	0.09	-	2.45	3.09	-	-	0.00	0.13	1.05	..	6.80
Transport Equipment	-	-	0.16	0.50	-	-	0.00	-	0.37	..	1.03
Machinery	0.01	-	0.24	0.56	-	-	0.00	0.00	0.60	..	1.41
Mining and Quarrying	-	-	0.16	0.04	-	-	-	-	0.13	..	0.33
Food and Tobacco	0.03	-	0.59	1.27	-	-	0.00	0.27	0.92	..	3.08
Paper, Pulp and Printing	-	-	0.21	0.96	-	-	-	0.46	0.66	..	2.29
Wood and Wood Products	-	-	0.04	0.25	-	-	-	0.36	0.21	..	0.86
Construction	-	-	0.15	0.07	-	-	0.00	0.00	0.19	..	0.43
Textile and Leather	-	-	0.18	0.44	-	-	0.00	0.01	0.38	..	1.00
Non-specified	0.06	-	0.31	0.86	-	-	-	0.11	0.60	..	1.94
TRANSPORT SECTOR	**-**	**-**	**38.43**	**-**	**-**	**-**	**-**	**0.23**	**0.45**	**-**	**39.11**
International Aviation	-	-	3.20	-	-	-	-	-	-	-	3.20
Domestic Aviation	-	-	1.99	-	-	-	-	-	-	-	1.99
Road	-	-	30.94	-	-	-	-	0.23 e	-	-	31.17
Rail	-	-	0.66	-	-	-	-	-	0.29	-	0.96
Pipeline Transport	-	-	-	-	-	-	-	-	-	-	-
Domestic Navigation	-	-	1.63	-	-	-	-	-	-	-	1.63
Non-specified	-	-	-	-	-	-	-	-	0.16	-	0.16
OTHER SECTORS	**0.17**	**-**	**8.97**	**4.06**	**-**	**-**	**0.06**	**2.10**	**10.66**	**-**	**26.01**
Residential	0.14	-	4.47	3.03	-	-	0.04	2.02	4.99	..	14.68
Comm. and Publ. Services	-	-	2.16	0.32	-	-	0.02	0.06	5.22	..	7.77
Agriculture/Forestry	-	-	2.34	0.56	-	-	0.01	0.01	0.45	..	3.37
Fishing	-	-	-	-	-	-	-	-	-	-	-
Non-specified	0.03	-	-	0.15	-	-	0.00	0.01	-	..	0.19
NON-ENERGY USE	**-**	**-**	**8.34**	**0.44**	**-**	**-**	**-**	**-**	**-**	**-**	**8.78**
in Industry/Transf./Energy	-	-	7.97	0.44	-	-	-	-	-	-	8.41
of which: Feedstocks	-	-	*5.03*	*0.44*	-	-	-	-	-	-	*5.47*
in Transport	-	-	0.35	-	-	-	-	-	-	-	0.35
in Other Sectors	-	-	0.02	-	-	-	-	-	-	-	0.02
Electricity Generated - TWh	***80.32***	**-**	***23.84***	***55.46***	***63.61***	***31.55***	***18.63***	***3.71***	**-**	**-**	***277.12***
Electricity Plants	*79.79 e*	-	*15.62*	*31.63*	*63.61*	*31.55*	*15.76*	*2.80*	-	-	*240.75*
CHP plants	*0.54*	-	*8.22*	*23.84*	-	-	*2.88*	*0.91*	-	-	*36.38*
Heat Generated - PJ	**-**	**-**	**-**	**-**	**-**	**-**	**-**	**..**	**-**	**-**	**-**
CHP plants	-	-	-	-	-	-	-	..	-	-	-
Heat Plants	-	-	-	-	-	-	-	-	-	-	-

Spain / Espagne : 2005

Million tonnes of oil equivalent / *Million de tonnes d'équivalent pétrole*

SUPPLY AND CONSUMPTION / ***APPROVISIONNEMENT ET DEMANDE***	Coal / *Charbon*	Crude Oil / *Pétrole brut*	Petroleum Products / *Produits pétroliers*	Gas / *Gaz*	Nuclear / *Nucléaire*	Hydro / *Hydro*	Geotherm. Solar etc. / *Géotherm. solaire etc.*	Combust. Renew. & Waste / *Comb. ren. & déchets*	Electricity / *Electricité*	Heat / *Chaleur*	Total / *Total*
Production	6.26	0.17	-	0.14	15.00	1.68	1.90 e	5.13	-	-	30.28
Imports	14.84	61.38	27.26	30.24	-	-	-	-	0.88	..	134.60
Exports	-0.44	-	-8.49	-	-	-	-	-	-0.99	..	-9.92
Intl. Marine Bunkers	-	-	-7.89	-	-	-	-	-	-	-	-7.89
Stock Changes	-0.17	-0.10	-1.06	-0.55	-	-	-	-	-	-	-1.88
TPES	**20.49**	**61.46**	**9.83**	**29.84**	**15.00**	**1.68**	**1.90** e	**5.13**	**-0.12**	**-**	**145.20**
Transfers	-	0.53	-0.59	-	-	-	-	-	-	-	-0.06
Statistical Differences	0.26	0.00	0.72	-0.72	-	-	-	-	-	-	0.25
Electricity Plants	-17.89 e	-	-4.41	-7.93	-15.00	-1.68	-1.83 e	-1.07	21.67	-	-28.15
CHP Plants	-0.07 e	-	-0.86	-2.86	-	-	-	-0.32	3.32	..	-0.79
Heat Plants	-	-	-	-	-	-	-	-	-	-	-
Gas Works	-	-	-0.06	0.04	-	-	-	-	-	-	-0.02
Petroleum Refineries	-	-62.04	61.76	-	-	-	-	-	-	-	-0.29
Coal Transformation	-0.85 e	-	-	-	-	-	-	-	-	-	-0.85
Liquefaction Plants	-	-	-	-	-	-	-	-	-	-	-
Other Transformation	-	0.07	-0.07	-	-	-	-	-	-	-	-0.00
Own Use	-0.45	-	-4.39	-	-	-	-0.00	-0.00	-1.81 e	..	-6.66
Distribution Losses	-0.02	-	-	-0.19	-	-	-	-	-2.23	..	-2.44
TFC	**1.45**	**0.01**	**61.92**	**18.17**	**-**	**-**	**0.07**	**3.74**	**20.83**	**-**	**106.19**
INDUSTRY SECTOR	**1.26**	**0.01**	**5.48**	**13.28**	**-**	**-**	**0.00**	**1.37**	**9.03**	**-**	**30.44**
Iron and Steel	0.86 e	-	0.42	1.12	-	-	-	0.00	1.58 e	..	3.97
Chemical and Petrochem.	0.16	0.01	0.61	2.74	-	-	-	0.01	1.15 e	..	4.68
Non-Ferrous Metals	0.06	-	0.09	0.15	-	-	0.00	-	0.88 e	..	1.18
Non-Metallic Minerals	0.10	-	2.39	3.70	-	-	0.00	0.13	1.14 e	..	7.46
Transport Equipment	-	-	0.15	0.31	-	-	0.00	-	0.38 e	..	0.84
Machinery	0.01	-	0.22	0.52	-	-	0.00	0.00	0.63 e	..	1.38
Mining and Quarrying	-	-	0.15	0.18	-	-	-	-	0.13 e	..	0.47
Food and Tobacco	0.02	-	0.56	1.05	-	-	0.00	0.28	0.99 e	..	2.89
Paper, Pulp and Printing	-	-	0.19	1.16	-	-	-	0.46	0.68 e	..	2.50
Wood and Wood Products	-	-	0.06	0.14	-	-	-	0.36	0.22 e	..	0.79
Construction	-	-	0.19	0.04	-	-	0.00	0.00	0.23 e	..	0.47
Textile and Leather	-	-	0.21	0.40	-	-	0.00	0.01	0.37 e	..	0.99
Non-specified	0.06	-	0.24	1.77	-	-	0.00	0.11	0.65 e	..	2.82
TRANSPORT SECTOR	**-**	**-**	**39.67**	**-**	**-**	**-**	**-**	**0.26**	**0.46**	**-**	**40.39**
International Aviation	-	-	3.21	-	-	-	-	-	-	-	3.21
Domestic Aviation	-	-	2.32	-	-	-	-	-	-	-	2.32
Road	-	-	31.85	-	-	-	-	0.26	-	-	32.11
Rail	-	-	0.72	-	-	-	-	-	0.31 e	..	1.04
Pipeline Transport	-	-	-	-	-	-	-	-	-	..	-
Domestic Navigation	-	-	1.57	-	-	-	-	-	-	-	1.57
Non-specified	-	-	-	-	-	-	-	-	0.15 e	..	0.15
OTHER SECTORS	**0.19**	**-**	**8.81**	**4.41**	**-**	**-**	**0.07**	**2.11**	**11.34**	**-**	**26.92**
Residential	0.16	-	4.36	3.19	-	-	0.04	2.02	5.38 e	..	15.15
Comm. and Publ. Services	-	-	2.17	0.71	-	-	0.02	0.06	5.49 e	..	8.44
Agriculture/Forestry	-	-	2.28	0.38	-	-	0.01	0.02	0.46 e	..	3.14
Fishing	-	-	-	-	-	-	-	-	-	-	-
Non-specified	0.03	-	-	0.14	-	-	0.00	0.01	0.01 e	..	0.19
NON-ENERGY USE	**-**	**-**	**7.96**	**0.48**	**-**	**-**	**-**	**-**	**-**	**-**	**8.44**
in Industry/Transf./Energy	-	-	7.58	0.48	-	-	-	-	-	-	8.06
of which: Feedstocks	-	-	*4.16*	*0.48*	-	-	-	-	-	-	*4.64*
in Transport	-	-	0.36	-	-	-	-	-	-	-	0.36
in Other Sectors	-	-	0.02	-	-	-	-	-	-	-	0.02
Electricity Generated - TWh	*80.77*	-	*24.42*	*79.01*	*57.54*	*19.55*	*26.24* e	*3.08*	-	-	*290.61*
Electricity Plants	*80.23* e	-	*17.45*	*53.56*	*57.54*	*19.55*	*21.31* e	*2.32*	-	-	*251.97*
CHP plants	*0.54*	-	*6.97*	*25.45*	-	-	*4.93*	*0.76*	-	-	*38.64*
Heat Generated - PJ	-	-	-	-	-	-	-	..	-	-	-
CHP plants	-	-	-	-	-	-	-	..	-	-	-
Heat Plants	-	-	-	-	-	-	-	-	-	-	-

Sweden / Suède
Key Indicators
Indicateurs principaux

	1960	1970	1973	1980	1990	1995
Energy Production (Mtoe)	5.48	6.49	9.25	16.13	29.75	31.93
Net Imports (Mtoe)	16.02	32.96	30.70	27.77	18.29	19.33
Total Primary Energy Supply (Mtoe)	20.54	37.95	39.32	40.75	47.57	50.92
Net Oil Imports (Mtoe)	13.57	30.80	28.96	26.04	15.29	16.07
Oil Supply (Mtoe)	12.56	29.19	28.39	22.90	14.67	15.82
Electricity Consumption (TWh)*	29.96	58.84	71.16	88.95	135.54	136.60
GDP (billion 2000 US$ using exch. rates)	84.09 e	132.35	142.08	160.63	199.58	206.42
GDP (billion 2000 US$ using PPPs)	83.81 e	131.90	141.60	160.09	198.91	205.72
Population (millions)	7.48 e	8.04	8.14	8.31	8.56	8.83
Industrial Production Index (2000=100)	25.90	47.20	51.90	51.70	69.10	83.40
Energy Production/TPES	0.2670	0.1711	0.2353	0.3959	0.6255	0.6271
Net Oil Imports/GDP (toe per thousand 2000 US$)	0.1613 e	0.2327	0.2038	0.1621	0.0766	0.0779
TPES/GDP (toe per thousand 2000 US$)	0.2442 e	0.2867	0.2768	0.2537	0.2383	0.2467
TPES/GDP (toe per thousand 2000 US$ PPP)	0.2450 e	0.2877	0.2777	0.2546	0.2391	0.2475
TPES/Population (toe per capita)	2.7455 e	4.7178	4.8327	4.9042	5.5575	5.7690
Oil Supply/GDP (toe per thousand 2000 US$)	0.1493 e	0.2206	0.1998	0.1426	0.0735	0.0766
Oil Supply/Population (toe per capita)	1.6788 e	3.6296	3.4888	2.7562	1.7141	1.7917
Elect. Cons./GDP (kWh per 2000 US$)	0.3562 e	0.4446	0.5008	0.5538	0.6791	0.6617
Elect. Cons./Population (kWh per capita)	4 005 e	7 316	8 745	10 704	15 836	15 475
Industry Cons.**/Industrial Production (2000=100)	237.97	198.27	194.37	170.38	130.25	120.03
Industry Oil Cons.**/Industrial Production (2000=100)	362.56	364.59	337.30	253.17	124.63	133.49

	2000	2001	2002	2003	2004	2005
Energy Production (Mtoe)	30.59	33.99	31.94	31.04	34.46	34.78
Net Imports (Mtoe)	19.22	19.18	19.84	22.72	20.22	20.11
Total Primary Energy Supply (Mtoe)	48.21	51.21	52.30	51.10	53.18	52.17
Net Oil Imports (Mtoe)	15.70	16.55	16.21	18.24	17.01	17.44
Oil Supply (Mtoe)	14.23	14.49	16.52	15.75	15.45	14.87
Electricity Consumption (TWh)*	139.13	142.52	140.21	137.60 e	138.69	139.34
GDP (billion 2000 US$ using exch. rates)	242.00	244.59	249.47	253.70	264.17	271.84
GDP (billion 2000 US$ using PPPs)	241.19	243.76	248.63	252.84	263.27	270.92
Population (millions)	8.87	8.90	8.93	8.96	8.99	9.03
Industrial Production Index (2000=100)	100.00	98.90	98.80	100.20	105.40	107.30
Energy Production/TPES	0.6345	0.6637	0.6106	0.6073	0.6480	0.6666
Net Oil Imports/GDP (toe per thousand 2000 US$)	0.0649	0.0677	0.0650	0.0719	0.0644	0.0642
TPES/GDP (toe per thousand 2000 US$)	0.1992	0.2094	0.2097	0.2014	0.2013	0.1919
TPES/GDP (toe per thousand 2000 US$ PPP)	0.1999	0.2101	0.2104	0.2021	0.2020	0.1926
TPES/Population (toe per capita)	5.4343	5.7561	5.8604	5.7049	5.9129	5.7779
Oil Supply/GDP (toe per thousand 2000 US$)	0.0588	0.0592	0.0662	0.0621	0.0585	0.0547
Oil Supply/Population (toe per capita)	1.6036	1.6288	1.8511	1.7580	1.7180	1.6463
Elect. Cons./GDP (kWh per 2000 US$)	0.5749	0.5827	0.5620	0.5424 e	0.5250	0.5126
Elect. Cons./Population (kWh per capita)	15 682	16 021	15 709	15 361 e	15 420	15 430
Industry Cons.**/Industrial Production (2000=100)	100.00	96.27	99.12	92.60	88.45	84.76
Industry Oil Cons.**/Industrial Production (2000=100)	100.00	99.60	106.15	90.21	85.17	75.67

* Electricity consumption equals domestic supply less distribution losses.
La consommation d'électricité représente l'approvisionnement intérieur diminué des pertes de distribution.

** Includes non-energy use in industry/transformation/energy sectors.
Comprend l'usage non-énergétique dans les secteurs de l'industrie/transformation/énergie.

Sweden / Suède

Figure 1. TPES* in 1973

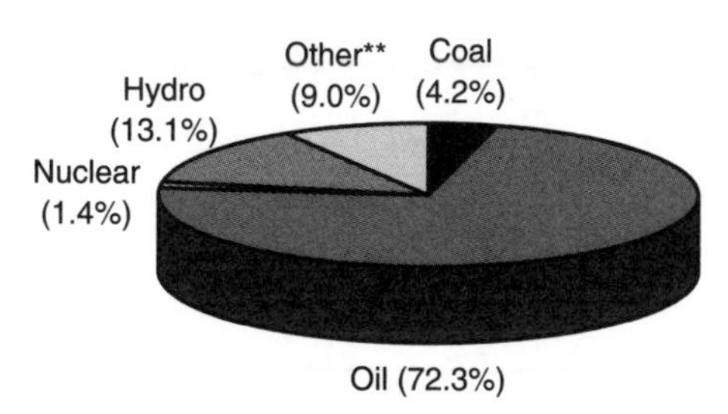

Figure 2. TPES* in 2005

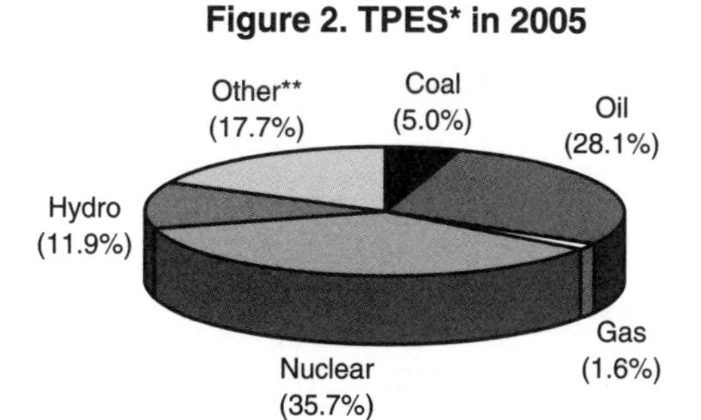

Figure 3. Final Consumption by Sector***

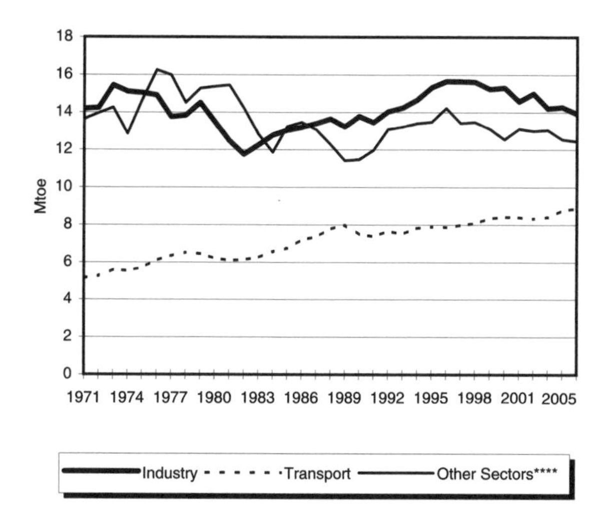

Figure 4. Breakdown of Sectorial Final Consumption by Source in 1973 and 2005***

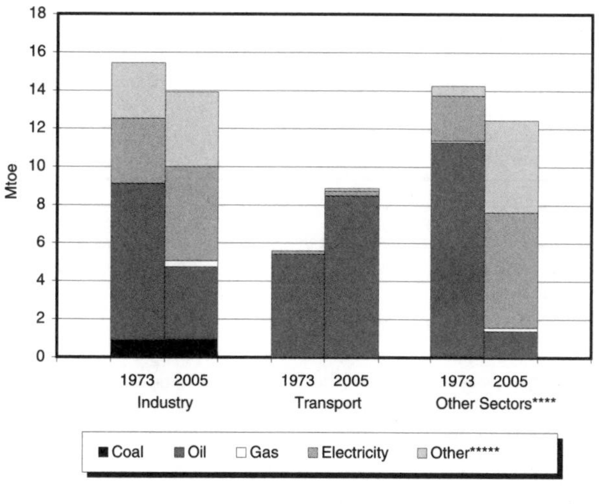

Figure 5. Electricity Generation by Fuel

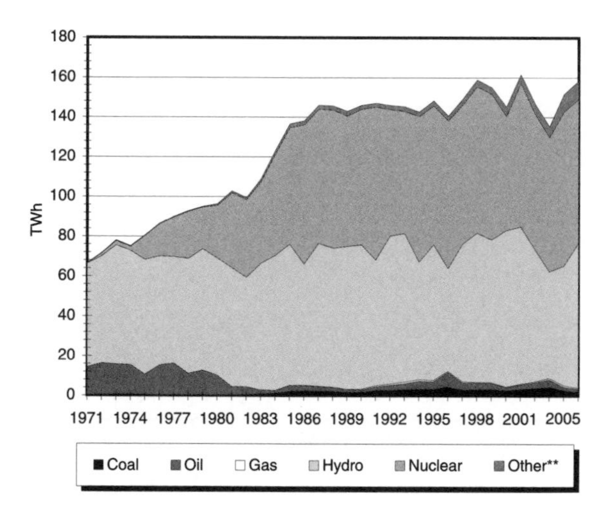

Figure 6. Electricity Consumption/GDP, TPES/GDP and Energy Production/TPES

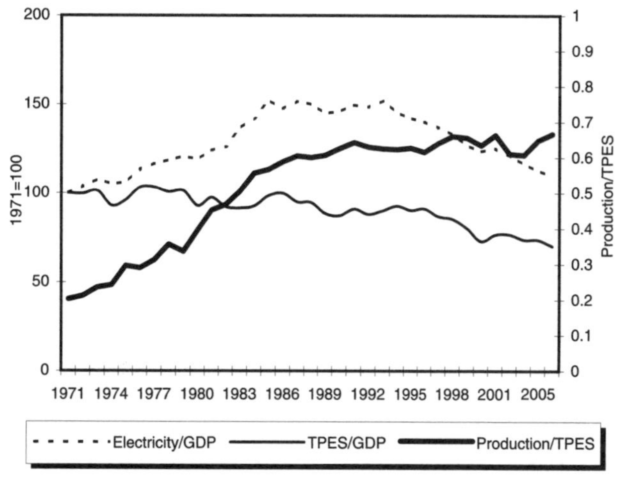

* Excluding electricity trade.

** Includes geothermal, solar, wind, combustible renewables & waste, etc.

*** Includes non-energy use.

**** Includes residential, commercial and public services, agriculture/forestry, fishing and non-specified.

***** Includes comb. renewables & waste, direct use of geothermal/solar thermal and heat produced in CHP/heat plants.

Sweden / Suède : 2004

Million tonnes of oil equivalent / *Million de tonnes d'équivalent pétrole*

SUPPLY AND CONSUMPTION / *APPROVISIONNEMENT ET DEMANDE*	Coal / *Charbon*	Crude Oil / *Pétrole brut*	Petroleum Products / *Produits pétroliers*	Gas / *Gaz*	Nuclear / *Nucléaire*	Hydro / *Hydro*	Geotherm. Solar etc. / *Géotherm. solaire etc.*	Combust. Renew. & Waste / *Comb. ren. & déchets*	Electricity / *Electricité*	Heat / *Chaleur*	Total / *Total*
Production	0.38	-	-	-	20.19	5.17	0.08	8.32 e	-	0.32	34.46
Imports	2.53	21.13	7.10	0.88	-	-	-	-	1.35	-	33.00
Exports	-0.03	-0.27	-10.95	-	-	-	-	-	-1.53	-	-12.78
Intl. Marine Bunkers	-	-	-1.89	-	-	-	-	-	-	-	-1.89
Stock Changes	0.06	0.02	0.31	-	-	-	-	-	-	-	0.39
TPES	**2.94**	**20.88**	**-5.43**	**0.88**	**20.19**	**5.17**	**0.08**	**8.32**	**-0.18**	**0.32**	**53.18**
Transfers	-	0.40	-0.37	-	-	-	-	-	-	-	0.04
Statistical Differences	0.07	0.25	0.72	-0.12	-	-	-	-	-	0.02	0.93
Electricity Plants	-0.06	-	-0.01	-	-20.19	-5.17	-0.07	-	11.93	-	-13.57
CHP Plants	-0.91	-	-0.45	-0.25	-	-	-	-2.86 e	1.11	2.56	-0.79
Heat Plants	-0.11	-	-0.15	-0.03	-	-	-	-0.96 e	-0.20	1.37	-0.07
Gas Works	-	-	-0.05	0.04	-	-	-	-	-	-	-0.01
Petroleum Refineries	-	-21.53	20.75	-	-	-	-	-	-	-	-0.78
Coal Transformation	-0.80 e	-	-0.00	-	-	-	-	-	-	-	-0.81
Liquefaction Plants	-	-	-	-	-	-	-	-	-	-	-
Other Transformation	-	-	-	-	-	-	-	-	-	-	-
Own Use	-0.10	-	-0.73	-0.01	-	-	-	-	-0.51	-0.00	-1.35
Distribution Losses	-0.04	-	-	-0.00	-	-	-	-	-0.94	-0.19	-1.17
TFC	**0.99**	**-**	**14.28**	**0.52**	**-**	**-**	**0.00**	**4.49**	**11.21**	**4.09**	**35.59**
INDUSTRY SECTOR	**0.98**	**-**	**2.23**	**0.32**	**-**	**-**	**-**	**3.42**	**4.92**	**0.41**	**12.27**
Iron and Steel	0.62 e	-	0.36	0.03	-	-	-	-	0.43	-	1.44
Chemical and Petrochem.	0.01	-	0.56	0.08	-	-	-	0.02	0.58	-	1.25
Non-Ferrous Metals	0.04	-	0.02	0.01	-	-	-	-	0.26	-	0.32
Non-Metallic Minerals	0.18	-	0.15	0.04	-	-	-	-	0.10	-	0.47
Transport Equipment	0.01	-	0.07	0.01	-	-	-	-	0.21	-	0.30
Machinery	-	-	0.12	0.01	-	-	-	-	0.16	-	0.29
Mining and Quarrying	0.09	-	0.06	-	-	-	-	-	0.23	-	0.37
Food and Tobacco	0.00	-	0.17	0.10	-	-	-	-	0.22	-	0.48
Paper, Pulp and Printing	0.02	-	0.54	0.03	-	-	-	2.95	1.98	-	5.52
Wood and Wood Products	-	-	0.04	-	-	-	-	0.42	0.20	-	0.65
Construction	-	-	-	0.00	-	-	-	-	0.07	-	0.07
Textile and Leather	-	-	0.03	0.00	-	-	-	-	0.03	-	0.06
Non-specified	0.01	-	0.12	0.01	-	-	-	0.04	0.46	0.41	1.05
TRANSPORT SECTOR	**-**	**-**	**8.15**	**0.02**	**-**	**-**	**-**	**0.14**	**0.26**	**-**	**8.56**
International Aviation	-	-	0.65	-	-	-	-	-	-	-	0.65
Domestic Aviation	-	-	0.23	-	-	-	-	-	-	-	0.23
Road	-	-	7.10	0.02	-	-	-	0.14	-	-	7.26
Rail	-	-	0.02	-	-	-	-	-	0.26	-	0.28
Pipeline Transport	-	-	-	-	-	-	-	-	-	-	-
Domestic Navigation	-	-	0.15	-	-	-	-	-	-	-	0.15
Non-specified	-	-	-	-	-	-	-	-	-	-	-
OTHER SECTORS	**-**	**-**	**1.70**	**0.18**	**-**	**-**	**0.00**	**0.93**	**6.04**	**3.68**	**12.54**
Residential	-	-	0.51	0.07	-	-	0.00	0.57	3.56	2.44	7.15
Comm. and Publ. Services	-	-	0.81	0.09	-	-	-	0.05	2.37	1.24	4.56
Agriculture/Forestry	-	-	0.32	0.02	-	-	-	0.30	0.11	0.01	0.76
Fishing	-	-	0.03	-	-	-	-	-	-	-	0.03
Non-specified	-	-	0.03	-	-	-	-	-	-	-	0.03
NON-ENERGY USE	**0.02**	**-**	**2.20**	**-**	**-**	**-**	**-**	**-**	**-**	**-**	**2.21**
in Industry/Transf./Energy	0.02	-	1.98	-	-	-	-	-	-	-	2.00
of which: Feedstocks	-	-	*1.23*	-	-	-	-	-	-	-	*1.23*
in Transport	-	-	0.21	-	-	-	-	-	-	-	0.21
in Other Sectors	-	-	-	-	-	-	-	-	-	-	-
Electricity Generated - TWh	***2.51***	**-**	***1.95***	***0.75***	***77.49***	***60.12***	***0.85***	***8.00***	**-**	**-**	***151.67***
Electricity Plants	*0.23*	-	*0.04*	-	*77.49*	*60.12*	*0.85*	-	-	-	*138.73*
CHP plants	*2.28*	-	*1.91*	*0.75*	-	-	-	*8.00*	-	-	*12.94*
Heat Generated - PJ	***27.07***	**-**	***12.76***	***8.13***	**-**	**-**	**-**	***105.11***	***1.29***	***24.03***	***178.39***
CHP plants	*22.74*	-	*7.85*	*6.84*	-	-	-	*69.93*	*0.58*	*5.97*	*113.90*
Heat Plants	*4.34*	-	*4.91*	*1.29*	-	-	-	*35.18*	*0.71*	*18.06*	*64.49*

Sweden / Suède : 2005

Million tonnes of oil equivalent / *Million de tonnes d'équivalent pétrole*

SUPPLY AND CONSUMPTION ***APPROVISIONNEMENT ET DEMANDE***	Coal *Charbon*	Crude Oil *Pétrole brut*	Petroleum Products *Produits pétroliers*	Gas *Gaz*	Nuclear *Nucléaire*	Hydro *Hydro*	Geotherm. Solar etc. *Géotherm. solaire etc.*	Combust. Renew. & Waste *Comb. ren. & déchets*	Electricity *Electricité*	Heat *Chaleur*	Total *Total*
Production	0.30	-	-	-	18.86	6.26	0.09	8.98	-	0.29	34.78
Imports	2.48	20.68	7.44	0.84	-	-	-	-	1.25	-	32.70
Exports	-0.03	-0.56	-10.12	-	-	-	-	-	-1.89	-	-12.60
Intl. Marine Bunkers	-	-	-1.93	-	-	-	-	-	-	-	-1.93
Stock Changes	-0.14	-0.18	-0.47	-	-	-	-	-	-	-	-0.79
TPES	**2.62**	**19.94**	**-5.07**	**0.84**	**18.86**	**6.26**	**0.09**	**8.98**	**-0.64**	**0.29**	**52.17**
Transfers	-	0.77	-0.70	-	-	-	-	-	-	-	0.07
Statistical Differences	0.13	0.15	0.48	-0.12	-	-	-	-	-	-	0.64
Electricity Plants	-0.07	-	-0.04	-	-18.86	-6.26	-0.08	-	12.60	-	-12.71
CHP Plants	-0.73	-	-0.28	-0.20	-	-	-	-3.16	1.02	2.56	-0.78
Heat Plants	-0.08	-	-0.13	-0.03	-	-	-	-1.10	-0.19	1.47	-0.06
Gas Works	-	-	-0.04	0.04	-	-	-	-	-	-	-0.01
Petroleum Refineries	-	-20.85	20.17	-	-	-	-	-	-	-	-0.68
Coal Transformation	-0.84 e	-	-0.03	-	-	-	-	-	-	-	-0.87
Liquefaction Plants	-	-	-	-	-	-	-	-	-	-	-
Other Transformation	-	-	-	-	-	-	-	-	-	-	-
Own Use	-0.10	-	-0.71	-0.00	-	-	-	-	-0.55	-	-1.36
Distribution Losses	-0.03	-	-	-0.00	-	-	-	-	-1.01	-0.15	-1.19
TFC	**0.91**	**-**	**13.65**	**0.53**	**-**	**-**	**0.01**	**4.72**	**11.24**	**4.17**	**35.23**
INDUSTRY SECTOR	**0.90**	**-**	**1.85**	**0.32**	**-**	**-**	**-**	**3.55**	**4.95**	**0.38**	**11.95**
Iron and Steel	0.55 e	-	0.34	0.03	-	-	-	-	0.46	-	1.37
Chemical and Petrochem.	0.01	-	0.24	0.09	-	-	-	0.02	0.57	-	0.92
Non-Ferrous Metals	0.03	-	0.02	0.01	-	-	-	-	0.28	-	0.34
Non-Metallic Minerals	0.17	-	0.16	0.02	-	-	-	-	0.09	-	0.44
Transport Equipment	0.01	-	0.06	0.01	-	-	-	-	0.22	-	0.31
Machinery	-	-	0.12	0.01	-	-	-	-	0.15	-	0.28
Mining and Quarrying	0.09	-	0.06	-	-	-	-	-	0.22	-	0.36
Food and Tobacco	0.00	-	0.13	0.12	-	-	-	-	0.21	-	0.46
Paper, Pulp and Printing	0.02	-	0.54	0.03	-	-	-	3.07	1.99	-	5.65
Wood and Wood Products	-	-	0.03	-	-	-	-	0.43	0.19	-	0.65
Construction	-	-	-	0.00	-	-	-	-	0.07	-	0.07
Textile and Leather	-	-	0.02	0.00	-	-	-	-	0.02	-	0.05
Non-specified	0.02	-	0.13	0.01	-	-	-	0.03	0.48	0.38	1.05
TRANSPORT SECTOR	**-**	**-**	**8.27**	**0.02**	**-**	**-**	**-**	**0.15**	**0.24**	**-**	**8.68**
International Aviation	-	-	0.65	-	-	-	-	-	-	-	0.65
Domestic Aviation	-	-	0.23	-	-	-	-	-	-	-	0.23
Road	-	-	7.24	0.02	-	-	-	0.15	-	-	7.41
Rail	-	-	0.00	-	-	-	-	-	0.24	-	0.25
Pipeline Transport	-	-	-	-	-	-	-	-	-	-	-
Domestic Navigation	-	-	0.14	-	-	-	-	-	-	-	0.14
Non-specified	-	-	-	-	-	-	-	-	-	-	-
OTHER SECTORS	**-**	**-**	**1.38**	**0.19**	**-**	**-**	**0.01**	**1.02**	**6.05**	**3.79**	**12.43**
Residential	-	-	0.42	0.07	-	-	0.01	0.63	3.67	2.51	7.31
Comm. and Publ. Services	-	-	0.63	0.10	-	-	-	0.06	2.25	1.27	4.30
Agriculture/Forestry	-	-	0.26	0.02	-	-	-	0.33	0.13	0.01	0.75
Fishing	-	-	0.05	-	-	-	-	-	-	-	0.05
Non-specified	-	-	0.02	-	-	-	-	-	-	-	0.02
NON-ENERGY USE	**0.01**	**-**	**2.15**	**-**	**-**	**-**	**-**	**-**	**-**	**-**	**2.16**
in Industry/Transf./Energy	0.01	-	1.96	-	-	-	-	-	-	-	1.97
of which: Feedstocks	-	-	*1.29*	-	-	-	-	-	-	-	*1.29*
in Transport	-	-	0.19	-	-	-	-	-	-	-	0.19
in Other Sectors	-	-	-	-	-	-	-	-	-	-	-
Electricity Generated - TWh	***1.93***	**-**	***1.38***	***0.59***	***72.38***	***72.80***	***0.94***	***8.36***	**-**	**-**	***158.36***
Electricity Plants	*0.23*	-	*0.18*	-	*72.38*	*72.80*	*0.94*	-	-	-	*146.53*
CHP plants	*1.69*	-	*1.20*	*0.59*	-	-	-	*8.36*	-	-	*11.84*
Heat Generated - PJ	***21.57***	**-**	***10.46***	***6.70***	**-**	**-**	**-**	***118.88***	***1.16***	***22.30***	***181.07***
CHP plants	*18.82*	-	*5.52*	*5.52*	-	-	-	*77.42*	*0.44*	*4.86*	*112.59*
Heat Plants	*2.75*	-	*4.93*	*1.18*	-	-	-	*41.46*	*0.72*	*17.44*	*68.48*

Switzerland / Suisse
Key Indicators
Indicateurs principaux

	1960	1970	1973	1980	1990	1995
Energy Production (Mtoe)	2.11	3.36	4.28	7.03	9.72	10.77
Net Imports (Mtoe)	5.78	13.52	15.23	14.22	15.18	13.91
Total Primary Energy Supply (Mtoe)	7.59	16.48	19.72	20.86	24.99	24.99
Net Oil Imports (Mtoe)	4.25	13.51	15.15	13.55	13.38	12.17
Oil Supply (Mtoe)	3.95	13.03	15.26	13.34	13.46	12.45
Electricity Consumption (TWh)*	16.39	26.62	31.60	37.87	50.39	52.09
GDP (billion 2000 US$ using exch. rates)	99.62 e	157.46	174.28	178.23	221.69	222.59
GDP (billion 2000 US$ using PPPs)	88.66 e	140.13	155.10	158.61	197.30	198.10
Population (millions)	5.40 e	6.27	6.44	6.39	6.80	7.08
Industrial Production Index (2000=100)	34.60	58.60	64.30	64.90	79.10	82.20
Energy Production/TPES	0.2780	0.2039	0.2170	0.3370	0.3888	0.4309
Net Oil Imports/GDP (toe per thousand 2000 US$)	0.0426 e	0.0858	0.0870	0.0760	0.0604	0.0547
TPES/GDP (toe per thousand 2000 US$)	0.0762 e	0.1047	0.1132	0.1170	0.1127	0.1123
TPES/GDP (toe per thousand 2000 US$ PPP)	0.0857 e	0.1176	0.1272	0.1315	0.1267	0.1261
TPES/Population (toe per capita)	1.4060 e	2.6299	3.0621	3.2672	3.6774	3.5290
Oil Supply/GDP (toe per thousand 2000 US$)	0.0396 e	0.0828	0.0876	0.0748	0.0607	0.0560
Oil Supply/Population (toe per capita)	0.7303 e	2.0795	2.3694	2.0886	1.9799	1.7589
Elect. Cons./GDP (kWh per 2000 US$)	0.1645 e	0.1690	0.1813	0.2125	0.2273	0.2340
Elect. Cons./Population (kWh per capita)	3 033 e	4 247	4 906	5 931	7 415	7 357
Industry Cons.**/Industrial Production (2000=100)	170.94	171.61	166.67	156.74	111.16	112.69
Industry Oil Cons.**/Industrial Production (2000=100)	273.80	402.83	399.15	296.56	113.05	107.61

	2000	2001	2002	2003	2004	2005
Energy Production (Mtoe)	11.47	12.02	11.58	11.79	11.82	10.88
Net Imports (Mtoe)	14.28	15.48	15.24	14.94	15.35	16.43
Total Primary Energy Supply (Mtoe)	26.16	27.68	26.77	26.87	27.13	27.15
Net Oil Imports (Mtoe)	12.26	13.72	13.04	12.50	12.56	13.00
Oil Supply (Mtoe)	12.73	13.87	12.96	12.58	12.53	12.79
Electricity Consumption (TWh)*	56.37	58.09	58.29	60.15	60.64	61.77
GDP (billion 2000 US$ using exch. rates)	246.04	248.61	249.37	248.95	254.66	259.57
GDP (billion 2000 US$ using PPPs)	218.97	221.25	221.92	221.55	226.63	231.00
Population (millions)	7.21	7.29	7.34	7.41	7.45	7.50
Industrial Production Index (2000=100)	100.00	99.30	94.20	94.50	98.40	101.00
Energy Production/TPES	0.4384	0.4345	0.4324	0.4389	0.4357	0.4008
Net Oil Imports/GDP (toe per thousand 2000 US$)	0.0498	0.0552	0.0523	0.0502	0.0493	0.0501
TPES/GDP (toe per thousand 2000 US$)	0.1063	0.1113	0.1074	0.1079	0.1066	0.1046
TPES/GDP (toe per thousand 2000 US$ PPP)	0.1195	0.1251	0.1206	0.1213	0.1197	0.1175
TPES/Population (toe per capita)	3.6287	3.7990	3.6462	3.6287	3.6402	3.6199
Oil Supply/GDP (toe per thousand 2000 US$)	0.0517	0.0558	0.0520	0.0505	0.0492	0.0493
Oil Supply/Population (toe per capita)	1.7655	1.9038	1.7651	1.6985	1.6810	1.7048
Elect. Cons./GDP (kWh per 2000 US$)	0.2291	0.2337	0.2337	0.2416	0.2381	0.2380
Elect. Cons./Population (kWh per capita)	7 820	7 974	7 938	8 123	8 135	8 235
Industry Cons.**/Industrial Production (2000=100)	100.00	104.28	105.99	106.66	105.03	104.13
Industry Oil Cons.**/Industrial Production (2000=100)	100.00	106.30	104.58	103.64	101.66	97.00

* Electricity consumption equals domestic supply less distribution losses.
La consommation d'électricité représente l'approvisionnement intérieur diminué des pertes de distribution.

** Includes non-energy use in industry/transformation/energy sectors.
Comprend l'usage non-énergétique dans les secteurs de l'industrie/transformation/énergie.

Switzerland / Suisse

Figure 1. TPES* in 1973

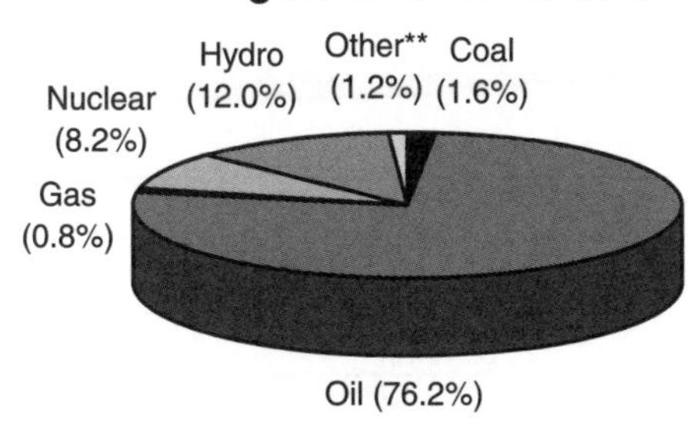

Figure 2. TPES* in 2005

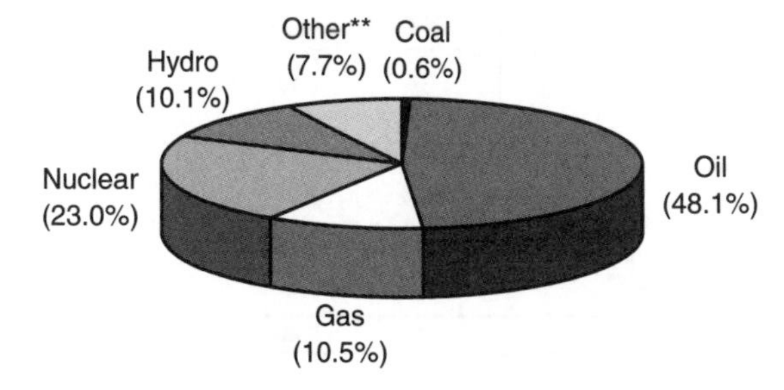

Figure 3. Final Consumption by Sector***

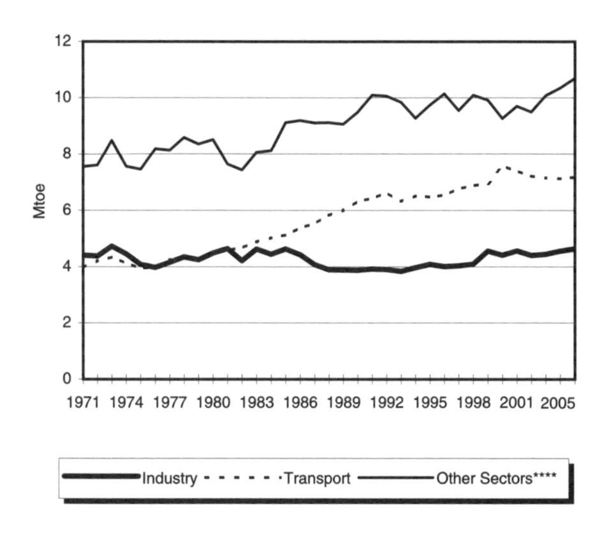

Figure 4. Breakdown of Sectorial Final Consumption by Source in 1973 and 2005***

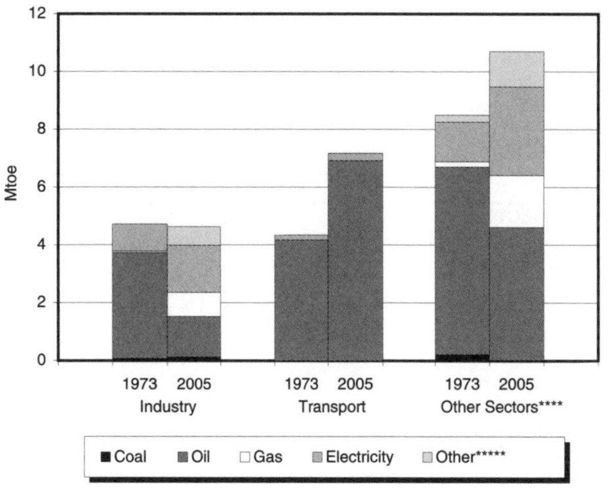

Figure 5. Electricity Generation by Fuel

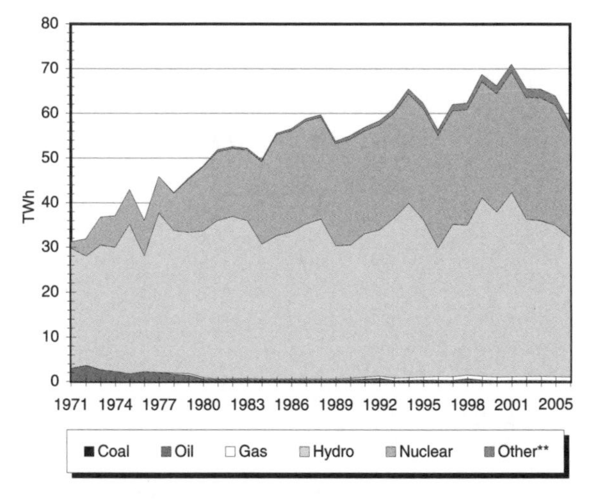

Figure 6. Electricity Consumption/GDP, TPES/GDP and Energy Production/TPES

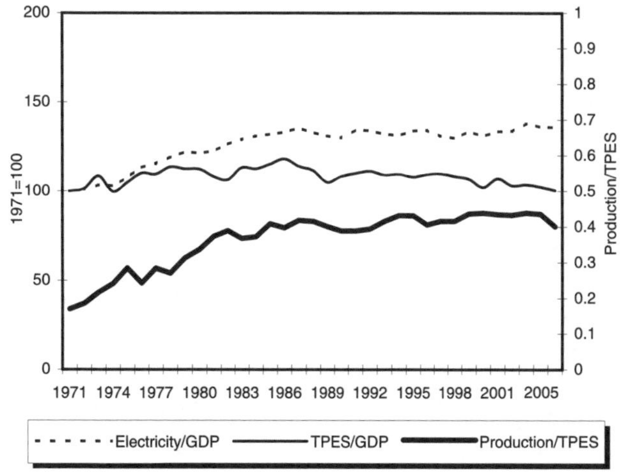

* Excluding electricity trade.

** Includes geothermal, solar, wind, combustible renewables & waste, etc.

*** Includes non-energy use.

**** Includes residential, commercial and public services, agriculture/forestry, fishing and non-specified.

***** Includes comb. renewables & waste, direct use of geothermal/solar thermal and heat produced in CHP/heat plants.

Switzerland / Suisse : 2004

Million tonnes of oil equivalent / *Million de tonnes d'équivalent pétrole*

SUPPLY AND CONSUMPTION *APPROVISIONNEMENT ET DEMANDE*	Coal *Charbon*	Crude Oil *Pétrole brut*	Petroleum Products *Produits pétroliers*	Gas *Gaz*	Nuclear *Nucléaire*	Hydro *Hydro*	Geotherm. Solar etc. *Géotherm. solaire etc.*	Combust. Renew. & Waste *Comb. ren. & déchets*	Electricity *Electricité*	Heat *Chaleur*	Total *Total*
Production	-	-	-	-	7.05	2.90	0.15	1.72 e	-	-	11.82
Imports	0.13	5.39	7.78	2.71	-	-	-	0.01	2.33	-	18.34
Exports	-	-	-0.60	-	-	-	-	-0.01	-2.39	-	-3.00
Intl. Marine Bunkers	-	-	-0.01	-	-	-	-	-	-	-	-0.01
Stock Changes	-	0.01	-0.04	-	-	-	-	-	-	-	-0.03
TPES	**0.13**	**5.40**	**7.13**	**2.71**	**7.05**	**2.90**	**0.15**	**1.71**	**-0.06**	**-**	**27.13**
Transfers	-	-	-	-	-	-	-	-	-	-	-
Statistical Differences	-	-0.00	0.64	-	-	-	-	-	-	-	0.64
Electricity Plants	-	-	-0.00	-	-7.03	-2.90	-0.00	-0.07	5.24	-	-4.77
CHP Plants	-	-	-0.02	-0.13	-0.03	-	-	-0.47	0.25	0.28	-0.13
Heat Plants	-	-	-	-	-	-	-	-0.01	-	0.12	0.11
Gas Works	-	-	-0.00	0.00	-	-	-	-	-	-	0.00
Petroleum Refineries	-	-5.40	5.43	-	-	-	-	-	-	-	0.03
Coal Transformation	-	-	-	-	-	-	-	-	-	-	-
Liquefaction Plants	-	-	-	-	-	-	-	-	-	-	-
Other Transformation	-	-	-	-	-	-	-	-	-	-	-
Own Use	-	-	-0.34	-	-	-	-	-	-0.24	-	-0.57
Distribution Losses	-	-	-	-0.02	-	-	-	-	-0.37	-0.03	-0.42
TFC	**0.13**	**-**	**12.84**	**2.56**	**-**	**-**	**0.15**	**1.16**	**4.83**	**0.37**	**22.04**
INDUSTRY SECTOR	**0.13**	**-**	**0.89**	**0.81**	**-**	**-**	**0.01**	**0.45**	**1.60**	**0.14**	**4.03**
Iron and Steel	-	-	0.01	0.07	-	-	-	0.00	0.13	-	0.21
Chemical and Petrochem.	-	-	0.10	0.25	-	-	-	0.04	0.29	0.03 e	0.71
Non-Ferrous Metals	-	-	0.00	0.02	-	-	-	0.00	0.04	0.00 e	0.07
Non-Metallic Minerals	0.11	-	0.11	0.01	-	-	-	0.12	0.03	0.00 e	0.39
Transport Equipment	-	-	-	-	-	-	-	-	-	-	-
Machinery	..	-	0.18	0.02	-	-	-	0.00	0.10	0.02 e	0.32
Mining and Quarrying	-	-	-	-	-	-	-	-	-	-	-
Food and Tobacco	..	-	0.13	0.14	-	-	-	0.00	0.16	0.01 e	0.44
Paper, Pulp and Printing	-	-	0.10	0.15	-	-	-	0.11	0.25	0.07 e	0.68
Wood and Wood Products	-	-	-	-	-	-	-	-	-	-	-
Construction	..	-	0.09	0.01	-	-	-	0.07	0.05	-	0.22
Textile and Leather	-	-	0.03	0.02	-	-	-	0.00	0.04	0.00 e	0.09
Non-specified	0.01	-	0.13	0.12	-	-	0.01	0.11	0.52	0.02 e	0.92
TRANSPORT SECTOR	**-**	**-**	**6.84**	**-**	**-**	**-**	**-**	**0.00**	**0.25**	**-**	**7.10**
International Aviation	-	-	1.19	-	-	-	-	-	-	-	1.19
Domestic Aviation	-	-	0.06	-	-	-	-	-	-	-	0.06
Road	-	-	5.57	-	-	-	-	0.00	-	-	5.58
Rail	-	-	0.01	-	-	-	-	-	0.25	-	0.26
Pipeline Transport	-	-	-	-	-	-	-	-	-	-	-
Domestic Navigation	-	-	0.01	-	-	-	-	-	-	-	0.01
Non-specified	-	-	-	-	-	-	-	-	-	-	-
OTHER SECTORS	**0.01**	**-**	**4.54**	**1.75**	**-**	**-**	**0.14**	**0.71**	**2.97**	**0.23**	**10.35**
Residential	0.01	-	3.12	0.99	-	-	0.11	0.25	1.47	0.13	6.08
Comm. and Publ. Services	-	-	1.25	0.55	-	-	0.02	0.43	1.41	0.10	3.76
Agriculture/Forestry	-	-	-	-	-	-	0.01	0.03	0.09	-	0.13
Fishing	-	-	-	-	-	-	-	-	-	-	-
Non-specified	-	-	0.17	0.21	-	-	0.00	0.00	-	-	0.39
NON-ENERGY USE	**-**	**-**	**0.56**	**-**	**-**	**-**	**-**	**-**	**-**	**-**	**0.56**
in Industry/Transf./Energy	-	-	0.53	-	-	-	-	-	-	-	0.53
of which: Feedstocks	-	-	*0.12*	-	-	-	-	-	-	-	*0.12*
in Transport	-	-	0.03	-	-	-	-	-	-	-	0.03
in Other Sectors	-	-	-	-	-	-	-	-	-	-	-
Electricity Generated - TWh	-	-	*0.21*	*0.95*	*26.96*	*33.75*	*0.02*	*1.99*	-	-	*63.88*
Electricity Plants	-	-	*0.02*	-	*26.96*	*33.75*	*0.02*	*0.22*	-	-	*60.97*
CHP plants	-	-	*0.20*	*0.95*	-	-	-	*1.77*	-	-	*2.91*
Heat Generated - PJ	-	-	*0.10*	*1.26*	*1.18*	-	-	*9.32*	-	*4.88*	*16.74*
CHP plants	-	-	*0.10*	*1.26*	*1.18*	-	-	*9.02*	-	-	*11.56*
Heat Plants	-	-	-	-	-	-	-	*0.30*	-	*4.88*	*5.18*

Switzerland / Suisse : 2005

Million tonnes of oil equivalent / *Million de tonnes d'équivalent pétrole*

SUPPLY AND CONSUMPTION / ***APPROVISIONNEMENT ET DEMANDE***	Coal / *Charbon*	Crude Oil / *Pétrole brut*	Petroleum Products / *Produits pétroliers*	Gas / *Gaz*	Nuclear / *Nucléaire*	Hydro / *Hydro*	Geotherm. Solar etc. / *Géotherm. solaire etc.*	Combust. Renew. & Waste / *Comb. ren. & déchets*	Electricity / *Electricité*	Heat / *Chaleur*	Total / *Total*
Production	-	-	-	-	6.11	2.69	0.16	1.92	-	-	10.88
Imports	0.10	5.03	8.46	2.78	-	-	-	0.01	3.30	-	19.67
Exports	-	-	-0.48	-	-	-	-	-0.01	-2.75	-	-3.24
Intl. Marine Bunkers	-	-	-0.01	-	-	-	-	-	-	-	-0.01
Stock Changes	0.06	0.01	-0.21	-	-	-	-	-	-	-	-0.15
TPES	**0.15**	**5.04**	**7.75**	**2.78**	**6.11**	**2.69**	**0.16**	**1.92**	**0.55**	**-**	**27.15**
Transfers	-	-	-	-	-	-	-	-	-	-	-
Statistical Differences	-	0.00	0.45	-	-	-	-	-	-	-	0.46
Electricity Plants	-	-	-0.00	-	-6.08	-2.69	-0.00	-0.06	4.71	-	-4.12
CHP Plants	-	-	-0.02	-0.13	-0.03	-	-	-0.49	0.25	0.29	-0.13
Heat Plants	-	-	-	-	-	-	-	-0.01	-	0.13	0.12
Gas Works	-	-	-0.00	0.00	-	-	-	-	-	-	-0.00
Petroleum Refineries	-	-5.04	5.05	-	-	-	-	-	-	-	0.02
Coal Transformation	-	-	-	-	-	-	-	-	-	-	-
Liquefaction Plants	-	-	-	-	-	-	-	-	-	-	-
Other Transformation	-	-	-	-	-	-	-	-	-	-	-
Own Use	-	-	-0.34	-	-	-	-	-	-0.22	-	-0.56
Distribution Losses	-	-	-	-0.02	-	-	-	-	-0.36	-0.03	-0.41
TFC	**0.15**	**-**	**12.89**	**2.64**	**-**	**-**	**0.16**	**1.36**	**4.93**	**0.38**	**22.52**
INDUSTRY SECTOR	**0.13**	**-**	**0.87**	**0.83**	**-**	**-**	**0.01**	**0.50**	**1.63**	**0.15**	**4.11**
Iron and Steel	-	-	0.01	0.06	-	-	-	0.00	0.12	-	0.20
Chemical and Petrochem.	-	-	0.10	0.29	-	-	-	0.04	0.32	0.03 e	0.78
Non-Ferrous Metals	-	-	0.00	0.02	-	-	-	0.00	0.10	0.00 e	0.12
Non-Metallic Minerals	0.12	-	0.10	0.02	-	-	-	0.12	0.04	0.00 e	0.39
Transport Equipment	-	-	-	-	-	-	-	-	-	-	-
Machinery	..	-	0.17	0.03	-	-	-	0.00	0.09	0.02 e	0.31
Mining and Quarrying	-	-	-	-	-	-	-	-	-	-	-
Food and Tobacco	..	-	0.12	0.14	-	-	-	0.00	0.15	0.01 e	0.43
Paper, Pulp and Printing	-	-	0.09	0.14	-	-	-	0.12	0.22	0.07 e	0.63
Wood and Wood Products	-	-	-	-	-	-	-	-	-	-	-
Construction	..	-	0.10	0.01	-	-	-	0.08	0.04	-	0.23
Textile and Leather	-	-	0.02	0.01	-	-	-	0.00	0.03	0.00 e	0.07
Non-specified	0.01	-	0.14	0.12	-	-	0.01	0.13	0.52	0.02 e	0.94
TRANSPORT SECTOR	**-**	**-**	**6.89**	**-**	**-**	**-**	**-**	**0.01**	**0.26**	**-**	**7.15**
International Aviation	-	-	1.22	-	-	-	-	-	-	-	1.22
Domestic Aviation	-	-	0.04	-	-	-	-	-	-	-	0.04
Road	-	-	5.60	-	-	-	-	0.01	-	-	5.61
Rail	-	-	0.01	-	-	-	-	-	0.26	-	0.27
Pipeline Transport	-	-	-	-	-	-	-	-	-	-	-
Domestic Navigation	-	-	0.01	-	-	-	-	-	-	-	0.01
Non-specified	-	-	-	-	-	-	-	-	-	-	-
OTHER SECTORS	**0.02**	**-**	**4.58**	**1.81**	**-**	**-**	**0.15**	**0.86**	**3.05**	**0.23**	**10.70**
Residential	0.02	-	3.15	1.02	-	-	0.12	0.31	1.52	0.14	6.28
Comm. and Publ. Services	-	-	1.26	0.56	-	-	0.02	0.51	1.44	0.09	3.89
Agriculture/Forestry	-	-	-	-	-	-	0.01	0.03	0.09	-	0.13
Fishing	-	-	-	-	-	-	-	-	-	-	-
Non-specified	-	-	0.17	0.22	-	-	0.00	0.00	-	-	0.39
NON-ENERGY USE	**-**	**-**	**0.56**	**-**	**-**	**-**	**-**	**-**	**-**	**-**	**0.56**
in Industry/Transf./Energy	-	-	0.53	-	-	-	-	-	-	-	0.53
of which: Feedstocks	-	-	*0.12*	-	-	-	-	-	-	-	*0.12*
in Transport	-	-	0.03	-	-	-	-	-	-	-	0.03
in Other Sectors	-	-	-	-	-	-	-	-	-	-	-
Electricity Generated - TWh	-	-	***0.19***	***0.87***	***23.34***	***31.23***	***0.03***	***2.10***	-	-	***57.75***
Electricity Plants	-	-	*0.02*	-	*23.34*	*31.23*	*0.03*	*0.18*	-	-	*54.79*
CHP plants	-	-	*0.18*	*0.87*	-	-	-	*1.92*	-	-	*2.96*
Heat Generated - PJ	-	-	***0.17***	***1.35***	***1.10***	-	-	***9.65***	-	***5.03***	***17.30***
CHP plants	-	-	*0.17*	*1.35*	*1.10*	-	-	*9.33*	-	-	*11.96*
Heat Plants	-	-	-	-	-	-	-	*0.32*	-	*5.03*	*5.34*

Turkey / Turquie
Key Indicators
Indicateurs principaux

	1960	1970	1973	1980	1990	1995
Energy Production (Mtoe)	9.37	13.99	15.52	17.14	25.82	26.48
Net Imports (Mtoe)	1.16	4.30	8.83	14.42	28.11	36.62
Total Primary Energy Supply (Mtoe)	10.71	18.22	24.37	31.51	52.97	61.86
Net Oil Imports (Mtoe)	1.18	4.48	8.82	13.77	21.28	26.54
Oil Supply (Mtoe)	1.54	7.72	12.50	15.69	23.61	28.74
Electricity Consumption (TWh)*	2.54	7.76	11.14	21.79	50.13	71.78
GDP (billion 2000 US$ using exch. rates)	33.54 e	56.64	66.33	84.37	140.20	164.20
GDP (billion 2000 US$ using PPPs)	77.38 e	130.66	153.01	194.63	323.42	378.79
Population (millions)	27.53 e	35.32	38.07	44.44	56.20	61.64
Industrial Production Index (2000=100)	..	..	..	..	70.50	82.50
Energy Production/TPES	0.8751	0.7676	0.6370	0.5438	0.4874	0.4281
Net Oil Imports/GDP (toe per thousand 2000 US$)	0.0351 e	0.0790	0.1329	0.1633	0.1518	0.1617
TPES/GDP (toe per thousand 2000 US$)	0.3192 e	0.3218	0.3674	0.3735	0.3778	0.3767
TPES/GDP (toe per thousand 2000 US$ PPP)	0.1384 e	0.1395	0.1593	0.1619	0.1638	0.1633
TPES/Population (toe per capita)	0.3889 e	0.5160	0.6401	0.7091	0.9424	1.0035
Oil Supply/GDP (toe per thousand 2000 US$)	0.0460 e	0.1364	0.1884	0.1860	0.1684	0.1750
Oil Supply/Population (toe per capita)	0.0561 e	0.2187	0.3283	0.3531	0.4201	0.4662
Elect. Cons./GDP (kWh per 2000 US$)	0.0756 e	0.1369	0.1680	0.2583	0.3576	0.4372
Elect. Cons./Population (kWh per capita)	92 e	220	293	490	892	1 165
Industry Cons.**/Industrial Production (2000=100)	..	..	..	..	83.86	83.89
Industry Oil Cons.**/Industrial Production (2000=100)	..	..	..	..	107.79	109.25

	2000	2001	2002	2003	2004	2005
Energy Production (Mtoe)	25.86	24.42	24.12	23.59	24.11	23.61
Net Imports (Mtoe)	51.06	46.16	51.34	56.55	58.20	61.89
Total Primary Energy Supply (Mtoe)	77.03	71.01	75.20	78.79	81.90	85.21
Net Oil Imports (Mtoe)	29.41	26.77	28.39	28.32	28.94	28.14
Oil Supply (Mtoe)	31.08	28.87	30.53	29.77	30.09	29.90
Electricity Consumption (TWh)*	104.52	103.54	108.62	117.10	126.77	136.75
GDP (billion 2000 US$ using exch. rates)	199.26	184.33	198.97	210.50	229.30	246.22
GDP (billion 2000 US$ using PPPs)	459.67	425.22	458.99	485.58	528.95	567.99
Population (millions)	67.46	68.62	69.63	70.71	71.79	72.07
Industrial Production Index (2000=100)	100.00	91.30	99.90	108.70	119.30	125.70
Energy Production/TPES	0.3357	0.3438	0.3207	0.2994	0.2944	0.2771
Net Oil Imports/GDP (toe per thousand 2000 US$)	0.1476	0.1452	0.1427	0.1346	0.1262	0.1143
TPES/GDP (toe per thousand 2000 US$)	0.3866	0.3852	0.3780	0.3743	0.3572	0.3461
TPES/GDP (toe per thousand 2000 US$ PPP)	0.1676	0.1670	0.1638	0.1623	0.1548	0.1500
TPES/Population (toe per capita)	1.1418	1.0348	1.0801	1.1143	1.1409	1.1823
Oil Supply/GDP (toe per thousand 2000 US$)	0.1560	0.1566	0.1535	0.1414	0.1312	0.1214
Oil Supply/Population (toe per capita)	0.4607	0.4208	0.4385	0.4211	0.4192	0.4148
Elect. Cons./GDP (kWh per 2000 US$)	0.5245	0.5617	0.5459	0.5563	0.5529	0.5554
Elect. Cons./Population (kWh per capita)	1 549	1 509	1 560	1 656	1 766	1 898
Industry Cons.**/Industrial Production (2000=100)	100.00	89.29	97.75	98.35	92.45	87.27
Industry Oil Cons.**/Industrial Production (2000=100)	100.00	100.05	98.83	92.27	83.49	75.84

* Electricity consumption equals domestic supply less distribution losses.
La consommation d'électricité représente l'approvisionnement intérieur diminué des pertes de distribution.

** Includes non-energy use in industry/transformation/energy sectors.
Comprend l'usage non-énergétique dans les secteurs de l'industrie/transformation/énergie.

Turkey / Turquie

Figure 1. TPES* in 1973

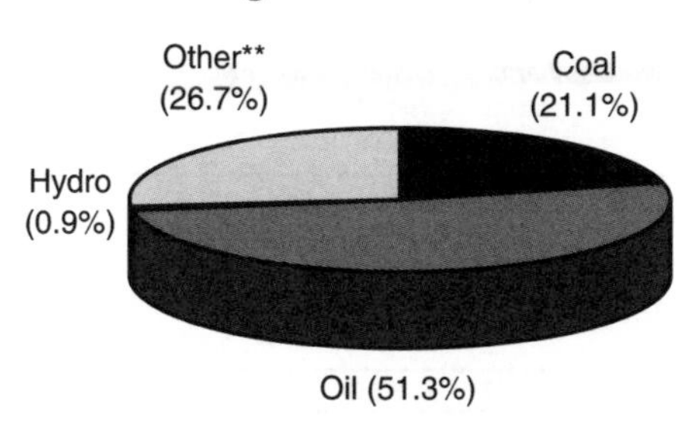

Figure 2. TPES* in 2005

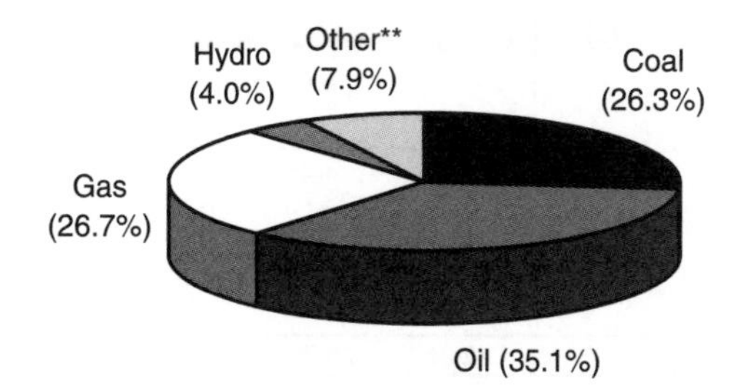

Figure 3. Final Consumption by Sector***

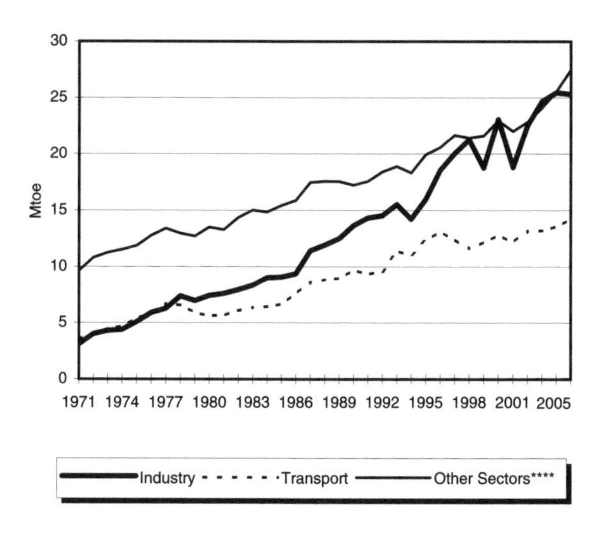

Figure 4. Breakdown of Sectorial Final Consumption by Source in 1973 and 2005***

Mtoe
1973 2005 Industry
1973 2005 Transport
1973 2005 Other Sectors****
Coal Oil Gas Electricity Other*****

Figure 5. Electricity Generation by Fuel

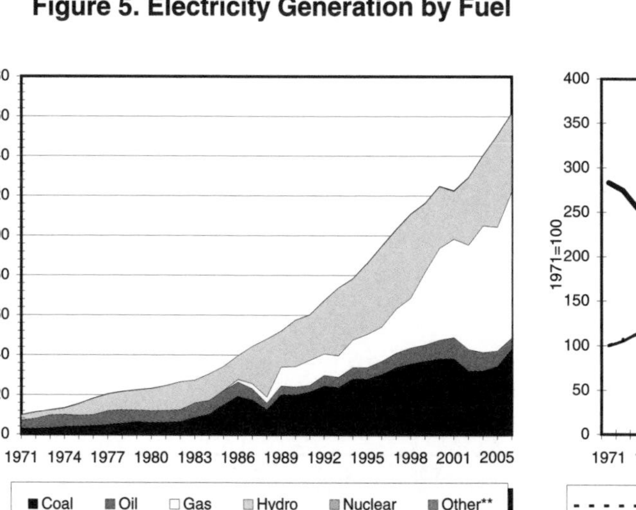

Figure 6. Electricity Consumption/GDP, TPES/GDP and Energy Production/TPES

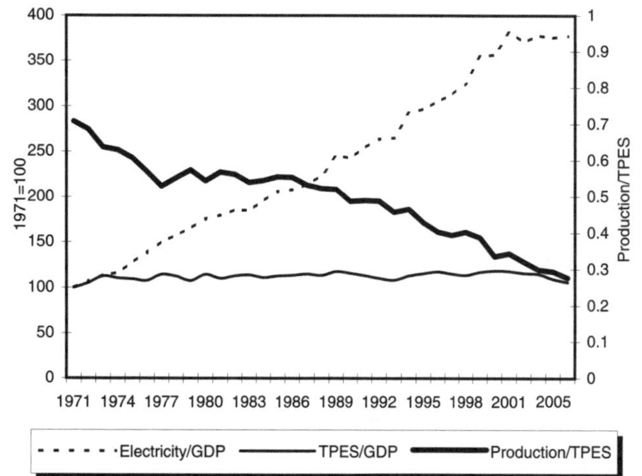

* Excluding electricity trade.
** Includes geothermal, solar, wind, combustible renewables & waste, etc.
*** Includes non-energy use.
**** Includes residential, commercial and public services, agriculture/forestry, fishing and non-specified.
***** Includes comb. renewables & waste, direct use of geothermal/solar thermal and heat produced in CHP/heat plants.

Turkey / Turquie : 2004

Million tonnes of oil equivalent / *Million de tonnes d'équivalent pétrole*

SUPPLY AND CONSUMPTION / *APPROVISIONNEMENT ET DEMANDE*	Coal / *Charbon*	Crude Oil / *Pétrole brut*	Petroleum Products / *Produits pétroliers*	Gas / *Gaz*	Nuclear / *Nucléaire*	Hydro / *Hydro*	Geotherm. Solar etc. / *Géotherm. solaire etc.*	Combust. Renew. & Waste / *Comb. ren. & déchets*	Electricity / *Electricité*	Heat / *Chaleur*	Total / *Total*
Production	10.53	2.22	-	0.57	-	3.96	1.27	5.56 e	-	-	24.11
Imports	11.20	23.75	10.48	18.12	-	-	-	-	0.04	-	63.59
Exports	-	-	-5.29	-	-	-	-	-	-0.10	-	-5.39
Intl. Marine Bunkers	-	-	-1.01	-	-	-	-	-	-	-	-1.01
Stock Changes	0.65	-0.18	0.11	0.02	-	-	-	-	-	-	0.60
TPES	**22.38**	**25.79**	**4.30**	**18.70**	**-**	**3.96**	**1.27**	**5.56**	**-0.06**	**-**	**81.90**
Transfers	-	-	-	-	-	-	-	-	-	-	-
Statistical Differences	0.05	0.19	-	-	-	-	-	-	-	-	0.24
Electricity Plants	-8.70	-	-1.57	-9.21	-	-3.96	-0.08	-0.02 e	12.44	-	-11.11
CHP Plants	-0.07	-	-0.20	-0.93	-	-	-	-0.01	0.52	0.45	-0.23
Heat Plants	-	-	-	-	-	-	-	-	-	-	-
Gas Works	-	-	-	-	-	-	-	-	-	-	-
Petroleum Refineries	-	-26.06	26.53	-	-	-	-	-	-	-	0.47
Coal Transformation	-1.91 e	-	-	-	-	-	-	-	-	-	-1.91
Liquefaction Plants	-	-	-	-	-	-	-	-	-	-	-
Other Transformation	-	0.09	-0.08	-	-	-	-	-	-	-	0.00
Own Use	-0.30	-	-1.71	-0.10	-	-	-	-	-0.62	-	-2.72
Distribution Losses	-0.03	-	-	-0.02	-	-	-	-	-2.00	-	-2.04
TFC	**11.41**	**-**	**27.28**	**8.45**	**-**	**-**	**1.19**	**5.53**	**10.29**	**0.45**	**64.59**
INDUSTRY SECTOR	**9.00**	**-**	**4.59**	**2.45**	**-**	**-**	**0.12**	**-**	**4.99**	**0.45**	**21.60**
Iron and Steel	0.75 e	-	0.24	0.43	-	-	-	-	0.94	-	2.36
Chemical and Petrochem.	0.05	-	1.59	0.50	-	-	-	-	0.38	-	2.52
Non-Ferrous Metals	0.07	-	0.27	0.32	-	-	-	-	0.23	-	0.89
Non-Metallic Minerals	0.09	-	0.05	0.47	-	-	-	-	0.52	-	1.14
Transport Equipment	-	-	-	0.05	-	-	-	-	-	-	0.05
Machinery	0.02	-	-	0.02	-	-	-	-	0.21	-	0.25
Mining and Quarrying	-	-	-	-	-	-	-	-	0.06	-	0.06
Food and Tobacco	0.44	-	0.23	0.11	-	-	-	-	0.30	-	1.08
Paper, Pulp and Printing	0.01	-	0.20	0.06	-	-	-	-	0.11	-	0.38
Wood and Wood Products	-	-	-	-	-	-	-	-	0.07	-	0.07
Construction	1.78	-	-	-	-	-	-	-	0.09	-	1.88
Textile and Leather	0.17	-	0.28	0.27	-	-	-	-	0.96	-	1.68
Non-specified	5.62	-	1.73	0.22	-	-	0.12	-	1.12	0.45	9.26
TRANSPORT SECTOR	**-**	**-**	**13.08**	**0.10**	**-**	**-**	**-**	**-**	**0.06**	**-**	**13.25**
International Aviation	-	-	1.01	-	-	-	-	-	-	-	1.01
Domestic Aviation	-	-	0.92	-	-	-	-	-	-	-	0.92
Road	-	-	10.58	0.00	-	-	-	-	-	-	10.58
Rail	-	-	0.18	-	-	-	-	-	0.02	-	0.20
Pipeline Transport	-	-	-	0.10	-	-	-	-	0.01	-	0.11
Domestic Navigation	-	-	0.39	-	-	-	-	-	-	-	0.39
Non-specified	-	-	-	-	-	-	-	-	0.03	-	0.03
OTHER SECTORS	**2.40**	**-**	**5.86**	**5.47**	**-**	**-**	**1.06**	**5.53**	**5.23**	**-**	**25.56**
Residential	2.40	-	2.88	3.90	-	-	1.06	5.53	2.38	-	18.15
Comm. and Publ. Services	-	-	-	1.57	-	-	-	-	2.52	-	4.10
Agriculture/Forestry	-	-	2.98	-	-	-	-	-	0.32	-	3.30
Fishing	-	-	-	-	-	-	-	-	0.02	-	0.02
Non-specified	-	-	-	-	-	-	-	-	-	-	-
NON-ENERGY USE	**-**	**-**	**3.75**	**0.43**	**-**	**-**	**-**	**-**	**-**	**-**	**4.18**
in Industry/Transf./Energy	-	-	3.42	0.43	-	-	-	-	-	-	3.85
of which: Feedstocks	-	-	*1.40*	*0.43*	-	-	-	-	-	-	*1.83*
in Transport	-	-	0.33	-	-	-	-	-	-	-	0.33
in Other Sectors	-	-	-	-	-	-	-	-	-	-	-
Electricity Generated - TWh	***34.45***	-	***7.67***	***62.24***	-	***46.08***	***0.15***	***0.10***	-	-	***150.70***
Electricity Plants	*33.96*	-	*6.83*	*57.49*	-	*46.08*	*0.15*	*0.08*	-	-	*144.60*
CHP plants	*0.49*	-	*0.84*	*4.75*	-	-	-	*0.02*	-	-	*6.10*
Heat Generated - PJ	-	-	***1.65***	***17.19***	-	-	-	-	-	-	***18.83***
CHP plants	-	-	*1.65*	*17.19*	-	-	-	-	-	-	*18.83*
Heat Plants	-	-	-	-	-	-	-	-	-	-	-

Turkey / Turquie : 2005

Million tonnes of oil equivalent / *Million de tonnes d'équivalent pétrole*

SUPPLY AND CONSUMPTION / ***APPROVISIONNEMENT ET DEMANDE***	Coal / *Charbon*	Crude Oil / *Pétrole brut*	Petroleum Products / *Produits pétroliers*	Gas / *Gaz*	Nuclear / *Nucléaire*	Hydro / *Hydro*	Geotherm. Solar etc. / *Géotherm. solaire etc.*	Combust. Renew. & Waste / *Comb. ren. & déchets*	Electricity / *Electricité*	Heat / *Chaleur*	Total / *Total*
Production	10.48	2.23	-	0.74	-	3.40	1.40	5.36	-	-	23.61
Imports	11.72	23.22	10.42	22.13	-	-	-	-	0.05	-	67.54
Exports	-	-	-5.50	-	-	-	-	-	-0.15	-	-5.65
Intl. Marine Bunkers	-	-	-1.07	-	-	-	-	-	-	-	-1.07
Stock Changes	0.27	0.15	0.44	-0.08	-	-	-	-	-	-	0.77
TPES	**22.47**	**25.61**	**4.29**	**22.79**	**-**	**3.40**	**1.40**	**5.36**	**-0.10**	**-**	**85.21**
Transfers	-	-	-	-	-	-	-	-	-	-	-
Statistical Differences	0.19	0.01	-0.01	-	-	-	-	-	-	-	0.19
Electricity Plants	-9.59	-	-0.99	-11.16	-	-3.40	-0.09	-0.03	13.31	-	-11.95
CHP Plants	-0.10	-	-0.22	-1.46	-	-	-	-0.00	0.62	0.85	-0.32
Heat Plants	-	-	-	-	-	-	-	-	-	-	-
Gas Works	-	-	-	-	-	-	-	-	-	-	-
Petroleum Refineries	-	-25.67	26.20	-	-	-	-	-	-	-	0.53
Coal Transformation	-1.89 e	-	-	-	-	-	-	-	-	-	-1.89
Liquefaction Plants	-	-	-	-	-	-	-	-	-	-	-
Other Transformation	-	0.06	-0.05	-	-	-	-	-	-	-	0.00
Own Use	-0.30	-	-1.56	-0.10	-	-	-	-	-0.70	-	-2.65
Distribution Losses	-0.05	-	-	-0.02	-	-	-	-	-2.07	-	-2.14
TFC	**10.74**	**-**	**27.65**	**10.05**	**-**	**-**	**1.31**	**5.32**	**11.06**	**0.85**	**66.98**
INDUSTRY SECTOR	**8.27**	**-**	**4.32**	**2.71**	**-**	**-**	**0.12**	**-**	**5.22**	**0.85**	**21.48**
Iron and Steel	0.79	-	0.25	0.47	-	-	-	-	1.00	-	2.50
Chemical and Petrochem.	0.05	-	1.59	0.67	-	-	-	-	0.34	-	2.64
Non-Ferrous Metals	0.08	-	0.27	0.38	-	-	-	-	0.21	-	0.94
Non-Metallic Minerals	0.10	-	0.05	0.53	-	-	-	-	0.52	-	1.19
Transport Equipment	-	-	-	0.05	-	-	-	-	-	-	0.05
Machinery	0.02	-	-	0.02	-	-	-	-	0.21	-	0.25
Mining and Quarrying	-	-	-	-	-	-	-	-	0.08	-	0.08
Food and Tobacco	0.50	-	0.18	0.11	-	-	-	-	0.32	-	1.11
Paper, Pulp and Printing	0.02	-	0.18	0.05	-	-	-	-	0.12	-	0.36
Wood and Wood Products	-	-	-	-	-	-	-	-	0.09	-	0.09
Construction	1.88	-	0.08	-	-	-	-	-	0.11	-	2.06
Textile and Leather	0.17	-	0.19	0.16	-	-	-	-	1.04	-	1.57
Non-specified	4.68	-	1.54	0.27	-	-	0.12	-	1.17	0.85	8.63
TRANSPORT SECTOR	**-**	**-**	**13.63**	**0.11**	**-**	**-**	**-**	**-**	**0.06**	**-**	**13.80**
International Aviation	-	-	1.12	-	-	-	-	-	-	-	1.12
Domestic Aviation	-	-	0.96	-	-	-	-	-	-	-	0.96
Road	-	-	10.91	0.00	-	-	-	-	-	-	10.92
Rail	-	-	0.22	-	-	-	-	-	0.02	-	0.24
Pipeline Transport	-	-	-	0.10	-	-	-	-	0.01	-	0.11
Domestic Navigation	-	-	0.41	-	-	-	-	-	-	-	0.41
Non-specified	-	-	-	-	-	-	-	-	0.03	-	0.03
OTHER SECTORS	**2.47**	**-**	**5.96**	**6.75**	**-**	**-**	**1.19**	**5.32**	**5.78**	**-**	**27.48**
Residential	2.47	-	2.96	4.78	-	-	1.19	5.32	2.66	-	19.39
Comm. and Publ. Services	-	-	-	1.96	-	-	-	-	2.77	-	4.73
Agriculture/Forestry	-	-	3.00	-	-	-	-	-	0.34	-	3.35
Fishing	-	-	-	-	-	-	-	-	0.01	-	0.01
Non-specified	-	-	-	-	-	-	-	-	-	-	-
NON-ENERGY USE	**-**	**-**	**3.74**	**0.49**	**-**	**-**	**-**	**-**	**-**	**-**	**4.22**
in Industry/Transf./Energy	-	-	3.35	0.49	-	-	-	-	-	-	3.83
of which: Feedstocks	-	-	*0.77*	*0.49*	-	-	-	-	-	-	*1.26*
in Transport	-	-	0.39	-	-	-	-	-	-	-	0.39
in Other Sectors	-	-	-	-	-	-	-	-	-	-	-
Electricity Generated - TWh	***43.19***	**-**	***5.48***	***73.45***	**-**	***39.56***	***0.15***	***0.12***	**-**	**-**	***161.96***
Electricity Plants	*42.62*	-	*4.40*	*67.92*	-	*39.56*	*0.15*	*0.12*	-	-	*154.77*
CHP plants	*0.57*	-	*1.08*	*5.53*	-	-	-	*0.00*	-	-	*7.19*
Heat Generated - PJ	***0.65***	**-**	***1.48***	***33.47***	**-**	**-**	**-**	**-**	**-**	**-**	***35.60***
CHP plants	*0.65*	-	*1.48*	*33.47*	-	-	-	-	-	-	*35.60*
Heat Plants	-	-	-	-	-	-	-	-	-	-	-

United Kingdom / Royaume-Uni
Key Indicators
Indicateurs principaux

	1960	1970	1973	1980	1990	1995
Energy Production (Mtoe)	114.81	101.34	108.49	197.85	208.00	257.53
Net Imports (Mtoe)	47.43	105.09	115.77	12.29	4.64	- 38.02
Total Primary Energy Supply (Mtoe)	160.46	207.31	220.72	201.28	212.18	223.44
Net Oil Imports (Mtoe)	51.26	106.67	115.97	1.89	- 11.09	- 50.50
Oil Supply (Mtoe)	45.23	101.28	111.55	82.19	82.63	84.61
Electricity Consumption (TWh)*	126.40	231.95	262.53	263.77	306.65	323.50
GDP (billion 2000 US$ using exch. rates)	548.14 e	725.19	820.74	877.03	1 135.30	1 232.53
GDP (billion 2000 US$ using PPPs)	572.66 e	757.63	857.46	916.26	1 186.08	1 287.66
Population (millions)	52.37 e	55.63	56.22	56.33	57.24	58.03
Industrial Production Index (2000=100)	53.40	68.10	75.10	73.50	87.70	93.20
Energy Production/TPES	0.7155	0.4888	0.4915	0.9829	0.9803	1.1526
Net Oil Imports/GDP (toe per thousand 2000 US$)	0.0935 e	0.1471	0.1413	0.0022	- 0.0098	- 0.0410
TPES/GDP (toe per thousand 2000 US$)	0.2927 e	0.2859	0.2689	0.2295	0.1869	0.1813
TPES/GDP (toe per thousand 2000 US$ PPP)	0.2802 e	0.2736	0.2574	0.2197	0.1789	0.1735
TPES/Population (toe per capita)	3.0637 e	3.7265	3.9258	3.5733	3.7070	3.8508
Oil Supply/GDP (toe per thousand 2000 US$)	0.0825 e	0.1397	0.1359	0.0937	0.0728	0.0686
Oil Supply/Population (toe per capita)	0.8636 e	1.8206	1.9841	1.4591	1.4436	1.4581
Elect. Cons./GDP (kWh per 2000 US$)	0.2306 e	0.3198	0.3199	0.3008	0.2701	0.2625
Elect. Cons./Population (kWh per capita)	2 413 e	4 169	4 669	4 683	5 358	5 575
Industry Cons.**/Industrial Production (2000=100)	179.15	201.92	193.63	141.66	109.24	105.57
Industry Oil Cons.**/Industrial Production (2000=100)	137.68	298.60	284.37	167.16	113.04	118.64

	2000	2001	2002	2003	2004	2005
Energy Production (Mtoe)	272.39	262.33	258.32	246.60	225.43	204.30
Net Imports (Mtoe)	- 40.04	- 21.99	- 29.02	- 15.24	10.91	32.26
Total Primary Energy Supply (Mtoe)	233.86	234.58	228.62	232.33	233.46	233.93
Net Oil Imports (Mtoe)	- 46.69	- 36.68	- 40.20	- 28.52	- 14.15	- 2.45
Oil Supply (Mtoe)	83.66	81.52	80.17	81.08	83.20	84.68
Electricity Consumption (TWh)*	360.10	363.11	364.70	368.30	368.71	376.63
GDP (billion 2000 US$ using exch. rates)	1 442.25	1 476.18	1 506.57	1 546.73	1 597.20	1 626.78
GDP (billion 2000 US$ using PPPs)	1 506.76	1 542.21	1 573.96	1 615.92	1 668.64	1 699.55
Population (millions)	58.89	59.11	59.32	59.55	59.84	60.22
Industrial Production Index (2000=100)	100.00	98.50	96.60	96.30	97.00	95.30
Energy Production/TPES	1.1647	1.1183	1.1299	1.0614	0.9656	0.8733
Net Oil Imports/GDP (toe per thousand 2000 US$)	- 0.0324	- 0.0248	- 0.0267	- 0.0184	- 0.0089	- 0.0015
TPES/GDP (toe per thousand 2000 US$)	0.1622	0.1589	0.1517	0.1502	0.1462	0.1438
TPES/GDP (toe per thousand 2000 US$ PPP)	0.1552	0.1521	0.1453	0.1438	0.1399	0.1376
TPES/Population (toe per capita)	3.9715	3.9684	3.8539	3.9011	3.9017	3.8847
Oil Supply/GDP (toe per thousand 2000 US$)	0.0580	0.0552	0.0532	0.0524	0.0521	0.0521
Oil Supply/Population (toe per capita)	1.4208	1.3791	1.3515	1.3615	1.3905	1.4063
Elect. Cons./GDP (kWh per 2000 US$)	0.2497	0.2460	0.2421	0.2381	0.2308	0.2315
Elect. Cons./Population (kWh per capita)	6 115	6 143	6 148	6 184	6 162	6 254
Industry Cons.**/Industrial Production (2000=100)	100.00	98.89	98.26	101.50	98.84	101.01
Industry Oil Cons.**/Industrial Production (2000=100)	100.00	97.46	99.53	109.94	110.56	116.78

* Electricity consumption equals domestic supply less distribution losses.
La consommation d'électricité représente l'approvisionnement intérieur diminué des pertes de distribution.

** Includes non-energy use in industry/transformation/energy sectors.
Comprend l'usage non-énergétique dans les secteurs de l'industrie/transformation/énergie.

United Kingdom / Royaume-Uni

Figure 1. TPES* in 1973

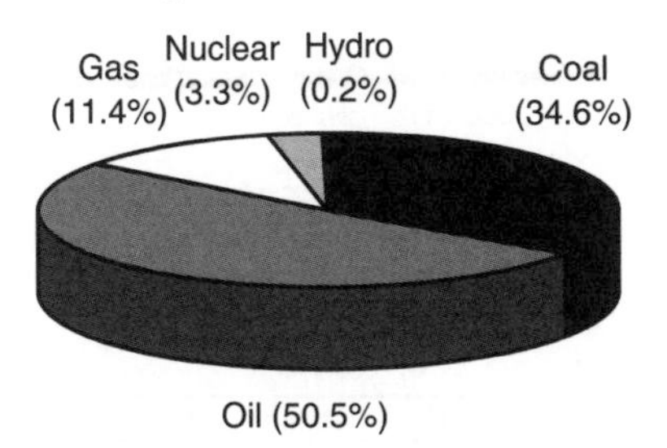

Figure 2. TPES* in 2005

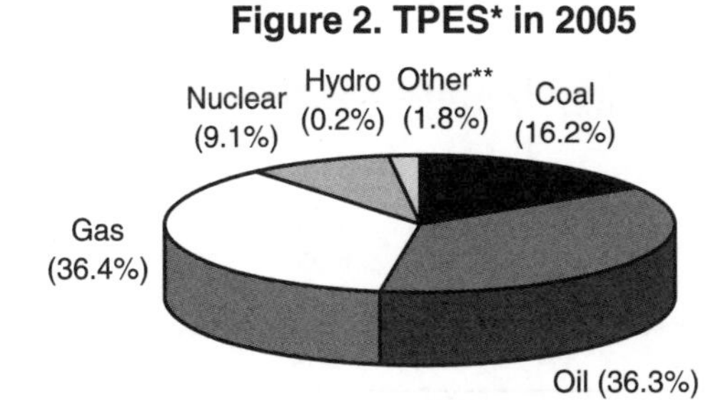

Figure 3. Final Consumption by Sector***

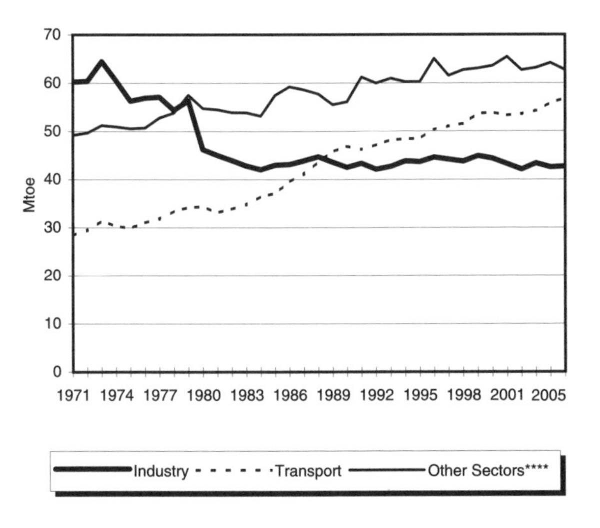

Figure 4. Breakdown of Sectorial Final Consumption by Source in 1973 and 2005***

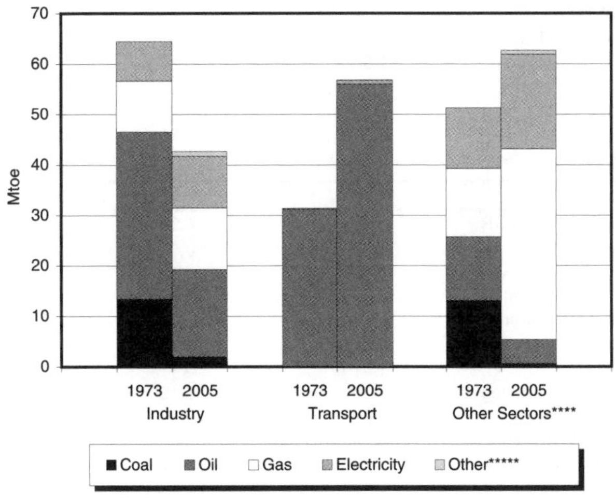

Figure 5. Electricity Generation by Fuel

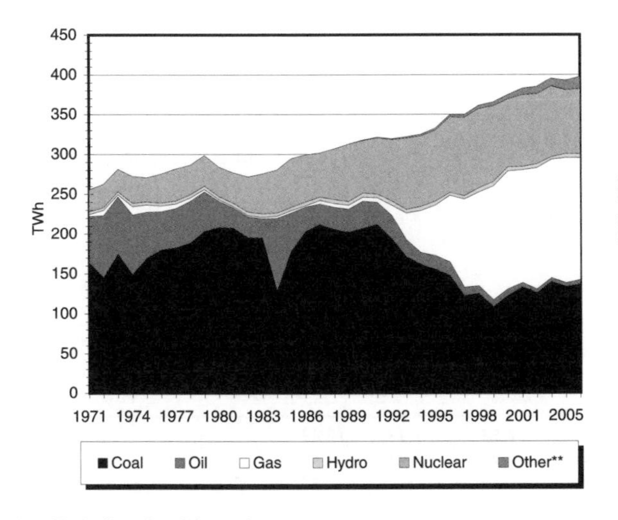

Figure 6. Electricity Consumption/GDP, TPES/GDP and Energy Production/TPES

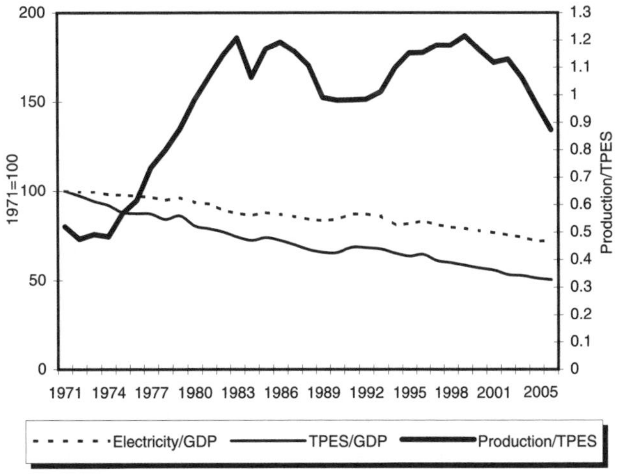

* Excluding electricity trade.

** Includes geothermal, solar, wind, combustible renewables & waste, etc.

*** Includes non-energy use.

**** Includes residential, commercial and public services, agriculture/forestry, fishing and non-specified.

***** Includes comb. renewables & waste, direct use of geothermal/solar thermal and heat produced in CHP/heat plants.

United Kingdom / Royaume-Uni : 2004

Million tonnes of oil equivalent / *Million de tonnes d'équivalent pétrole*

SUPPLY AND CONSUMPTION *APPROVISIONNEMENT ET DEMANDE*	Coal *Charbon*	Crude Oil *Pétrole brut*	Petroleum Products *Produits pétroliers*	Gas *Gaz*	Nuclear *Nucléaire*	Hydro *Hydro*	Geotherm. Solar etc. *Géotherm. solaire etc.*	Combust. Renew. & Waste *Comb. ren. & déchets*	Electricity *Electricité*	Heat *Chaleur*	Total *Total*
Production	14.90	99.60	-	86.38	20.85	0.42	0.19	3.08	-	-	225.43
Imports	23.15	64.68	19.11	10.29	-	-	-	0.35	0.84	-	118.42
Exports	-0.56	-67.07	-30.86	-8.83	-	-	-	-	-0.20	-	-107.52
Intl. Marine Bunkers	-	-	-2.08	-	-	-	-	-	-	-	-2.08
Stock Changes	-0.14	-0.14	-0.03	-0.48	-	-	-	-	-	-	-0.80
TPES	**37.35**	**97.07**	**-13.86**	**87.36**	**20.85**	**0.42**	**0.19**	**3.44**	**0.64**	**-**	**233.46**
Transfers	-	-3.95	3.95	-	-	-	-	-	-	-	-0.01
Statistical Differences	-0.12	0.06	0.67	-0.06	-	-	-	-	-	-	0.55
Electricity Plants	-30.72	-	-0.83	-22.94	-20.85	-0.42	-0.17	-2.30	31.43	-	-46.79
CHP Plants	-0.21	-	-0.21	-3.45	-	-	-	-0.56	2.34	-	-2.10
Heat Plants	-0.34	-	-0.08	-1.54	-	-	-	-	-	1.27	-0.69
Gas Works	-	-	-	-	-	-	-	-	-	-	-
Petroleum Refineries	-	-93.18	92.95	-	-	-	-	-	-	-	-0.23
Coal Transformation	-1.96 e	-	-0.26	-	-	-	-	-	-	-	-2.22
Liquefaction Plants	-	-	-	-	-	-	-	-	-	-	-
Other Transformation	0.00	-	-	-0.00	-	-	-	-	-	-	-0.00
Own Use	-0.81	-	-5.80	-6.81	-	-	-	-	-2.33	-0.01	-15.76
Distribution Losses	-0.19	-	-	-0.56	-	-	-	-	-2.93	-	-3.69
TFC	**2.99**	**-**	**76.52**	**52.00**	**-**	**-**	**0.03**	**0.58**	**29.16**	**1.25**	**162.53**
INDUSTRY SECTOR	**2.17**	**-**	**6.38**	**11.89**	**-**	**-**	**-**	**0.22**	**9.97**	**0.84**	**31.46**
Iron and Steel	0.92 e	-	0.06	0.75	-	-	-	-	0.47	-	2.20
Chemical and Petrochem.	0.09	-	0.12	3.24	-	-	-	-	1.90	0.39	5.75
Non-Ferrous Metals	0.01	-	0.05	0.25	-	-	-	-	0.63	-	0.94
Non-Metallic Minerals	0.70	-	0.19	1.04	-	-	-	-	0.67	-	2.60
Transport Equipment	0.05	-	0.14	0.79	-	-	-	-	-	-	0.98
Machinery	0.01	-	0.11	0.98	-	-	-	-	1.81	0.00	2.91
Mining and Quarrying	-	-	0.18	-	-	-	-	-	-	-	0.18
Food and Tobacco	0.02	-	0.33	2.18	-	-	-	-	1.06	0.00	3.60
Paper, Pulp and Printing	0.09	-	0.05	1.07	-	-	-	-	1.11	0.03	2.35
Wood and Wood Products	-	-	0.02	-	-	-	-	-	-	-	0.02
Construction	-	-	0.15	0.23	-	-	-	-	0.16	-	0.53
Textile and Leather	0.05	-	0.07	0.55	-	-	-	-	0.29	-	0.96
Non-specified	0.23	-	4.92	0.80	-	-	-	0.22	1.87	0.41	8.44
TRANSPORT SECTOR	**-**	**-**	**54.77**	**-**	**-**	**-**	**-**	**0.02**	**0.73**	**-**	**55.51**
International Aviation	-	-	11.10	-	-	-	-	-	-	-	11.10
Domestic Aviation	-	-	1.58	-	-	-	-	-	-	-	1.58
Road	-	-	40.14	-	-	-	-	0.02	-	-	40.15
Rail	-	-	0.82	-	-	-	-	-	0.73	-	1.55
Pipeline Transport	-	-	-	-	-	-	-	-	-	-	-
Domestic Navigation	-	-	1.13	-	-	-	-	-	-	-	1.13
Non-specified	-	-	-	-	-	-	-	-	-	-	-
OTHER SECTORS	**0.82**	**-**	**4.61**	**39.34**	**-**	**-**	**0.03**	**0.35**	**18.46**	**0.42**	**64.02**
Residential	0.81	-	3.10	30.67	-	-	-	0.19	9.94	0.05	44.75
Comm. and Publ. Services	0.01	-	0.84	6.85	-	-	-	0.09	8.17	0.36	16.32
Agriculture/Forestry	0.00	-	0.26	0.18	-	-	-	0.06	0.36	-	0.87
Fishing	-	-	-	-	-	-	-	-	-	-	-
Non-specified	0.00	-	0.41	1.64	-	-	0.03	0.01	-	-	2.09
NON-ENERGY USE	**-**	**-**	**10.75**	**0.78**	**-**	**-**	**-**	**-**	**-**	**-**	**11.53**
in Industry/Transf./Energy	-	-	10.27	0.78	-	-	-	-	-	-	11.04
of which: Feedstocks	-	-	*6.34*	*0.78*	-	-	-	-	-	-	*7.11*
in Transport	-	-	0.33	-	-	-	-	-	-	-	0.33
in Other Sectors	-	-	0.15	-	-	-	-	-	-	-	0.15
Electricity Generated - TWh	***133.30***	**-**	***4.87***	***157.33***	***80.00***	***4.93***	***1.94***	***10.28***	**-**	**-**	***392.66***
Electricity Plants	*132.31*	-	*1.98*	*136.47*	*80.00*	*4.93*	*1.94*	*7.82*	-	-	*365.45*
CHP plants	*0.99*	-	*2.89*	*20.86*	-	-	-	*2.47*	-	-	*27.21*
Heat Generated - PJ	***8.66***	**-**	***1.66***	***42.79***	**-**	**-**	**-**	**-**	**-**	**-**	***53.10***
CHP plants	-	-	-	-	-	-	-	-	-	-	-
Heat Plants	*8.66*	-	*1.66*	*42.79*	-	-	-	-	-	-	*53.10*

United Kingdom / Royaume-Uni : 2005

Million tonnes of oil equivalent / *Million de tonnes d'équivalent pétrole*

SUPPLY AND CONSUMPTION / ***APPROVISIONNEMENT ET DEMANDE***	Coal / *Charbon*	Crude Oil / *Pétrole brut*	Petroleum Products / *Produits pétroliers*	Gas / *Gaz*	Nuclear / *Nucléaire*	Hydro / *Hydro*	Geotherm. Solar etc. / *Géotherm. solaire etc.*	Combust. Renew. & Waste / *Comb. ren. & déchets*	Electricity / *Electricité*	Heat / *Chaleur*	Total / *Total*
Production	11.77	88.46	-	78.80	21.27	0.43	0.28	3.29	-	-	204.30
Imports	27.81	60.91	23.31	13.41	-	-	-	0.70	0.96	-	127.11
Exports	-0.49	-56.31	-30.36	-7.44	-	-	-	-	-0.24	-	-94.85
Intl. Marine Bunkers	-	-	-2.04	-	-	-	-	-	-	-	-2.04
Stock Changes	-1.40	-0.39	1.09	0.10	-	-	-	-	-	-	-0.60
TPES	**37.68**	**92.68**	**-7.99**	**84.87**	**21.27**	**0.43**	**0.28**	**4.00**	**0.72**	**-**	**233.93**
Transfers	-	-3.44	3.78	-	-	-	-	-	-	-	0.34
Statistical Differences	-1.33	-0.11	0.41	-0.05	-	-	-	-	-	-	-1.08
Electricity Plants	-30.29	-	-0.83	-22.33	-21.27	-0.43	-0.25	-2.79	31.90	-	-46.28
CHP Plants	-0.19	-	-0.20	-3.50	-	-	-	-0.67	2.29	-	-2.27
Heat Plants	-0.31	-	-0.06	-1.60	-	-	-	-	-	1.35	-0.61
Gas Works	-	-	-	-	-	-	-	-	-	-	-
Petroleum Refineries	-	-89.29	88.96	-	-	-	-	-	-	-	-0.33
Coal Transformation	-2.04 e	-	-0.24	-	-	-	-	-	-	-	-2.28
Liquefaction Plants	-	-	-	-	-	-	-	-	-	-	-
Other Transformation	0.00	0.16	-0.18	-0.00	-	-	-	-	-	-	-0.02
Own Use	-0.78	-	-5.62	-6.58	-	-	-	-	-2.45	-0.04	-15.47
Distribution Losses	-0.21	-	-	-0.76	-	-	-	-	-2.77	-	-3.73
TFC	**2.54**	**-**	**78.02**	**50.05**	**-**	**-**	**0.03**	**0.54**	**29.69**	**1.32**	**162.20**
INDUSTRY SECTOR	**1.95**	**-**	**6.70**	**11.51**	**-**	**-**	**-**	**0.12**	**10.22**	**0.86**	**31.36**
Iron and Steel	0.83 e	-	0.03	0.65	-	-	-	-	0.43	-	1.94
Chemical and Petrochem.	0.08	-	0.18	3.20	-	-	-	-	1.99	0.39	5.85
Non-Ferrous Metals	0.02	-	0.05	0.24	-	-	-	-	0.66	-	0.98
Non-Metallic Minerals	0.65	-	0.20	1.00	-	-	-	-	0.68	-	2.53
Transport Equipment	0.03	-	0.13	0.77	-	-	-	-	-	-	0.93
Machinery	0.01	-	0.11	0.99	-	-	-	-	1.89	0.00	3.00
Mining and Quarrying	-	-	0.18	-	-	-	-	-	-	-	0.18
Food and Tobacco	0.01	-	0.31	2.14	-	-	-	-	1.08	0.00	3.55
Paper, Pulp and Printing	0.08	-	0.08	1.01	-	-	-	-	1.12	0.06	2.35
Wood and Wood Products	-	-	0.01	-	-	-	-	-	-	-	0.01
Construction	-	-	0.18	0.20	-	-	-	-	0.17	-	0.55
Textile and Leather	0.04	-	0.10	0.52	-	-	-	-	0.30	-	0.97
Non-specified	0.19	-	5.13	0.78	-	-	-	0.12	1.89	0.41	8.53
TRANSPORT SECTOR	**-**	**-**	**55.78**	**-**	**-**	**-**	**-**	**0.08**	**0.74**	**-**	**56.60**
International Aviation	-	-	12.51	-	-	-	-	-	-	-	12.51
Domestic Aviation	-	-	0.85	-	-	-	-	-	-	-	0.85
Road	-	-	40.29	-	-	-	-	0.08	-	-	40.37
Rail	-	-	0.82	-	-	-	-	-	0.74	-	1.56
Pipeline Transport	-	-	-	-	-	-	-	-	-	-	-
Domestic Navigation	-	-	1.29	-	-	-	-	-	-	-	1.29
Non-specified	-	-	-	-	-	-	-	-	-	-	-
OTHER SECTORS	**0.59**	**-**	**4.59**	**37.79**	**-**	**-**	**0.03**	**0.34**	**18.73**	**0.46**	**62.54**
Residential	0.57	-	2.93	29.54	-	-	-	0.19	10.05	0.05	43.34
Comm. and Publ. Services	0.01	-	0.88	6.53	-	-	-	0.09	8.33	0.40	16.24
Agriculture/Forestry	0.01	-	0.35	0.17	-	-	-	0.06	0.36	-	0.94
Fishing	-	-	-	-	-	-	-	-	-	-	-
Non-specified	0.00	-	0.44	1.56	-	-	0.03	0.01	-	-	2.03
NON-ENERGY USE	**-**	**-**	**10.95**	**0.75**	**-**	**-**	**-**	**-**	**-**	**-**	**11.70**
in Industry/Transf./Energy	-	-	10.57	0.75	-	-	-	-	-	-	11.33
of which: Feedstocks	-	-	*6.82*	*0.75*	-	-	-	-	-	-	*7.57*
in Transport	-	-	0.23	-	-	-	-	-	-	-	0.23
in Other Sectors	-	-	0.14	-	-	-	-	-	-	-	0.14
Electricity Generated - TWh	***136.56***	**-**	***5.42***	***153.23***	***81.62***	***4.96***	***2.92***	***12.89***	**-**	**-**	***397.59***
Electricity Plants	*135.61*	-	*2.78*	*133.12*	*81.62*	*4.96*	*2.92*	*9.96*	-	-	*370.96*
CHP plants	*0.95*	-	*2.64*	*20.11*	-	-	-	*2.93*	-	-	*26.63*
Heat Generated - PJ	***8.60***	**-**	***1.73***	***46.38***	**-**	**-**	**-**	**-**	**-**	**-**	***56.71***
CHP plants	-	-	-	-	-	-	-	-	-	-	-
Heat Plants	*8.60*	-	*1.73*	*46.38*	-	-	-	-	-	-	*56.71*

United States / États-Unis
Key Indicators
Indicateurs principaux

	1960	1970	1973	1980	1990	1995
Energy Production (Mtoe)	964.89	1 450.87	1 455.47	1 553.26	1 650.29	1 663.69
Net Imports (Mtoe)	65.88	139.25	298.43	307.30	343.44	435.98
Total Primary Energy Supply (Mtoe)	1 021.36	1 557.36	1 736.45	1 811.65	1 927.46	2 090.00
Net Oil Imports (Mtoe)	83.46	163.68	305.41	340.34	374.92	420.00
Oil Supply (Mtoe)	469.16	703.57	823.99	803.90	770.25	801.54
Electricity Consumption (TWh)*	731.68	1 483.89	1 816.74	2 240.98	2 923.92	3 370.98
GDP (billion 2000 US$ using exch. rates)	2 553.59 e	3 721.70	4 304.80	5 128.00	7 055.00	7 972.80
GDP (billion 2000 US$ using PPPs)	2 553.59 e	3 721.70	4 304.80	5 128.00	7 055.00	7 972.80
Population (millions)	180.70 e	205.09	211.94	227.73	250.18	266.59
Industrial Production Index (2000=100)	25.10	40.40	48.60	54.20	66.30	77.00
Energy Production/TPES	0.9447	0.9316	0.8382	0.8574	0.8562	0.7960
Net Oil Imports/GDP (toe per thousand 2000 US$)	0.0327 e	0.0440	0.0709	0.0664	0.0531	0.0527
TPES/GDP (toe per thousand 2000 US$)	0.4000 e	0.4185	0.4034	0.3533	0.2732	0.2621
TPES/GDP (toe per thousand 2000 US$ PPP)	0.4000 e	0.4185	0.4034	0.3533	0.2732	0.2621
TPES/Population (toe per capita)	5.6521 e	7.5936	8.1931	7.9554	7.7042	7.8398
Oil Supply/GDP (toe per thousand 2000 US$)	0.1837 e	0.1890	0.1914	0.1568	0.1092	0.1005
Oil Supply/Population (toe per capita)	2.5963 e	3.4305	3.8879	3.5301	3.0788	3.0066
Elect. Cons./GDP (kWh per 2000 US$)	0.2865 e	0.3987	0.4220	0.4370	0.4144	0.4228
Elect. Cons./Population (kWh per capita)	4 049 e	7 235	8 572	9 841	11 687	12 645
Industry Cons.**/Industrial Production (2000=100)	263.70	231.19	205.98	187.19	124.94	110.50
Industry Oil Cons.**/Industrial Production (2000=100)	286.89	216.41	207.98	222.24	139.62	123.58

	2000	2001	2002	2003	2004	2005
Energy Production (Mtoe)	1 678.77	1 699.61	1 667.34	1 634.52	1 647.02	1 630.68
Net Imports (Mtoe)	608.35	645.92	629.67	662.41	711.74	734.87
Total Primary Energy Supply (Mtoe)	2 306.64	2 259.71	2 289.80	2 282.78	2 328.55	2 340.29
Net Oil Imports (Mtoe)	550.23	575.27	557.94	594.72	641.07	660.16
Oil Supply (Mtoe)	891.00	903.78	900.20	921.41	947.47	952.84
Electricity Consumption (TWh)*	3 857.28 e	3 717.66	3 824.06	3 860.31	3 919.88	4 046.60
GDP (billion 2000 US$ using exch. rates)	9 764.80	9 838.90	9 997.60	10 249.80	10 651.70	10 995.80
GDP (billion 2000 US$ using PPPs)	9 764.80	9 838.90	9 997.60	10 249.80	10 651.70	10 995.80
Population (millions)	282.43	285.37	288.25	291.11	293.93	296.68
Industrial Production Index (2000=100)	100.00	96.50	96.50	97.60	100.00	103.20
Energy Production/TPES	0.7278	0.7521	0.7282	0.7160	0.7073	0.6968
Net Oil Imports/GDP (toe per thousand 2000 US$)	0.0563	0.0585	0.0558	0.0580	0.0602	0.0600
TPES/GDP (toe per thousand 2000 US$)	0.2362	0.2297	0.2290	0.2227	0.2186	0.2128
TPES/GDP (toe per thousand 2000 US$ PPP)	0.2362	0.2297	0.2290	0.2227	0.2186	0.2128
TPES/Population (toe per capita)	8.1671	7.9185	7.9437	7.8415	7.9221	7.8883
Oil Supply/GDP (toe per thousand 2000 US$)	0.0912	0.0919	0.0900	0.0899	0.0890	0.0867
Oil Supply/Population (toe per capita)	3.1548	3.1670	3.1230	3.1651	3.2234	3.2117
Elect. Cons./GDP (kWh per 2000 US$)	0.3950 e	0.3779	0.3825	0.3766	0.3680	0.3680
Elect. Cons./Population (kWh per capita)	13 658 e	13 028	13 266	13 261	13 336	13 640
Industry Cons.**/Industrial Production (2000=100)	100.00	98.89	98.33	94.68	96.43	90.48
Industry Oil Cons.**/Industrial Production (2000=100)	100.00	109.10	111.72	109.11	117.71	111.88

* Electricity consumption equals domestic supply less distribution losses.
La consommation d'électricité représente l'approvisionnement intérieur diminué des pertes de distribution.

** Includes non-energy use in industry/transformation/energy sectors.
Comprend l'usage non-énergétique dans les secteurs de l'industrie/transformation/énergie.

United States / États-Unis

Figure 1. TPES* in 1973

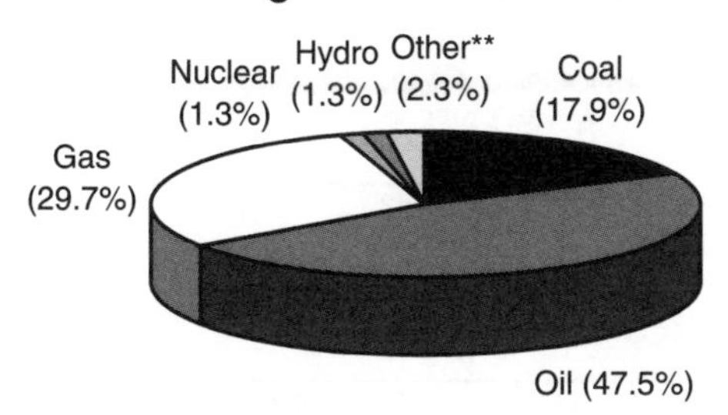

Figure 2. TPES* in 2005

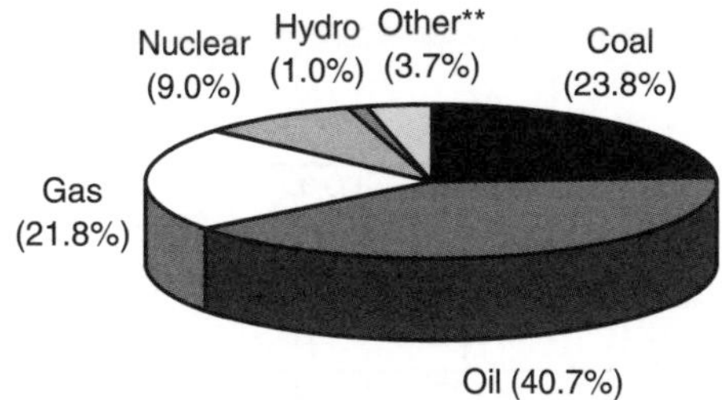

Figure 3. Final Consumption by Sector***

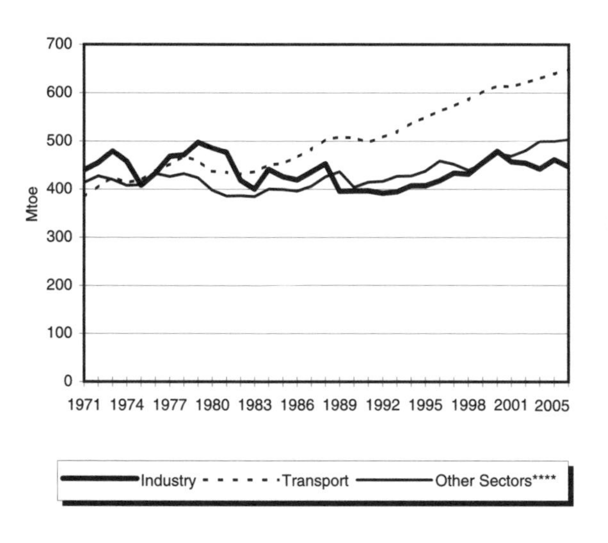

Figure 4. Breakdown of Sectorial Final Consumption by Source in 1973 and 2005***

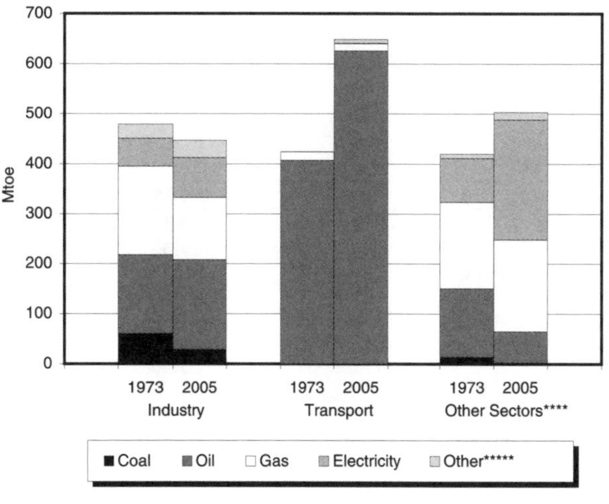

Figure 5. Electricity Generation by Fuel

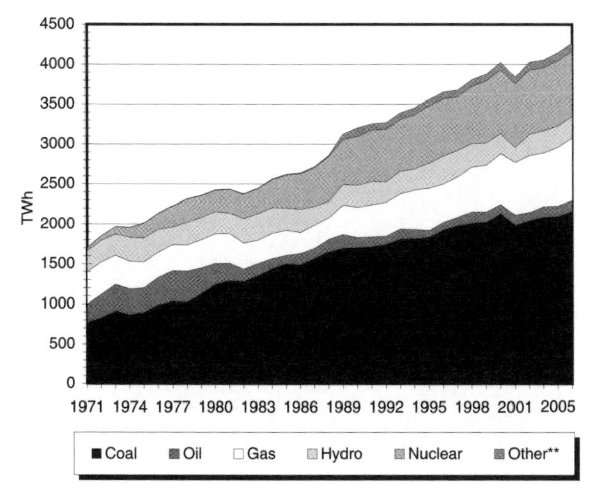

Figure 6. Electricity Consumption/GDP, TPES/GDP and Energy Production/TPES

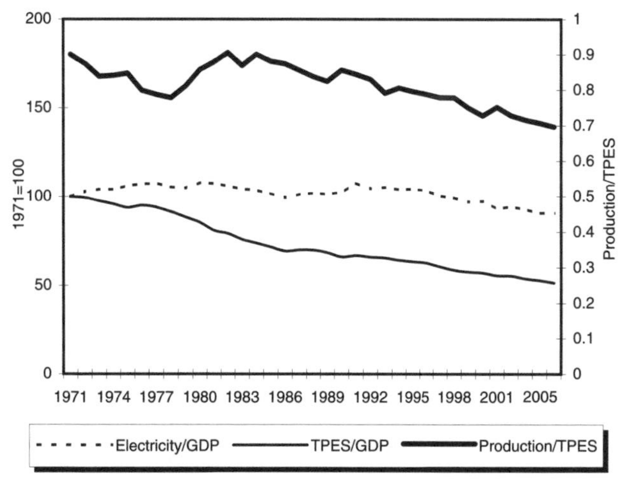

* Excluding electricity trade.

** Includes geothermal, solar, wind, combustible renewables & waste, etc.

*** Includes non-energy use.

**** Includes residential, commercial and public services, agriculture/forestry, fishing and non-specified.

***** Includes comb. renewables & waste, direct use of geothermal/solar thermal and heat produced in CHP/heat plants.

United States / États-Unis : 2004

Million tonnes of oil equivalent / *Million de tonnes d'équivalent pétrole*

SUPPLY AND CONSUMPTION / ***APPROVISIONNEMENT ET DEMANDE***	Coal / *Charbon*	Crude Oil / *Pétrole brut*	Petroleum Products / *Produits pétroliers*	Gas / *Gaz*	Nuclear / *Nucléaire*	Hydro / *Hydro*	Geotherm. Solar etc. / *Géotherm. solaire etc.*	Combust. Renew. & Waste / *Comb. ren. & déchets*	Electricity / *Electricité*	Heat / *Chaleur*	Total / *Total*
Production	553.16	339.09	-	435.83	211.96	23.32	11.23	72.42	-	-	1647.02
Imports	20.25	593.89	99.29	99.07	-	-	-	0.23	2.94	-	815.68
Exports	-30.31	-3.82	-48.29	-19.55	-	-	-	-	-1.97	-	-103.94
Intl. Marine Bunkers	-	-	-24.39	-	-	-	-	-	-	-	-24.39
Stock Changes	5.67	-7.26	-1.04	-3.23	-	-	-	0.06	-	-	-5.81
TPES	**548.77**	**921.90**	**25.57**	**512.12**	**211.96**	**23.32**	**11.23**	**72.71**	**0.97**	**-**	**2328.55**
Transfers	-	-56.41	57.55	-	-	-	-	-	-	-	1.13
Statistical Differences	-10.39	-9.41	-1.31	8.13	-	-	-	-0.00	-	-	-12.99
Electricity Plants	-478.37	-	-27.04	-96.85	-211.96	-23.32	-9.22	-11.61	326.94	-	-531.42
CHP Plants	-17.33	-	-6.89	-49.23	-	-	-	-11.74	29.76	5.64	-49.78
Heat Plants	-	-	-	-	-	-	-	-	-	-	-
Gas Works	-1.74	-	-	1.04	-	-	-	-	-	-	-0.70
Petroleum Refineries	-	-856.07	867.13	-	-	-	-	-	-	-	11.06
Coal Transformation	-4.81 e	-	-	-	-	-	-	-	-	-	-4.81
Liquefaction Plants	-	-	-	-	-	-	-	-	-	-	-
Other Transformation	-	-	-	-	-	-	-	-	-	-	-
Own Use	-2.42	-	-48.73	-41.28	-	-	-	-	-23.45	-1.88 e	-117.77
Distribution Losses	-	-	-	-	-	-	-	-	-22.87	-0.68 e	-23.55
TFC	**33.72**	**-**	**866.28**	**333.93**	**-**	**-**	**2.02**	**49.36**	**311.35**	**3.08**	**1599.74**
INDUSTRY SECTOR	**30.68**	**-**	**34.55**	**119.09**	**-**	**-**	**0.10**	**30.44**	**79.32**	**2.43**	**296.61**
Iron and Steel	4.29 e	-	1.50	10.02	-	-	-	-	6.49	0.09 e	22.40
Chemical and Petrochem.	5.24	-	8.27	44.54	-	-	-	0.61	21.70	1.49 e	81.84
Non-Ferrous Metals	-	-	0.52	6.11	-	-	-	-	6.63	0.05 e	13.30
Non-Metallic Minerals	7.52	-	4.50	10.09	-	-	-	0.41	3.60	0.00 e	26.13
Transport Equipment	0.21	-	0.74	4.84	-	-	-	0.01	4.21	0.06 e	10.06
Machinery	0.07	-	1.50	9.82	-	-	-	-	10.19	0.04 e	21.63
Mining and Quarrying	-	-	-	..	-	-	-	-	2.21	-	2.21
Food and Tobacco	3.76	-	3.32	14.87	-	-	-	0.91	7.31	0.27 e	30.44
Paper, Pulp and Printing	4.55	-	5.09	13.12	-	-	-	21.07	10.99	0.23 e	55.04
Wood and Wood Products	0.02	-	1.83	1.99	-	-	-	5.30	2.51	0.12 e	11.77
Construction	-	-	1.82	..	-	-	-	-	-	-	1.82
Textile and Leather	0.11	-	0.72	2.95	-	-	-	0.03	2.60	0.07 e	6.48
Non-specified	4.92	-	4.73	0.74	-	-	0.10	2.12	0.87	0.01 e	13.49
TRANSPORT SECTOR	**-**	**-**	**617.83**	**13.66**	**-**	**-**	**-**	**6.96**	**0.62**	**-**	**639.08**
International Aviation	-	-	17.00	-	-	-	-	-	-	-	17.00
Domestic Aviation	-	-	64.96	-	-	-	-	-	-	-	64.96
Road	-	-	520.53	0.48	-	-	-	6.91	-	-	527.92
Rail	-	-	10.99	-	-	-	-	-	0.62	-	11.61
Pipeline Transport	-	-	-	13.18	-	-	-	-	-	-	13.18
Domestic Navigation	-	-	3.16	-	-	-	-	0.05	-	-	3.22
Non-specified	-	-	1.19	-	-	-	-	-	-	-	1.19
OTHER SECTORS	**3.03**	**-**	**65.03**	**185.17**	**-**	**-**	**1.92**	**11.96**	**231.42**	**0.65**	**499.17**
Residential	-	-	30.73	113.38	-	-	1.62	9.81	111.11	-	266.65
Comm. and Publ. Services	2.46	-	17.88	71.79	-	-	0.30	2.11	105.82	0.65 e	201.00
Agriculture/Forestry	0.57	-	16.43	-	-	-	-	0.03	-	-	17.04
Fishing	-	-	-	-	-	-	-	-	-	-	-
Non-specified	-	-	-	-	-	-	-	-	14.49	-	14.49
NON-ENERGY USE	**-**	**-**	**148.87**	**16.01**	**-**	**-**	**-**	**-**	**-**	**-**	**164.88**
in Industry/Transf./Energy	-	-	148.68	16.01	-	-	-	-	-	-	164.69
of which: Feedstocks	-	-	*88.72*	*14.91*	-	-	-	-	-	-	*103.64*
in Transport	-	-	0.19	-	-	-	-	-	-	-	0.19
in Other Sectors	-	-	-	-	-	-	-	-	-	-	-
Electricity Generated - TWh	***2090.50***	-	***139.09***	***731.55***	***813.34***	***271.12***	***31.08***	***71.04***	-	-	***4147.71***
Electricity Plants	*2030.98 e*	-	*115.06*	*508.36*	*813.34*	*271.12*	*30.82*	*31.98*	-	-	*3801.65*
CHP plants	*59.52 e*	-	*24.03*	*223.19*	-	-	*0.26*	*39.06*	-	-	*346.06*
Heat Generated - PJ	***41.37***	-	***10.66***	***171.23***	-	-	-	***12.84***	-	-	***236.10***
CHP plants	*41.37 e*	-	*10.66*	*171.23*	-	-	-	*12.84*	-	-	*236.10*
Heat Plants	-	-	-	-	-	-	-	-	-	-	-

United States / États-Unis : 2005

Million tonnes of oil equivalent / *Million de tonnes d'équivalent pétrole*

SUPPLY AND CONSUMPTION / ***APPROVISIONNEMENT ET DEMANDE***	Coal / *Charbon*	Crude Oil / *Pétrole brut*	Petroleum Products / *Produits pétroliers*	Gas / *Gaz*	Nuclear / *Nucléaire*	Hydro / *Hydro*	Geotherm. Solar etc. / *Géotherm. solaire etc.*	Combust. Renew. & Waste / *Comb. ren. & déchets*	Electricity / *Electricité*	Heat / *Chaleur*	Total / *Total*
Production	564.20	322.55	-	423.84	211.28	23.43	11.54	73.83 e	-	-	1630.68
Imports	20.17	599.51	118.07	100.85	-	-	-	0.21	3.83	-	842.63
Exports	-31.95	-4.91	-52.51	-16.69	-	-	-	-	-1.70	-	-107.76
Intl. Marine Bunkers	-	-	-25.90	-	-	-	-	-	-	-	-25.90
Stock Changes	3.23	-5.52	1.54	1.42	-	-	-	-0.03	-	-	0.64
TPES	**555.66**	**911.64**	**41.20**	**509.41**	**211.28**	**23.43**	**11.54**	**74.01**	**2.13**	**-**	**2340.29**
Transfers	-	-46.12	47.03	-	-	-	-	-	-	-	0.91
Statistical Differences	-11.07	-13.13	-2.62	8.28	-	-	-	0.12	0.00	-	-18.41
Electricity Plants	-488.59	-	-27.52	-107.85	-211.28	-23.43	-9.45	-11.49 e	338.52	-	-541.10
CHP Plants	-17.26	-	-6.23	-46.76	-	-	-	-10.29	28.56	5.96	-46.01
Heat Plants	-	-	-	-	-	-	-	-	-	-	-
Gas Works	-1.89	-	-	1.13	-	-	-	-	-	-	-0.76
Petroleum Refineries	-	-852.39	863.23	-	-	-	-	-	-	-	10.84
Coal Transformation	-4.39 e	-	-	-	-	-	-	-	-	-	-4.39
Liquefaction Plants	-	-	-	-	-	-	-	-	-	-	-
Other Transformation	-	-	-	-	-	-	-	-	-	-	-
Own Use	-2.05	-	-47.38	-41.87	-	-	-	-	-26.51	-1.99 e	-119.80
Distribution Losses	-	-	-	-	-	-	-	-	-22.75	-0.72 e	-23.46
TFC	**30.41**	**-**	**867.71**	**322.34**	**-**	**-**	**2.08**	**52.35**	**319.95**	**3.26**	**1598.10**
INDUSTRY SECTOR	**28.07**	**-**	**35.49**	**110.01**	**-**	**-**	**0.11**	**31.99**	**79.45**	**2.58**	**287.69**
Iron and Steel	2.21 e	-	1.56	9.26	-	-	-	-	6.92	0.09 e	20.05
Chemical and Petrochem.	4.91	-	8.68	41.15	-	-	-	0.75	21.87	1.58 e	78.94
Non-Ferrous Metals	-	-	0.54	5.64	-	-	-	-	7.07	0.05 e	13.30
Non-Metallic Minerals	7.32	-	4.68	9.32	-	-	-	0.41	3.66	0.00 e	25.40
Transport Equipment	0.16	-	0.77	4.47	-	-	-	-	4.01	0.06 e	9.47
Machinery	0.07	-	1.55	9.07	-	-	-	-	9.93	0.05 e	20.67
Mining and Quarrying	-	-	-	..	-	-	-	-	2.21	-	2.21
Food and Tobacco	3.82	-	3.46	13.74	-	-	-	0.93	7.32	0.28 e	29.56
Paper, Pulp and Printing	4.56	-	5.35	12.12	-	-	-	22.10	10.58	0.24 e	54.95
Wood and Wood Products	0.04	-	1.89	1.83	-	-	-	5.49	2.52	0.13 e	11.90
Construction	-	-	1.69	..	-	-	-	-	-	-	1.69
Textile and Leather	0.26	-	0.75	2.72	-	-	-	0.03	2.47	0.08 e	6.30
Non-specified	4.72	-	4.56	0.69	-	-	0.11	2.28	0.88	0.01 e	13.25
TRANSPORT SECTOR	**-**	**-**	**625.48**	**14.16**	**-**	**-**	**-**	**8.13**	**0.65**	**-**	**648.41**
International Aviation	-	-	17.57	-	-	-	-	-	-	-	17.57
Domestic Aviation	-	-	67.12	-	-	-	-	-	-	-	67.12
Road	-	-	523.64	0.52	-	-	-	8.07	-	-	532.23
Rail	-	-	12.27	-	-	-	-	-	0.65	-	12.92
Pipeline Transport	-	-	-	13.64	-	-	-	-	-	-	13.64
Domestic Navigation	-	-	3.96	-	-	-	-	0.05	-	-	4.02
Non-specified	-	-	0.91	-	-	-	-	-	-	-	0.91
OTHER SECTORS	**2.33**	**-**	**62.34**	**183.38**	**-**	**-**	**1.98**	**12.24**	**239.85**	**0.68**	**502.81**
Residential	-	-	29.10	112.14	-	-	1.63	10.05	116.89	-	269.81
Comm. and Publ. Services	1.90	-	16.87	71.25	-	-	0.34	2.00	109.66	0.68 e	202.70
Agriculture/Forestry	0.43	-	16.37	-	-	-	-	0.19	-	-	16.99
Fishing	-	-	-	-	-	-	-	-	-	-	-
Non-specified	-	-	-	-	-	-	-	-	13.30	-	13.30
NON-ENERGY USE	**-**	**-**	**144.40**	**14.79**	**-**	**-**	**-**	**-**	**-**	**-**	**159.19**
in Industry/Transf./Energy	-	-	144.22	14.79	-	-	-	-	-	-	159.01
of which: Feedstocks	-	-	*84.68*	*13.78*	-	-	-	-	-	-	*98.46*
in Transport	-	-	0.18	-	-	-	-	-	-	-	0.18
in Other Sectors	-	-	-	-	-	-	-	-	-	-	-
Electricity Generated - TWh	***2153.93***	-	***141.32***	***782.83***	***810.73***	***272.45***	***35.92***	***71.22***	-	-	***4268.38***
Electricity Plants	*2093.69 e*	-	*117.72*	*573.86*	*810.73*	*272.45*	*35.55*	*32.25*	-	-	*3936.23*
CHP plants	*60.24 e*	-	*23.60*	*208.97*	-	-	*0.37*	*38.97*	-	-	*332.15*
Heat Generated - PJ	***50.81***	-	***26.19***	***156.07***	-	-	-	***16.71***	-	-	***249.77***
CHP plants	*50.81 e*	-	*26.19*	*156.07*	-	-	-	*16.71*	-	-	*249.77*
Heat Plants	-	-	-	-	-	-	-	-	-	-	-

SUMMARY TABLES

TABLEAUX RECAPITULATIFS

Production of Coal (Mtoe)
Production de charbon (Mtep)
Erzeugung von Kohle (Mtoe)

Produzione di carbone (Mtep)

石炭の生産量（石油換算百万トン）

Producción de carbón (Mtep)

Производство угля (мил.тон нефтяного эквивалента (Мтнэ))

	1960	1970	1973	1980	1990	2000	2003	2004	2005
Australia	16.87	33.77	40.25	52.58	106.11	164.60 e	185.24	192.61	204.70
Austria	1.84	1.01	1.02	0.84	0.64	0.29	0.27	0.06	0.00
Belgium	13.93	7.04	6.42	4.71	1.18	0.21	0.07	0.09	0.06
Canada	5.73	8.33	11.70	20.51	37.93	34.41	30.26 e	32.18 e	31.77 e
Czech Republic	..	..	38.01 e	40.45	36.31	25.00	24.33	24.84	23.52
Denmark	0.99	0.06	-	-	-	-	-	-	-
Finland	0.03	0.02	0.06	0.73	1.81	1.21	1.83	0.88	2.13
France	37.23	25.54	18.04	13.38	8.24	2.48	1.39	0.54	0.38
Germany	117.85	151.47	141.40	143.15	121.77	60.63	57.73	58.33	56.49
Greece	0.28	1.01	1.69	2.95	7.12	8.22	8.18	8.55	8.54
Hungary	..	6.31	6.05	6.34	4.14	2.89	2.71	2.18	1.75
Iceland	-	-	-	-	-	-	-	-	-
Ireland	1.30	1.35	1.06	1.08	1.43	0.97	1.06	0.89	0.81
Italy	0.71	0.55	0.30	0.32	0.28	0.00	0.16	0.06	0.06
Japan	40.79	28.71	17.90	10.90	4.51	1.55	-	-	-
Korea	..	..	6.65 e	8.20	7.58	1.79	1.41	1.37	1.21
Luxembourg	-	-	-	-	-	-	-	-	-
Mexico	..	..	1.52	1.73	3.39	5.42	4.61	4.75	5.16
Netherlands	7.96	2.82	1.14	-	-	-	-	-	-
New Zealand	1.60	1.24	1.29	1.14	1.39	2.33	3.09	3.01	3.06
Norway	0.28	0.32	0.29	0.20	0.20	0.42	1.98	1.95	0.99
Poland	63.22	89.71	100.72	115.93	94.46	71.30	70.82	69.18	68.86
Portugal	0.29	0.16	0.13	0.07	0.12	-	-	-	-
Slovak Republic	..	..	1.70	1.70	1.40	1.02	0.82	0.82	0.64
Spain	8.43	6.88	6.48	9.82	11.75	7.97	6.98	6.45	6.26
Sweden	0.17	-	0.01	0.01	0.24	0.23	0.34	0.38	0.30
Switzerland	-	-	-	-	-	-	-	-	-
Turkey	3.04	4.11	5.21	6.15	12.37	12.49	10.77	10.53	10.48
United Kingdom	113.75	84.59	75.89	73.96	53.62	18.58	16.80	14.90	11.77
United States	243.64	343.18	333.36	447.92	539.15	544.83	526.12	553.16	564.20
OECD TOTAL	**..**	**..**	**818.29**	**964.77**	**1 057.12**	**968.84**	**956.96**	**987.72**	**1 003.14**
OECD N. AMERICA	..	..	346.58	470.16	580.46	584.65	560.99	590.09	601.14
OECD PACIFIC	..	..	66.09	72.82	119.59	170.27	189.74	196.99	208.97
OECD EUROPE	..	..	405.62	421.79	357.07	213.91	206.23	200.65	193.03
IEA	..	..	714.36	845.42	957.87	891.10	880.71	912.98	928.49

Production of Crude Oil and NGL (Mtoe)
Production de pétrole brut et LGN (Mtep)

Erzeugung von Rohöl und Kondensaten (Mtoe)

Produzione di petrolio grezzo e LGN (Mtep)

原油及びNGLの生産量（石油換算百万トン）

Producción de petróleo crudo y líquidos de gas natural (Mtep)

Производство сырой нефти и газовых конденсатов (Мтнэ)

	1960	1970	1973	1980	1990	2000	2003	2004	2005
Australia	-	8.42	19.83	21.30	29.03	33.91	30.67	27.64	24.13
Austria	2.50	2.86	2.65	1.52	1.21	1.09	1.03	1.08	0.98
Belgium	-	-	-	-	-	-	-	-	-
Canada	26.59	67.96	96.33	83.64	94.14	128.43	144.20	149.29	147.44
Czech Republic	..	..	0.04	0.24	0.21	0.38	0.47	0.57	0.58
Denmark	-	-	0.07	0.30	6.07	18.26	18.63	19.78	19.02
Finland	-	-	-	-	-	0.06	0.06	0.08	0.09
France	2.02	2.96	2.11	2.26	3.47	1.81	1.52	1.53	1.31
Germany	5.64	7.95	6.85	5.66	4.71	3.94	4.41	4.42	4.57
Greece	-	-	-	-	0.84	0.26	0.13	0.12	0.09
Hungary	..	1.98	2.02	2.52	2.27	1.68	1.61	1.59	1.41
Iceland	-	-	-	-	-	-	-	-	-
Ireland	-	-	-	-	-	-	-	-	-
Italy	2.10	1.55	1.13	1.73	4.47	4.69	5.76	5.62	6.26
Japan	0.51	0.87	0.81	0.55	0.67	0.76	0.69	0.71	0.75
Korea	..	..	-	-	-	0.67	0.50	0.44	0.53
Luxembourg	-	-	-	-	-	-	-	-	-
Mexico	..	..	27.49	115.23	154.11	171.27	185.83	195.02	197.29
Netherlands	1.96	1.96	1.59	1.61	4.07	2.42	3.16	2.97	2.34
New Zealand	-	-	0.18	0.37	1.96	1.92	1.30	1.15	1.06
Norway	-	-	1.52	24.56	84.51	169.50	156.86	155.58	143.42
Poland	0.19	0.43	0.39	0.34	0.18	0.72	0.78	0.92	0.89
Portugal	-	-	-	-	-	-	-	-	-
Slovak Republic	..	..	0.13	0.04	0.08	0.06	0.22	0.22	0.26
Spain	0.07	0.16	0.67	1.79	1.17	0.23	0.33	0.26	0.17
Sweden	0.10	-	-	0.03	0.00	-	-	-	-
Switzerland	-	-	-	-	-	-	-	-	-
Turkey	0.37	3.62	3.59	2.27	3.61	2.73	2.32	2.22	2.23
United Kingdom	0.15	0.17	0.53	82.59	95.25	131.66	110.73	99.60	88.46
United States	392.59	553.73	533.83	498.35	432.56	365.61	350.77	339.09	322.55
OECD TOTAL	**..**	**..**	**701.75**	**846.90**	**924.58**	**1 042.07**	**1 021.97**	**1 009.92**	**965.84**
OECD N. AMERICA	..	..	657.65	697.21	680.81	665.31	680.80	683.40	667.28
OECD PACIFIC	..	..	20.82	22.22	31.66	37.27	33.16	29.94	26.47
OECD EUROPE	..	..	23.28	127.46	212.10	339.49	308.01	296.57	272.09
IEA	..	..	673.73	731.29	770.21	870.02	835.15	813.76	767.41

Production of Petroleum Products (Mtoe)

Production de produits pétroliers (Mtep)

Erzeugung von Ölprodukten (Mtoe)

Produzione di prodotti petroliferi (Mtep)

石油製品の生産量（石油換算百万トン）

Producción de productos petrolíferos (Mtep)

Производство нефтепродуктов (Мтнэ)

	1960	1970	1973	1980	1990	2000	2003	2004	2005
Australia	12.74	23.94	26.03	30.20	32.10	38.38	36.61	35.85	34.29
Austria	1.91	5.93	8.88	10.35	9.15	9.01	9.34	9.02	9.43
Belgium	6.62	28.55	35.93	34.05	30.00	38.76	45.96	43.69	37.50
Canada	38.10	64.52	84.75	95.74	86.96	96.69	106.56	108.45	105.47
Czech Republic	..	..	7.53	9.71	8.11	6.26	6.93	7.20	8.35
Denmark	0.14	9.76	9.89	6.75	8.06	8.54	8.47	8.25	7.79
Finland	1.10	8.24	9.21	12.76	10.75	13.43	13.57	13.98	13.30
France	31.39	102.47	135.84	118.28	80.81	91.55	90.48	91.28	89.07
Germany	29.17	123.01	141.81	139.84	109.49	120.19	120.49	124.27	127.07
Greece	1.71	5.04	12.50	14.28	16.80	22.71	22.56	21.41	21.70
Hungary	..	5.91	8.05	10.42	8.58	7.68	7.50	7.59	8.60
Iceland	-	-	-	-	-	-	-	-	-
Ireland	1.36	2.67	2.71	2.04	1.76	3.35	3.21	2.96	3.20
Italy	30.77	116.87	131.48	99.23	92.74	97.17	100.72	100.92	103.33
Japan	25.69	161.46	223.95	203.80	182.32	214.03	209.20	206.33	212.37
Korea	..	..	14.96	25.65	43.10	125.32	113.63	119.68	123.88
Luxembourg	-	-	-	-	-	-	-	-	-
Mexico	..	..	26.27	51.32	67.07	64.94	68.48	70.31	71.30
Netherlands	18.67	62.25	74.01	58.68	70.52	83.61	85.84	87.13	88.59
New Zealand	-	3.06	3.33	3.00	4.91	5.29	5.42	5.33	5.46
Norway	0.14	5.69	6.18	7.96	13.61	15.84	15.23	14.65	16.07
Poland	0.86	7.30	10.91	15.64	13.05	19.06	18.55	19.14	19.09
Portugal	1.22	3.57	4.27	7.67	11.69	12.60	13.63	13.67	13.95
Slovak Republic	..	..	6.06	8.10	7.13	6.06	6.40	6.86	6.47
Spain	6.24	32.57	42.73	48.77	54.01	61.16	58.99	60.86	61.76
Sweden	2.75	11.38	10.57	17.71	18.37	23.09	19.82	20.75	20.17
Switzerland	-	5.47	6.24	4.71	3.16	4.83	4.79	5.43	5.05
Turkey	0.28	7.10	12.67	12.83	23.25	24.14	27.01	26.53	26.20
United Kingdom	44.52	101.62	114.56	87.21	90.99	89.38	87.55	92.95	88.96
United States	440.76	606.67	692.71	746.01	755.16	845.41	850.45	867.13	863.23
OECD TOTAL	**..**	**..**	**1 864.06**	**1 882.73**	**1 853.64**	**2 148.46**	**2 157.38**	**2 191.62**	**2 191.63**
OECD N. AMERICA	..	..	803.73	893.07	909.19	1 007.04	1 025.49	1 045.89	1 040.00
OECD PACIFIC	..	..	268.27	262.65	262.43	383.02	364.86	367.19	376.00
OECD EUROPE	..	..	792.06	727.02	682.02	758.40	767.02	778.54	775.63
IEA	..	..	1 820.81	1 807.67	1 766.38	2 058.40	2 063.95	2 095.30	2 094.76

Production of Natural Gas (Mtoe)
Production de gaz naturel (Mtep)

Erzeugung von Erdgas (Mtoe)

Produzione di gas naturale (Mtep)

天然ガスの生産量（石油換算百万トン）

Producción de gas natural (Mtep)

Производство природного газа (Мтнэ)

	1960	1970	1973	1980	1990	2000	2003	2004	2005
Australia	-	1.20	3.38	7.46	17.13	28.53	31.30	31.99	35.42
Austria	1.27	1.64	1.96	1.67	1.10	1.53	1.78	1.67	1.40
Belgium	0.05	0.04	0.04	0.03	0.01	0.00	-	-	-
Canada	11.53	47.08	61.36	63.62	88.55	148.32	151.12	150.79	154.06
Czech Republic	..	..	0.36	0.32	0.20	0.17	0.13	0.16	0.15
Denmark	-	-	0.00	0.00	2.77	7.41	7.20	8.49	9.38
Finland	-	-	-	-	-	-	-	-	-
France	2.50	5.82	6.29	6.33	2.52	1.50	1.28	1.11	0.83
Germany	0.74	9.54	16.44	16.26	13.53	15.80	15.92	14.73	14.22
Greece	-	-	-	-	0.14	0.04	0.03	0.03	0.02
Hungary	..	2.96	4.03	5.09	3.81	2.47	2.29	2.37	2.33
Iceland	-	-	-	-	-	-	-	-	-
Ireland	-	-	-	0.74	1.87	0.96	0.54	0.69	0.46
Italy	5.28	10.82	12.61	10.26	14.03	13.62	11.37	10.61	9.88
Japan	0.64	2.08	2.29	1.94	1.92	2.29	2.60	2.69	2.86
Korea	..	..	-	-	-	-	-	-	0.44
Luxembourg	-	-	-	-	-	-	-	-	-
Mexico	..	..	10.54	21.55	22.75	31.34	33.94 e	35.49 e	36.89
Netherlands	0.28	23.99	53.75	68.89	54.60	51.89	52.20	61.57	56.25
New Zealand	0.06	0.09	0.28	0.79	3.90	5.05	3.86	3.45	3.19
Norway	-	-	-	22.77	24.14	45.80	66.25	70.40	76.26
Poland	0.47	4.40	4.87	4.54	2.38	3.31	3.61	3.93	3.88
Portugal	-	-	-	-	-	-	-	-	-
Slovak Republic	..	..	0.39	0.14	0.34	0.13	0.17	0.14	0.13
Spain	-	0.00	0.00	-	1.27	0.15	0.20	0.31	0.14
Sweden	-	-	-	-	-	-	-	-	-
Switzerland	-	-	-	-	0.00	-	-	-	-
Turkey	-	-	-	-	0.17	0.53	0.46	0.57	0.74
United Kingdom	0.06	9.42	24.44	31.31	40.91	97.53	92.61	86.38	78.80
United States	283.43	490.80	502.61	454.56	419.04	450.34	447.87	435.83	423.84
OECD TOTAL	**..**	**..**	**705.65**	**718.28**	**717.07**	**908.72**	**926.71**	**923.39**	**911.59**
OECD N. AMERICA	..	..	574.52	539.74	530.34	630.00	632.93	622.11	614.80
OECD PACIFIC	..	..	5.95	10.20	22.95	35.87	37.75	38.14	41.92
OECD EUROPE	..	..	125.17	168.35	163.78	242.85	256.02	263.14	254.88
IEA	..	..	689.85	692.05	691.61	873.94	888.99	883.83	870.69

Production of Nuclear Energy (Mtoe)
Production d'énergie nucléaire (Mtep)

Erzeugung von Kernenergie (Mtoe)

Produzione di energia nucleare (Mtep)

原子力の生産量（石油換算百万トン）

Producción de energía nuclear (Mtep)

Производство атомной энергии (Мтнэ)

	1960	1970	1973	1980	1990	2000	2003	2004	2005
Australia	-	-	-	-	-	-	-	-	-
Austria	-	-	-	-	-	-	-	-	-
Belgium	-	0.01	0.02	3.27	11.13	12.55	12.35	12.33	12.40
Canada	-	0.27	4.07	10.40	19.40	18.97	19.52	23.56	23.99
Czech Republic	..	..	-	-	3.28	3.54	6.74	6.89	6.47
Denmark	-	-	-	-	-	-	-	-	-
Finland	-	-	-	1.83	5.01	5.86	5.92	5.92	6.06
France	0.04	1.49	3.84	15.96	81.85	108.19	114.95	116.81	117.67
Germany	-	1.69	3.15	14.50	39.84	44.20	43.02	43.54	42.49
Greece	-	-	-	-	-	-	-	-	-
Hungary	..	-	-	-	3.58	3.71	2.89	3.12	3.62
Iceland	-	-	-	-	-	-	-	-	-
Ireland	-	-	-	-	-	-	-	-	-
Italy	-	0.83	0.82	0.58	-	-	-	-	-
Japan	-	1.20	2.53	21.52	52.71	83.93	62.55	73.61	79.42
Korea	..	..	-	0.91	13.78	28.40	33.79	34.07	38.25
Luxembourg	-	-	-	-	-	-	-	-	-
Mexico	..	..	-	-	0.77	2.14	2.74	2.40	2.82
Netherlands	-	0.10	0.29	1.09	0.91	1.02	1.05	1.00	1.04
New Zealand	-	-	-	-	-	-	-	-	-
Norway	-	-	-	-	-	-	-	-	-
Poland	-	-	-	-	-	-	-	-	-
Portugal	-	-	-	-	-	-	-	-	-
Slovak Republic	..	..	0.06	1.18	3.14	4.30	4.70	4.49	4.67
Spain	-	0.24	1.71	1.35	14.14	16.21	16.13	16.58	15.00
Sweden	-	0.01	0.55	6.90	17.77	14.94	17.57	20.19	18.86
Switzerland	-	0.46	1.64	3.74	6.18	6.92	7.19	7.05	6.11
Turkey	-	-	-	-	-	-	-	-	-
United Kingdom	0.58	6.78	7.30	9.65	17.13	22.17	23.11	20.85	21.27
United States	0.14	6.08	23.24	69.37	159.38	207.89	205.31	211.96	211.28
OECD TOTAL	**..**	**..**	**49.22**	**162.25**	**450.01**	**584.94**	**579.51**	**604.35**	**611.43**
OECD N. AMERICA	..	..	27.31	79.77	179.55	229.00	227.56	237.91	238.08
OECD PACIFIC	..	..	2.53	22.43	66.50	112.32	96.34	107.67	117.67
OECD EUROPE	..	..	19.38	60.05	203.96	243.61	255.61	258.77	255.67
IEA	..	..	49.16	161.07	446.11	578.50	572.07	597.46	603.94

Production of Hydro Energy (Mtoe)

Production d'énergie hydraulique (Mtep)

Erzeugung von Wasserkraft (Mtoe)

Produzione di energia idroelettrica (Mtep)

水力の生産量（石油換算百万トン）

Producción de energía hidráulica (Mtep)

Производство гидроэнергии (Мтнэ)

	1960	1970	1973	1980	1990	2000	2003	2004	2005
Australia	0.34	0.76	0.98	1.11	1.22	1.44	1.38	1.35	1.35
Austria	0.98	1.78	1.61	2.47	2.71	3.60	2.83	3.13	3.09
Belgium	0.01	0.02	0.01	0.02	0.02	0.04	0.02	0.03	0.02
Canada	9.18	13.60	16.74	21.60	25.52	30.83	29.02	29.31	31.26
Czech Republic	..	..	0.09	0.21	0.10	0.15	0.12	0.17	0.20
Denmark	0.00	0.00	0.00	0.00	0.00	0.00	0.00	0.00	0.00
Finland	0.45	0.80	0.90	0.88	0.93	1.26	0.82	1.30	1.19
France	3.52	4.87	4.10	5.98	4.63	5.77	5.09	5.14	4.45
Germany	1.03	1.51	1.31	1.64	1.50	1.87	1.66	1.81	1.68
Greece	0.04	0.23	0.19	0.29	0.15	0.32	0.41	0.40	0.43
Hungary	..	0.01	0.01	0.01	0.02	0.02	0.01	0.02	0.02
Iceland	0.05	0.12	0.19	0.27	0.36	0.55	0.61	0.61	0.60
Ireland	0.08	0.07	0.06	0.07	0.06	0.07	0.05	0.05	0.05
Italy	3.94	3.47	3.23	3.89	2.72	3.80	2.91	3.41	2.89
Japan	5.03	6.48	5.74	7.59	7.68	7.50	8.14	8.09	6.73
Korea	..	..	0.11	0.17	0.55	0.34	0.42	0.37	0.32
Luxembourg	0.00	0.01	0.00	0.01	0.01	0.01	0.01	0.01	0.01
Mexico	..	..	1.39	1.45	2.02	2.85	1.71	2.17	2.38
Netherlands	-	-	-	-	0.01	0.01	0.01	0.01	0.01
New Zealand	0.48	0.98	1.23	1.63	2.01	2.10	2.04	2.34	2.02
Norway	2.69	4.97	6.27	7.19	10.42	11.95	9.08	9.36	11.68
Poland	0.05	0.15	0.13	0.20	0.12	0.18	0.14	0.18	0.19
Portugal	0.27	0.50	0.63	0.69	0.79	0.97	1.35	0.85	0.41
Slovak Republic	..	..	0.11	0.19	0.16	0.40	0.30	0.35	0.40
Spain	1.34	2.39	2.49	2.54	2.19	2.54 e	3.53	2.71	1.68
Sweden	2.67	3.57	5.15	5.06	6.24	6.76	4.60	5.17	6.26
Switzerland	1.76	2.66	2.40	2.82	2.56	3.17	2.99	2.90	2.69
Turkey	0.09	0.26	0.22	0.98	1.99	2.66	3.04	3.96	3.40
United Kingdom	0.27	0.39	0.33	0.33	0.45	0.44	0.28	0.42	0.43
United States	12.68	21.54	22.82	23.98	23.49	21.78	23.96	23.32	23.43
OECD TOTAL	**..**	**..**	**78.46**	**93.28**	**100.61**	**113.38**	**106.53**	**108.96**	**109.26**
OECD N. AMERICA	..	..	40.96	47.03	51.03	55.46	54.69	54.80	57.08
OECD PACIFIC	..	..	8.07	10.50	11.45	11.39	11.98	12.15	10.41
OECD EUROPE	..	..	29.44	35.75	38.13	46.53	39.87	42.02	41.78
IEA	..	..	76.64	91.17	97.94	109.40	103.77	105.65	105.69

Does not include electricity output from pumped storage plants.

Ne comprend pas la production d'électricité des centrales à accumulation par pompage.

Production of Geothermal Energy (Mtoe)
Production d'énergie géothermique (Mtep)
Erzeugung von geothermischer Energie (Mtoe)
Produzione di energia geotermica (Mtep)
地熱エネルギーの生産量（石油換算百万トン）
Producción de energía geotérmica (Mtep)
Производство геотермальной энергии (Мтнэ)

	1960	1970	1973	1980	1990	2000	2003	2004	2005
Australia	-	-	-	-	-	-	-	-	-
Austria	-	-	-	-	0.00	0.02 e	0.03 e	0.03	0.03
Belgium	-	-	-	-	0.00	0.00	0.00	0.00	0.00
Canada	-	-	-	-	-	-	-	-	-
Czech Republic	..	..	-	-	-	-	-	-	-
Denmark	-	-	-	-	0.00 e	0.00 e	0.00	0.00 e	0.00
Finland	-	-	-	-	-	-	-	-	-
France	-	-	0.00	0.01	0.11	0.13	0.13	0.13	0.13
Germany	-	-	-	-	0.01 e	0.12	0.14 e	0.14 e	0.15 e
Greece	-	-	-	-	0.00	0.00	0.00	0.00	0.00
Hungary	..	-	-	-	0.09	0.09	0.09 e	0.09	0.09
Iceland	0.11	0.27	0.35	0.64	1.04	1.76	1.85	1.90	2.03
Ireland	-	-	-	-	0.00	0.00	0.00	0.00	0.00
Italy	1.81	2.34	2.13	2.30	2.97	4.26 e	4.81	4.89	4.79
Japan	-	-	0.23	0.77	1.58	3.10	3.22	3.12	2.99
Korea	..	..	-	-	-	-	0.00	0.00	0.00
Luxembourg	-	-	-	-	-	-	-	-	-
Mexico	..	..	0.14	0.79	4.41	5.07	5.40	5.65	6.27
Netherlands	-	-	-	-	-	-	-	-	-
New Zealand	0.35	1.09	1.07	1.02	2.21	2.73	1.88	1.91	1.93
Norway	-	-	-	-	-	-	-	-	-
Poland	-	-	-	-	-	0.00	0.01	0.01	0.01
Portugal	-	-	-	0.00	0.00	0.07	0.08	0.08	0.07
Slovak Republic	..	..	-	-	-	-	0.01	0.01 e	0.01
Spain	-	-	-	-	-	0.01	0.01	0.01	0.01
Sweden	-	-	-	-	-	-	-	-	-
Switzerland	-	-	-	-	0.06	0.09	0.12	0.12	0.14
Turkey	-	0.02	0.05	0.06	0.43	0.68	0.86	0.89	1.01
United Kingdom	-	-	-	-	0.00	0.00	0.00	0.00	0.00
United States	0.03	0.48	2.11	4.60	14.10	13.09	8.39	8.59	8.63
OECD TOTAL	**..**	**..**	**6.08**	**10.19**	**27.01**	**31.22**	**27.03**	**27.59**	**28.29**
OECD N. AMERICA	..	..	2.25	5.39	18.51	18.16	13.79	14.25	14.91
OECD PACIFIC	..	..	1.30	1.79	3.79	5.83	5.11	5.03	4.92
OECD EUROPE	..	..	2.53	3.01	4.72	7.24	8.13	8.31	8.46
IEA	..	..	5.59	8.76	21.57	24.39	19.77	20.01	19.97

Production of Energy from Solar, Wind, Tide, etc. (Mtoe)

Production d'énergie d'origine solaire, éolienne, marémotrice, etc. (Mtep)

Erzeugung von Sonnenenergie, Windenergie, Gezeitenenergie usw. (Mtoe)

Produzione di energia solare, eolica, dalle maree, etc. (Mtep)

太陽光、風力、潮力、その他エネルギーの生産量（石油換算百万トン）

Producción de energía solar, eólica, maremotriz, etc. (Mtep)

Производство солнечной энергии, энергии ветра, приливов, и т.д. (Мтнэ)

	1960	1970	1973	1980	1990	2000	2003	2004	2005
Australia	-	-	-	0.02	0.08	0.09	0.15	0.12	0.14
Austria	-	-	-	-	0.01	0.07	0.11	0.17	0.21
Belgium	-	-	-	-	0.00	0.00	0.01	0.01	0.02
Canada	-	-	-	-	0.00	0.03 e	0.08 e	0.09	0.13
Czech Republic	..	..	-	-	-	-	0.00	0.00	0.00
Denmark	-	-	-	0.00	0.05	0.37 e	0.49 e	0.58 e	0.58 e
Finland	-	-	-	-	0.00	0.01	0.01	0.10	0.10
France	-	0.04	0.05	0.05	0.07	0.07	0.10	0.12	0.15
Germany	-	-	-	-	0.02	0.92	1.86	2.46	2.71
Greece	-	-	-	-	0.06	0.14	0.19	0.20	0.21
Hungary	..	-	-	-	-	-	0.00	0.00	0.00
Iceland	-	-	-	-	-	-	-	-	-
Ireland	-	-	-	-	0.00	0.02	0.04	0.06	0.10
Italy	-	-	-	-	0.01	0.06 e	0.14 e	0.18 e	0.22
Japan	-	-	-	-	1.17	0.82	0.71	0.69	0.73
Korea	..	..	-	-	0.01	0.04 e	0.04 e	0.04 e	0.05
Luxembourg	-	-	-	-	-	0.00	0.00	0.00	0.01
Mexico	..	..	-	-	-	0.05	0.07	0.08	0.08
Netherlands	-	-	-	-	0.01	0.10	0.15	0.20	0.22
New Zealand	-	-	-	-	-	0.01	0.02	0.04	0.06
Norway	-	-	-	-	-	0.00	0.02	0.02	0.04
Poland	-	-	-	-	-	0.00	0.01	0.01	0.01
Portugal	-	-	-	-	0.01	0.03	0.06	0.09	0.18
Slovak Republic	..	..	-	-	-	-	0.00	0.00	0.00
Spain	-	-	-	-	0.00	0.44	1.09	1.41	1.89 e
Sweden	-	-	-	-	0.00	0.04	0.06	0.08	0.09
Switzerland	-	-	-	-	0.01	0.02	0.02	0.03	0.03
Turkey	-	-	-	-	0.03	0.26	0.36	0.38	0.39
United Kingdom	-	-	-	-	0.01	0.09	0.13	0.19	0.28
United States	-	-	-	-	0.32	2.06 e	2.37	2.64	2.91
OECD TOTAL	**..**	**..**	**0.05**	**0.07**	**1.87**	**5.76**	**8.28**	**9.98**	**11.53**
OECD N. AMERICA	..	..	-	-	0.32	2.13	2.52	2.80	3.12
OECD PACIFIC	..	..	-	0.02	1.26	0.96	0.91	0.89	0.97
OECD EUROPE	..	..	0.05	0.05	0.29	2.67	4.85	6.29	7.44
IEA	..	..	0.05	0.07	1.87	5.72	8.20	9.89	11.44

Production of Combustible Renewables and Waste (Mtoe)
Production d'énergies renouvelables combustibles et de déchets (Mtep)

Erzeugung von erneuerbaren Brennstoffen und Abfällen (Mtoe)

Produzione di energia da combustibili rinnovabili e da rifiuti (Mtep)

可燃性再生可能エネルギー及び廃棄物の生産量（石油換算百万トン）

Producción de combustibles renovables y desechos (Mtep)

Производство возобновляемых видов топлива и отходов (Мтнэ)

	1960	1970	1973	1980	1990	2000	2003	2004	2005
Australia	4.09	3.54	3.53	3.61	3.96	5.03 e	5.14	5.30	5.24
Austria	0.77	0.66	0.70	1.13	2.43	3.14	3.75	3.91	4.10
Belgium	-	-	0.01	0.06	0.75	0.93	1.25	1.28	1.32 e
Canada	4.06	7.52	7.81	7.65 e	8.19 e	11.53 e	11.74 e	12.23 e	12.60 e
Czech Republic	..	..	-	-	-	0.64	1.57	1.84	1.93
Denmark	..	0.32 e	0.35	0.64	1.14 e	1.69	2.14	2.25	2.32
Finland	4.81	4.18	3.92	3.48	4.33	6.69	7.27	7.41	6.92
France	..	9.36	9.79	8.64	11.55	12.11	12.03	11.93	11.97
Germany	..	2.54	2.50	4.42 e	4.80 e	7.86 e	9.91	10.75	12.19
Greece	..	0.45	0.45	0.45	0.89	1.01	0.97	0.99	1.01
Hungary	..	0.51	0.59	0.53	0.42	0.41	0.82	0.87	1.11
Iceland	-	-	-	-	-	0.00	0.00	0.00	0.00
Ireland	-	-	-	-	0.11	0.16	0.17	0.20	0.24
Italy	..	0.30 e	0.24 e	0.82 e	0.85 e	1.74 e	2.44 e	3.39 e	3.52
Japan	-	-	-	-	4.97 e	5.84 e	6.10 e	6.10 e	6.29 e
Korea	..	..	-	-	0.71	1.35	1.78	1.98	2.12
Luxembourg	..	..	..	0.02	0.02	0.04	0.05	0.06	0.06
Mexico	..	..	6.21	6.88	7.34	7.95	8.01	8.05	8.31
Netherlands	..	..	..	0.23	0.95	1.74	1.88	1.92	2.04
New Zealand	..	..	..	0.52 e	0.55 e	0.71	0.79	0.83	0.87
Norway	..	..	..	0.58	1.03	1.35	1.29	1.26	1.29
Poland	0.87	1.08	1.29	1.22	2.23	4.07	4.49	4.60	4.80
Portugal	0.71	0.75	0.64	0.72	2.48	2.77	2.85	2.88	2.94
Slovak Republic	..	..	0.18	0.18	0.17	0.42 e	0.38 e	0.42 e	0.50
Spain	-	0.01	0.01	0.27	4.07 e	4.13 e	4.74 e	4.94 e	5.13
Sweden	2.55	2.91	3.54	4.13	5.51	8.26	8.14	8.32 e	8.98
Switzerland	0.35	0.24	0.24	0.47	0.90 e	1.27	1.47 e	1.72 e	1.92
Turkey	5.88	5.97	6.45	7.68	7.21	6.51 e	5.78 e	5.56 e	5.36
United Kingdom	-	-	-	-	0.63	1.92	2.94	3.08	3.29
United States	32.36	35.07	37.50	54.49	62.26 e	73.17	69.72	72.42	73.83 e
OECD TOTAL	**..**	**..**	**..**	**108.80**	**140.44**	**174.47**	**179.60**	**186.50**	**192.19**
OECD N. AMERICA	..	..	..	69.01	77.79	92.65	89.48	92.70	94.74
OECD PACIFIC	..	..	..	4.13	10.19	12.94	13.81	14.21	14.52
OECD EUROPE	..	..	..	35.66	52.46	68.88	76.32	79.59	82.93
IEA	..	..	..	100.53	130.69	162.02	166.72	173.42	178.58

Total Production of Energy (Mtoe)
Production totale d'énergie (Mtep)
Gesamte Energieerzeugung (Mtoe)
Produzione totale di energia (Mtep)
エネルギー総生産量（石油換算百万トン）
Producción total de energía (Mtep)
Общее производство топлива и энергии (Мтнэ)

	1960	1970	1973	1980	1990	2000	2003	2004	2005
Australia	21.31	47.70	67.97	86.10	157.53	233.61	253.89	259.02	270.98
Austria	7.36	7.95	7.93	7.63	8.10	9.75	9.79	10.04	9.81
Belgium	14.00	7.12	6.51	8.09	13.10	13.73	13.70	13.75	13.90
Canada	57.09	144.76	198.02	207.42	273.73	372.51	385.93	397.44	401.26
Czech Republic	..	..	38.51	41.21	40.10	29.88	33.36	34.49	32.87
Denmark	1.00	0.38	0.43	0.95	10.04	27.73	28.47	31.10	31.30
Finland	5.29	5.00	4.88	6.91	12.08	15.08	15.92	15.77	16.56
France	45.30	50.09	44.21	52.60	112.43	132.08	136.48	137.31	136.89
Germany	125.26	174.69	171.65	185.63	186.16	135.34	134.64	136.19	134.50
Greece	0.32	1.69	2.33	3.70	9.20	9.99	9.90	10.29	10.30
Hungary	..	11.77	12.70	14.49	14.33	11.27	10.41	10.24	10.33
Iceland	0.15	0.39	0.54	0.90	1.40	2.31	2.46	2.52	2.64
Ireland	1.38	1.42	1.12	1.89	3.47	2.18	1.86	1.89	1.66
Italy	13.84	19.87	20.46	19.90	25.31	28.17	27.59	28.15	27.63
Japan	46.98	39.34	29.50	43.28	75.21	105.79	84.00	95.01	99.77
Korea	..	..	6.76	9.27	22.62	32.59	37.94	38.27	42.93
Luxembourg	0.00	0.01	0.00	0.03	0.03	0.06	0.06	0.07	0.07
Mexico	..	..	47.29	147.62	194.78	226.09	242.31	253.60	259.20
Netherlands	10.20	28.87	56.76	71.82	60.54	57.19	58.44	67.66	61.90
New Zealand	2.49	3.40	4.05	5.47	12.01	14.86	12.97	12.74	12.20
Norway	2.97	5.29	8.08	55.31	120.32	229.05	235.50	238.60	233.70
Poland	64.81	95.76	107.40	122.22	99.37	79.59	79.86	78.83	78.63
Portugal	1.27	1.41	1.40	1.48	3.39	3.85	4.34	3.90	3.58
Slovak Republic	..	..	2.57	3.43	5.28	6.33	6.59	6.45	6.61
Spain	9.84	9.68	11.35	15.77	34.58	31.68	32.99	32.67	30.28
Sweden	5.48	6.49	9.25	16.13	29.75	30.59	31.04	34.46	34.78
Switzerland	2.11	3.36	4.28	7.03	9.72	11.47	11.79	11.82	10.88
Turkey	9.37	13.99	15.52	17.14	25.82	25.86	23.59	24.11	23.61
United Kingdom	114.81	101.34	108.49	197.85	208.00	272.39	246.60	225.43	204.30
United States	964.89	1 450.87	1 455.47	1 553.26	1 650.29	1 678.77	1 634.52	1 647.02	1 630.68
OECD TOTAL	**..**	**..**	**2 445.46**	**2 904.54**	**3 418.72**	**3 829.77**	**3 806.93**	**3 858.86**	**3 833.78**
OECD N. AMERICA	..	..	1 700.78	1 908.30	2 118.81	2 277.37	2 262.76	2 298.06	2 291.14
OECD PACIFIC	..	..	108.28	144.12	267.38	386.85	388.79	405.04	425.89
OECD EUROPE	..	..	636.39	852.12	1 032.54	1 165.55	1 155.37	1 155.75	1 116.75
IEA	..	..	2 287.65	2 630.36	3 117.89	3 515.47	3 475.71	3 517.46	3 486.69

Net Imports of Coal (Mtoe)
Importations nettes de charbon (Mtep)
Nettoimporte von Kohle (Mtoe)
Importazioni nette di carbone (Mtep)
石炭の純輸入量（石油換算百万トン）
Importaciones netas de carbón (Mtep)
Чистый импорт угля (Мтнэ)

	1960	1970	1973	1980	1990	2000	2003	2004	2005
Australia	- 0.75	- 11.16	- 17.65	- 28.49	- 67.26	- 121.45	- 135.50	- 141.70	- 150.34
Austria	3.37	3.55	3.01	2.80	3.17	3.00	3.50	3.93	3.97
Belgium	0.52	5.06	4.55	7.18	9.70	7.24	5.80	5.87	5.16
Canada	7.15	9.27	2.83	0.34	- 11.90	- 7.05	- 2.00 e	- 4.52 e	- 5.25 e
Czech Republic	..	..	- 2.41 e	- 6.78	- 5.69	- 4.74	- 3.36	- 2.90	- 3.28
Denmark	3.43	2.24	1.87	6.05	6.22	3.78	5.57	4.42	3.51
Finland	2.01	2.61	2.43	3.79	4.39	3.54	6.63	5.53	3.35
France	9.40	10.13	9.49	20.23	13.01	13.00	11.76	13.11	13.65
Germany	- 12.94	- 3.84	- 3.06	- 1.33	3.34	21.66	25.14	27.70	25.72
Greece	0.10	0.31	0.45	0.38	0.92	0.77	0.42	0.46	0.37
Hungary	..	2.01	1.63	2.20	1.63	1.08	1.00	1.10	1.30
Iceland	0.02	0.00	0.00	0.02	0.06	0.10	0.09	0.10	0.10
Ireland	1.15	0.79	0.50	0.81	2.01	1.70	1.75	1.92	1.97
Italy	7.23	8.97	7.73	11.65	13.74	13.14	14.53	16.78	16.37
Japan	6.09	35.63	40.89	47.55	72.59	96.52	106.48	116.48	112.47
Korea	..	..	0.34 e	3.47 e	15.73 e	38.45 e	46.51 e	50.25	46.90
Luxembourg	3.09	2.70	2.44	1.84	1.13	0.13	0.08	0.09	0.08
Mexico	..	..	0.27	0.59	0.23	1.70	3.79	2.36	3.77
Netherlands	1.56	1.90	1.54	3.72	9.46	8.22	9.23	8.58	8.31
New Zealand	- 0.01	- 0.00	- 0.02	- 0.05	- 0.22	- 1.12	- 1.60	- 0.93	- 1.13
Norway	0.54	0.80	0.58	0.79	0.67	0.60	- 1.10	- 1.01	- 0.41
Poland	- 13.02	- 20.40	- 26.17	- 20.50	- 18.91	- 16.31	- 14.72	- 14.97	- 12.99
Portugal	0.24	0.51	0.27	0.35	2.99	3.91	3.27	3.21	3.22
Slovak Republic	..	..	6.26	6.28	6.10	3.43	3.66	3.76	3.75
Spain	0.21	1.61	2.15	4.13	7.08	12.81	12.72	14.14	14.40
Sweden	2.52	1.81	1.68	1.68	2.57	2.34	2.49	2.50	2.46
Switzerland	1.76	0.49	0.22	0.51	0.34	0.19	0.08	0.13	0.10
Turkey	- 0.02	- 0.18	0.01	0.53	4.21	9.31	10.90	11.20	11.72
United Kingdom	- 3.83	- 2.38	- 0.87	1.40	8.53	14.74	20.01	22.59	27.32
United States	- 21.36	- 42.13	- 30.31	- 57.01	- 64.83	- 26.99	- 8.96	- 10.06	- 11.78
OECD TOTAL	..	..	**10.65**	**14.12**	**21.01**	**83.70**	**128.17**	**140.14**	**124.78**
OECD N. AMERICA	..	..	- 27.21	- 56.08	- 76.50	- 32.34	- 7.16	- 12.21	- 13.27
OECD PACIFIC	..	..	23.55	22.48	20.84	12.39	15.89	24.09	7.91
OECD EUROPE	..	..	14.31	47.72	76.67	103.64	119.44	128.27	130.14
IEA	..	..	30.28	27.73	33.52	94.79	135.34	148.89	130.16

A negative number shows net exports.
Un chiffre négatif correspond à des exportations nettes.

Net Imports of Oil (Mtoe)
Importations nettes de pétrole (Mtep)

Netto-Ölimporte (Mtoe)

Importazioni nette di petrolio (Mtep)

石油の純輸入量（石油換算百万トン）

Importaciones netas de petróleo (Mtep)

Чистый импорт нефти и нефтепродуктов (Мтнэ)

	1960	1970	1973	1980	1990	2000	2003	2004	2005
Australia	12.74	17.75	9.16	11.15	4.94	3.45	5.84	7.19	14.70
Austria	0.56	6.75	9.74	11.02	9.65	11.03	13.35	13.57	13.38
Belgium	7.75	27.28	31.29	26.26	22.51	29.20	31.93	30.72	30.72
Canada	16.16	4.25	- 14.28	8.39	- 14.94	- 39.12	- 49.32	- 51.81	- 47.15
Czech Republic	..	..	8.87	10.91	8.60	7.54	8.42	9.02	9.75
Denmark	5.24	19.34	18.69	13.36	2.75	- 8.48	- 9.29	- 10.70	- 9.41
Finland	2.70	12.51	13.84	14.35	10.79	10.78	11.59	11.38	11.18
France	28.96	98.87	131.35	112.28	86.16	89.99	93.78	93.87	94.18
Germany	29.09	135.30	161.22	149.34	122.70	127.38	126.30	122.41	123.43
Greece	2.64	6.69	11.56	13.19	14.31	19.27	19.68	21.53	20.10
Hungary	..	4.27	6.48	8.33	6.43	5.21	4.81	5.00	5.93
Iceland	0.39	0.54	0.70	0.59	0.74	0.95	0.86	0.98	0.98
Ireland	1.43	4.30	5.48	5.88	5.11	8.11	8.71	8.99	8.64
Italy	23.65	90.87	107.00	92.73	85.07	87.81	83.97	81.29	78.25
Japan	29.40	201.46	273.75	251.71	263.14	270.74	260.62	256.84	258.73
Korea	..	..	13.25	27.18	51.68	109.93	108.69	107.84	103.23
Luxembourg	0.23	1.34	1.67	1.12	1.65	2.39	2.75	3.01	3.14
Mexico	..	..	5.72	- 47.58	- 69.96	- 76.71	- 94.40	- 97.77	- 92.21
Netherlands	12.01	37.05	41.46	37.90	30.86	41.86	41.29	44.53	48.34
New Zealand	1.83	4.19	4.60	4.27	2.33	4.50	5.73	6.20	6.05
Norway	3.73	8.45	6.65	- 14.83	- 73.63	- 158.84	- 145.41	- 144.89	- 127.92
Poland	2.02	7.81	11.78	17.76	14.35	19.87	20.26	21.22	22.16
Portugal	1.77	4.74	6.22	9.45	12.43	16.08	16.37	15.72	16.85
Slovak Republic	..	..	5.25	7.45	4.50	2.60	3.05	3.15	3.15
Spain	6.41	28.82	40.95	49.95	49.56	71.58	75.71	77.47	80.16
Sweden	13.57	30.80	28.96	26.04	15.29	15.70	18.24	17.01	17.44
Switzerland	4.25	13.51	15.15	13.55	13.38	12.26	12.50	12.56	13.00
Turkey	1.18	4.48	8.82	13.77	21.28	29.41	28.32	28.94	28.14
United Kingdom	51.26	106.67	115.97	1.89	- 11.09	- 46.69	- 28.52	- 14.15	- 2.45
United States	83.46	163.68	305.41	340.34	374.92	550.23	594.72	641.07	660.16
OECD TOTAL	**..**	**..**	**1 386.70**	**1 217.76**	**1 065.50**	**1 218.01**	**1 270.56**	**1 322.21**	**1 392.65**
OECD N. AMERICA	..	..	296.85	301.15	290.02	434.39	451.00	491.49	520.79
OECD PACIFIC	..	..	300.76	294.32	322.09	388.62	380.88	378.07	382.70
OECD EUROPE	..	..	789.09	622.30	453.39	395.00	438.68	452.65	489.16
IEA	..	..	1 363.24	1 239.54	1 115.87	1 271.31	1 340.79	1 394.64	1 458.58

A negative number shows net exports.

Un chiffre négatif correspond à des exportations nettes.

Net Imports of Gas (Mtoe)

Importations nettes de gaz naturel (Mtep)

Nettoimporte von Erdgas (Mtoe)

Importazioni nette di gas naturale (Mtep)

ガスの純輸入量（石油換算百万トン）

Importaciones netas de gas natural (Mtep)

Чистый импорт природного газа (Мтнэ)

	1960	1970	1973	1980	1990	2000	2003	2004	2005
Australia	-	-	-	-	- 2.35	- 9.26	- 9.15	- 9.25	- 12.38
Austria	0.00	0.84	1.34	2.66	4.44	5.25	5.95	5.85	7.29
Belgium	- 0.02	3.38	7.11	8.89	8.21	13.27	14.24	14.55	14.19
Canada	- 2.43	- 17.29	- 22.77	- 18.37	- 32.51	- 81.33	- 75.35	- 77.52	- 79.55
Czech Republic	..	..	0.72 e	2.41	4.78	7.48	7.70	7.09	7.53
Denmark	-	-	-	-	- 0.93	- 2.88	- 2.59	- 3.69	- 5.01
Finland	-	-	-	0.77	2.18	3.42	4.08	3.95	3.60
France	0.10	2.86	7.56	16.17	24.36	35.77	37.52	38.66	40.71
Germany	- 0.00	2.83	12.29	35.31	41.74	56.85	62.42	65.88	65.72
Greece	-	-	-	-	-	1.69	2.00	2.17	2.33
Hungary	..	0.16	0.15	3.19	5.17	7.28	9.94	9.28	9.80
Iceland	-	-	-	-	-	-	-	-	-
Ireland	-	-	-	-	-	2.48	3.13	2.96	3.01
Italy	-	-	1.64	11.76	25.30	46.99	51.10	55.28	59.82
Japan	-	0.97	2.78	19.53	42.33	63.49	68.65	68.04	67.78
Korea	..	..	-	-	2.68	17.07	22.73	25.91	26.10
Luxembourg	-	0.02	0.22	0.42	0.43	0.67	1.06	1.20	1.18
Mexico	..	..	- 0.05	- 2.42	0.37	2.17	8.06	9.35 e	7.28
Netherlands	0.01	- 8.56	- 25.25	- 38.47	- 23.79	- 17.19	- 16.20	- 24.85	- 20.94
New Zealand	-	-	-	-	-	-	-	-	-
Norway	-	-	-	- 21.90	- 22.17	- 42.17	- 60.93	- 65.32	- 71.10
Poland	0.20	0.80	1.39	4.30	6.78	6.61	7.50	8.12	8.53
Portugal	-	-	-	-	-	2.04	2.64	3.30	3.89
Slovak Republic	..	..	1.17	3.28	5.35	5.71	5.50	5.68	5.73
Spain	-	0.09	0.93	1.41	3.69	15.46	21.16	24.61	30.24
Sweden	-	-	-	-	0.58	0.78	0.89	0.88	0.84
Switzerland	- 0.00	0.04	0.15	0.87	1.63	2.43	2.63	2.71	2.78
Turkey	-	-	-	-	2.68	12.05	17.28	18.12	22.13
United Kingdom	0.00	0.76	0.67	9.00	6.18	- 9.31	- 7.02	1.46	5.97
United States	3.39	17.53	22.11	21.68	33.18	82.18	76.08	79.52	84.16
OECD TOTAL	**..**	**..**	**12.16**	**60.50**	**140.32**	**228.99**	**261.01**	**273.93**	**291.64**
OECD N. AMERICA	..	..	- 0.72	0.89	1.04	3.02	8.79	11.35	11.89
OECD PACIFIC	..	..	2.78	19.53	42.67	71.29	82.23	84.70	81.51
OECD EUROPE	..	..	10.09	40.08	96.62	154.67	169.99	177.88	198.25
IEA	..	..	9.65	55.33	127.83	214.51	239.95	250.79	270.10

A negative number shows net exports.

Un chiffre négatif correspond à des exportations nettes.

Net Imports of Electricity (Mtoe)
Importations nettes d'électricité (Mtep)
Nettoimporte von Elektrizität (Mtoe)

Importazioni nette di energia elettrica (Mtep)

電力の純輸入量（石油換算百万トン）

Importaciones netas de electricidad (Mtep)

Чистый импорт электроэнергии (Мтнэ)

	1960	1970	1973	1980	1990	2000	2003	2004	2005
Australia	-	-	-	-	-	-	-	-	-
Austria	- 0.16	- 0.47	- 0.13	- 0.34	- 0.04	- 0.12	0.48	0.26	0.23
Belgium	0.00	0.03	- 0.06	- 0.23	- 0.32	0.37	0.55	0.67	0.54
Canada	- 0.44	- 0.21	- 1.21	- 2.34	- 0.03	- 3.07	- 0.58	- 0.93	- 2.05
Czech Republic	..	..	- 0.19	- 0.13	- 0.06	- 0.86	- 1.39	- 1.35	- 1.09
Denmark	0.01	- 0.36	- 0.02	- 0.11	0.61	0.06	- 0.73	- 0.25	0.12
Finland	0.04	0.05	0.37	0.10	0.92	1.02	0.42	0.42	1.46
France	- 0.01	- 0.04	- 0.25	0.28	- 3.91	- 5.98	- 5.71	- 5.32	- 5.19
Germany	0.36	0.70	0.99	0.61	0.08	0.26	- 0.04 e	- 0.23	- 0.39
Greece	0.00	0.00	0.00	0.05	0.06	- 0.00	0.18	0.24	0.33
Hungary	..	0.29	0.40	0.64	0.96	0.30	0.60	0.64	0.54
Iceland	-	-	-	-	-	-	-	-	-
Ireland	-	-	0.00	-	-	0.01	0.10	0.14	0.18
Italy	- 0.01	0.34	0.08	0.52	2.98	3.81	4.38	3.92	4.23
Japan	-	-	-	-	-	-	-	-	-
Korea	..	..	-	-	-	-	-	-	-
Luxembourg	0.00	0.13	0.18	0.24	0.34	0.49	0.32	0.29	0.28
Mexico	..	..	0.03	0.05	- 0.12	0.08	- 0.07	- 0.08	- 0.10
Netherlands	0.01	- 0.03	- 0.12	- 0.03	0.79	1.63	1.46	1.39	1.57
New Zealand	-	-	-	-	-	-	-	-	-
Norway	0.01	- 0.07	- 0.45	- 0.04	- 1.37	- 1.64	0.68	0.99	- 1.04
Poland	0.03	0.00	- 0.15	- 0.02	- 0.09	- 0.55	- 0.87	- 0.80	- 0.96
Portugal	0.00	0.00	- 0.00	0.16	0.00	0.08	0.24	0.56	0.59
Slovak Republic	..	..	0.24	0.29	0.45	- 0.23	- 0.19	- 0.16	- 0.28
Spain	- 0.01	- 0.13	- 0.17	- 0.12	- 0.04	0.38	0.11	- 0.26	- 0.12
Sweden	- 0.07	0.35	0.06	0.05	- 0.15	0.40	1.10	- 0.18	- 0.64
Switzerland	- 0.22	- 0.52	- 0.30	- 0.70	- 0.18	- 0.61	- 0.27	- 0.06	0.55
Turkey	-	-	-	0.12	- 0.06	0.29	0.05	- 0.06	- 0.10
United Kingdom	- 0.00	0.05	0.01	0.00	1.03	1.22	0.19	0.64	0.72
United States	0.39	0.17	1.23	2.30	0.17	2.92	0.55	0.97	2.13
OECD TOTAL	**..**	**..**	**0.54**	**1.35**	**2.01**	**0.27**	**1.54**	**1.47**	**1.49**
OECD N. AMERICA	..	..	0.05	0.01	0.02	- 0.07	- 0.11	- 0.04	- 0.03
OECD PACIFIC	..	..	-	-	-	-	-	-	-
OECD EUROPE	..	..	0.49	1.35	1.99	0.34	1.64	1.51	1.52
IEA	..	..	0.42	1.03	1.77	0.97	2.68	2.51	2.84

A negative number shows net exports.

Un chiffre négatif correspond à des exportations nettes.

Total Net Imports of Energy (Mtoe)

Importations nettes totales d'énergie (Mtep)

Gesamte Nettoimporte von Energie (Mtoe)

Importazioni nette totali di energia (Mtep)

エネルギー純輸入量（石油換算百万トン）

Importaciones netas totales de energía (Mtep)

Общий чистый импорт топлива и энергии (Мтнэ)

	1960	1970	1973	1980	1990	2000	2003	2004	2005
Australia	11.99	6.59	- 8.49	- 17.34	- 64.67	- 127.26	- 138.81	- 143.76	- 148.02
Austria	3.77	10.68	13.97	16.15	17.27	19.12	23.17	23.55	24.76
Belgium	8.25	35.75	42.89	42.11	40.10	50.20	52.68	52.02	50.89
Canada	20.44	- 3.98	- 35.43	- 11.99	- 59.38	- 130.52	- 127.20	- 134.72	- 133.96
Czech Republic	..	..	6.99	6.41	7.63	9.41	11.31	11.71	12.72
Denmark	8.68	21.22	20.54	19.30	8.65	- 7.46	- 6.88	- 9.99	- 10.52
Finland	4.75	15.17	16.64	19.01	18.28	18.77	22.67	21.21	19.51
France	38.45	111.82	148.15	148.96	119.62	132.79	137.31	140.27	143.30
Germany	16.50	134.98	171.44	183.86	167.85	206.14	213.81	215.76	214.47
Greece	2.74	7.00	12.01	13.63	15.29	21.72	22.29	24.41	23.13
Hungary	..	6.73	8.66	14.36	14.16	13.86	16.35	16.01	17.58
Iceland	0.41	0.54	0.70	0.60	0.80	1.05	0.95	1.08	1.08
Ireland	2.59	5.09	5.99	6.69	7.12	12.29	13.70	14.00	13.80
Italy	30.87	100.18	116.44	116.77	127.19	152.28	154.64	157.93	159.33
Japan	35.49	238.06	317.43	318.80	378.07	430.74	435.75	441.36	438.98
Korea	..	..	13.58	30.66	70.11	165.48	177.96	184.02	176.26
Luxembourg	3.32	4.20	4.51	3.63	3.55	3.68	4.21	4.59	4.68
Mexico	..	..	5.97	- 49.35	- 69.48	- 72.77	- 82.61	- 86.15	- 81.27
Netherlands	13.58	30.35	17.64	3.12	17.32	34.53	35.84	29.92	37.86
New Zealand	1.82	4.18	4.58	4.22	2.11	3.38	4.13	5.27	4.92
Norway	4.28	9.18	6.79	- 35.98	- 96.49	- 202.05	- 206.71	- 210.21	- 200.44
Poland	- 10.78	- 11.79	- 13.15	1.55	2.12	9.61	12.17	13.57	16.68
Portugal	2.01	5.26	6.49	9.95	15.43	22.11	22.52	22.79	24.55
Slovak Republic	..	..	12.94	17.29	16.40	11.50	12.00	12.41	12.31
Spain	6.62	30.39	43.86	55.37	60.29	100.24	109.71	115.96	124.68
Sweden	16.02	32.96	30.70	27.77	18.29	19.22	22.72	20.22	20.11
Switzerland	5.78	13.52	15.23	14.22	15.18	14.28	14.94	15.35	16.43
Turkey	1.16	4.30	8.83	14.42	28.11	51.06	56.55	58.20	61.89
United Kingdom	47.43	105.09	115.77	12.29	4.64	- 40.04	- 15.24	10.91	32.26
United States	65.88	139.25	298.43	307.30	343.44	608.35	662.41	711.74	734.87
OECD TOTAL	..	..	**1 410.07**	**1 293.78**	**1 229.00**	**1 531.69**	**1 662.32**	**1 739.44**	**1 812.81**
OECD N. AMERICA	..	..	268.97	245.96	214.58	405.05	452.59	490.87	519.64
OECD PACIFIC	..	..	327.09	336.33	385.62	472.33	479.02	486.89	472.14
OECD EUROPE	..	..	814.01	711.49	628.80	654.30	730.70	761.68	821.03
IEA	..	..	1 403.61	1 323.69	1 279.15	1 582.30	1 719.81	1 798.53	1 864.02

A negative number shows net exports.

Un chiffre négatif correspond à des exportations nettes.

Primary Supply of Coal (Mtoe)

Approvisionnement primaire en charbon (Mtep)

Primäraufkommen von Kohle (Mtoe)

Disponibilità primaria di carbone (Mtep)

石炭の一次供給量（石油換算百万トン）

Suministro primario de carbón (Mtep)

Первичная поставка угля (Мтнэ)

	1960	1970	1973	1980	1990	2000	2003	2004	2005
Australia	15.89	21.40	22.58	27.32	34.98	48.15	48.29	49.47	54.32
Austria	5.06	4.54	3.87	3.65	4.10	3.58	4.06	4.05	4.06
Belgium	15.96	12.34	11.18	11.40	10.65	7.95	5.95	5.79	5.09
Canada	12.56	17.11	15.26	21.22	24.28	28.84	30.00	28.44	27.98
Czech Republic	..	..	35.59	33.42	31.46	21.53	20.97	20.96	20.19
Denmark	4.11	2.19	1.93	5.88	6.09	3.99	5.67	4.36	3.72
Finland	1.93	2.34	2.55	4.95	5.32	5.09	8.33	7.52	4.93
France	44.62	37.08	29.24	32.89	20.21	15.04	14.36	13.90	14.42
Germany	109.44	147.79	139.37	141.03	128.53	84.83	85.02	85.83	81.69
Greece	0.40	1.33	2.10	3.26	8.07	9.04	8.91	9.10	8.95
Hungary	..	7.97	7.91	8.43	6.12	3.97	3.75	3.47	3.07
Iceland	0.02	0.00	0.00	0.02	0.06	0.10	0.09	0.10	0.10
Ireland	2.46	2.11	1.59	1.91	3.45	2.53	2.49	2.24	2.69
Italy	7.96	9.17	8.10	11.68	14.63	12.56	14.88	16.60	16.47
Japan	47.51	61.62	57.86	59.56	77.19	97.95	106.44	116.48	112.07
Korea	..	..	8.13	13.49	25.56	39.45	48.18	50.09	49.47
Luxembourg	3.08	2.65	2.44	1.82	1.13	0.13	0.08	0.09	0.08
Mexico	..	..	1.84	2.37	3.47	6.85	8.23	7.13	8.74
Netherlands	9.91	4.71	2.87	3.79	8.93	8.05	8.84	8.70	8.19
New Zealand	1.57	1.19	1.26	1.02	1.13	1.04	1.81	1.81	2.00
Norway	0.78	1.08	0.91	1.01	0.86	1.08	0.79	0.93	0.78
Poland	50.48	69.17	74.69	95.98	75.41	56.31	56.19	54.19	54.61
Portugal	0.55	0.71	0.51	0.43	2.76	3.81	3.28	3.37	3.35
Slovak Republic	..	..	7.96	8.20	7.82	4.27	4.59	4.52	4.24
Spain	8.83	9.02	9.03	12.43	19.29	20.92	20.11	21.02	20.49
Sweden	2.83	1.91	1.63	1.71	2.96	2.45	2.67	2.94	2.62
Switzerland	1.76	0.57	0.33	0.33	0.36	0.14	0.14	0.13	0.15
Turkey	3.20	4.24	5.15	6.99	16.91	22.91	21.22	22.38	22.47
United Kingdom	114.31	88.65	76.43	68.80	63.11	36.99	38.64	37.35	37.68
United States	222.86	291.42	311.05	376.23	458.30	543.58	531.17	548.77	555.66
OECD TOTAL	**..**	**..**	**843.35**	**961.19**	**1 063.14**	**1 093.10**	**1 105.14**	**1 131.74**	**1 130.27**
OECD N. AMERICA	..	..	328.15	399.82	486.05	579.26	569.40	584.34	592.37
OECD PACIFIC	..	..	89.84	101.38	138.86	186.60	204.72	217.85	217.86
OECD EUROPE	..	..	425.36	459.99	438.23	327.25	331.02	329.55	320.04
IEA	..	..	758.86	854.63	976.38	1 025.58	1 036.04	1 065.79	1 062.59

Primary Supply of Oil (Mtoe)

Approvisionnement primaire en pétrole (Mtep)

Primäraufkommen von Öl (Mtoe)

Disponibilità primaria di petrolio (Mtep)

石油の一次供給量（石油換算百万トン）

Suministro primario de petróleo (Mtep)

Первичная поставка нефти и нефтепродуктов (Мтнэ)

	1960	1970	1973	1980	1990	2000	2003	2004	2005
Australia	11.22	24.42	27.15	30.84	32.52	36.50	35.93	34.56	37.87
Austria	3.01	9.20	12.28	12.23	10.63	12.27	14.28	14.30	14.50
Belgium	7.22	24.42	28.02	23.58	18.75	23.77	24.76	23.02	22.79
Canada	42.11	71.06	79.89	88.92	77.33	87.77	92.84	97.95	97.37
Czech Republic	..	..	8.91	11.15	8.96	7.89	8.77	9.62	9.98
Denmark	4.91	18.12	17.57	13.36	8.18	8.74	8.39	8.40	8.21
Finland	2.55	10.71	13.57	13.41	10.25	9.63	10.75	11.23	10.70
France	28.80	93.64	124.32	108.12	87.28	87.25	91.13	92.13	91.44
Germany	31.08	137.92	161.88	147.07	126.47	131.72	126.51	125.21	123.40
Greece	2.09	6.09	9.61	11.64	12.81	15.61	17.19	17.30	17.69
Hungary	..	6.05	8.21	10.93	8.51	6.86	6.30	6.44	7.23
Iceland	0.39	0.54	0.70	0.61	0.71	0.84	0.84	0.88	0.89
Ireland	1.25	4.08	5.54	5.77	4.87	8.05	8.49	8.82	8.57
Italy	20.94	82.52	100.11	89.55	84.73	88.45	86.87	83.77	81.78
Japan	27.73	184.86	252.18	235.68	255.01	262.76	256.87	253.60	251.69
Korea	..	..	13.40	26.81	50.03	103.53	101.20	101.43	96.16
Luxembourg	0.23	1.34	1.67	1.12	1.64	2.34	2.74	3.02	3.16
Mexico	..	..	33.10	66.47	83.34	91.83	91.71	96.12	103.84
Netherlands	10.94	29.07	30.91	29.48	24.35	28.60	31.53	31.96	32.88
New Zealand	1.66	3.87	4.42	4.22	3.96	6.31	6.74	7.03	6.82
Norway	3.48	7.58	7.90	9.04	8.57	9.41	9.89	10.58	14.17
Poland	2.10	7.91	10.89	16.89	13.27	19.46	20.23	21.71	22.14
Portugal	1.48	4.04	5.45	8.30	11.71	15.53	15.28	15.42	15.90
Slovak Republic	..	..	5.37	7.47	4.49	2.82	3.19	3.21	3.46
Spain	6.00	26.72	38.38	50.66	46.46	64.85	69.04	70.77	71.28
Sweden	12.56	29.19	28.39	22.90	14.67	14.23	15.75	15.45	14.87
Switzerland	3.95	13.03	15.26	13.34	13.46	12.73	12.58	12.53	12.79
Turkey	1.54	7.72	12.50	15.69	23.61	31.08	29.77	30.09	29.90
United Kingdom	45.23	101.28	111.55	82.19	82.63	83.66	81.08	83.20	84.68
United States	469.16	703.57	823.99	803.90	770.25	891.00	921.41	947.47	952.84
OECD TOTAL	**..**	**..**	**1 993.13**	**1 961.34**	**1 899.44**	**2 165.51**	**2 202.07**	**2 237.22**	**2 249.00**
OECD N. AMERICA	..	..	936.98	959.29	930.92	1 070.60	1 105.96	1 141.54	1 154.05
OECD PACIFIC	..	..	297.15	297.56	341.53	409.11	400.74	396.62	392.55
OECD EUROPE	..	..	759.00	704.50	626.99	685.81	695.36	699.05	702.40
IEA	..	..	1 943.07	1 869.90	1 797.64	2 050.56	2 086.10	2 115.30	2 118.67

Primary Supply of Gas (Mtoe)
Approvisionnement primaire en gaz (Mtep)

Primäraufkommen von Gas (Mtoe)

Disponibilità primaria di gas (Mtep)

ガスの一次供給量（石油換算百万トン）

Suministro primario de gas natural (Mtep)

Первичная поставка газа (Мтнэ)

	1960	1970	1973	1980	1990	2000	2003	2004	2005
Australia	-	1.20	3.38	7.46	14.79	19.27	22.15	22.74	23.04
Austria	1.27	2.46	3.30	4.16	5.18	6.52	7.55	7.46	8.26
Belgium	0.03	3.41	7.14	8.91	8.17	13.36	14.40	14.76	14.11
Canada	8.80	29.18	37.27	45.55	54.73	74.24	79.71	78.00	80.63
Czech Republic	..	..	1.01	2.60	5.26	7.50	7.84	7.79	7.70
Denmark	-	-	0.00	0.00	1.82	4.45	4.66	4.63	4.40
Finland	-	-	-	0.77	2.18	3.42	4.08	3.95	3.60
France	2.50	8.24	13.56	21.64	26.02	35.76	39.31	40.14	40.98
Germany	0.73	12.30	28.67	51.18	54.99	71.83	79.11	78.71	80.83
Greece	-	-	-	-	0.14	1.70	2.03	2.23	2.35
Hungary	..	3.12	4.17	7.97	8.91	9.65	11.88	11.71	12.09
Iceland	-	-	-	-	-	-	-	-	-
Ireland	-	-	-	0.74	1.87	3.43	3.65	3.64	3.47
Italy	5.28	10.61	14.22	22.72	38.99	57.92	63.60	66.00	70.63
Japan	0.64	3.05	5.07	21.40	44.16	65.65	71.30	70.56	70.54
Korea	..	..	-	-	2.72	17.01	22.00	25.28	27.37
Luxembourg	-	0.02	0.22	0.42	0.43	0.67	1.06	1.20	1.18
Mexico	..	..	10.49	19.13	23.12	33.51	41.97	43.70	44.19
Netherlands	0.29	15.42	28.50	30.42	30.80	34.70	35.99	36.73	35.31
New Zealand	0.06	0.09	0.28	0.79	3.90	5.06	3.86	3.45	3.19
Norway	-	-	-	0.87	1.98	3.63	5.32	5.07	5.16
Poland	0.66	5.20	6.25	8.77	8.94	9.96	11.26	11.88	12.23
Portugal	-	-	-	-	-	2.03	2.64	3.30	3.75
Slovak Republic	..	..	1.56	3.42	5.09	5.77	5.67	5.50	5.88
Spain	-	0.11	0.94	1.45	4.97	15.21	21.35	25.16	29.84
Sweden	-	-	-	-	0.58	0.78	0.89	0.88	0.84
Switzerland	- 0.00	0.04	0.15	0.87	1.63	2.43	2.63	2.71	2.78
Turkey	-	-	-	-	2.85	12.63	17.72	18.70	22.79
United Kingdom	0.06	10.17	25.11	40.31	47.19	87.37	85.86	87.36	84.87
United States	283.73	499.03	514.51	476.78	439.18	551.10	519.80	512.12	509.41
OECD TOTAL	**..**	**..**	**705.83**	**778.34**	**840.58**	**1 156.59**	**1 189.26**	**1 195.39**	**1 211.44**
OECD N. AMERICA	..	..	562.28	541.47	517.03	658.85	641.47	633.83	634.24
OECD PACIFIC	..	..	8.74	29.65	65.56	106.98	119.31	122.04	124.14
OECD EUROPE	..	..	134.81	207.22	257.98	390.75	428.48	439.52	453.06
IEA	..	..	687.52	747.02	803.43	1 107.34	1 130.37	1 134.31	1 149.13

Total Primary Energy Supply (TPES) (Mtoe)

Approvisionnements totaux en énergie primaire (ATEP) (Mtep)

Gesamtaufkommen von Primärenergie (TPES) (Mtoe)

Disponibilità totale di energia primaria (DTEP) (Mtep)

一次エネルギー総供給量（石油換算百万トン）

Suministro total de energía primaria (TPES) (Mtep)

Общая первичная поставка топлива и энергии (ОППТЭ) (Мтнэ)

	1960	1970	1973	1980	1990	2000	2003	2004	2005
Australia	31.55	51.33	57.62	70.37	87.55	110.49	113.05	113.54	121.96
Austria	10.93	18.18	21.65	23.30	25.07	29.04	32.99	33.25	34.36
Belgium	23.24	40.24	46.32	47.01	49.16	59.09	59.44	58.10	56.65
Canada	76.27	138.52	159.84	193.00	209.41	249.18	262.36	268.70	271.95
Czech Republic	..	..	45.42	47.25	48.99	40.39	44.58	45.77	45.21
Denmark	9.03	20.27	19.83	19.78	17.90	19.36	20.78	20.20	19.61
Finland	9.78	18.07	21.35	25.41	29.17	32.98	37.55	37.85	34.96
France	79.47	154.69	184.65	193.57	227.82	258.36	271.33	274.93	275.97
Germany	142.65	304.45	337.88	360.39	356.22	343.62	347.18	348.22	344.75
Greece	2.53	8.09	12.35	15.70	22.18	27.82	29.88	30.47	30.98
Hungary	..	17.94	21.33	28.49	28.56	25.01	26.34	26.36	27.76
Iceland	0.56	0.93	1.24	1.53	2.17	3.24	3.39	3.50	3.63
Ireland	3.78	6.26	7.19	8.49	10.37	14.28	15.00	15.15	15.29
Italy	39.93	109.58	128.93	132.15	147.97	173.12	180.68	182.80	185.19
Japan	80.92	257.21	323.62	346.53	444.47	527.56	515.32	532.26	530.46
Korea	..	..	21.64	41.37	93.39	190.15	207.44	213.28	213.77
Luxembourg	3.31	4.15	4.50	3.64	3.57	3.68	4.26	4.68	4.78
Mexico	..	..	53.20	97.13	124.34	150.32	159.76	165.22	176.53
Netherlands	21.15	49.26	62.44	64.98	66.75	75.86	80.97	82.17	81.85
New Zealand	4.12	7.23	8.27	9.20	13.76	17.95	17.13	17.43	16.91
Norway	6.97	13.56	14.63	18.65	21.51	25.81	27.14	28.27	32.12
Poland	54.19	83.51	93.08	123.03	99.88	89.43	91.45	91.79	92.97
Portugal	3.00	5.99	7.23	10.29	17.75	25.29	25.78	26.55	27.17
Slovak Republic	..	..	15.50	20.93	21.32	17.74	18.63	18.33	18.83
Spain	16.16	38.35	52.39	68.58	91.07	124.69	136.09	142.34	145.20
Sweden	20.54	37.95	39.32	40.75	47.57	48.21	51.10	53.18	52.17
Switzerland	7.59	16.48	19.72	20.86	24.99	26.16	26.87	27.13	27.15
Turkey	10.71	18.22	24.37	31.51	52.97	77.03	78.79	81.90	85.21
United Kingdom	160.46	207.31	220.72	201.28	212.18	233.86	232.33	233.46	233.93
United States	1 021.36	1 557.36	1 736.45	1 811.65	1 927.46	2 306.64	2 282.78	2 328.55	2 340.29
OECD TOTAL	..	..	**3 762.69**	**4 076.85**	**4 525.49**	**5 326.37**	**5 400.40**	**5 505.39**	**5 547.60**
OECD N. AMERICA	..	..	1 949.49	2 101.78	2 261.21	2 706.14	2 704.91	2 762.48	2 788.77
OECD PACIFIC	..	..	411.15	467.47	639.16	846.15	852.94	876.51	883.10
OECD EUROPE	..	..	1 402.06	1 507.60	1 625.12	1 774.08	1 842.56	1 866.41	1 875.72
IEA	..	..	3 599.68	3 834.22	4 277.78	5 065.64	5 127.17	5 226.56	5 255.64

Electricity Generation from Coal (% of total)

Production d'électricité à partir du charbon (% du total)

Elektrizitätserzeugung auf Kohlebasis (in %)

Produzione di energia termoelettrica da carbone (% del totale)

石炭からの発電量(%)

Generación de electricidad a partir del carbón (% del total)

Производство электроэнергии за счет потребления угля (в % к общему производству)

	1960	1970	1973	1980	1990	2000	2003	2004	2005
Australia	74.42	75.97	74.88	73.25	77.12	77.43	77.17	79.41	80.14
Austria	13.86	9.72	10.32	7.02	14.22	11.09	16.36	14.79	13.47
Belgium	85.36	33.64	21.68	29.36	28.25	19.37	13.89	13.61	12.24
Canada	3.38	17.93	12.92	16.02	17.06	19.42	19.17	16.94	16.91
Czech Republic	..	..	85.14	84.75	76.43	72.53	61.51	60.32	60.76
Denmark	71.62	31.21	35.80	81.84	90.68	46.25	54.80	46.19	42.64
Finland	29.68	30.35	28.07	42.63	33.04	18.86	31.78	27.56	16.53
France	36.47	30.55	19.66	27.35	8.49	5.76	5.21	4.79	5.37
Germany	87.03	74.46	69.00	62.94	58.73	52.72	52.75	50.27	49.81
Greece	53.36	38.32	35.45	44.85	72.37	64.23	60.74	60.16	59.81
Hungary	..	65.03	66.01	50.44	30.49	27.58	27.10	24.74	19.99
Iceland	-	-	-	-	-	-	-	-	-
Ireland	53.32	32.36	24.92	16.40	57.37	36.27	33.11	30.60	34.49
Italy	3.82	4.90	3.60	9.95	16.78	11.31	15.57	17.36	16.79
Japan	32.21	16.94	8.01	9.60	13.97	22.27	27.45	27.49	28.27
Korea	..	..	9.05	6.66	16.76	37.03	39.11	38.80	38.36
Luxembourg	97.81	74.72	58.82	51.63	76.44	-	-	-	-
Mexico	..	..	0.56	-	6.26	9.37	14.33	10.66	14.02
Netherlands	79.69	19.81	6.04	13.69	38.26	28.39	28.39	26.04	26.87
New Zealand	14.42	6.12	8.52	1.89	1.90	4.18	10.02	11.13	13.54
Norway	-	-	0.03	0.02	0.07	0.05	0.12	0.10	0.10
Poland	97.46	91.70	93.90	94.71	97.49	96.15	95.06	94.06	93.44
Portugal	1.10	4.93	3.94	2.30	32.11	33.87	31.23	33.15	32.97
Slovak Republic	..	..	64.40	37.86	31.86	19.84	20.73	20.14	19.14
Spain	12.90	21.72	18.87	30.01	40.13	36.38	29.45	28.98	27.79
Sweden	1.08	0.28	0.64	0.19	1.09	1.75	3.20	1.65	1.22
Switzerland	-	-	-	0.13	0.07	-	-	-	-
Turkey	54.67	32.75	26.11	25.61	35.07	30.57	22.94	22.86	26.67
United Kingdom	81.09	68.81	62.06	73.18	64.97	32.67	35.36	33.95	34.35
United States	53.91	46.39	46.16	51.20	53.07	52.90	51.38	50.40	50.46
OECD TOTAL	**..**	**..**	**38.03**	**41.06**	**40.42**	**38.64**	**38.88**	**37.91**	**37.98**
OECD N. AMERICA	..	..	41.47	45.43	46.99	46.87	45.82	44.57	44.69
OECD PACIFIC	..	..	15.71	17.54	22.52	31.64	36.29	36.71	37.45
OECD EUROPE	..	..	40.98	43.30	38.60	29.62	30.09	28.88	28.37
IEA	..	..	37.21	40.41	40.01	38.49	38.65	37.75	37.77

Electricity Generation from Oil (% of total)

Production d'électricité à partir du pétrole (% du total)

Elektrizitätserzeugung auf Ölbasis (in %)

Produzione di energia termoelettrica da prodotti petroliferi (% del totale)

石油からの発電量 (%)

Generación de electricidad a partir del petróleo (% del total)

Производство электроэнергии за счет потребления нефти (в % к общему производству)

	1960	1970	1973	1980	1990	2000	2003	2004	2005
Australia	5.52	4.64	2.61	5.43	2.73	1.31	1.00	0.65	0.77
Austria	4.28	7.03	14.06	13.96	3.82	2.58	3.03	2.95	2.61
Belgium	13.23	52.08	53.72	34.67	1.87	0.96	1.21	1.99	2.03
Canada	1.03	3.06	3.36	3.70	3.42	2.43	3.66	3.87	3.10
Czech Republic	..	..	11.30	9.55	0.87	0.51	0.44	0.42	0.40
Denmark	27.92	68.67	64.07	18.00	3.38	12.30	5.08	4.04	3.78
Finland	9.09	27.55	31.65	10.84	3.09	0.87	1.11	0.72	0.70
France	3.55	21.97	40.17	18.83	2.08	1.34	1.26	1.15	1.27
Germany	2.71	12.21	11.98	5.73	1.90	0.84	0.79	1.66	1.73
Greece	26.33	34.84	49.54	40.12	22.27	16.63	15.04	14.26	15.49
Hungary	..	19.86	17.19	13.89	4.75	12.51	4.76	2.29	1.27
Iceland	4.54	2.96	3.75	1.48	0.13	0.07	0.07	0.05	0.06
Ireland	5.48	53.79	66.32	60.43	10.04	19.59	9.87	12.73	13.03
Italy	6.67	49.19	62.36	57.00	48.19	31.81	26.81	20.10	16.01
Japan	17.06	59.24	73.24	46.23	29.85	13.82	13.73	12.34	13.34
Korea	..	..	82.29	78.67	17.90	9.34	9.21	8.04	6.70
Luxembourg	0.82	18.05	27.62	10.89	1.44	-	-	-	-
Mexico	..	..	41.13	57.94	56.68	47.71	29.94	31.06	29.26
Netherlands	19.42	32.60	12.33	38.42	4.33	3.49	2.95	2.80	2.26
New Zealand	-	3.31	6.11	0.17	0.02	-	0.05	0.05	0.01
Norway	0.70	0.63	0.19	0.15	0.00	0.01	0.03	0.03	0.01
Poland	0.11	2.19	2.34	2.89	1.17	1.34	1.64	1.64	1.54
Portugal	2.44	14.53	19.21	42.89	33.15	19.42	13.48	12.71	19.03
Slovak Republic	..	..	17.71	17.94	6.41	0.66	2.28	2.42	2.36
Spain	3.16	27.23	33.19	35.19	5.69	10.16	9.31	8.60	8.40
Sweden	10.10	30.95	19.44	10.38	0.89	1.06	2.86	1.29	0.87
Switzerland	0.87	6.04	7.07	1.02	0.70	0.35	0.38	0.33	0.33
Turkey	8.28	30.15	51.36	25.05	6.85	7.45	6.54	5.09	3.39
United Kingdom	15.04	18.57	25.65	11.67	10.91	2.26	1.16	1.24	1.36
United States	6.42	12.12	17.09	10.84	4.08	2.94	3.38	3.35	3.31
OECD TOTAL	**..**	**..**	**25.26**	**17.34**	**9.16**	**6.07**	**5.70**	**5.33**	**5.18**
OECD N. AMERICA	..	..	15.85	11.01	5.71	4.76	4.60	4.66	4.47
OECD PACIFIC	..	..	63.19	41.12	24.17	11.06	10.70	9.50	9.79
OECD EUROPE	..	..	25.28	17.75	7.72	5.61	4.81	4.21	3.86
IEA	..	..	25.60	17.17	8.51	5.25	5.22	4.81	4.68

Electricity Generation from Gas (% of total)
Production d'électricité à partir du gaz (% du total)

Elektrizitätserzeugung auf Gasbasis (in %)

Produzione di energia termoelettrica da gas (% del totale)

ガスからの発電量 (%)

Generación de electricidad a partir del gas natural (% del total)

Производство электроэнергии за счет потребления газа (в % к общему производству)

	1960	1970	1973	1980	1990	2000	2003	2004	2005
Australia	-	0.87	4.27	7.33	10.60	12.62	13.84	12.32	11.68
Austria	8.30	12.42	14.32	9.19	15.66	13.66	19.44	17.80	20.70
Belgium	0.28	13.29	23.70	11.24	7.69	19.30	25.86	25.46	26.66
Canada	3.50	3.04	6.00	2.46	2.00	5.53	5.60	5.73	5.78
Czech Republic	..	..	0.93	1.14	0.63	4.92	4.53	4.57	4.83
Denmark	-	-	-	-	2.67	24.34	21.14	24.59	24.31
Finland	-	-	-	4.22	8.56	14.40	16.55	14.89	15.95
France	5.32	4.50	5.53	2.72	0.73	2.12	3.45	3.63	4.02
Germany	0.07	4.72	10.94	14.15	7.39	9.26	9.82	10.32	11.32
Greece	-	-	-	-	0.26	11.08	13.81	15.29	13.75
Hungary	..	14.50	16.22	35.21	15.73	18.76	34.80	34.77	34.62
Iceland	-	-	-	-	-	-	-	-	-
Ireland	-	-	-	15.24	27.70	39.13	52.44	51.14	45.17
Italy	3.84	4.89	3.11	5.03	18.63	37.55	41.39	44.28	50.70
Japan	0.09	1.27	2.26	14.17	19.85	23.17	24.53	22.83	21.15
Korea	..	..	-	-	9.11	10.69	12.38	16.20	16.02
Luxembourg	-	0.15	10.19	23.53	5.45	53.12	93.92	93.17	92.72
Mexico	..	..	14.25	15.48	11.65	19.47	37.76	38.85	36.08
Netherlands	0.88	46.69	79.53	39.83	50.89	58.76	58.75	60.55	57.73
New Zealand	-	0.06	1.41	7.54	17.62	24.39	24.13	16.48	22.04
Norway	-	-	-	-	-	0.15	0.28	0.34	0.26
Poland	0.23	3.16	1.68	0.12	0.09	0.65	1.62	2.06	2.30
Portugal	-	-	-	-	-	16.46	16.64	26.08	29.46
Slovak Republic	..	..	5.26	10.24	7.15	10.86	7.73	7.95	6.97
Spain	-	0.01	1.01	2.67	1.00	9.08	15.27	20.01	27.19
Sweden	-	-	-	-	0.27	0.32	0.52	0.49	0.37
Switzerland	-	-	-	0.61	0.60	1.30	1.42	1.48	1.50
Turkey	-	-	-	-	17.71	37.00	45.20	41.30	45.35
United Kingdom	-	0.33	0.97	0.75	1.57	39.55	37.65	40.07	38.54
United States	21.14	24.58	18.56	15.26	11.92	15.76	16.53	17.64	18.34
OECD TOTAL	**..**	**..**	**11.68**	**10.94**	**10.17**	**15.94**	**17.63**	**18.35**	**18.84**
OECD N. AMERICA	..	..	17.00	13.60	10.65	14.63	16.16	17.16	17.62
OECD PACIFIC	..	..	2.40	12.34	17.52	19.69	20.52	19.80	18.71
OECD EUROPE	..	..	7.44	6.73	6.33	16.09	18.34	19.36	20.70
IEA	..	..	11.88	11.14	10.35	16.13	17.47	18.18	18.74

Electricity Generation from Nuclear Energy (% of total)

Production d'électricité à partir d'énergie nucléaire (% du total)

Elektrizitätserzeugung auf Kernkraftbasis (in %)

Produzione di energia nucleotermoelettrica (% del totale)

原子力からの発電量 (%)

Generación de electricidad a partir de energía nuclear (% del total)

Производство атомной электроэнергии (в % к общему производству)

	1960	1970	1973	1980	1990	2000	2003	2004	2005
Australia	-	-	-	-	-	-	-	-	-
Austria	-	-	-	-	-	-	-	-	-
Belgium	-	0.19	0.19	23.64	60.78	58.18	56.70	56.09	55.53
Canada	-	0.49	5.65	10.19	15.14	12.02	12.70	15.06	14.65
Czech Republic	..	..	-	-	20.21	18.64	31.24	31.42	30.18
Denmark	-	-	-	-	-	-	-	-	-
Finland	-	-	-	17.23	35.34	32.12	26.99	26.46	32.99
France	0.19	3.89	8.08	23.80	75.28	77.44	78.51	78.83	79.13
Germany	-	2.10	3.23	11.92	27.84	29.91	27.71	27.39	26.59
Greece	-	-	-	-	-	-	-	-	-
Hungary	..	-	-	-	48.29	40.29	32.25	35.35	38.69
Iceland	-	-	-	-	-	-	-	-	-
Ireland	-	-	-	-	-	-	-	-	-
Italy	-	2.73	2.18	1.20	-	-	-	-	-
Japan	-	1.30	2.09	14.43	24.17	30.63	23.04	26.37	27.85
Korea	..	..	-	9.34	50.19	41.37	37.78	35.65	37.84
Luxembourg	-	-	-	-	-	-	-	-	-
Mexico	..	..	-	-	2.37	4.04	4.82	4.10	4.60
Netherlands	-	0.90	2.11	6.48	4.87	4.38	4.15	3.79	3.99
New Zealand	-	-	-	-	-	-	-	-	-
Norway	-	-	-	-	-	-	-	-	-
Poland	-	-	-	-	-	-	-	-	-
Portugal	-	-	-	-	-	-	-	-	-
Slovak Republic	..	..	1.89	22.65	47.21	53.56	57.65	55.90	56.54
Spain	-	1.64	8.65	4.75	35.90	27.99	23.99	22.95	19.80
Sweden	-	0.09	2.70	27.50	46.71	39.47	49.80	51.09	45.70
Switzerland	-	5.08	17.14	29.78	42.98	39.99	42.03	42.20	40.42
Turkey	-	-	-	-	-	-	-	-	-
United Kingdom	1.60	10.49	9.95	13.03	20.69	22.72	22.43	20.37	20.53
United States	0.07	1.44	4.54	10.97	19.10	19.82	19.43	19.61	18.99
OECD TOTAL	**..**	**..**	**4.23**	**11.00**	**22.79**	**23.40**	**22.54**	**22.90**	**22.57**
OECD N. AMERICA	..	..	4.59	10.61	18.05	18.18	17.96	18.36	17.80
OECD PACIFIC	..	..	1.72	11.83	22.61	27.61	22.35	24.03	25.43
OECD EUROPE	..	..	4.60	11.24	29.72	29.25	29.27	28.92	28.14
IEA	..	..	4.36	11.34	23.48	24.11	23.21	23.61	23.26

Electricity Generation from Hydro Energy (% of total)

Production d'électricité à partir d'énergie hydraulique (% du total)

Elektrizitätserzeugung auf Wasserkraftbasis (in %)

Produzione di energia idroelettrica (% del totale)

水力からの発電量 (%)

Generación de electricidad a partir de energía hidráulica (% del total)

Производство гидроэлектроэнергии (в % к общему производству)

	1960	1970	1973	1980	1990	2000	2003	2004	2005
Australia	18.64	18.00	17.72	13.59	9.17	8.09	7.04	6.57	6.25
Austria	73.56	70.22	60.65	69.05	63.92	69.55	57.00	59.13	56.96
Belgium	1.14	0.81	0.42	0.52	0.38	0.56	0.30	0.38	0.34
Canada	92.09	75.48	72.07	67.28	61.57	59.21	57.21	56.79	57.88
Czech Republic	..	..	2.63	4.56	1.86	2.41	1.67	2.41	2.90
Denmark	0.45	0.12	0.13	0.11	0.11	0.08	0.05	0.07	0.06
Finland	61.23	42.10	40.28	25.07	19.97	20.95	11.39	17.55	19.54
France	54.47	38.60	26.13	27.02	12.90	12.52	10.53	10.52	9.06
Germany	10.19	5.68	4.07	4.09	3.18	3.83	3.23	3.46	3.19
Greece	20.31	26.84	15.00	15.03	5.09	6.91	8.23	7.94	8.44
Hungary	..	0.61	0.57	0.47	0.63	0.51	0.50	0.61	0.56
Iceland	95.46	96.17	95.13	96.95	93.22	82.72	83.39	82.73	80.81
Ireland	41.20	13.85	8.76	7.93	4.90	3.57	2.41	2.50	2.46
Italy	81.90	34.66	26.07	24.66	14.84	16.38	11.92	13.52	11.42
Japan	50.65	21.25	14.35	15.42	10.67	8.30	9.08	8.78	7.15
Korea	..	..	8.66	5.33	6.04	1.52	1.43	1.18	0.95
Luxembourg	1.37	7.07	3.37	10.68	11.22	27.71	2.77	3.15	2.95
Mexico	..	..	43.64	25.22	18.91	16.27	9.12	11.25	11.81
Netherlands	-	-	-	-	0.12	0.16	0.07	0.09	0.09
New Zealand	79.75	81.41	77.25	83.77	72.32	62.17	57.45	63.56	54.64
Norway	99.30	99.37	99.78	99.84	99.62	99.50	98.89	98.80	98.88
Poland	2.16	2.75	1.74	1.94	1.05	1.47	1.11	1.36	1.42
Portugal	95.09	78.03	74.81	52.71	32.29	26.11	33.80	22.02	10.24
Slovak Republic	..	..	10.75	11.30	7.37	14.98	11.23	13.46	14.79
Spain	83.94	49.33	38.21	27.05	16.81	13.31 e	15.92	11.39	6.73
Sweden	88.82	68.47	76.70	61.12	49.67	54.11	39.55	39.64	45.97
Switzerland	99.13	88.88	75.79	68.10	54.18	55.70	53.24	52.83	54.07
Turkey	35.60	35.17	20.95	48.76	40.23	24.72	25.13	30.58	24.43
United Kingdom	2.27	1.81	1.37	1.37	1.64	1.36	0.82	1.26	1.25
United States	18.44	15.42	13.50	11.49	8.53	6.29	6.87	6.54	6.38
OECD TOTAL	**..**	**..**	**20.48**	**19.22**	**15.45**	**13.75**	**12.56**	**12.52**	**12.23**
OECD N. AMERICA	..	..	20.95	19.07	15.58	13.34	13.08	12.82	12.93
OECD PACIFIC	..	..	16.65	16.79	11.80	8.48	8.42	8.22	6.82
OECD EUROPE	..	..	21.15	20.29	16.84	16.94	13.84	14.23	13.94
IEA	..	..	20.64	19.51	15.64	13.82	12.76	12.65	12.34

Other Electricity Generation (% of total)
Autre Production d'électricité (% du total)

Sonstige Elektrizitätserzeugung (in %)

Produzione di energia elettrica da altre fonti (% del totale)

その他の電力発電量 (%)

Otra electricidad generada (% del total)

Производство электричества из других видов энергии (в % от общего)

	1960	1970	1973	1980	1990	2000	2003	2004	2005
Australia	1.41	0.53	0.52	0.40	0.39	0.54	0.95	1.06	1.16
Austria	-	0.61	0.65	0.78	2.39	3.13	4.17	5.33	6.27
Belgium	-	-	0.29	0.57	1.04	1.63	2.05	2.48	3.20
Canada	-	-	-	0.35	0.81	1.39 e	1.66 e	1.61	1.68
Czech Republic	..	..	-	-	-	0.99	0.60	0.87	0.93
Denmark	-	-	-	0.04	3.16	17.02	18.93	25.12	29.21
Finland	-	-	-	-	-	12.80	12.19	12.83	14.30
France	-	0.49	0.44	0.28	0.53	0.82	1.04	1.08	1.15
Germany	-	0.82	0.78	1.17	0.96	3.44	5.69	6.90	7.36
Greece	-	-	-	-	0.01	1.15	2.19	2.35	2.51
Hungary	..	-	-	-	0.12	0.34	0.58	2.25	4.87
Iceland	-	0.87	1.12	1.57	6.65	17.22	16.54	17.22	19.13
Ireland	-	-	-	-	-	1.43	2.17	3.03	4.85
Italy	3.77	3.63	2.67	2.16	1.56	2.96 e	4.31 e	4.74 e	5.08
Japan	-	-	0.06	0.16	1.48	1.80	2.17	2.18	2.24
Korea	..	..	-	-	0.00	0.05	0.08	0.12	0.13
Luxembourg	-	-	-	3.27	5.45	19.17	3.31	3.68	4.33
Mexico	..	..	0.43	1.37	4.13	3.14	4.03	4.08	4.23
Netherlands	-	-	-	1.58	1.54	4.83	5.68	6.73	9.07
New Zealand	5.83	9.10	6.71	6.63	8.14	9.25	8.35	8.78	9.77
Norway	-	-	-	-	0.31	0.29	0.68	0.74	0.76
Poland	0.04	0.20	0.35	0.34	0.19	0.39	0.58	0.87	1.31
Portugal	1.37	2.50	2.04	2.10	2.45	4.15	4.85	6.05	8.30
Slovak Republic	..	..	-	-	-	0.10	0.37	0.13	0.20
Spain	-	0.08	0.07	0.33	0.46	3.08	6.06	8.06	10.09 e
Sweden	-	0.21	0.51	0.81	1.38	3.30	4.07	5.83	5.87
Switzerland	-	-	-	0.36	1.46	2.66	2.94	3.15	3.68
Turkey	1.46	1.93	1.59	0.58	0.14	0.26	0.19	0.17	0.17
United Kingdom	-	-	-	-	0.22	1.44	2.59	3.11	3.98
United States	0.02	0.05	0.14	0.24	3.31	2.30	2.40	2.46	2.51
OECD TOTAL	**..**	**..**	**0.31**	**0.44**	**2.00**	**2.20**	**2.70**	**2.99**	**3.21**
OECD N. AMERICA	..	..	0.13	0.28	3.02	2.22	2.39	2.43	2.49
OECD PACIFIC	..	..	0.33	0.38	1.38	1.53	1.72	1.75	1.81
OECD EUROPE	..	..	0.56	0.68	0.78	2.49	3.65	4.41	4.99
IEA	..	..	0.31	0.43	2.00	2.20	2.70	2.99	3.21

Includes geothermal, solar, biomass, waste, tide, wave, ocean, wind and other fuel sources.

Inclut l'énergie géothermique et solaire, la biomasse, les déchets, les énergies marémotrice, houlomotrice et éolienne ainsi que diverses autres sources.

Total Electricity Generation (GWh)

Production totale d'électricité (GWh)

Gesamte Elektrizitätserzeugung (GWh)

Produzione totale di energia elettrica (GWh)

総発電量 (GWh)

Generación total de electricidad (GWh)

Общее производство электроэнергии (ГВт. ч)

	1960	1970	1973	1980	1990	2000	2003	2004	2005
Australia	21 449	49 381	64 411	95 234	154 345	207 397	227 918	238 842	250 920
Austria	15 442	29 536	30 916	41 600	49 296	60 161	57 683	61 601	62 980
Belgium	15 152	30 523	40 615	53 091	70 292	82 773	83 561	84 353	85 709
Canada	115 966	209 512	270 081	373 278	481 943	605 462	589 856	600 128	628 083
Czech Republic	..	..	41 174	52 656	62 271	72 911	82 816	83 790	81 931
Denmark	5 540	20 024	19 120	26 765	25 977	36 049	46 181	40 432	36 275
Finland	8 605	21 991	26 102	40 747	54 377	69 991	84 230	85 847	70 550
France	75 059	146 822	182 508	257 308	417 206	536 100	561 774	568 584	570 646
Germany	118 069	308 771	374 352	466 340	547 650	567 122	595 646	609 988	613 164
Greece	2 290	9 820	14 817	22 653	34 775	53 425	57 905	58 813	59 427
Hungary	..	14 542	17 643	23 876	28 436	35 191	34 145	33 708	35 756
Iceland	551	1 488	2 320	3 184	4 510	7 684	8 500	8 623	8 686
Ireland	2 262	5 791	7 348	10 566	14 229	23 673	24 861	25 215	25 626
Italy	55 990	116 496	143 916	183 474	213 147	269 947	283 392	293 047	294 380
Japan	115 500	354 800	465 387	572 531	836 742	1 051 282	1 041 680	1 071 249	1 094 191
Korea	..	..	14 825	37 239	105 371	263 386	343 191	366 612	387 874
Luxembourg	1 464	1 357	1 394	918	624	433	2 780	3 368	3 351
Mexico	..	..	37 100	66 962	124 127	203 645	217 867	224 077	234 895
Netherlands	16 516	40 858	52 627	64 806	71 938	89 652	96 763	100 770	100 219
New Zealand	6 978	13 983	18 531	22 596	32 272	39 223	41 249	42 794	42 956
Norway	31 444	58 177	73 029	83 750	121 611	139 608	106 801	110 189	137 332
Poland	29 282	64 417	83 908	120 941	134 415	143 174	150 009	152 550	155 359
Portugal	3 279	7 438	9 792	15 206	28 355	43 372	46 521	44 827	46 188
Slovak Republic	..	..	12 299	19 967	25 497	30 798	30 986	30 460	31 352
Spain	18 614	56 303	75 660	109 226	151 150	222 235	257 884	277 122	290 607
Sweden	34 936	60 596	78 060	96 316	145 984	145 230	135 377	151 671	158 363
Switzerland	20 700	34 776	36 817	48 175	54 988	66 126	65 403	63 876	57 752
Turkey	2 815	8 623	12 425	23 275	57 543	124 922	140 581	150 698	161 956
United Kingdom	138 748	248 014	281 352	284 071	317 755	374 375	395 473	392 657	397 594
United States	799 679	1 623 891	1 965 509	2 427 320	3 202 813	4 025 705	4 054 351	4 147 708	4 268 381
OECD TOTAL	**..**	**..**	**4 454 038**	**5 644 071**	**7 569 639**	**9 591 052**	**9 865 384**	**10 123 599**	**10 392 503**
OECD N. AMERICA	..	..	2 272 690	2 867 560	3 808 883	4 834 812	4 862 074	4 971 913	5 131 359
OECD PACIFIC	..	..	563 154	727 600	1 128 730	1 561 288	1 654 038	1 719 497	1 775 941
OECD EUROPE	..	..	1 618 194	2 048 911	2 632 026	3 194 952	3 349 272	3 432 189	3 485 203
IEA	..	..	4 318 411	5 433 017	7 281 090	9 205 751	9 458 022	9 707 889	9 962 211

Final Consumption of Coal (Mtoe)

Consommation finale de charbon (Mtep)

Endverbrauch von Kohle (Mtoe)

Consumo finale di carbone (Mtep)

石炭の最終消費量（石油換算百万トン）

Consumo final de carbón (Mtep)

Конечное потребление угля (Мтнэ)

	1960	1970	1973	1980	1990	2000	2003	2004	2005
Australia	5.55	5.06	4.94	4.20	4.28	4.11	2.74	3.32	3.47
Austria	3.38	2.71	1.99	1.94	1.27	0.82	0.73	0.68	0.64
Belgium	8.65	6.65	5.71	4.24	3.53	2.62	1.66	1.47	1.25
Canada	10.32	6.36	5.22	4.33	3.09	3.51	3.29	3.50	3.41
Czech Republic	..	..	19.25	18.43	13.35	4.61	3.92	3.86	3.47
Denmark	2.00	0.49	0.34	0.46	0.40	0.29	0.23	0.26	0.24
Finland	1.60	0.92	1.06	1.11	1.56	1.15	1.04	0.99	1.00
France	27.26	17.95	13.07	8.56	7.52	4.28	3.59	3.55	3.38
Germany	60.22	66.93	53.14	46.87	37.26	8.94	7.68	8.43	8.16
Greece	0.16	0.44	0.52	0.47	1.20	0.88	0.60	0.56	0.44
Hungary	..	5.02	4.17	3.73	2.68	0.71	0.66	0.70	0.72
Iceland	0.02	0.00	0.00	0.02	0.06	0.10	0.09	0.10	0.10
Ireland	1.45	1.30	0.93	1.27	1.72	0.71	0.66	0.67	0.70
Italy	5.34	4.27	3.26	3.34	3.38	2.68	2.75	3.08	2.92
Japan	25.95	21.93	20.17	21.37	31.80	23.67	24.69	25.46	26.06
Korea	..	..	6.49	9.74	11.72	8.35	9.22	8.93	8.05
Luxembourg	1.30	1.00	0.98	1.04	0.55	0.13	0.08	0.09	0.08
Mexico	..	..	1.37	1.61	1.55	1.38	1.04	1.28	1.28
Netherlands	5.13	1.67	1.08	0.78	1.38	0.83	0.86	0.98	0.93
New Zealand	1.16	0.87	0.87	0.80	0.68	0.46	0.66	0.52	0.49
Norway	0.76	0.96	0.81	0.87	0.78	0.95	0.70	0.79	0.67
Poland	25.69	28.66	27.99	31.26	17.39	13.30	11.02	11.40	11.33
Portugal	0.49	0.40	0.19	0.20	0.59	0.43	0.14	0.09	0.02
Slovak Republic	..	..	3.84	4.06	4.11	1.41	1.25	1.34	1.14
Spain	6.70	4.06	3.96	2.48	3.25	1.26	1.58	1.61	1.45
Sweden	1.90	0.97	0.93	0.84	1.04	0.74	0.93	0.99	0.91
Switzerland	1.54	0.46	0.29	0.31	0.35	0.14	0.14	0.13	0.15
Turkey	2.25	2.46	2.93	4.16	7.52	10.85	10.94	11.41	10.74
United Kingdom	64.45	37.58	26.46	14.07	10.77	3.97	3.11	2.99	2.54
United States	89.76	89.74	73.75	56.16	54.39	31.34	31.66	33.72	30.41
OECD TOTAL	**..**	**..**	**285.69**	**248.72**	**229.17**	**134.60**	**127.65**	**132.90**	**126.18**
OECD N. AMERICA	..	..	80.34	62.10	59.03	36.23	35.99	38.49	35.10
OECD PACIFIC	..	..	32.46	36.11	48.48	36.60	37.31	38.23	38.07
OECD EUROPE	..	..	172.89	150.51	121.66	61.77	54.35	56.18	53.00
IEA	..	..	252.49	211.77	206.05	118.41	114.26	118.78	112.32

For the United States, coal used by autoproducers of electricity and heat has been included in final consumption prior to 1992.

Pour les États-Unis, avant 1992, le charbon utilisé par les autoproducteurs d'électricité et de chaleur est inclus dans la consommation finale.

Final Consumption of Oil (Mtoe)

Consommation finale de pétrole (Mtep)

Endverbrauch von Öl (Mtoe)

Consumo finale di petrolio (Mtep)

石油の最終消費量（石油換算百万トン）

Consumo final de petróleo (Mtep)

Конечное потребление нефти и нефтепродуктов (Мтнэ)

	1960	1970	1973	1980	1990	2000	2003	2004	2005
Australia	11.61	22.09	24.67	27.65	30.52	37.22	37.34	37.49	39.16
Austria	2.87	7.97	10.17	10.01	9.23	11.00	13.16	13.01	13.30
Belgium	6.36	18.83	20.98	17.56	17.32	21.98	22.56	20.93	20.87
Canada	37.46	66.33	76.49	80.79	69.86	81.96	87.36	91.62	91.60
Czech Republic	..	..	8.06	9.68	8.54	7.56	8.39	9.40	9.72
Denmark	4.51	14.27	14.26	12.04	7.56	7.44	7.44	7.65	7.65
Finland	2.25	9.00	11.50	10.30	9.67	8.00	8.91	8.94	8.87
France	24.07	80.31	99.37	90.64	79.53	87.67	88.19	88.49	87.37
Germany	28.08	116.01	138.22	127.47	117.70	122.75	116.80	115.59	111.79
Greece	1.73	4.97	7.15	8.96	10.75	13.46	15.25	14.93	15.16
Hungary	..	4.55	6.71	9.37	7.41	5.52	5.72	6.09	6.86
Iceland	0.37	0.49	0.66	0.58	0.68	0.84	0.84	0.87	0.89
Ireland	1.04	3.06	3.86	4.16	4.15	7.21	7.80	7.98	8.46
Italy	17.50	62.00	72.13	66.55	64.16	65.14	67.89	68.24	67.92
Japan	20.70	130.68	171.49	157.68	189.61	217.14	213.15	212.93	208.36
Korea	..	..	9.81	18.81	43.82	86.20	87.74	86.79	84.97
Luxembourg	0.23	1.28	1.53	1.09	1.64	2.34	2.74	3.03	3.16
Mexico	..	..	22.88	41.27	56.73	62.99	64.46	68.29	70.56
Netherlands	7.80	21.26	24.66	21.09	19.90	24.47	26.78	27.19	28.76
New Zealand	1.66	3.31	3.67	3.80	4.43	5.84	6.54	6.80	6.79
Norway	3.43	7.33	7.68	8.45	7.95	7.99	9.20	8.91	8.79
Poland	1.96	6.72	9.28	13.43	11.45	18.07	18.52	19.95	20.53
Portugal	1.25	3.38	4.59	6.16	8.97	13.10	13.09	13.37	13.21
Slovak Republic	..	..	3.87	5.08	4.94	3.08	3.00	2.95	3.08
Spain	4.90	22.50	30.13	38.15	39.91	55.77	59.93	61.47	61.93
Sweden	11.92	24.45	24.84	20.61	14.64	15.14	14.54	14.28	13.65
Switzerland	3.86	12.19	14.30	12.94	12.85	13.12	12.90	12.84	12.89
Turkey	1.41	6.15	9.70	12.91	20.87	27.11	26.65	27.28	27.65
United Kingdom	31.33	69.88	76.98	63.54	68.80	74.00	74.52	76.52	78.02
United States	434.48	622.98	701.02	697.69	697.84	814.41	837.14	866.28	867.71
OECD TOTAL	**..**	**..**	**1 610.68**	**1 598.48**	**1 641.42**	**1 918.52**	**1 958.57**	**2 000.14**	**1 999.70**
OECD N. AMERICA	..	..	800.39	819.74	824.44	959.36	988.95	1 026.19	1 029.87
OECD PACIFIC	..	..	209.64	207.95	268.38	346.40	344.77	344.02	339.29
OECD EUROPE	..	..	600.65	570.79	548.61	612.76	624.84	629.92	630.54
IEA	..	..	1 573.98	1 538.12	1 567.62	1 833.54	1 871.75	1 908.06	1 904.64

Final Consumption of Gas (Mtoe)
Consommation finale de gaz (Mtep)

Endverbrauch von Gas (Mtoe)

Consumo finale di gas (Mtep)

ガスの最終消費量（石油換算百万トン）

Consumo final de gas natural (Mtep)

Конечное потребление газа (Мтнэ)

	1960	1970	1973	1980	1990	2000	2003	2004	2005
Australia	0.49	0.96	2.37	5.34	8.82	11.46	11.51	11.83	11.98
Austria	0.74	1.31	1.81	2.86	3.05	4.28	4.66	4.73	5.07
Belgium	0.36	2.48	4.60	7.08	6.82	10.16	10.49	10.81	10.40
Canada	6.32	18.75	23.72	36.22	43.30	53.41	53.10	52.56	51.02
Czech Republic	..	..	1.81	2.38	4.80	5.91	6.32	6.21	6.18
Denmark	0.13	0.13	0.12	0.12	1.16	1.67	1.74	1.70	1.70
Finland	0.00	0.01	0.01	0.44	0.98	1.00	0.97	0.86	0.87
France	2.48	7.05	11.17	19.32	23.92	32.14	33.93	34.46	34.68
Germany	2.66	11.01	21.13	35.81	41.04	55.12	61.01	62.45	61.28
Greece	0.00	0.00	0.00	0.00	0.11	0.38	0.51	0.59	0.71
Hungary	..	2.36	3.07	4.80	6.20	6.69	7.73	7.75	8.05
Iceland	-	-	-	-	-	-	-	-	-
Ireland	0.05	0.08	0.10	0.43	1.00	1.58	1.28	1.32	1.34
Italy	5.05	9.14	12.78	20.21	30.58	38.58	41.88	42.97	44.71
Japan	1.84	5.54	7.02	9.71	14.35	21.97	24.24	25.48	27.96
Korea	..	..	-	-	0.67	10.92	14.01	14.51	15.98
Luxembourg	0.01	0.02	0.18	0.36	0.42	0.62	0.63	0.68	0.65
Mexico	..	..	7.26	12.84	14.16	15.15	13.63	14.13	13.78
Netherlands	0.63	10.76	19.29	24.25	23.00	23.07	23.31	23.26	22.29
New Zealand	0.09	0.10	0.14	0.37	1.29	3.08	1.86	2.00	1.37
Norway	0.02	0.01	0.01	0.00	-	0.59	0.70	0.80	0.75
Poland	1.79	4.23	5.45	7.66	7.90	8.15	9.08	9.50	9.97
Portugal	0.03	0.04	0.05	0.05	0.05	0.83	1.21	1.28	1.31
Slovak Republic	..	..	1.40	2.99	3.91	4.17	3.89	3.66	4.31
Spain	0.09	0.31	0.70	1.05	4.60	12.38	15.82	16.85	18.17
Sweden	0.12	0.10	0.11	0.08	0.36	0.48	0.53	0.52	0.53
Switzerland	0.13	0.17	0.24	0.72	1.54	2.29	2.48	2.56	2.64
Turkey	0.03	0.04	0.04	0.04	0.72	4.91	7.65	8.45	10.05
United Kingdom	6.01	12.97	23.64	37.31	41.77	52.42	51.79	52.00	50.05
United States	194.20	346.37	367.31	337.41	302.99	359.89	342.23	333.93	322.34
OECD TOTAL	..	..	**515.53**	**569.85**	**589.53**	**743.28**	**748.20**	**747.86**	**740.12**
OECD N. AMERICA	..	..	398.30	386.47	360.45	428.45	408.96	400.62	387.14
OECD PACIFIC	..	..	9.54	15.42	25.13	47.42	51.62	53.82	57.29
OECD EUROPE	..	..	107.70	167.96	203.95	267.41	287.62	293.41	295.69
IEA	..	..	501.42	546.36	563.56	715.82	721.60	720.57	712.06

For the United States, gas used by autoproducers of electricity and heat has been included in final consumption prior to 1989.

Pour les États-Unis, avant 1989, le gaz utilisé par les autoproducteurs d'électricité et de chaleur est inclus dans la consommation finale.

Final Consumption of Electricity (Mtoe)
Consommation finale d'électricité (Mtep)
Endverbrauch von Elektrizität (Mtoe)

Consumo finale di energia elettrica (Mtep)

電力の最終消費量（石油換算百万トン）

Consumo final de electricidad (Mtep)

Конечное потребление электроэнергии (Мтнэ)

	1960	1970	1973	1980	1990	2000	2003	2004	2005
Australia	1.51	3.61	4.51	6.81	11.11	14.86	16.37	17.09	17.76
Austria	0.98	1.77	2.18	2.84	3.68	4.49	4.72	4.80	4.90
Belgium	0.98	2.25	2.94	3.73	4.99	6.67	6.86	6.93	6.90
Canada	8.38	15.80	18.93	26.08	35.95	41.41	43.07	43.58	43.93
Czech Republic	..	..	2.54	3.26	4.14	4.25	4.51	4.63	4.76
Denmark	0.40	1.11	1.38	1.86	2.44	2.79	2.78	2.84	2.88
Finland	0.69	1.72	2.32	3.20	5.07	6.50	6.95	7.15	6.96
France	5.19	10.29	12.78	17.98	25.99	33.10	35.11	36.09	36.34
Germany	8.30	21.86	26.91	33.70	39.14	42.16	43.80	44.15	44.51
Greece	0.16	0.72	1.09	1.71	2.45	3.71	4.18	4.28	4.38
Hungary	..	1.20	1.51	2.20	2.72	2.53	2.70	2.74	2.78
Iceland	0.04	0.11	0.18	0.25	0.34	0.60	0.65	0.67	0.67
Ireland	0.16	0.41	0.53	0.74	1.02	1.74	1.98	1.98	2.09
Italy	4.03	8.89	10.58	13.74	18.46	23.48	25.06	25.42	25.88
Japan	8.18	26.92	35.70	44.14	64.57	81.36	80.73	83.02	84.63
Korea	..	..	1.10	2.82	8.12	20.08	27.35	29.06	30.71
Luxembourg	0.12	0.21	0.26	0.31	0.36	0.49	0.52	0.55	0.53
Mexico	..	..	2.71	4.92	8.62	13.94	14.36	14.62	15.25
Netherlands	1.17	3.00	3.81	4.94	6.32	8.42	8.64	8.87	8.99
New Zealand	0.49	1.01	1.37	1.68	2.39	2.89	3.02	3.23	3.19
Norway	2.34	4.42	5.23	6.43	8.33	9.42	8.87	9.28	9.62
Poland	1.72	3.89	5.01	7.31	8.28	8.35	8.48	8.61	8.54
Portugal	0.24	0.54	0.70	1.23	2.02	3.30	3.71	3.84	3.98
Slovak Republic	..	..	1.06	1.64	2.01	1.89	1.98	2.07	1.97
Spain	1.18	3.75	5.08	7.72	10.82	16.21	18.74	19.84	20.83
Sweden	2.52	4.90	5.95	7.30	10.35	11.07	11.13	11.21	11.24
Switzerland	1.37	2.15	2.49	3.03	4.04	4.50	4.74	4.83	4.93
Turkey	0.18	0.59	0.85	1.68	3.87	8.25	9.49	10.29	11.06
United Kingdom	9.44	17.62	20.04	20.15	23.60	28.33	28.91	29.16	29.69
United States	59.17	115.88	143.39	174.19	226.49	300.94	306.80	311.35	319.95
OECD TOTAL	**..**	**..**	**323.15**	**407.59**	**547.66**	**707.73**	**736.22**	**752.18**	**769.83**
OECD N. AMERICA	..	..	165.03	205.19	271.06	356.29	364.23	369.56	379.12
OECD PACIFIC	..	..	42.69	55.45	86.19	119.19	127.47	132.41	136.28
OECD EUROPE	..	..	115.43	146.95	190.42	232.25	244.52	250.22	254.42
IEA	..	..	314.19	393.48	528.42	682.95	710.76	726.21	743.41

Total Final Consumption of Energy (Mtoe)

Consommation finale totale d'énergie (Mtep)

Gesamter Endverbrauch von Energie (Mtoe)

Consumo finale totale di energia (Mtep)

最終エネルギー総消費量（石油換算百万トン）

Consumo final total de energía (Mtep)

Общее конечное потребление топлива и энергии (Мтнэ)

	1960	1970	1973	1980	1990	2000	2003	2004	2005
Australia	23.21	35.23	39.98	47.52	58.07	72.07	72.30	73.95	76.48
Austria	8.74	14.41	16.83	18.90	20.03	24.13	27.18	27.33	28.16
Belgium	16.35	30.21	34.55	32.99	33.26	42.46	42.79	41.37	40.62
Canada	66.47	114.57	132.08	155.86	160.13	190.79	197.47	202.46	201.33
Czech Republic	..	..	31.66	35.11	33.79	25.19	27.02	28.05	28.06
Denmark	7.03	16.06	16.26	15.45	13.88	15.10	15.48	15.75	15.77
Finland	9.36	16.22	19.43	19.64	22.72	24.39	26.32	26.70	25.85
France	59.00	124.39	145.56	144.57	147.76	170.80	175.03	176.81	176.40
Germany	99.27	222.21	246.64	253.45	247.28	240.73	250.59	252.56	261.01
Greece	2.05	6.58	9.21	11.59	15.47	19.50	21.61	21.43	21.81
Hungary	..	14.62	17.14	22.32	21.02	17.33	18.99	19.21	20.36
Iceland	0.53	0.85	1.14	1.32	1.72	2.26	2.36	2.39	2.38
Ireland	2.70	4.85	5.42	6.61	7.99	11.38	11.87	12.12	12.81
Italy	31.92	84.30	98.75	104.58	117.65	131.84	139.36	146.31	148.07
Japan	56.67	185.07	234.41	233.02	304.39	348.36	346.68	350.65	350.85
Korea	..	..	17.40	31.36	65.07	128.15	143.13	145.34	146.07
Luxembourg	1.65	2.52	2.94	2.80	2.96	3.62	4.03	4.42	4.50
Mexico	..	..	40.44	67.50	88.41	100.64	100.47	105.33	108.11
Netherlands	14.72	36.69	48.85	51.05	51.28	59.52	62.28	63.25	64.37
New Zealand	3.40	5.29	6.05	7.09	9.52	13.05	12.94	13.43	12.74
Norway	6.54	12.73	13.73	16.34	18.03	20.27	20.76	21.02	21.10
Poland	36.61	55.26	60.87	78.43	62.21	58.63	58.74	60.89	61.56
Portugal	2.68	4.99	6.11	8.30	14.00	20.23	20.86	21.34	21.38
Slovak Republic	..	..	10.90	14.41	15.80	11.20	11.45	11.36	11.79
Spain	12.88	30.62	39.87	49.57	62.50	89.08	99.74	103.50	106.19
Sweden	19.00	33.26	35.28	35.05	32.74	36.26	35.66	35.59	35.23
Switzerland	7.24	15.21	17.57	17.52	19.70	21.24	21.69	22.04	22.52
Turkey	9.75	15.25	20.03	26.53	40.58	58.83	61.98	64.59	66.98
United Kingdom	111.23	138.05	147.13	135.21	145.38	161.79	160.75	162.53	162.20
United States	809.95	1 209.98	1 322.89	1 319.84	1 306.78	1 565.97	1 570.93	1 599.74	1 598.10
OECD TOTAL	..	..	**2 839.11**	**2 963.93**	**3 140.11**	**3 684.82**	**3 760.45**	**3 831.47**	**3 852.78**
OECD N. AMERICA	..	..	1 495.40	1 543.20	1 555.32	1 857.40	1 868.87	1 907.53	1 907.54
OECD PACIFIC	..	..	297.85	319.00	437.05	561.63	575.05	583.38	586.13
OECD EUROPE	..	..	1 045.86	1 101.73	1 147.74	1 265.79	1 316.53	1 340.57	1 359.11
IEA	..	..	2 725.76	2 802.27	2 971.96	3 512.10	3 587.43	3 651.50	3 668.94

For the U.S., fuels used by autoproducers of electricity and heat have been included in final consumption for some years.

Pour les É.U., les combustibles utilisés par les autoproducteurs d'électricité et de chaleur sont inclus dans la consommation pour certaines années.

Industry Consumption of Coal (Mtoe)

Consommation industrielle de charbon (Mtep)

Industrieverbrauch von Kohle (Mtoe)

Consumo di carbone nell'industria (Mtep)

石炭の産業用消費量（石油換算百万トン）

Consumo industrial de carbón (Mtep)

Потребление угля промышленным сектором (Мтнэ)

	1960	1970	1973	1980	1990	2000	2003	2004	2005
Australia	4.06	4.55	4.63	3.98	4.07	3.98	2.62	3.16	3.27
Austria	1.59	0.89	0.74	0.91	0.59	0.57	0.55	0.51	0.48
Belgium	3.98	3.32	3.54	3.20	3.01	2.42	1.51	1.30	1.13
Canada	5.95	5.08	4.70	4.22	3.04	3.48	3.26 e	3.47 e	3.39 e
Czech Republic	..	..	11.43	11.69	6.93	3.28	2.91	2.83	2.81
Denmark	0.21	0.17	0.21	0.38	0.32	0.27	0.20	0.24	0.20
Finland	1.19	0.69	0.94	1.01	1.54	1.12	1.01	0.96	0.97
France	12.82	9.47	7.17	5.36	5.86	3.64	3.16	3.14	3.02
Germany	31.22	32.90	28.71	26.10	20.68	7.65	6.61	7.13	7.27
Greece	0.07	0.37	0.46	0.42	1.18	0.85	0.60	0.55	0.44
Hungary	..	1.94	1.86	1.62	0.80	0.46	0.38	0.45	0.47
Iceland	0.01	-	-	0.02	0.06	0.10	0.09	0.10	0.10
Ireland	0.32	0.11	0.04	0.10	0.26	0.12	0.13	0.15	0.16
Italy	2.76	2.67	2.65	2.97	3.28	2.44	2.60	2.93	2.75
Japan	17.67	17.71	18.22	20.82	30.83	23.05	24.08	24.87	25.42
Korea	..	..	0.39	1.35	3.05	7.78	8.66	8.27	7.10
Luxembourg	1.10	0.94	0.94	1.02	0.54	0.12	0.08	0.09	0.08
Mexico	..	..	1.37	1.61	1.55	1.38	1.04	1.28	1.28
Netherlands	1.62	0.71	0.76	0.69	1.33 e	0.80	0.83	0.94	0.90
New Zealand	0.74	0.62	0.69	0.55	0.55	0.35	0.54	0.34	0.36
Norway	0.46	0.61	0.76	0.84	0.77	0.95	0.70	0.79	0.67
Poland	7.80	9.67	10.15	10.39	6.87	7.60	5.32	5.46	4.75
Portugal	0.20	0.24	0.14	0.19	0.59	0.43	0.14	0.09	0.02
Slovak Republic	..	..	2.66	1.76	1.93	1.16	1.13	1.11	1.06
Spain	3.33	3.13	3.63	2.21	2.94	1.20	1.50	1.44	1.26
Sweden	1.11	0.72	0.88	0.82	1.00	0.74	0.93	0.99	0.91
Switzerland	0.62	0.17	0.08	0.22	0.33	0.13	0.13	0.13	0.13
Turkey	0.72	0.74	1.14	2.17	4.50	8.83	8.87	9.00	8.27
United Kingdom	24.34	19.00	13.34	5.95	6.38	2.36	2.15	2.17	1.95
United States	64.45	80.20	60.15	48.25	44.84	29.08	29.33	30.68	28.07
OECD TOTAL	**..**	**..**	**182.38**	**160.82**	**159.63**	**116.33**	**111.07**	**114.60**	**108.68**
OECD N. AMERICA	..	..	66.22	54.08	49.43	33.93	33.63	35.43	32.75
OECD PACIFIC	..	..	23.93	26.70	38.51	35.17	35.90	36.64	36.16
OECD EUROPE	..	..	92.24	80.05	71.69	47.24	41.53	42.52	39.77
IEA	..	..	168.21	147.05	149.20	106.10	103.49	106.65	101.49

Includes non-energy use for industry/transformation/energy sectors.

Comprend l'usage non-énergétique pour les secteurs de l'industrie/transformation/énergie.

For the United States, coal used by autoproducers of electricity and heat has been included in final consumption prior to 1992.

Pour les États-Unis, avant 1992, le charbon utilisé par les autoproducteurs d'électricité et de chaleur est inclus dans la consommation finale.

Industry Consumption of Oil (Mtoe)

Consommation industrielle de pétrole (Mtep)

Industrieverbrauch von Öl (Mtoe)

Consumo di petrolio nell'industria (Mtep)

石油の産業用消費量（石油換算百万トン）

Consumo industrial de petróleo (Mtep)

Потребление нефти и нефтепродуктов промышленным сектором (Мтнэ)

	1960	1970	1973	1980	1990	2000	2003	2004	2005
Australia	4.40	7.95	7.71	7.75	6.31	7.54	5.97	5.91	6.62
Austria	1.22	2.65	3.09	1.92	2.05	2.46	2.81	2.86	2.77
Belgium	2.47	7.67	7.86	4.51	4.18	6.84	5.94	4.90	5.07
Canada	8.09	15.10	20.90	20.30	17.03	20.29	22.22	23.93	23.43
Czech Republic	..	..	5.08	6.04	4.49	2.57	2.33	3.08	2.97
Denmark	1.70	3.64	3.41	2.54	1.19	1.01	1.02	1.07	1.01
Finland	0.81	3.38	5.05	3.77	2.59	1.86	2.50	2.43	2.40
France	9.54	38.41	34.79	30.30	17.44	19.03	18.74	19.06	19.01
Germany	8.76	40.28	46.54	36.49	26.79	27.83	26.74	27.03	26.50
Greece	0.48	1.61	2.39	3.06	2.07	2.52	2.63	2.42	2.37
Hungary	..	1.52	2.34	3.38	2.11	1.54	1.37	1.58	2.15
Iceland	0.05	0.07	0.13	0.15	0.15	0.23	0.25	0.27	0.27
Ireland	0.37	1.41	1.62	1.61	0.84	1.30	1.29	1.24	1.32
Italy	7.92	27.35	29.69	22.41	16.57	13.59	14.92	15.12	15.04
Japan	10.81	73.08	93.74	66.33	70.64	75.59	73.07	74.31	72.79
Korea	..	..	6.22	9.85	17.42	37.93	38.48	39.34	40.23
Luxembourg	0.05	0.74	0.81	0.21	0.29	0.09	0.06	0.07	0.10
Mexico	..	..	5.34	9.09	15.75	14.09	12.06	12.48	12.25
Netherlands	3.15	7.79	10.25	9.34	8.04	9.03	10.81	10.85	12.25
New Zealand	0.25	0.86	0.96	0.81	0.59	0.62	0.58	0.67	0.65
Norway	1.16	2.90	3.01	3.59	2.79	2.45	3.10	2.76	2.70
Poland	0.50	2.03	2.95	4.66	3.02	3.90	3.71	3.82	3.79
Portugal	0.36	1.28	1.76	2.56	3.86	4.61	4.02	4.03	3.91
Slovak Republic	..	..	1.74	2.92	2.92	1.50	1.23	1.18	1.12
Spain	0.81	10.34	13.41	15.95	11.02	14.40	14.67	13.69	13.07
Sweden	4.41	8.08	8.21	6.14	4.04	4.69	4.24	4.21	3.81
Switzerland	1.35	3.36	3.65	2.74	1.27	1.42	1.39	1.42	1.39
Turkey	0.13	1.52	2.60	4.20	6.11	8.04	8.07	8.01	7.67
United Kingdom	11.41	31.57	33.15	19.07	15.39	15.52	16.43	16.65	17.28
United States	112.09	136.08	157.33	187.49	144.08	155.65	165.75	183.22	179.71
OECD TOTAL	**..**	**..**	**515.72**	**489.17**	**411.04**	**458.14**	**466.44**	**487.62**	**483.68**
OECD N. AMERICA	..	..	183.58	216.88	176.87	190.03	200.04	219.63	215.39
OECD PACIFIC	..	..	108.62	84.75	94.95	121.67	118.09	120.23	120.30
OECD EUROPE	..	..	223.52	187.55	139.22	146.44	148.30	147.76	147.99
IEA	..	..	505.56	472.35	389.21	438.41	449.17	469.86	466.23

Includes non-energy use for industry/transformation/energy sectors.

Comprend l'usage non-énergétique pour les secteurs de l'industrie/transformation/énergie.

Industry Consumption of Gas (Mtoe)
Consommation industrielle de gaz (Mtep)

Industrieverbrauch von Gas (Mtoe)

Consumo di gas nell'industria (Mtep)

ガスの産業用消費量（石油換算百万トン）

Consumo industrial de gas natural (Mtep)

Потребление газа промышленным сектором (Мтнэ)

	1960	1970	1973	1980	1990	2000	2003	2004	2005
Australia	0.49	0.77	1.75	3.85	6.12	7.50	7.52 e	7.72	7.70
Austria	0.48	0.88	1.31	2.11	1.98	2.35	2.36	2.41	2.73
Belgium	0.13	1.70	3.15	3.63	3.30	5.33	5.23	5.28	4.88
Canada	2.73	8.98	11.87	18.53	20.23	23.40	23.07	23.46	21.55
Czech Republic	..	..	0.46	0.28	2.65	2.60	2.52	2.48	2.42
Denmark	0.04	0.02	0.02	0.01	0.54	0.78	0.75	0.72	0.72
Finland	0.00	0.00	0.01	0.40	0.94	0.92	0.87	0.77	0.77
France	1.23	3.70	5.77	9.47	11.09	14.67	15.16	13.86	14.18
Germany	1.07	7.55	13.31	19.89	19.69	21.41 e	21.35	21.13	21.39
Greece	0.00	0.00	0.00	0.00	0.10	0.36	0.45	0.50	0.55
Hungary	..	1.83	2.29	3.55	3.76	1.70	1.69	1.56	1.62
Iceland	-	-	-	-	-	-	-	-	-
Ireland	0.01	0.02	0.02	0.36	0.79	0.85	0.44	0.43	0.43
Italy	3.99	6.66	8.65	11.11	14.65	17.60	17.89	18.18	17.83
Japan	0.73	1.85	2.07	2.73	3.10	4.17	4.66	5.08	5.51
Korea	..	..	-	-	0.07	2.88	3.74	3.94	4.17
Luxembourg	-	0.01	0.14	0.25	0.28	0.41	0.40	0.43	0.42
Mexico	..	..	6.87	12.37	13.35	13.73	12.05	12.47	11.99
Netherlands	0.10	4.77	8.14	8.41	8.79	8.25	8.03	8.15	8.21
New Zealand	0.01	0.04	0.05	0.27	1.06	2.62	1.50	1.66	1.06
Norway	0.01	0.00	0.00	0.00	-	0.59	0.69	0.78	0.70
Poland	1.39	3.62	4.65	5.86	4.56	4.10	4.28	4.61	4.80
Portugal	0.00	0.00	0.00	0.00	-	0.66	0.92	0.95	0.96
Slovak Republic	..	..	0.82	1.42	1.33	1.12	1.31	1.21	1.35
Spain	0.01	0.09	0.41	0.61	3.77	9.62	12.09	12.78	13.76
Sweden	0.02	0.01	0.01	0.01	0.26	0.31	0.34	0.32	0.32
Switzerland	0.03	0.03	0.05	0.36	0.59	0.76	0.78	0.81	0.83
Turkey	0.00	0.00	0.00	0.00	0.67	1.76	2.64	2.88	3.19
United Kingdom	1.99	3.21	10.13	13.51	11.96	15.26	13.63	12.66	12.26
United States	95.56	160.28	177.30	151.53	123.77	155.30	135.43	135.10	124.80
OECD TOTAL	**..**	**..**	**259.25**	**270.52**	**259.42**	**321.00**	**301.79**	**302.33**	**291.11**
OECD N. AMERICA	..	..	196.04	182.43	157.35	192.43	170.55	171.03	158.34
OECD PACIFIC	..	..	3.87	6.85	10.36	17.17	17.42	18.40	18.44
OECD EUROPE	..	..	59.34	81.24	91.71	111.39	113.82	112.91	114.33
IEA	..	..	246.90	250.87	240.18	302.05	284.15	284.04	272.97

Includes non-energy use for industry/transformation/energy sectors.
Comprend l'usage non-énergétique pour les secteurs de l'industrie/transformation/énergie.

For the United States, gas used by autoproducers of electricity and heat has been included in final consumption prior to 1989.
Pour les États-Unis, avant 1989, le gaz utilisé par les autoproducteurs d'électricité et de chaleur est inclus dans la consommation finale.

Industry Consumption of Electricity (Mtoe)
Consommation industrielle d'électricité (Mtep)

Industrieverbrauch von Elektrizität (Mtoe)

Consumo di energia elettrica nell'industria (Mtep)

電力の産業用消費量（石油換算百万トン）

Consumo industrial de electricidad (Mtep)

Потребление электроэнергии промышленным сектором (Мтнэ)

	1960	1970	1973	1980	1990	2000	2003	2004	2005
Australia	0.86	2.24	1.99	2.80	5.09	6.62	7.30	7.69	7.94
Austria	0.59	0.90	1.04	1.22	1.55	1.79	1.87	2.03	2.08
Belgium	0.69	1.50	1.93	2.06	2.62	3.43	3.44	3.47	3.39
Canada	5.49	8.13	9.10	11.67	14.44	17.48	17.79	17.81	18.17
Czech Republic	..	..	1.61	1.91	2.32	1.63	1.77	1.92	1.99
Denmark	0.12	0.33	0.40	0.50	0.73	0.86	0.84	0.86	0.88
Finland	0.53	1.21	1.55	1.96	2.80	3.68	3.81	3.97	3.72
France	3.56	6.23	7.22	8.20	9.86	11.58	11.51	11.75	11.51
Germany	5.59	12.68	15.34	17.16	18.62	19.74	19.93	20.11	19.96
Greece	0.08	0.43	0.63	0.90	1.04	1.17	1.22	1.20	1.24
Hungary	..	0.82	0.92	1.19	1.18	0.76	0.82	0.82	0.80
Iceland	0.02	0.08	0.13	0.17	0.22	0.45	0.50	0.51	0.51
Ireland	0.05	0.14	0.19	0.28	0.39	0.66	0.63	0.59	0.66
Italy	2.79	5.82	6.63	8.09	9.54	12.20	12.42	12.40	12.45
Japan	6.32	19.77	25.06	28.19	29.11	31.33	29.96	30.12	29.83
Korea	..	..	0.76	1.95	4.97	10.92	14.49	15.25	15.82
Luxembourg	0.10	0.17	0.20	0.21	0.24	0.33	0.34	0.36	0.34
Mexico	..	..	1.56	2.60	4.59	8.55	8.56	8.75	9.12
Netherlands	0.61	1.55	1.95	2.41	2.86	3.49	3.50	3.56	3.58
New Zealand	0.20	0.25	0.48	0.66	0.96	1.21	1.19	1.30	1.28
Norway	1.53	2.79	3.20	3.43	3.94	4.43	4.11	4.41	4.51
Poland	1.15	2.64	3.28	4.48	3.68	3.48	3.46	3.65	3.55
Portugal	0.16	0.34	0.44	0.71	1.05	1.37	1.45	1.47	1.48
Slovak Republic	..	..	0.72	1.11	1.29	0.84	0.88	0.92	0.95
Spain	0.83	2.42	3.26	4.64	5.44	7.37	8.28	8.73	9.03
Sweden	1.62	2.95	3.40	3.49	4.64	4.90	4.83	4.92	4.95
Switzerland	0.61	0.88	0.95	1.02	1.48	1.55	1.57	1.60	1.63
Turkey	0.12	0.37	0.55	1.05	2.35	3.96	4.62	4.99	5.22
United Kingdom	4.67	7.20	7.85	7.51	8.66	9.81	9.75	9.97	10.22
United States	27.86	45.28	55.54	64.17	74.52	98.22	78.93	79.32	79.45
OECD TOTAL	**..**	**..**	**157.91**	**185.73**	**220.18**	**273.83**	**259.76**	**264.45**	**266.27**
OECD N. AMERICA	..	..	66.20	78.43	93.56	124.26	105.28	105.87	106.75
OECD PACIFIC	..	..	28.30	33.60	40.14	50.08	52.94	54.35	54.87
OECD EUROPE	..	..	63.41	73.69	86.49	99.49	101.54	104.23	104.65
IEA	..	..	152.23	177.37	210.40	260.51	246.36	250.62	252.14

Total Industry Consumption of Energy (Mtoe)
Consommation industrielle totale d'énergie (Mtep)

Gesamtindustrieverbrauch von Energie (Mtoe)

Consumo totale di energia nell'industria (Mtep)

産業用エネルギー総消費量（石油換算百万トン）

Consumo total industrial de energía (Mtep)

Общее потребление топлива и энергии промышленным сектором (Мтнэ)

	1960	1970	1973	1980	1990	2000	2003	2004	2005
Australia	13.86	17.01	17.59	20.27	23.08	28.10	25.80	27.03	28.12
Austria	3.88	5.34	6.22	6.36	6.86	8.09	8.65	8.97	9.18
Belgium	7.29	14.19	16.81	13.76	13.50	18.83	17.08	15.87	15.41
Canada	24.34	42.71	52.37	61.23	61.06	73.17	75.01	77.87	75.68
Czech Republic	..	..	18.58	19.93	17.47	10.99	10.59	11.47	11.38
Denmark	2.07	4.16	4.10	3.59	2.96	3.19	3.10	3.17	3.08
Finland	2.53	5.33	7.62	7.26	10.50	12.18	13.00	13.35	12.55
France	27.15	58.84	56.12	54.46	45.69	50.37	50.04	49.30	49.25
Germany	46.64	94.75	105.51	101.65	88.98	77.99	82.35	83.19	82.87
Greece	0.63	2.41	3.49	4.38	4.58	5.14	5.10	4.88	4.84
Hungary	..	6.78	7.90	10.39	8.08	5.03	4.82	4.84	5.52
Iceland	0.07	0.17	0.29	0.36	0.48	0.84	0.90	0.94	0.92
Ireland	0.75	1.68	1.88	2.35	2.33	3.04	2.59	2.55	2.74
Italy	17.46	42.51	47.62	44.70	44.26	46.12	48.11	48.91	48.35
Japan	35.53	112.41	139.08	118.08	136.21	136.75	134.19	136.70	135.95
Korea	..	..	7.37	13.15	25.80	60.56	68.45	71.04	71.65
Luxembourg	1.26	1.86	2.09	1.68	1.35	0.97	0.90	0.98	0.97
Mexico	..	..	16.47	27.20	36.99	38.91	34.70	36.00	35.91
Netherlands	5.47	14.82	21.11	20.86	21.08	22.79	24.47	25.05	26.73
New Zealand	1.20	1.77	2.18	2.60	3.76	5.32	4.41	4.60	4.01
Norway	3.16	6.30	6.96	8.04	7.89	9.04	9.02	9.15	9.01
Poland	14.25	25.55	29.49	36.79	27.45	21.52	19.80	20.57	19.81
Portugal	1.07	2.21	2.65	3.79	6.71	8.46	8.06	8.09	8.02
Slovak Republic	..	..	6.15	7.40	7.66	4.66	4.99	4.82	4.86
Spain	4.98	15.98	20.71	23.58	25.03	33.89	37.89	38.01	38.50
Sweden	9.44	14.33	15.44	13.48	13.78	15.31	14.20	14.27	13.92
Switzerland	2.61	4.44	4.73	4.49	3.88	4.41	4.45	4.56	4.64
Turkey	0.98	2.64	4.30	7.41	13.64	23.08	24.67	25.45	25.32
United Kingdom	42.41	60.97	64.47	46.16	42.48	44.34	43.34	42.51	42.68
United States	316.64	446.83	478.90	485.37	396.27	478.39	442.08	461.30	446.70
OECD TOTAL	**..**	**..**	**1 168.17**	**1 170.77**	**1 099.79**	**1 251.47**	**1 222.74**	**1 255.43**	**1 238.55**
OECD N. AMERICA	..	..	547.74	573.80	494.32	590.47	551.79	575.16	558.29
OECD PACIFIC	..	..	166.21	154.11	188.85	230.74	232.84	239.37	239.73
OECD EUROPE	..	..	454.22	442.86	416.62	430.26	438.11	440.90	440.53
IEA	..	..	1 115.79	1 099.02	1 027.22	1 185.54	1 162.35	1 193.10	1 177.05

Includes non-energy use for industry/transformation/energy sectors.

Comprend l'usage non-énergétique pour les secteurs de l'industrie/transformation/énergie.

For the U.S., fuels used by autoproducers of electricity and heat have been included in final consumption for some years.

Pour les É.U., les combustibles utilisés par les autoproducteurs d'électricité et de chaleur sont inclus dans la consommation pour certaines années.

Consumption of Oil in Transport (Mtoe)

Consommation de pétrole dans les transports (Mtep)

Ölverbrauch im Verkehrssektor (Mtoe)

Consumo di petrolio nel settore dei trasporti (Mtep)

運輸部門の石油消費量（石油換算百万トン）

Consumo de petróleo en el transporte (Mtep)

Потребление нефти и нефтепродуктов в транспорте (Мтнэ)

	1960	1970	1973	1980	1990	2000	2003	2004	2005
Australia	5.61	11.25	13.43	17.62	22.45	27.65	28.63	28.74	29.56
Austria	1.24	3.07	4.01	4.23	4.61	6.06	7.37	7.60	7.87
Belgium	1.92	4.28	4.96	5.94	7.85	9.77	10.30	10.36	10.02
Canada	16.59	27.84	33.78	43.08	41.26	48.29	49.75	51.73	52.10
Czech Republic	..	..	2.38	2.51	2.78	4.81	5.86	6.22	6.67
Denmark	1.19	3.11	3.51	3.63	4.12	4.87	5.02	5.26	5.38
Finland	0.73	2.10	2.53	2.99	4.33	4.45	4.67	4.84	4.87
France	9.53	20.35	26.86	32.59	42.06	50.76	50.63	50.97	50.44
Germany	11.59	31.77	37.51	47.03	59.33	65.99	61.23	62.43	60.36
Greece	0.80	1.92	2.68	4.02	6.06	7.38	8.00	8.17	8.29
Hungary	..	1.55	1.92	2.83	3.05	3.24	3.77	3.95	4.24
Iceland	0.10	0.16	0.24	0.19	0.29	0.35	0.33	0.35	0.37
Ireland	0.47	1.20	1.44	1.81	2.07	4.12	4.55	4.72	5.10
Italy	5.62	16.63	19.95	25.57	34.74	41.79	43.19	43.91	43.65
Japan	7.66	32.03	41.62	54.40	76.16	94.32	93.30	93.71	92.10
Korea	..	..	2.58	5.04	14.84	30.31	34.28	34.30	31.92
Luxembourg	0.10	0.19	0.29	0.51	1.03	1.92	2.38	2.64	2.77
Mexico	..	..	13.06	24.33	31.36	37.40	41.52	44.45	46.84
Netherlands	2.71	6.17	7.39	8.69	10.51	14.47	14.97	15.35	15.41
New Zealand	1.00	1.86	2.15	2.48	3.37	4.78	5.47	5.66	5.58
Norway	1.22	2.51	2.57	3.12	4.15	4.45	4.63	4.82	4.89
Poland	1.23	3.99	5.29	7.32	7.02	9.74	10.14	11.36	12.14
Portugal	0.54	1.42	1.95	2.65	3.86	6.70	7.26	7.46	7.20
Slovak Republic	..	..	1.65	1.23	1.37	1.40	1.57	1.55	1.76
Spain	3.48	8.19	11.81	16.07	22.77	33.43	37.01	38.78	40.03
Sweden	2.81	4.97	5.40	6.00	7.28	8.13	8.07	8.36	8.46
Switzerland	1.44	3.49	4.17	4.33	6.11	7.34	6.90	6.87	6.92
Turkey	0.77	2.67	3.95	5.43	9.66	12.69	13.09	13.41	14.02
United Kingdom	14.62	26.93	31.16	34.02	46.36	53.13	53.55	55.11	56.01
United States	230.26	349.22	406.89	421.83	490.96	595.38	609.53	618.02	625.66
OECD TOTAL	**..**	**..**	**697.14**	**791.51**	**971.77**	**1 195.13**	**1 226.96**	**1 251.11**	**1 260.63**
OECD N. AMERICA	..	..	453.73	489.23	563.58	681.07	700.80	714.20	724.60
OECD PACIFIC	..	..	59.78	79.55	116.82	157.05	161.68	162.41	159.17
OECD EUROPE	..	..	183.63	222.72	291.37	357.01	364.48	374.49	376.86
IEA	..	..	676.90	758.44	931.73	1 146.24	1 173.41	1 193.40	1 199.52

Includes non-energy use for this sector.

Comprend l'usage non-énergétique pour ce secteur.

Consumption of Electricity in Transport (Mtoe)

Consommation d'électricité dans les transports (Mtep)

Elektrizitätsverbrauch im Verkehrssektor (Mtoe)

Consumo di energia elettrica nel settore dei trasporti (Mtep)

運輸部門の電力消費量（石油換算百万トン）

Consumo de electricidad en el transporte (Mtep)

Потребление электроэнергии в транспорте (Мтнэ)

	1960	1970	1973	1980	1990	2000	2003	2004	2005
Australia	0.06	0.06	0.06	0.08	0.16	0.20	0.18	0.20	0.21
Austria	0.08	0.13	0.15	0.20	0.24	0.30	0.28	0.27	0.28
Belgium	0.05	0.06	0.07	0.08	0.11	0.12	0.13	0.13	0.15
Canada	0.05	0.15	0.28	0.20	0.28	0.39	0.36	0.37	0.37
Czech Republic	..	..	0.16	0.20	0.27	0.20	0.19	0.19	0.19
Denmark	0.01	0.01	0.01	0.01	0.02	0.03	0.03	0.03	0.03
Finland	0.00	0.00	0.01	0.02	0.04	0.05	0.05	0.05	0.06
France	0.30	0.50	0.55	0.59	0.76	1.00	1.04	1.07	1.05
Germany	0.33	0.76	0.85	1.03	1.18	1.37	1.39	1.39	1.39
Greece	0.00	0.00	0.00	0.01	0.01	0.02	0.02	0.02	0.02
Hungary	..	0.05	0.07	0.09	0.10	0.09	0.09	0.09	0.09
Iceland	-	-	-	-	-	0.00	0.00	0.00	0.00
Ireland	-	-	-	-	0.00	0.00	0.00	0.00	0.01
Italy	0.28	0.31	0.33	0.41	0.58	0.73	0.81	0.83	0.85
Japan	0.43	0.97	1.14	1.31	1.45	1.60	1.58	1.61	1.64
Korea	..	..	0.01	0.03	0.09	0.18	0.20	0.21	0.18
Luxembourg	0.00	0.00	0.00	0.00	0.00	0.01	0.01	0.01	0.01
Mexico	..	..	0.03	0.04	0.07	0.09	0.10	0.10	0.10
Netherlands	0.06	0.08	0.08	0.08	0.11	0.14	0.14	0.14	0.14
New Zealand	-	0.00	0.00	0.00	0.01	0.04	0.04	0.04	0.04
Norway	0.03	0.05	0.04	0.06	0.07	0.13	0.14	0.13	0.13
Poland	0.06	0.24	0.30	0.41	0.47	0.40	0.41	0.40	0.38
Portugal	0.01	0.02	0.02	0.02	0.03	0.03	0.04	0.04	0.04
Slovak Republic	..	..	0.05	0.08	0.10	0.08	0.06	0.06	0.05
Spain	0.06	0.11	0.12	0.16	0.32	0.36	0.44	0.45	0.46
Sweden	0.14	0.18	0.18	0.20	0.21	0.27	0.24	0.26	0.24
Switzerland	0.12	0.17	0.17	0.18	0.22	0.23	0.26	0.25	0.26
Turkey	0.00	0.02	0.01	0.01	0.03	0.07	0.06	0.06	0.06
United Kingdom	0.19	0.24	0.22	0.26	0.45	0.74	0.71	0.73	0.74
United States	0.47	0.40	0.37	0.27	0.35	0.38	0.59	0.62	0.65
OECD TOTAL	..	..	**5.29**	**6.05**	**7.72**	**9.25**	**9.57**	**9.76**	**9.81**
OECD N. AMERICA	..	..	0.68	0.50	0.71	0.86	1.04	1.09	1.11
OECD PACIFIC	..	..	1.21	1.42	1.69	2.01	1.99	2.06	2.07
OECD EUROPE	..	..	3.40	4.13	5.32	6.38	6.54	6.61	6.63
IEA	..	..	4.90	5.51	7.08	8.67	9.00	9.20	9.28

Total Consumption of Energy in Transport (Mtoe)

Consommation totale d'énergie dans les transports (Mtep)

Gesamtenergieverbrauch im Verkehrssektor (Mtoe)

Consumo totale di energia nel settore dei trasporti (Mtep)

運輸部門のエネルギー総消費量（石油換算百万トン）

Consumo total de energía en el transporte (Mtep)

Общее потребление топлива и энергии в транспорте (Мтнэ)

	1960	1970	1973	1980	1990	2000	2003	2004	2005
Australia	7.04	11.49	13.51	17.70	22.69	28.24	29.18	29.34	30.24
Austria	1.87	3.40	4.29	4.47	4.95	6.60	7.88	8.08	8.42
Belgium	2.49	4.37	5.04	6.03	7.95	9.89	10.42	10.49	10.17
Canada	17.22	28.20	34.18	44.91	44.44	53.57	54.10	55.85	56.93
Czech Republic	..	..	2.66	2.81	3.05	5.10	6.16	6.49	6.91
Denmark	1.30	3.12	3.52	3.64	4.13	4.90	5.05	5.29	5.41
Finland	0.94	2.13	2.55	3.01	4.36	4.51	4.76	4.92	4.94
France	12.14	21.13	27.49	33.21	42.82	52.13	52.04	52.45	51.96
Germany	17.31	34.88	40.09	48.37	60.52	67.59	63.33	64.80	63.70
Greece	0.88	1.95	2.70	4.03	6.07	7.40	8.03	8.20	8.32
Hungary	..	2.19	2.37	3.05	3.15	3.33	3.87	4.05	4.35
Iceland	0.10	0.16	0.24	0.19	0.29	0.36	0.33	0.36	0.37
Ireland	0.51	1.20	1.44	1.81	2.07	4.12	4.55	4.73	5.10
Italy	6.69	17.21	20.54	26.24	35.53	42.85	44.36	45.34	45.06
Japan	11.91	34.34	42.96	55.71	77.60	95.92	94.89	95.32	93.74
Korea	..	..	2.60	5.08	14.93	30.48	34.61	34.75	32.43
Luxembourg	0.14	0.20	0.29	0.51	1.03	1.92	2.39	2.65	2.78
Mexico	..	..	13.09	24.36	31.43	38.13	42.20	45.15	47.67
Netherlands	2.82	6.26	7.47	8.77	10.62	14.61	15.11	15.49	15.54
New Zealand	1.10	1.87	2.15	2.49	3.43	4.81	5.51	5.71	5.63
Norway	1.32	2.55	2.62	3.18	4.22	4.58	4.78	4.95	5.04
Poland	7.01	8.70	9.25	9.53	7.66	10.20	10.70	11.95	12.81
Portugal	0.61	1.47	1.99	2.67	3.88	6.73	7.31	7.51	7.25
Slovak Republic	..	..	1.70	1.32	1.47	1.48	2.10	2.21	2.42
Spain	5.06	8.39	11.95	16.25	23.08	33.87	37.64	39.46	40.75
Sweden	3.04	5.15	5.58	6.20	7.49	8.41	8.41	8.77	8.87
Switzerland	1.57	3.66	4.34	4.51	6.33	7.57	7.16	7.13	7.18
Turkey	1.59	3.27	4.49	5.62	9.70	12.80	13.20	13.58	14.19
United Kingdom	20.27	27.34	31.44	34.32	46.81	53.87	54.27	55.85	56.83
United States	232.05	366.65	424.10	436.84	506.72	614.13	629.91	639.27	648.60
OECD TOTAL	**..**	**..**	**726.64**	**816.85**	**998.45**	**1 230.13**	**1 264.25**	**1 290.13**	**1 303.59**
OECD N. AMERICA	..	..	471.38	506.11	582.59	705.83	726.21	740.27	753.20
OECD PACIFIC	..	..	61.22	80.99	118.65	159.45	164.18	165.12	162.03
OECD EUROPE	..	..	194.04	229.75	297.21	364.85	373.86	384.75	388.36
IEA	..	..	702.36	781.45	957.60	1 179.96	1 208.92	1 230.46	1 240.33

Includes non-energy use for this sector.

Comprend l'usage non-énergétique pour ce secteur.

Other Sectors' Consumption of Coal (Mtoe)

Consommation de charbon des autres secteurs (Mtep)

Kohleverbrauch in sonstigen Sektoren (Mtoe)

Consumo di carbone negli altri settori (Mtep)

他の部門の石炭消費量（石油換算百万トン）

Consumo de carbón de otros sectores (Mtep)

Потребление угля другими секторами (Мтнэ)

	1960	1970	1973	1980	1990	2000	2003	2004	2005
Australia	0.13	0.33	0.28	0.21	0.14	0.05	0.06	0.09	0.11
Austria	1.24	1.64	1.13	1.01	0.68	0.25	0.18	0.16	0.17
Belgium	4.15	3.30	2.15	1.03	0.52	0.20	0.15	0.16	0.13
Canada	3.79	1.07	0.40	0.10	0.05	0.04	0.02	0.03	0.02
Czech Republic	..	..	7.70	6.64	6.42	1.33	1.01	1.03	0.66
Denmark	1.69	0.32	0.12	0.08	0.08	0.03	0.03	0.02	0.04
Finland	0.22	0.20	0.11	0.10	0.02	0.03	0.03	0.03	0.03
France	12.19	8.21	5.84	3.18	1.66	0.63	0.42	0.41	0.36
Germany	23.61	31.68	22.71	20.52	16.57	1.28	1.07	1.30	0.89
Greece	0.02	0.04	0.04	0.04	0.03	0.02	0.01	0.01	0.01
Hungary	..	2.49	1.93	1.98	1.88	0.24	0.27	0.24	0.25
Iceland	0.01	0.00	0.00	-	-	-	-	-	-
Ireland	1.08	1.18	0.88	1.17	1.46	0.58	0.53	0.52	0.54
Italy	1.98	1.42	0.47	0.36	0.10	0.23	0.15	0.15	0.17
Japan	4.46	2.89	1.75	0.55	0.97	0.62	0.60	0.59	0.64
Korea	..	..	6.08	8.39	8.67	0.57	0.56	0.66	0.95
Luxembourg	0.17	0.06	0.03	0.02	0.01	0.00	0.00	0.00	0.00
Mexico	..	..	-	-	-	-	-	-	-
Netherlands	3.47	0.95	0.32	0.08	0.05	0.03	0.03	0.03	0.03
New Zealand	0.31	0.24	0.18	0.25	0.13	0.11	0.12	0.18	0.12
Norway	0.22	0.35	0.06	0.03	0.01	0.00	0.00	0.00	0.00
Poland	12.17	14.52	14.19	19.08	10.34	5.69	5.69	5.94	6.58
Portugal	0.23	0.13	0.04	0.01	0.00	-	-	-	-
Slovak Republic	..	..	1.19	2.30	2.18	0.26	0.12	0.23	0.08
Spain	1.85	0.84	0.31	0.26	0.30	0.06	0.08	0.17	0.19
Sweden	0.70	0.24	0.05	0.02	0.04	-	-	-	-
Switzerland	0.92	0.29	0.21	0.09	0.01	0.01	0.01	0.01	0.02
Turkey	0.71	1.14	1.27	1.81	3.00	2.02	2.07	2.40	2.47
United Kingdom	34.65	18.41	13.07	8.08	4.39	1.61	0.96	0.82	0.59
United States	23.99	9.38	13.59	7.92	9.55	2.27	2.33	3.03	2.33
OECD TOTAL	**..**	**..**	**96.10**	**85.35**	**69.26**	**18.17**	**16.51**	**18.23**	**17.40**
OECD N. AMERICA	..	..	13.99	8.02	9.60	2.30	2.35	3.06	2.36
OECD PACIFIC	..	..	8.30	9.41	9.90	1.35	1.35	1.52	1.82
OECD EUROPE	..	..	73.81	67.92	49.76	14.52	12.81	13.65	13.22
IEA	..	..	80.72	63.96	56.74	12.22	10.70	12.05	10.73

Includes non-energy use for this sector.
Comprend l'usage non-énergétique pour ce secteur.

Includes residential, commerce/public services, agriculture/forestry and non-specified other sectors.
Comprend les secteurs résidentiel, commerce/services publics, agriculture/sylviculture et autres secteurs non spécifiés.

For the United States, coal used by autoproducers of electricity and heat has been included in final consumption prior to 1992.
Pour les États-Unis, avant 1992, le charbon utilisé par les autoproducteurs d'électricité et de chaleur est inclus dans la consommation finale.

Other Sectors' Consumption of Oil (Mtoe)

Consommation de pétrole des autres secteurs (Mtep)

Ölverbrauch in sonstigen Sektoren (Mtoe)

Consumo di petrolio negli altri settori (Mtep)

他の部門の石油消費量（石油換算百万トン）

Consumo de petróleo de otros sectores (Mtep)

Потребление нефти и нефтепродуктов другими секторами (Мтнэ)

	1960	1970	1973	1980	1990	2000	2003	2004	2005
Australia	1.59	2.89	3.52	2.27	1.76	2.04	2.74	2.84	2.98
Austria	0.41	2.26	3.07	3.87	2.57	2.48	2.98	2.55	2.67
Belgium	1.96	6.88	8.16	7.10	5.30	5.37	6.33	5.67	5.78
Canada	12.78	23.39	21.81	17.42	11.57	13.38	15.39	15.96	16.08
Czech Republic	..	..	0.60	1.13	1.27	0.19	0.20	0.09	0.07
Denmark	1.62	7.51	7.34	5.86	2.25	1.56	1.41	1.32	1.27
Finland	0.71	3.53	3.92	3.55	2.75	1.70	1.74	1.68	1.60
France	5.00	21.55	37.72	27.75	20.03	17.88	18.82	18.46	17.92
Germany	7.73	43.96	54.17	43.94	31.59	28.93	28.83	26.13	24.93
Greece	0.45	1.44	2.08	1.89	2.63	3.56	4.63	4.35	4.50
Hungary	..	1.48	2.45	3.16	2.25	0.74	0.57	0.56	0.46
Iceland	0.22	0.26	0.29	0.24	0.24	0.26	0.26	0.25	0.25
Ireland	0.20	0.45	0.79	0.74	1.24	1.78	1.96	2.01	2.04
Italy	3.95	18.01	22.49	18.56	12.85	9.76	9.78	9.22	9.23
Japan	2.24	25.57	36.13	36.95	42.81	47.22	46.78	44.92	43.47
Korea	..	..	1.02	3.92	11.56	17.97	14.99	13.15	12.82
Luxembourg	0.07	0.35	0.44	0.38	0.31	0.33	0.30	0.33	0.29
Mexico	..	..	4.48	7.85	9.63	11.51	10.88	11.37	11.47
Netherlands	1.94	7.29	7.02	3.06	1.34	0.96	0.99	0.99	1.11
New Zealand	0.41	0.59	0.57	0.52	0.48	0.45	0.50	0.47	0.56
Norway	1.04	1.93	2.10	1.74	1.02	1.09	1.47	1.34	1.20
Poland	0.23	0.70	1.05	1.45	1.42	4.42	4.68	4.77	4.59
Portugal	0.35	0.68	0.89	0.95	1.25	1.79	1.81	1.88	2.10
Slovak Republic	..	..	0.48	0.93	0.66	0.18	0.20	0.22	0.20
Spain	0.62	3.97	4.92	6.13	6.12	7.93	8.25	8.99	8.83
Sweden	4.70	11.40	11.22	8.47	3.32	2.31	2.23	1.70	1.38
Switzerland	1.07	5.35	6.48	5.87	5.46	4.36	4.60	4.54	4.58
Turkey	0.51	1.96	3.15	3.29	5.11	6.38	5.49	5.86	5.96
United Kingdom	5.29	11.38	12.67	10.45	7.05	5.34	4.54	4.76	4.74
United States	92.13	137.67	136.79	88.37	62.80	63.38	61.85	65.03	62.34
OECD TOTAL	**..**	**..**	**397.82**	**317.80**	**258.62**	**265.25**	**265.17**	**261.41**	**255.40**
OECD N. AMERICA	..	..	163.08	113.64	83.99	88.27	88.12	92.36	89.88
OECD PACIFIC	..	..	41.24	43.65	56.61	67.68	65.00	61.38	59.82
OECD EUROPE	..	..	193.50	160.51	118.02	109.31	112.06	107.67	105.69
IEA	..	..	391.52	307.33	246.68	248.88	249.17	244.80	238.90

Includes non-energy use for this sector.
Comprend l'usage non-énergétique pour ce secteur.

Includes residential, commerce/public services, agriculture/forestry, fishing and non-specified other sectors.
Comprend les secteurs résidentiel, commerce/services publics, agriculture/sylviculture, pêche et autres secteurs non spécifiés.

Other Sectors' Consumption of Gas (Mtoe)

Consommation de gaz des autres secteurs (Mtep)

Gasverbrauch in sonstigen Sektoren (Mtoe)

Consumo di gas negli altri settori (Mtep)

他の部門のガス消費量（石油換算百万トン）

Consumo de gas natural de otros sectores (Mtep)

Потребление газа другими секторами (Мтнэ)

	1960	1970	1973	1980	1990	2000	2003	2004	2005
Australia	-	0.19	0.62	1.49	2.68	3.65	3.67	3.77	3.93
Austria	0.25	0.41	0.48	0.72	0.97	1.71	2.08	2.13	2.10
Belgium	0.23	0.79	1.45	3.45	3.52	4.84	5.27	5.53	5.51
Canada	3.59	9.78	11.86	16.06	20.17	25.26	26.17	25.50	25.17
Czech Republic	..	..	1.35	2.10	2.15	3.28	3.76	3.69	3.73
Denmark	0.09	0.12	0.10	0.11	0.62	0.89	0.99	0.99	0.98
Finland	0.00	0.01	0.00	0.04	0.04	0.06	0.07	0.07	0.07
France	1.19	3.33	5.39	9.84	12.83	17.47	18.73	20.56	20.45
Germany	1.60	3.46	7.82	15.86	21.34	33.71	39.66	41.32	39.90
Greece	0.00	0.00	0.00	0.00	0.01	0.01	0.05	0.08	0.15
Hungary	..	0.53	0.78	1.25	2.44	4.99	6.04	6.18	6.43
Iceland	-	-	-	-	-	-	-	-	-
Ireland	0.04	0.06	0.08	0.07	0.21	0.73	0.84	0.89	0.91
Italy	0.89	2.40	4.00	8.84	15.73	20.66	23.63	24.43	26.49
Japan	1.11	3.69	4.96	6.98	11.24	17.79	19.58	20.40	22.45
Korea	..	..	-	-	0.60	8.04	10.14	10.34	11.49
Luxembourg	0.01	0.01	0.04	0.11	0.14	0.21	0.24	0.25	0.24
Mexico	..	..	0.39	0.47	0.81	0.78	1.00	1.06	1.06
Netherlands	0.52	5.99	11.15	15.84	14.21	14.82	15.28	15.11	14.09
New Zealand	0.09	0.06	0.09	0.10	0.18	0.46	0.35	0.34	0.30
Norway	0.01	0.01	0.01	0.00	-	0.00	0.01	0.01	0.03
Poland	0.39	0.61	0.80	1.79	3.34	3.98	4.68	4.71	4.93
Portugal	0.03	0.04	0.05	0.05	0.05	0.17	0.28	0.32	0.34
Slovak Republic	..	..	0.58	1.57	2.58	3.05	2.11	1.85	2.36
Spain	0.07	0.22	0.30	0.44	0.83	2.74	3.73	4.06	4.41
Sweden	0.10	0.09	0.10	0.07	0.11	0.16	0.18	0.18	0.19
Switzerland	0.10	0.14	0.19	0.37	0.95	1.53	1.69	1.75	1.81
Turkey	0.03	0.04	0.04	0.04	0.05	3.11	4.96	5.47	6.75
United Kingdom	4.02	9.76	13.51	23.81	29.82	37.16	38.16	39.34	37.79
United States	98.64	169.23	173.17	171.13	163.81	189.40	192.55	185.17	183.38
OECD TOTAL	**..**	**..**	**239.28**	**282.58**	**311.44**	**400.68**	**425.89**	**425.50**	**427.42**
OECD N. AMERICA	..	..	185.41	187.66	184.79	215.44	219.71	211.72	209.61
OECD PACIFIC	..	..	5.67	8.57	14.71	29.94	33.75	34.85	38.16
OECD EUROPE	..	..	48.20	86.36	111.94	155.30	172.43	178.93	179.64
IEA	..	..	237.52	278.75	304.71	392.87	418.10	417.89	419.07

Includes residential, commerce/public services, agriculture/forestry and non-specified other sectors.

Comprend les secteurs résidentiel, commerce/services publics, agriculture/sylviculture et autres secteurs non spécifiés.

Total Other Sectors' Consumption of Energy (Mtoe)

Consommation totale d'énergie des autres secteurs (Mtep)

Gesamtenergieverbrauch in sonstigen Sektoren (Mtoe)

Consumo totale di energia negli altri settori (Mtep)

他の部門のエネルギー総消費量（石油換算百万トン）

Consumo total de energía de otros sectores (Mtep)

Общее потребление топлива и энергии другими секторами (Мтнэ)

	1960	1970	1973	1980	1990	2000	2003	2004	2005
Australia	2.31	6.72	8.88	9.55	12.30	15.73	17.33	17.58	18.13
Austria	2.99	5.67	6.32	8.06	8.23	9.44	10.64	10.29	10.56
Belgium	6.57	11.64	12.71	13.21	11.81	13.74	15.28	15.01	15.04
Canada	24.91	43.67	45.52	49.72	54.63	64.05	68.36	68.75	68.72
Czech Republic	..	..	10.42	12.38	13.27	9.09	10.28	10.10	9.78
Denmark	3.67	8.77	8.64	8.22	6.78	7.01	7.34	7.28	7.28
Finland	5.89	8.76	9.26	9.38	7.86	7.70	8.56	8.43	8.35
France	19.72	44.42	61.95	56.90	59.25	68.31	72.95	75.06	75.19
Germany	35.31	92.58	101.04	103.43	97.78	95.16	104.91	104.57	114.44
Greece	0.55	2.22	3.03	3.18	4.82	6.96	8.48	8.35	8.65
Hungary	..	5.65	6.88	8.88	9.79	8.97	10.30	10.32	10.49
Iceland	0.35	0.52	0.62	0.76	0.96	1.06	1.13	1.10	1.09
Ireland	1.44	1.97	2.09	2.44	3.59	4.22	4.74	4.85	4.97
Italy	7.77	24.59	30.58	33.63	37.86	42.87	46.88	52.06	54.66
Japan	9.24	38.32	52.37	59.22	90.58	115.69	117.60	118.63	121.16
Korea	..	..	7.43	13.14	24.34	37.11	40.08	39.56	41.98
Luxembourg	0.25	0.46	0.56	0.61	0.57	0.72	0.74	0.80	0.76
Mexico	..	..	10.88	15.94	20.00	23.60	23.58	24.18	24.53
Netherlands	6.43	15.62	20.27	21.42	19.58	22.12	22.70	22.71	22.10
New Zealand	1.10	1.65	1.72	2.00	2.32	2.91	3.02	3.12	3.10
Norway	2.05	3.87	4.15	5.12	5.92	6.66	6.96	6.92	7.05
Poland	15.35	21.00	22.14	32.11	27.10	26.91	28.24	28.37	28.95
Portugal	1.00	1.31	1.47	1.84	3.41	5.04	5.50	5.74	6.11
Slovak Republic	..	..	3.05	5.69	6.67	5.06	4.36	4.33	4.51
Spain	2.84	6.26	7.21	9.75	14.39	21.32	24.20	26.03	26.94
Sweden	6.53	13.79	14.26	15.37	11.47	12.54	13.05	12.54	12.43
Switzerland	3.06	7.12	8.49	8.52	9.49	9.26	10.08	10.35	10.70
Turkey	7.18	9.33	11.25	13.50	17.23	22.96	24.10	25.56	27.48
United Kingdom	48.54	49.74	51.22	54.72	56.09	63.58	63.14	64.17	62.69
United States	261.26	396.50	419.89	397.62	403.79	473.45	498.94	499.17	502.81
OECD TOTAL	**..**	**..**	**944.30**	**976.30**	**1 041.87**	**1 203.22**	**1 273.47**	**1 285.91**	**1 310.64**
OECD N. AMERICA	..	..	476.29	463.28	478.41	561.11	590.88	592.10	596.05
OECD PACIFIC	..	..	70.41	83.90	129.55	171.44	178.03	178.89	184.37
OECD EUROPE	..	..	397.60	429.12	433.91	470.68	504.56	514.92	530.22
IEA	..	..	907.61	921.80	987.14	1 146.60	1 216.16	1 227.94	1 251.56

Includes non-energy use for this sector.
Comprend l'usage non-énergétique pour ce secteur.

Includes residential, commerce/public services, agriculture/forestry, fishing and non-specified other sectors.
Comprend les secteurs résidentiel, commerce/services publics, agriculture/sylviculture et autres secteurs non spécifiés.

For the United States, coal used by autoproducers of electricity and heat has been included in final consumption prior to 1992.
Pour les États-Unis, avant 1992, le charbon utilisé par les autoproducteurs d'électricité et de chaleur est inclus dans la consommation finale.

GDP using Exchange Rates (billion US$2000)

PIB sur la base des taux de change (milliards US$2000)

BIP auf Wechselkursbasis (Milliarden US$2000)

PIL utilizzando i tassi di cambio (miliardi di US$ 2000)

為替換算による国内総生産（十億米ドル, 2000 年価格）

PIB basado en los tipos de cambio (millardos US$2000)

ВВП по валютному курсу (млрд.долл.США в ценах 2000 г.)

	1960	1970	1973	1980	1990	2000	2003	2004	2005
Australia	93.49 e	156.95	174.25	210.03	280.98	399.61	445.07	456.98	469.81
Austria	53.35 e	84.52	98.97	120.44	150.67	193.84	199.27	204.14	208.31
Belgium	69.26 e	110.54	128.11	153.98	187.89	231.93	240.06	246.28	249.35
Canada	168.91 e	276.91	325.18	411.94	543.65	724.91	773.42	798.93	822.39
Czech Republic	27.82 e	37.14 e	41.03 e	48.67 e	55.30	56.72	61.35	63.93	67.82
Denmark	52.17 e	80.80	89.96	101.00	123.89	160.08	163.08	166.13	171.08
Finland	32.36 e	51.73	61.03	74.45	100.29	121.87	129.39	133.93	137.84
France	351.91 e	604.94	697.97	841.13	1 088.25	1 327.96	1 381.34	1 413.38	1 430.13
Germany	597.23 e	921.64	1 038.75	1 225.93	1 543.20	1 900.22	1 920.17	1 944.12	1 961.79
Greece	33.09 e	68.99	88.59	108.14	115.79	145.96	166.11	173.96	180.45
Hungary	13.33 e	25.10 e	30.96 e	39.65 e	44.41 e	47.96	54.23	56.88	59.29
Iceland	1.77 e	2.79	3.57	5.15	6.75	8.64	9.17	9.87	10.61
Ireland	14.14 e	21.32	24.60	33.87	48.34	96.33	112.75	117.61	124.11
Italy	292.05 e	508.83	575.48	738.95	937.38	1 097.34	1 121.28	1 133.23	1 132.83
Japan	667.96 e	1 805.00	2 213.40	2 793.09	4 111.27	4 649.64	4 756.80	4 866.31	4 994.13
Korea	27.75 e	61.05	77.34	122.81	283.56	511.66	585.92	613.63	637.95
Luxembourg	4.19 e	5.93	7.02	7.65	12.40	20.27	21.87	22.66	23.56
Mexico	94.97 e	182.13	223.14	345.12	412.80	580.79	593.22	617.90	636.16
Netherlands	104.50 e	171.22	192.61	228.29	284.85	385.08	394.11	401.81	407.95
New Zealand	19.41 e	27.79	32.68	33.07	39.83	52.67	59.34	61.53	62.70
Norway	38.14 e	57.47	66.30	91.05	115.80	166.91	175.31	180.71	184.79
Poland	54.78 e	83.69 e	102.92 e	119.10 e	118.29	171.33	182.43	192.03	198.26
Portugal	20.90 e	38.72	49.60	61.53	84.74	112.65	114.50	115.86	116.32
Slovak Republic	9.23 e	12.32 e	13.61 e	16.15 e	18.70 e	20.45	22.89	24.13	25.61
Spain	113.17 e	231.11	281.94	329.98	440.64	580.67	636.96	657.62	680.84
Sweden	84.09 e	132.35	142.08	160.63	199.58	242.00	253.70	264.17	271.84
Switzerland	99.62 e	157.46	174.28	178.23	221.69	246.04	248.95	254.66	259.57
Turkey	33.54 e	56.64	66.33	84.37	140.20	199.26	210.50	229.30	246.22
United Kingdom	548.14 e	725.19	820.74	877.03	1 135.30	1 442.25	1 546.73	1 597.20	1 626.78
United States	2 553.59 e	3 721.70	4 304.80	5 128.00	7 055.00	9 764.80	10 249.80	10 651.70	10 995.80
OECD TOTAL	**6 274.87**	**10 421.94**	**12 147.22**	**14 689.43**	**19 901.40**	**25 659.84**	**26 829.70**	**27 670.56**	**28 394.27**
OECD N. AMERICA	2 817.48	4 180.74	4 853.12	5 885.07	8 011.45	11 070.51	11 616.44	12 068.54	12 454.35
OECD PACIFIC	808.61	2 050.79	2 497.67	3 158.99	4 715.64	5 613.58	5 847.13	5 998.45	6 164.59
OECD EUROPE	2 648.78	4 190.42	4 796.43	5 645.37	7 174.32	8 975.76	9 366.13	9 603.57	9 775.33
IEA	6 114.12	10 141.01	11 803.98	14 203.91	19 344.86	24 878.63	26 022.00	26 826.62	27 523.63

GDP using Purchasing Power Parities (billion US$2000)

PIB sur la base des parités de pouvoir d'achat (milliards US$2000)

BIP auf Kaufkraftparitätenbasis (Milliarden US$2000)

PIL utilizzando i PPA (miliardi di US$ 2000)

購買力平価換算による国内総生産（十億米ドル, 2000 年価格）

PIB basado en la paridad de poder adquisitivo (millardos US$2000)

ВВП по ППС (млрд.долл.США в ценах 2000 г.)

	1960	1970	1973	1980	1990	2000	2003	2004	2005
Australia	122.73 e	206.03	228.75	275.72	368.85	524.59	584.26	599.90	616.75
Austria	63.33 e	100.34	117.49	142.98	178.87	230.12	236.57	242.35	247.30
Belgium	81.57 e	130.18	150.87	181.35	221.28	273.16	282.73	290.05	293.67
Canada	203.43 e	333.49	391.63	496.13	654.75	873.06	931.48	962.21	990.45
Czech Republic	74.74 e	99.76 e	110.23 e	130.75 e	148.56	152.37	164.81	171.75	182.19
Denmark	50.14 e	77.66	86.46	97.08	119.07	153.86	156.74	159.68	164.43
Finland	35.87 e	57.34	67.65	82.53	111.17	135.08	143.42	148.45	152.80
France	417.32 e	717.39	827.71	997.49	1 290.53	1 574.81	1 638.11	1 676.10	1 695.97
Germany	660.44 e	1 019.19	1 148.69	1 355.69	1 706.54	2 101.35	2 123.41	2 149.89	2 169.43
Greece	51.83 e	108.05	138.75	169.37	181.36	228.60	260.16	272.46	282.62
Hungary	35.03 e	65.96 e	81.35 e	104.21 e	116.70 e	126.04	142.53	149.47	155.82
Iceland	1.68 e	2.63	3.37	4.87	6.38	8.16	8.66	9.32	10.02
Ireland	16.09 e	24.27	28.00	38.54	55.01	109.64	128.33	133.86	141.26
Italy	392.30 e	683.48	773.01	992.59	1 259.12	1 473.99	1 506.14	1 522.19	1 521.65
Japan	464.61 e	1 255.51	1 539.58	1 942.80	2 859.69	3 234.16	3 308.70	3 384.87	3 473.78
Korea	41.67 e	91.67	116.14	184.41	425.79	768.29	879.80	921.41	957.92
Luxembourg	4.61 e	6.51	7.71	8.40	13.62	22.26	24.02	24.89	25.88
Mexico	146.70 e	281.34	344.69	533.12	637.66	897.16	916.36	954.49	982.69
Netherlands	122.64 e	200.95	226.06	267.93	334.31	451.93	462.54	471.57	478.78
New Zealand	29.55 e	42.30	49.74	50.33	60.63	80.18	90.34	93.67	95.45
Norway	37.24 e	56.13	64.75	88.92	113.08	162.99	171.20	176.47	180.46
Poland	130.79 e	199.82 e	245.72 e	284.37 e	282.42	409.07	435.56	458.50	473.37
Portugal	34.86 e	64.61	82.75	102.66	141.37	187.94	191.03	193.30	194.07
Slovak Republic	26.44 e	35.29 e	38.99 e	46.25 e	53.56 e	58.58	65.57	69.13	73.36
Spain	165.47 e	337.91	412.23	482.48	644.28	849.03	931.32	961.53	995.48
Sweden	83.81 e	131.90	141.60	160.09	198.91	241.19	252.84	263.27	270.92
Switzerland	88.66 e	140.13	155.10	158.61	197.30	218.97	221.55	226.63	231.00
Turkey	77.38 e	130.66	153.01	194.63	323.42	459.67	485.58	528.95	567.99
United Kingdom	572.66 e	757.63	857.46	916.26	1 186.08	1 506.76	1 615.92	1 668.64	1 699.55
United States	2 553.59 e	3 721.70	4 304.80	5 128.00	7 055.00	9 764.80	10 249.80	10 651.70	10 995.80
OECD TOTAL	**6 787.19**	**11 079.82**	**12 894.29**	**15 618.53**	**20 945.29**	**27 277.80**	**28 609.47**	**29 536.68**	**30 320.83**
OECD N. AMERICA	2 903.73	4 336.54	5 041.13	6 157.25	8 347.41	11 535.02	12 097.64	12 568.40	12 968.95
OECD PACIFIC	658.56	1 595.51	1 934.21	2 453.26	3 714.96	4 607.22	4 863.10	4 999.85	5 143.90
OECD EUROPE	3 224.90	5 147.77	5 918.96	7 008.02	8 882.92	11 135.56	11 648.73	11 968.44	12 207.98
IEA	6 481.58	10 560.74	12 261.52	14 749.93	19 965.27	25 904.83	27 183.33	28 045.25	28 781.40

Population (millions)

Population (millions)

Bevölkerung (Millionen)

Popolazione (milioni)

人口（100万人）

Población (millones)

Численность населения (млн. человек)

	1960	1970	1973	1980	1990	2000	2003	2004	2005
Australia	10.40 e	12.66	13.61	14.81	17.17	19.27	19.98	20.20	20.47
Austria	7.05 e	7.47	7.59	7.55	7.68	8.01	8.12	8.18	8.23
Belgium	9.13 e	9.63	9.73	9.83	9.97	10.25	10.37	10.42	10.47
Canada	17.89 e	21.32	22.49	24.52	27.70	30.69	31.67	31.97	32.27
Czech Republic	9.58 e	9.81	9.92	10.33	10.36	10.27	10.20	10.21	10.23
Denmark	4.59 e	4.94	5.02	5.12	5.14	5.34	5.39	5.40	5.42
Finland	4.43 e	4.61	4.67	4.78	4.99	5.18	5.21	5.23	5.25
France	46.71 e	51.91	53.30	55.11	58.17	60.71	61.93	62.32	62.70
Germany	71.22 e	77.71	78.96	78.30	79.36	82.19	82.52	82.50	82.46
Greece	8.47 e	8.95	9.08	9.81	10.34	10.92	11.02	11.06	11.10
Hungary	9.98 e	10.34	10.43	10.71	10.37	10.21	10.13	10.11	10.09
Iceland	0.18 e	0.20	0.21	0.23	0.26	0.28	0.29	0.29	0.30
Ireland	2.83 e	2.95	3.07	3.40	3.51	3.80	3.99	4.06	4.15
Italy	49.94 e	53.82	54.75	56.43	56.72	56.94	57.61	58.18	58.53
Japan	93.46 e	103.73	108.67	116.81	123.48	126.84	127.71	127.75	127.76
Korea	25.01 e	32.24	34.10	38.12	42.87	47.01	47.85	48.08	48.29
Luxembourg	0.31 e	0.34	0.35	0.36	0.38	0.44	0.45	0.45	0.46
Mexico	34.61 e	48.26	53.27	65.70	81.25	98.66	102.71	104.00	105.30
Netherlands	11.48 e	13.03	13.44	14.15	14.95	15.92	16.22	16.28	16.32
New Zealand	2.38 e	2.82	2.97	3.14	3.36	3.86	4.01	4.06	4.10
Norway	3.58 e	3.88	3.96	4.09	4.24	4.49	4.57	4.59	4.62
Poland	29.56 e	32.53	33.37	35.58	38.12	38.26	38.20	38.18	38.16
Portugal	9.23 e	8.81	8.72	9.86	10.00	10.23	10.44	10.50	10.55
Slovak Republic	3.99	4.53	4.64	4.98	5.30	5.40	5.38	5.38	5.39
Spain	30.40 e	34.02	34.96	37.67	39.01	40.26	42.01	42.69	43.40
Sweden	7.48 e	8.04	8.14	8.31	8.56	8.87	8.96	8.99	9.03
Switzerland	5.40 e	6.27	6.44	6.39	6.80	7.21	7.41	7.45	7.50
Turkey	27.53 e	35.32	38.07	44.44	56.20	67.46	70.71	71.79	72.07
United Kingdom	52.37 e	55.63	56.22	56.33	57.24	58.89	59.55	59.84	60.22
United States	180.70 e	205.09	211.94	227.73	250.18	282.43	291.11	293.93	296.68
OECD TOTAL	**769.91**	**870.84**	**902.09**	**964.58**	**1 043.65**	**1 130.28**	**1 155.72**	**1 164.11**	**1 171.52**
OECD N. AMERICA	233.20	274.68	287.70	317.94	359.13	411.78	425.49	429.91	434.25
OECD PACIFIC	131.25	151.45	159.36	172.88	186.88	196.98	199.55	200.10	200.63
OECD EUROPE	405.46	444.71	455.03	473.76	497.64	521.53	530.68	534.10	536.64
IEA	701.57	785.32	810.59	858.09	918.73	987.69	1 009.15	1 016.25	1 022.37

Energy Production/TPES (Self Sufficiency)

Production d'énergie/ATEP (indépendance énergétique)

Energieerzeugung/TPES (Eigenversorgung)

Produzione di energia/ATEP (indice di autosufficienza energetica)

エネルギー生産量／一次エネルギー総供給量（自給率）

Producción energética/TPES (autosuficiencia energética)

Производство топлива и энергии/ОППТЭ (самостоятельность)

	1960	1970	1973	1980	1990	2000	2003	2004	2005
Australia	0.6753	0.9291	1.1797	1.2235	1.7995	2.1143	2.2459	2.2813	2.2220
Austria	0.6735	0.4374	0.3664	0.3275	0.3232	0.3358	0.2969	0.3020	0.2854
Belgium	0.6024	0.1769	0.1405	0.1721	0.2666	0.2324	0.2304	0.2367	0.2453
Canada	0.7485	1.0450	1.2388	1.0747	1.3072	1.4950	1.4710	1.4791	1.4755
Czech Republic	..	..	0.8478	0.8721	0.8185	0.7397	0.7484	0.7535	0.7271
Denmark	0.1102	0.0186	0.0215	0.0481	0.5610	1.4325	1.3699	1.5396	1.5962
Finland	0.5412	0.2764	0.2288	0.2720	0.4141	0.4573	0.4239	0.4166	0.4737
France	0.5700	0.3238	0.2394	0.2717	0.4935	0.5112	0.5030	0.4994	0.4960
Germany	0.8781	0.5738	0.5080	0.5151	0.5226	0.3939	0.3878	0.3911	0.3902
Greece	0.1275	0.2086	0.1889	0.2355	0.4148	0.3590	0.3315	0.3377	0.3326
Hungary	..	0.6562	0.5952	0.5085	0.5016	0.4507	0.3952	0.3883	0.3721
Iceland	0.2712	0.4235	0.4365	0.5891	0.6448	0.7107	0.7256	0.7202	0.7270
Ireland	0.3655	0.2264	0.1558	0.2232	0.3345	0.1527	0.1242	0.1246	0.1087
Italy	0.3466	0.1813	0.1587	0.1505	0.1711	0.1627	0.1527	0.1540	0.1492
Japan	0.5806	0.1530	0.0912	0.1249	0.1692	0.2005	0.1630	0.1785	0.1881
Korea	..	..	0.3124	0.2241	0.2422	0.1714	0.1829	0.1794	0.2008
Luxembourg	0.0005	0.0020	0.0009	0.0081	0.0086	0.0154	0.0141	0.0155	0.0155
Mexico	..	..	0.8890	1.5198	1.5665	1.5040	1.5167	1.5349	1.4683
Netherlands	0.4824	0.5860	0.9090	1.1052	0.9070	0.7539	0.7218	0.8234	0.7563
New Zealand	0.6033	0.4703	0.4896	0.5950	0.8728	0.8276	0.7571	0.7312	0.7216
Norway	0.4259	0.3904	0.5518	2.9650	5.5937	8.8748	8.6757	8.4405	7.2749
Poland	1.1958	1.1467	1.1539	0.9934	0.9949	0.8900	0.8732	0.8588	0.8458
Portugal	0.4215	0.2351	0.1938	0.1439	0.1912	0.1521	0.1683	0.1469	0.1319
Slovak Republic	..	..	0.1661	0.1641	0.2479	0.3566	0.3538	0.3519	0.3510
Spain	0.6091	0.2525	0.2166	0.2300	0.3797	0.2540	0.2424	0.2295	0.2086
Sweden	0.2670	0.1711	0.2353	0.3959	0.6255	0.6345	0.6073	0.6480	0.6666
Switzerland	0.2780	0.2039	0.2170	0.3370	0.3888	0.4384	0.4389	0.4357	0.4008
Turkey	0.8751	0.7676	0.6370	0.5438	0.4874	0.3357	0.2994	0.2944	0.2771
United Kingdom	0.7155	0.4888	0.4915	0.9829	0.9803	1.1647	1.0614	0.9656	0.8733
United States	0.9447	0.9316	0.8382	0.8574	0.8562	0.7278	0.7160	0.7073	0.6968
OECD TOTAL	**..**	**..**	**0.6499**	**0.7124**	**0.7554**	**0.7190**	**0.7049**	**0.7009**	**0.6911**
OECD N. AMERICA	..	..	0.8724	0.9079	0.9370	0.8416	0.8365	0.8319	0.8216
OECD PACIFIC	..	..	0.2634	0.3083	0.4183	0.4572	0.4558	0.4621	0.4823
OECD EUROPE	..	..	0.4539	0.5652	0.6354	0.6570	0.6270	0.6192	0.5954
IEA	..	..	0.6355	0.6860	0.7289	0.6940	0.6779	0.6730	0.6634

TPES/GDP (toe per thousand 2000 US$)
ATEP/PIB (tep par millier de $US 2000)

TPES/BIP (in toe pro tausend 2000er US$)

DTEP/PIL (tep per migliaia di $US 2000)

一次エネルギー供給／GDP（石油換算トン／千米ドル、2000 年価格）

TPES/PIB (tep por mile de 2000 US$)

ОППТЭ / ВВП (тнэ на тыс.долл.США в ценах и по валютному курсу 2000 г.)

	1960	1970	1973	1980	1990	2000	2003	2004	2005
Australia	0.3375 e	0.3271	0.3307	0.3351	0.3116	0.2765	0.2540	0.2485	0.2596
Austria	0.2048 e	0.2151	0.2188	0.1935	0.1664	0.1498	0.1655	0.1629	0.1650
Belgium	0.3355 e	0.3641	0.3616	0.3053	0.2616	0.2548	0.2476	0.2359	0.2272
Canada	0.4515 e	0.5002	0.4915	0.4685	0.3852	0.3437	0.3392	0.3363	0.3307
Czech Republic	..	..	1.1069 e	0.9709 e	0.8860	0.7122	0.7266	0.7159	0.6666
Denmark	0.1732 e	0.2509	0.2205	0.1959	0.1445	0.1209	0.1274	0.1216	0.1146
Finland	0.3022 e	0.3493	0.3498	0.3413	0.2909	0.2706	0.2902	0.2826	0.2536
France	0.2258 e	0.2557	0.2646	0.2301	0.2093	0.1946	0.1964	0.1945	0.1930
Germany	0.2389 e	0.3303	0.3253	0.2940	0.2308	0.1808	0.1808	0.1791	0.1757
Greece	0.0764 e	0.1173	0.1395	0.1451	0.1916	0.1906	0.1799	0.1752	0.1717
Hungary	..	0.7147 e	0.6891 e	0.7186 e	0.6431 e	0.5216	0.4857	0.4634	0.4682
Iceland	0.3135 e	0.3348	0.3471	0.2979	0.3217	0.3754	0.3694	0.3544	0.3417
Ireland	0.2675 e	0.2935	0.2922	0.2506	0.2144	0.1483	0.1330	0.1288	0.1232
Italy	0.1367 e	0.2154	0.2240	0.1788	0.1579	0.1578	0.1611	0.1613	0.1635
Japan	0.1211 e	0.1425	0.1462	0.1241	0.1081	0.1135	0.1083	0.1094	0.1062
Korea	..	..	0.2798	0.3369	0.3293	0.3716	0.3540	0.3476	0.3351
Luxembourg	0.7892 e	0.6998	0.6414	0.4762	0.2880	0.1817	0.1949	0.2065	0.2027
Mexico	..	..	0.2384	0.2814	0.3012	0.2588	0.2693	0.2674	0.2775
Netherlands	0.2024 e	0.2877	0.3242	0.2847	0.2343	0.1970	0.2054	0.2045	0.2006
New Zealand	0.2123 e	0.2601	0.2531	0.2781	0.3454	0.3409	0.2887	0.2832	0.2697
Norway	0.1827 e	0.2359	0.2207	0.2049	0.1858	0.1546	0.1548	0.1564	0.1738
Poland	0.9893 e	0.9978 e	0.9044 e	1.0330 e	0.8444	0.5220	0.5013	0.4780	0.4689
Portugal	0.1438 e	0.1546	0.1458	0.1672	0.2094	0.2245	0.2251	0.2291	0.2335
Slovak Republic	..	..	1.1387 e	1.2961 e	1.1400 e	0.8675	0.8139	0.7597	0.7354
Spain	0.1428 e	0.1660	0.1858	0.2078	0.2067	0.2147	0.2137	0.2164	0.2133
Sweden	0.2442 e	0.2867	0.2768	0.2537	0.2383	0.1992	0.2014	0.2013	0.1919
Switzerland	0.0762 e	0.1047	0.1132	0.1170	0.1127	0.1063	0.1079	0.1066	0.1046
Turkey	0.3192 e	0.3218	0.3674	0.3735	0.3778	0.3866	0.3743	0.3572	0.3461
United Kingdom	0.2927 e	0.2859	0.2689	0.2295	0.1869	0.1622	0.1502	0.1462	0.1438
United States	0.4000 e	0.4185	0.4034	0.3533	0.2732	0.2362	0.2227	0.2186	0.2128
OECD TOTAL	**..**	**..**	**0.3098**	**0.2775**	**0.2274**	**0.2076**	**0.2013**	**0.1990**	**0.1954**
OECD N. AMERICA	..	..	0.4017	0.3571	0.2822	0.2444	0.2329	0.2289	0.2239
OECD PACIFIC	..	..	0.1646	0.1480	0.1355	0.1507	0.1459	0.1461	0.1433
OECD EUROPE	..	..	0.2923	0.2671	0.2265	0.1977	0.1967	0.1943	0.1919
IEA	..	..	0.3050	0.2699	0.2211	0.2036	0.1970	0.1948	0.1910

TPES/GDP (toe per thousand 2000 US$ PPP)

ATEP/PIB (tep par millier de $US 2000 PPA)

TPES/BIP (in toe pro tausend 2000er US$ Kaufkraftparität)

DTEP/PIL (tep per migliaia di $US 2000 PPA)

一次エネルギー供給／ＧＤＰ（石油換算トン／千米ドル、2000 年価格、購買力平価）

TPES/PIB (tep por mile de 2000 US$ PPP)

ОППТЭ / ВВП (тнэ на тыс.долл.США в ценах и по ППС 2000 г.)

	1960	1970	1973	1980	1990	2000	2003	2004	2005
Australia	0.2571 e	0.2492	0.2519	0.2552	0.2373	0.2106	0.1935	0.1893	0.1977
Austria	0.1725 e	0.1812	0.1843	0.1630	0.1402	0.1262	0.1394	0.1372	0.1390
Belgium	0.2848 e	0.3091	0.3070	0.2592	0.2222	0.2163	0.2102	0.2003	0.1929
Canada	0.3749 e	0.4154	0.4081	0.3890	0.3198	0.2854	0.2817	0.2793	0.2746
Czech Republic	..	..	0.4120 e	0.3614 e	0.3298	0.2651	0.2705	0.2665	0.2481
Denmark	0.1802 e	0.2610	0.2294	0.2038	0.1503	0.1258	0.1326	0.1265	0.1193
Finland	0.2726 e	0.3152	0.3155	0.3079	0.2624	0.2441	0.2618	0.2550	0.2288
France	0.1904 e	0.2156	0.2231	0.1941	0.1765	0.1641	0.1656	0.1640	0.1627
Germany	0.2160 e	0.2987	0.2941	0.2658	0.2087	0.1635	0.1635	0.1620	0.1589
Greece	0.0488 e	0.0749	0.0890	0.0927	0.1223	0.1217	0.1148	0.1118	0.1096
Hungary	..	0.2720 e	0.2622 e	0.2734 e	0.2447 e	0.1985	0.1848	0.1763	0.1782
Iceland	0.3320 e	0.3545	0.3675	0.3155	0.3406	0.3975	0.3911	0.3753	0.3618
Ireland	0.2350 e	0.2578	0.2567	0.2201	0.1884	0.1303	0.1169	0.1132	0.1082
Italy	0.1018 e	0.1603	0.1668	0.1331	0.1175	0.1175	0.1200	0.1201	0.1217
Japan	0.1742 e	0.2049	0.2102	0.1784	0.1554	0.1631	0.1557	0.1572	0.1527
Korea	..	..	0.1863	0.2243	0.2193	0.2475	0.2358	0.2315	0.2232
Luxembourg	0.7186 e	0.6372	0.5841	0.4336	0.2622	0.1654	0.1775	0.1880	0.1846
Mexico	..	..	0.1543	0.1822	0.1950	0.1676	0.1743	0.1731	0.1796
Netherlands	0.1724 e	0.2452	0.2762	0.2425	0.1997	0.1679	0.1751	0.1743	0.1710
New Zealand	0.1395 e	0.1709	0.1662	0.1827	0.2269	0.2239	0.1896	0.1861	0.1771
Norway	0.1870 e	0.2416	0.2260	0.2098	0.1902	0.1583	0.1586	0.1602	0.1780
Poland	0.4144 e	0.4179 e	0.3788 e	0.4327 e	0.3537	0.2186	0.2100	0.2002	0.1964
Portugal	0.0862 e	0.0927	0.0874	0.1002	0.1255	0.1346	0.1349	0.1373	0.1400
Slovak Republic	..	..	0.3975 e	0.4524 e	0.3979 e	0.3028	0.2841	0.2652	0.2567
Spain	0.0976 e	0.1135	0.1271	0.1421	0.1414	0.1469	0.1461	0.1480	0.1459
Sweden	0.2450 e	0.2877	0.2777	0.2546	0.2391	0.1999	0.2021	0.2020	0.1926
Switzerland	0.0857 e	0.1176	0.1272	0.1315	0.1267	0.1195	0.1213	0.1197	0.1175
Turkey	0.1384 e	0.1395	0.1593	0.1619	0.1638	0.1676	0.1623	0.1548	0.1500
United Kingdom	0.2802 e	0.2736	0.2574	0.2197	0.1789	0.1552	0.1438	0.1399	0.1376
United States	0.4000 e	0.4185	0.4034	0.3533	0.2732	0.2362	0.2227	0.2186	0.2128
OECD TOTAL	**..**	**..**	**0.2918**	**0.2610**	**0.2161**	**0.1953**	**0.1888**	**0.1864**	**0.1830**
OECD N. AMERICA	..	..	0.3867	0.3414	0.2709	0.2346	0.2236	0.2198	0.2150
OECD PACIFIC	..	..	0.2126	0.1905	0.1721	0.1837	0.1754	0.1753	0.1717
OECD EUROPE	..	..	0.2369	0.2151	0.1829	0.1593	0.1582	0.1559	0.1536
IEA	..	..	0.2936	0.2599	0.2143	0.1955	0.1886	0.1864	0.1826

TPES/Population (toe per capita)

ATEP/Population (tep par habitant)

TPES/Bevölkerung (toe pro Kopf)

DTEP/Popolazione (tep per abitante)

一人当たり一次エネルギー供給（石油換算トン／人）

TPES/ población (tep per capita)

ОППТЭ / Численность населения (тнэ на человека)

	1960	1970	1973	1980	1990	2000	2003	2004	2005
Australia	3.0327 e	4.0538	4.2324	4.7526	5.0988	5.7336	5.6580	5.6196	5.9566
Austria	1.5504 e	2.4349	2.8540	3.0869	3.2653	3.6241	4.0636	4.0677	4.1738
Belgium	2.5464 e	4.1810	4.7628	4.7808	4.9319	5.7667	5.7296	5.5768	5.4095
Canada	4.2623 e	6.4960	7.1066	7.8724	7.5605	8.1195	8.2846	8.4037	8.4272
Czech Republic	..	..	4.5774	4.5757	4.7277	3.9319	4.3693	4.4842	4.4172
Denmark	1.9680 e	4.1052	3.9495	3.8608	3.4816	3.6270	3.8560	3.7384	3.6187
Finland	2.2075 e	3.9235	4.5748	5.3165	5.8506	6.3717	7.2034	7.2419	6.6655
France	1.7014 e	2.9798	3.4645	3.5124	3.9163	4.2553	4.3812	4.4113	4.4013
Germany	2.0030 e	3.9178	4.2794	4.6024	4.4884	4.1809	4.2073	4.2208	4.1806
Greece	0.2984 e	0.9049	1.3602	1.5999	2.1458	2.5485	2.7102	2.7545	2.7898
Hungary	..	1.7354	2.0460	2.6613	2.7552	2.4497	2.6003	2.6079	2.7523
Iceland	3.1600 e	4.5724	5.8490	6.7312	8.5157	11.5450	11.7179	11.9376	12.2494
Ireland	1.3344 e	2.1211	2.3396	2.4950	2.9565	3.7583	3.7577	3.7327	3.6850
Italy	0.7995 e	2.0361	2.3548	2.3417	2.6088	3.0403	3.1365	3.1422	3.1639
Japan	0.8659 e	2.4797	2.9781	2.9667	3.5996	4.1592	4.0351	4.1664	4.1520
Korea	..	..	0.6346	1.0852	2.1784	4.0450	4.3353	4.4358	4.4265
Luxembourg	10.5389 e	12.2317	12.8344	10.0078	9.3494	8.3898	9.4715	10.3315	10.4516
Mexico	..	..	0.9986	1.4785	1.5303	1.5237	1.5555	1.5887	1.6765
Netherlands	1.8419 e	3.7803	4.6468	4.5932	4.4658	4.7646	4.9909	5.0487	5.0165
New Zealand	1.7342 e	2.5625	2.7834	2.9248	4.0922	4.6514	4.2720	4.2895	4.1231
Norway	1.9441 e	3.4976	3.6955	4.5651	5.0720	5.7469	5.9462	6.1573	6.9504
Poland	1.8333 e	2.5675	2.7893	3.4582	2.6202	2.3376	2.3943	2.4040	2.4362
Portugal	0.3257 e	0.6800	0.8292	1.0435	1.7755	2.4731	2.4689	2.5280	2.5753
Slovak Republic	..	..	3.3393	4.1985	4.0232	3.2842	3.4627	3.4063	3.4957
Spain	0.5315 e	1.1274	1.4986	1.8205	2.3344	3.0969	3.2399	3.3341	3.3457
Sweden	2.7455 e	4.7178	4.8327	4.9042	5.5575	5.4343	5.7049	5.9129	5.7779
Switzerland	1.4060 e	2.6299	3.0621	3.2672	3.6774	3.6287	3.6287	3.6402	3.6199
Turkey	0.3889 e	0.5160	0.6401	0.7091	0.9424	1.1418	1.1143	1.1409	1.1823
United Kingdom	3.0637 e	3.7265	3.9258	3.5733	3.7070	3.9715	3.9011	3.9017	3.8847
United States	5.6521 e	7.5936	8.1931	7.9554	7.7042	8.1671	7.8415	7.9221	7.8883
OECD TOTAL	**..**	**..**	**4.1711**	**4.2266**	**4.3362**	**4.7124**	**4.6728**	**4.7293**	**4.7354**
OECD N. AMERICA	..	..	6.7760	6.6106	6.2964	6.5719	6.3571	6.4258	6.4221
OECD PACIFIC	..	..	2.5801	2.7040	3.4202	4.2956	4.2743	4.3803	4.4016
OECD EUROPE	..	..	3.0813	3.1822	3.2656	3.4017	3.4721	3.4945	3.4953
IEA	..	..	4.4408	4.4683	4.6562	5.1288	5.0807	5.1430	5.1406

Index of Industry Consumption/Industrial Production (2000=100)

Indice de Consommation industrielle/Production industrielle (2000=100)

Index des Industrieverbrauchs/Industrieerzeugung (2000=100)

Indice di Consumo industriale/ Produzione industriale (2000=100)

産業部門エネルギー消費原単位 (2000=100)

Indice del Consumo industrial / Producción industrial (2000=100)

Потребление промышленным сектором/Объем промышленной продукции (Индекс 2000=100)

	1960	1970	1973	1980	1990	2000	2003	2004	2005
Australia	..	..	..	116.54	102.15	100.00	88.77	92.74	95.38
Austria	233.15	185.54	179.18	149.59	122.87	100.00	101.34	98.76	96.78
Belgium	111.54	133.20	136.09	103.53	83.46	100.00	89.73	80.81	78.80
Canada	..	146.65	140.61	149.97	120.77	100.00	104.50	106.32	102.00
Czech Republic	..	..	..	..	132.52	100.00	83.95	82.99	77.22
Denmark	..	..	..	195.42	122.55	100.00	93.97	96.34	91.93
Finland	146.27	149.78	175.74	130.94	142.96	100.00	103.43	101.09	95.13
France	159.45	204.21	161.47	142.44	104.86	100.00	99.73	95.86	95.58
Germany	167.53	194.08	194.12	173.32	125.80	100.00	106.02	103.98	100.16
Greece	..	120.42	119.90	112.77	107.15	100.00	99.92	94.89	94.73
Hungary	..	..	..	298.20	237.71	100.00	84.77	79.19	84.51
Iceland	..	..	..	..	..	..	..	..	..
Ireland	..	..	..	460.38	248.31	100.00	68.98	67.66	70.54
Italy	136.64	169.72	166.79	126.52	111.06	100.00	107.64	110.12	109.75
Japan	206.19	183.89	179.68	129.26	101.12	100.00	102.86	99.46	97.75
Korea	..	..	..	151.86	98.83	100.00	98.62	92.87	88.22
Luxembourg	298.44	347.35	338.02	312.24	175.50	100.00	84.01	85.54	79.50
Mexico	..	..	..	123.52	141.25	100.00	92.60	92.24	90.57
Netherlands	82.21	109.83	130.99	115.99	110.24	100.00	107.26	107.13	115.64
New Zealand	..	..	..	..	85.04	100.00	76.58	77.48	69.27
Norway	215.73	254.55	238.54	192.65	122.16	100.00	104.45	103.92	102.91
Poland	..	..	..	..	209.06	100.00	83.11	76.60	70.87
Portugal	70.43	89.62	79.04	81.85	90.89	100.00	92.84	95.67	94.48
Slovak Republic	..	..	..	..	152.51	100.00	89.68	83.31	80.92
Spain	..	114.16	107.39	103.69	91.29	100.00	111.82	110.40	111.07
Sweden	237.97	198.27	194.37	170.38	130.25	100.00	92.60	88.45	84.76
Switzerland	170.94	171.61	166.67	156.74	111.16	100.00	106.66	105.03	104.13
Turkey	..	..	..	..	83.86	100.00	98.35	92.45	87.27
United Kingdom	179.15	201.92	193.63	141.66	109.24	100.00	101.50	98.84	101.01
United States	263.70	231.19	205.98	187.19	124.94	100.00	94.68	96.43	90.48
OECD TOTAL	**..**	**..**	**..**	**150.65**	**112.52**	**100.00**	**98.29**	**97.58**	**94.17**
OECD N. AMERICA	..	..	..	..	..	..	..	..	..
OECD PACIFIC	..	..	..	..	..	..	..	..	..
OECD EUROPE	..	..	..	146.83	115.55	100.00	101.12	98.72	97.33
IEA	..	..	..	..	..	..	..	..	..

RENEWABLE ENERGY AND WASTES

ENERGIES RENOUVELABLES ET DECHETS

OECD Total / OCDE Total

Contribution from Renewable Energies and Energy from Wastes

Part des énergies renouvables et de l'énergie tirée des déchets

	1990	1995	2000	2001	2002	2003	2004	2005
TPES / ATEP (ktoe / ktep)								
TOTAL PRIMARY ENERGY SUPPLY	**4 525 492**	**4 890 802**	**5 326 373**	**5 302 613**	**5 349 037**	**5 400 403**	**5 505 394**	**5 547 598**
% contribution of Renewables and Wastes	-	6.2	6.1	5.9	5.9	6.0	6.1	6.2
Renewables	..	**290 545**	**308 801**	**293 542**	**296 157**	**304 828**	**317 808**	**327 598**
% contribution	-	5.9	5.8	5.5	5.5	5.6	5.8	5.9
Hydro	..	112 051	113 377	104 499	108 781	106 532	108 961	109 263
Geothermal (transformation *)	..	25 895	28 214	27 687	22 273	23 571	24 088	24 620
Geothermal (direct use **)	..	2 703	3 010	3 149	3 214	3 456	3 499	3 670
Solar Photovoltaic (transformation *)	..	5	16	23	31	48	70	138
Solar Thermal (transformation *)	..	71	134	143	142	138	145	136
Solar Thermal (direct use **)	..	1 514	3 085	3 025	3 065	3 001	3 006	3 042
Tide/Wave/Ocean	..	52	52	49	49	49	47	49
Wind	..	632	2 455	2 978	4 156	5 025	6 610	8 059
Ambient Heat (Heat Pumps)	..	339	378	395	406	336	450	497
Municipal Waste (Renewable)	..	6 535	8 914	8 690	9 293	9 399	9 666	10 140
Solid Biomass	..	135 433	139 604	132 251	131 799	138 158	143 423	146 685
Biogasoline	..	2 676	3 147	3 211	4 124	5 873	7 331	8 446
Biodiesel	..	185	657	764	961	1 260	1 762	2 842
Other Liquid Biomass	..	11	17	23	149	296	429	1 015
Biogas	..	2 442	5 740	6 653	7 712	7 686	8 322	8 997
Non-Renewable Wastes	..	**13 285**	**17 119**	**16 758**	**17 421**	**18 017**	**17 277**	**16 226**
% contribution	-	0.3	0.3	0.3	0.3	0.3	0.3	0.3
Industrial Waste	..	6 999	8 676	8 570	8 678	9 039	8 016	6 492
Municipal Waste (Non-Renewable)	..	6 285	8 443	8 188	8 743	8 978	9 261	9 734
Not separately identified * **	..	-	-	-	-	-	-	-
% contribution	-	-	-	-	-	-	-	-
*Memo: Total Wastes *******	..	*19 820*	*26 033*	*25 448*	*26 714*	*27 416*	*26 943*	*26 366*
ELECTRICITY / ELECTRICITE (GWh)								
TOTAL ELECTRICITY GENERATED	**7 569 639**	**8 471 338**	**9 591 052**	**9 460 971**	**9 761 488**	**9 865 384**	**10 123 599**	**10 392 503**
% contribution of Renewables and Wastes	-	17.2	15.9	15.1	15.5	15.2	15.4	15.4
Renewables	..	**1 433 827**	**1 496 269**	**1 394 849**	**1 471 593**	**1 465 492**	**1 525 667**	**1 561 972**
% contribution	-	16.9	15.6	14.7	15.1	14.9	15.1	15.0
Hydro (excl. pumped storage)	..	1 302 916	1 318 341	1 215 107	1 264 900	1 238 746	1 266 988	1 270 497
Geothermal	..	29 809	32 975	32 236	32 876	34 334	35 291	37 304
Solar Photovoltaic	..	55	186	268	365	553	815	1 605
Solar Thermal Electric	..	824	526	565	569	548	587	596
Tide/Wave/Ocean	..	601	605	575	568	572	549	565
Wind	..	7 348	28 545	34 632	48 330	58 433	76 859	93 711
Municipal Waste (Renewable)	..	13 178	18 903	19 561	20 588	21 787	22 393	24 543
Solid Biomass	..	72 943	83 178	77 652	86 071	91 516	101 424	108 422
Biogas/Liquid Biomass	..	6 153	13 010	14 253	17 326	19 003	20 761	24 729
Non-Renewable Wastes	..	**22 238**	**31 725**	**35 229**	**37 165**	**37 473**	**38 429**	**34 516**
% contribution	-	0.3	0.3	0.4	0.4	0.4	0.4	0.3
Industrial Waste	..	9 399	13 747	16 550	17 519	16 613	16 578	10 736
Municipal Waste (Non-Renewable)	..	12 839	17 978	18 679	19 646	20 860	21 851	23 780
Not separately identified * **	..	-	-	-	-	-	-	-
% contribution	-	-	-	-	-	-	-	-
*Memo: Total Wastes *******	..	*35 416*	*50 628*	*54 790*	*57 753*	*59 260*	*60 822*	*59 059*

* Primary energy used in the production of electricity and heat by main activity producers or autoproducers in electricity plants, CHP plants and heat plants (e.g. solar thermal power plants, geothermal power plants, etc.).
Energie primaire utilisée pour la production d'électricité, de cogénération et de chaleur par des producteurs dont c'est l'activité principale ou des autoproducteurs (installations héliothermiques, géothermiques, etc.).

** Primary energy used elsewhere than in transformation as described above (e.g. remote photovoltaic electricity production for households, heating of buildings/greenhouses by geothermal, etc.).
Energie primaire utilisée ailleurs que dans la transformation décrite ci-dessus (ex : production isolée d'électricité photovoltaïque, chauffage des bâtiments/serres à partir d'énergie géothermique, etc.).

*** Includes non-specified combustible renewables and waste.
Comprend les énergies renouvelables combustibles et les déchets non spécifiés.

**** Includes municipal waste and industrial waste.
Comprend les déchets municipaux et les déchets industriels.

OECD North America / OCDE Amérique du Nord

Contribution from Renewable Energies and Energy from Wastes

Part des énergies renouvables et de l'énergie tirée des déchets

	1990	1995	2000	2001	2002	2003	2004	2005
TPES / ATEP (ktoe / ktep)								
TOTAL PRIMARY ENERGY SUPPLY	**2 261 209**	**2 454 096**	**2 706 139**	**2 657 866**	**2 695 402**	**2 704 906**	**2 762 476**	**2 788 775**
% contribution of Renewables and Wastes	-	6.7	6.2	5.7	5.8	5.9	6.0	6.1
Renewables	..	**158 577**	**160 212**	**144 014**	**147 994**	**153 358**	**158 487**	**163 897**
% contribution	-	6.5	5.9	5.4	5.5	5.7	5.7	5.9
Hydro	..	58 271	55 457	47 306	55 258	54 690	54 796	57 078
Geothermal (transformation *)	..	17 718	17 642	17 103	12 314	13 039	13 497	14 054
Geothermal (direct use **)	..	406	519	569	600	751	751	852
Solar Photovoltaic (transformation *)	..	1	4	5	5	5	5	6
Solar Thermal (transformation *)	..	71	133	143	141	137	144	135
Solar Thermal (direct use **)	..	-	1 483	1 412	1 386	1 330	1 338	1 307
Tide/Wave/Ocean	..	3	3	3	3	3	3	3
Wind	..	280	510	616	936	1 044	1 312	1 665
Ambient Heat (Heat Pumps)	..	-	-	-	-	-	-	-
Municipal Waste (Renewable)	..	3 231	4 099	3 468	3 853	3 585	3 543	3 551
Solid Biomass	..	74 918	74 122	66 777	65 564	68 998	71 833	72 815
Biogasoline	..	2 644	3 067	3 119	3 940	5 606	6 952	7 826
Biodiesel	..	-	21	21	50	79	108	296
Other Liquid Biomass	..	-	-	-	106	255	265	291
Biogas	..	1 034	3 152	3 472	3 838	3 835	3 942	4 019
Non-Renewable Wastes	..	**6 384**	**8 287**	**6 992**	**7 374**	**7 259**	**6 401**	**6 163**
% contribution	-	0.3	0.3	0.3	0.3	0.3	0.2	0.2
Industrial Waste	..	3 153	4 187	3 524	3 521	3 674	2 858	2 612
Municipal Waste (Non-Renewable)	..	3 231	4 099	3 468	3 853	3 585	3 543	3 551
Not separately identified *	..	-	-	-	-	-	-	-
% contribution	-	-	-	-	-	-	-	-
*Memo: Total Wastes ***	..	*9 615*	*12 386*	*10 459*	*11 226*	*10 845*	*9 945*	*9 715*
ELECTRICITY / ELECTRICITE (GWh)								
TOTAL ELECTRICITY GENERATED	**3 808 883**	**4 275 738**	**4 834 812**	**4 637 419**	**4 841 793**	**4 862 074**	**4 971 913**	**5 131 359**
% contribution of Renewables and Wastes	-	18.0	15.6	14.0	15.6	15.4	15.2	15.4
Renewables	..	**759 083**	**736 606**	**637 004**	**738 669**	**736 041**	**741 662**	**776 433**
% contribution	-	17.8	15.2	13.7	15.3	15.1	14.9	15.1
Hydro (excl. pumped storage)	..	677 567	644 846	550 073	642 539	635 934	637 159	663 694
Geothermal	..	20 610	20 522	19 813	20 337	21 152	22 064	24 077
Solar Photovoltaic	..	8	48	53	57	58	54	68
Solar Thermal Electric	..	824	526	565	569	548	587	596
Tide/Wave/Ocean	..	33	32	32	32	33	31	31
Wind	..	3 261	5 927	7 161	10 883	12 140	15 260	19 366
Municipal Waste (Renewable)	..	7 396	8 374	8 112	8 262	8 103	8 138	8 517
Solid Biomass	..	46 052	50 384	45 064	48 837	50 323	50 862	52 670
Biogas/Liquid Biomass	..	3 332	5 947	6 131	7 153	7 750	7 507	7 414
Non-Renewable Wastes	..	**11 664**	**15 542**	**14 219**	**15 143**	**14 735**	**15 734**	**14 264**
% contribution	-	0.3	0.3	0.3	0.3	0.3	0.3	0.3
Industrial Waste	..	4 268	7 170	6 108	6 881	6 635	7 599	5 748
Municipal Waste (Non-Renewable)	..	7 396	8 372	8 111	8 262	8 100	8 135	8 516
Not separately identified *	..	-	-	-	-	-	-	-
% contribution	-	-	-	-	-	-	-	-
*Memo: Total Wastes ***	..	*19 060*	*23 916*	*22 331*	*23 405*	*22 838*	*23 872*	*22 781*

* Primary energy used in the production of electricity and heat by main activity producers or autoproducers in electricity plants, CHP plants and heat plants (e.g. solar thermal power plants, geothermal power plants, etc.).
Energie primaire utilisée pour la production d'électricité, de cogénération et de chaleur par des producteurs dont c'est l'activité principale ou des autoproducteurs (installations héliothermiques, géothermiques, etc.).

** Primary energy used elsewhere than in transformation as described above (e.g. remote photovoltaic electricity production for households, heating of buildings/greenhouses by geothermal, etc.).
Energie primaire utilisée ailleurs que dans la transformation décrite ci-dessus (ex : production isolée d'électricité photovoltaïque, chauffage des bâtiments/serres à partir d'énergie géothermique, etc.).

*** Includes non-specified combustible renewables and waste.
Comprend les énergies renouvelables combustibles et les déchets non spécifiés.

**** Includes municipal waste and industrial waste.
Comprend les déchets municipaux et les déchets industriels.

OECD Pacific / OCDE Pacifique

Contribution from Renewable Energies and Energy from Wastes

Part des énergies renouvables et de l'énergie tirée des déchets

	1990	1995	2000	2001	2002	2003	2004	2005
				TPES / ATEP (ktoe / ktep)				
TOTAL PRIMARY ENERGY SUPPLY	**639 163**	**757 246**	**846 152**	**838 709**	**852 338**	**852 938**	**876 507**	**883 099**
% contribution of Renewables and Wastes	-	3.7	3.7	3.6	3.6	3.7	3.7	3.5
Renewables	..	**27 006**	**29 290**	**28 486**	**28 540**	**29 583**	**29 865**	**28 485**
% contribution	-	3.6	3.5	3.4	3.3	3.5	3.4	3.2
Hydro	..	11 010	11 389	10 852	10 896	11 976	12 150	10 409
Geothermal (transformation *)	..	4 489	5 238	5 239	4 471	4 504	4 436	4 332
Geothermal (direct use **)	..	674	590	596	603	601	594	591
Solar Photovoltaic (transformation *)	..	-	1	1	1	1	2	2
Solar Thermal (transformation *)	..	-	-	-	-	-	-	-
Solar Thermal (direct use **)	..	1 107	931	871	866	762	682	682
Tide/Wave/Ocean	..	-	-	-	-	-	-	-
Wind	..	1	26	52	81	147	208	291
Ambient Heat (Heat Pumps)	..	-	-	-	-	-	24	24
Municipal Waste (Renewable)	..	321	598	732	864	964	989	1 011
Solid Biomass	..	9 197	10 186	9 718	10 264	10 128	10 226	10 561
Biogasoline	..	-	-	-	-	-	-	11
Biodiesel	..	-	-	-	1	2	4	11
Other Liquid Biomass	..	-	-	-	-	-	-	-
Biogas	..	207	332	425	492	498	550	561
Non-Renewable Wastes	..	**1 291**	**1 853**	**1 881**	**1 973**	**2 241**	**2 463**	**2 389**
% contribution	-	0.2	0.2	0.2	0.2	0.3	0.3	0.3
Industrial Waste	..	976	1 292	1 210	1 191	1 364	1 568	1 480
Municipal Waste (Non-Renewable)	..	315	562	672	782	878	895	910
Not separately identified ***	..	-	-	-	-	-	-	-
% contribution	-	-	-	-	-	-	-	-
*Memo: Total Wastes *****	..	*1 612*	*2 452*	*2 613*	*2 837*	*3 205*	*3 452*	*3 400*
				ELECTRICITY / ELECTRICITE (GWh)				
TOTAL ELECTRICITY GENERATED	**1 128 730**	**1 351 446**	**1 561 288**	**1 570 110**	**1 649 201**	**1 654 038**	**1 719 497**	**1 775 941**
% contribution of Renewables and Wastes	-	10.9	10.0	9.6	9.3	10.1	10.0	8.6
Renewables	..	**146 241**	**153 773**	**147 441**	**150 043**	**164 198**	**167 630**	**149 425**
% contribution	-	10.8	9.8	9.4	9.1	9.9	9.7	8.4
Hydro (excl. pumped storage)	..	128 022	132 426	126 188	126 695	139 256	141 274	121 040
Geothermal	..	5 345	6 269	6 270	6 240	6 253	6 128	6 078
Solar Photovoltaic	..	2	10	12	14	17	21	28
Solar Thermal Electric	..	-	-	-	-	-	-	-
Tide/Wave/Ocean	..	-	-	-	-	-	-	-
Wind	..	9	302	609	947	1 705	2 415	3 381
Municipal Waste (Renewable)	..	1 401	2 374	2 695	3 088	3 506	3 515	3 517
Solid Biomass	..	11 228	11 902	11 193	12 006	12 557	13 249	14 205
Biogas/Liquid Biomass	..	234	490	474	1 053	904	1 028	1 176
Non-Renewable Wastes	..	**1 402**	**2 468**	**2 727**	**3 121**	**3 557**	**3 662**	**3 647**
% contribution	-	0.1	0.2	0.2	0.2	0.2	0.2	0.2
Industrial Waste	..	-	100	39	51	70	168	151
Municipal Waste (Non-Renewable)	..	1 402	2 368	2 688	3 070	3 487	3 494	3 496
Not separately identified ***	..	-	-	-	-	-	-	-
% contribution	-	-	-	-	-	-	-	-
*Memo: Total Wastes *****	..	*2 803*	*4 842*	*5 422*	*6 209*	*7 063*	*7 177*	*7 164*

* Primary energy used in the production of electricity and heat by main activity producers or autoproducers in electricity plants, CHP plants and heat plants (e.g. solar thermal power plants, geothermal power plants, etc.).
Energie primaire utilisée pour la production d'électricité, de cogénération et de chaleur par des producteurs dont c'est l'activité principale ou des autoproducteurs (installations héliothermiques, géothermiques, etc.).

** Primary energy used elsewhere than in transformation as described above (e.g. remote photovoltaic electricity production for households, heating of buildings/greenhouses by geothermal, etc.).
Energie primaire utilisée ailleurs que dans la transformation décrite ci-dessus (ex : production isolée d'électricité photovoltaïque, chauffage des bâtiments/serres à partir d'énergie géothermique, etc.).

*** Includes non-specified combustible renewables and waste.
Comprend les énergies renouvelables combustibles et les déchets non spécifiés.

**** Includes municipal waste and industrial waste.
Comprend les déchets municipaux et les déchets industriels.

OECD Europe / OCDE Europe

Contribution from Renewable Energies and Energy from Wastes

Part des énergies renouvables et de l'énergie tirée des déchets

	1990	1995	2000	2001	2002	2003	2004	2005
TPES / ATEP (ktoe / ktep)								
TOTAL PRIMARY ENERGY SUPPLY	**1 625 119**	**1 679 460**	**1 774 083**	**1 806 037**	**1 801 298**	**1 842 559**	**1 866 411**	**1 875 724**
% contribution of Renewables and Wastes	-	6.6	7.1	7.1	7.1	7.1	7.4	7.6
Renewables	..	**104 962**	**119 298**	**121 042**	**119 623**	**121 887**	**129 455**	**135 215**
% contribution	-	6.2	6.7	6.7	6.6	6.6	6.9	7.2
Hydro	..	42 770	46 532	46 341	42 627	39 866	42 016	41 776
Geothermal (transformation *)	..	3 688	5 334	5 345	5 488	6 028	6 155	6 233
Geothermal (direct use **)	..	1 622	1 901	1 983	2 011	2 104	2 153	2 228
Solar Photovoltaic (transformation *)	..	4	11	17	25	41	64	130
Solar Thermal (transformation *)	..	-	1	1	1	1	1	1
Solar Thermal (direct use **)	..	406	671	743	813	908	986	1 053
Tide/Wave/Ocean	..	49	49	47	46	46	45	46
Wind	..	351	1 919	2 310	3 139	3 835	5 090	6 103
Ambient Heat (Heat Pumps)	..	339	378	395	406	336	426	473
Municipal Waste (Renewable)	..	2 984	4 216	4 490	4 576	4 849	5 134	5 579
Solid Biomass	..	51 318	55 296	55 756	55 972	59 032	61 364	63 310
Biogasoline	..	33	80	92	184	268	379	609
Biodiesel	..	185	636	743	910	1 179	1 650	2 535
Other Liquid Biomass	..	11	17	23	43	41	163	723
Biogas	..	1 201	2 256	2 756	3 381	3 353	3 830	4 416
Non-Renewable Wastes	..	**5 610**	**6 979**	**7 885**	**8 074**	**8 517**	**8 413**	**7 673**
% contribution	-	0.3	0.4	0.4	0.4	0.5	0.5	0.4
Industrial Waste	..	2 870	3 197	3 836	3 966	4 002	3 590	2 400
Municipal Waste (Non-Renewable)	..	2 740	3 782	4 049	4 108	4 515	4 823	5 273
Not separately identified * **	..	-	-	-	-	-	-	-
% contribution	-	-	-	-	-	-	-	-
*Memo: Total Wastes **** *	..	*8 593*	*11 195*	*12 375*	*12 651*	*13 366*	*13 547*	*13 252*
ELECTRICITY / ELECTRICITE (GWh)								
TOTAL ELECTRICITY GENERATED	**2 632 026**	**2 844 154**	**3 194 952**	**3 253 442**	**3 270 494**	**3 349 272**	**3 432 189**	**3 485 203**
% contribution of Renewables and Wastes	-	18.9	19.4	19.3	18.4	17.4	18.5	18.7
Renewables	..	**528 503**	**605 890**	**610 404**	**582 881**	**565 253**	**616 375**	**636 114**
% contribution	-	18.6	19.0	18.8	17.8	16.9	18.0	18.3
Hydro (excl. pumped storage)	..	497 327	541 069	538 846	495 666	463 556	488 555	485 763
Geothermal	..	3 854	6 184	6 153	6 299	6 929	7 099	7 149
Solar Photovoltaic	..	45	128	203	294	478	740	1 509
Solar Thermal Electric	..	-	-	-	-	-	-	-
Tide/Wave/Ocean	..	568	573	543	536	539	518	534
Wind	..	4 078	22 316	26 862	36 500	44 588	59 184	70 964
Municipal Waste (Renewable)	..	4 381	8 155	8 754	9 238	10 178	10 740	12 509
Solid Biomass	..	15 663	20 892	21 395	25 228	28 636	37 313	41 547
Biogas/Liquid Biomass	..	2 587	6 573	7 648	9 120	10 349	12 226	16 139
Non-Renewable Wastes	..	**9 172**	**13 715**	**18 283**	**18 901**	**19 181**	**19 033**	**16 605**
% contribution	-	0.3	0.4	0.6	0.6	0.6	0.6	0.5
Industrial Waste	..	5 131	6 477	10 403	10 587	9 908	8 811	4 837
Municipal Waste (Non-Renewable)	..	4 041	7 238	7 880	8 314	9 273	10 222	11 768
Not separately identified * **	..	-	-	-	-	-	-	-
% contribution	-	-	-	-	-	-	-	-
*Memo: Total Wastes **** *	..	*13 553*	*21 870*	*27 037*	*28 139*	*29 359*	*29 773*	*29 114*

* Primary energy used in the production of electricity and heat by main activity producers or autoproducers in electricity plants, CHP plants and heat plants (e.g. solar thermal power plants, geothermal power plants, etc.).
Energie primaire utilisée pour la production d'électricité, de cogénération et de chaleur par des producteurs dont c'est l'activité principale ou des autoproducteurs (installations héliothermiques, géothermiques, etc.).

** Primary energy used elsewhere than in transformation as described above (e.g. remote photovoltaic electricity production for households, heating of buildings/greenhouses by geothermal, etc.).
Energie primaire utilisée ailleurs que dans la transformation décrite ci-dessus (ex : production isolée d'électricité photovoltaïque, chauffage des bâtiments/serres à partir d'énergie géothermique, etc.).

*** Includes non-specified combustible renewables and waste.
Comprend les énergies renouvelables combustibles et les déchets non spécifiés.

**** Includes municipal waste and industrial waste.
Comprend les déchets municipaux et les déchets industriels.

IEA / AIE

Contribution from Renewable Energies and Energy from Wastes

Part des énergies renouvables et de l'énergie tirée des déchets

	1990	1995	2000	2001	2002	2003	2004	2005
TPES / ATEP (ktoe / ktep)								
TOTAL PRIMARY ENERGY SUPPLY	**4 277 785**	**4 638 249**	**5 065 641**	**5 038 537**	**5 082 275**	**5 127 172**	**5 226 558**	**5 255 639**
% contribution of Renewables and Wastes	-	6.1	6.0	5.7	5.7	5.8	6.0	6.1
Renewables	..	**269 488**	**286 291**	**270 917**	**273 999**	**282 385**	**294 289**	**302 623**
% contribution	-	5.8	5.7	5.4	5.4	5.5	5.6	5.8
Hydro	..	108 699	109 403	100 859	105 387	103 770	105 648	105 686
Geothermal (transformation *)	..	20 409	22 012	21 627	16 357	16 945	17 168	16 894
Geothermal (direct use **)	..	2 154	2 378	2 527	2 614	2 821	2 845	3 074
Solar Photovoltaic (transformation *)	..	5	14	20	29	45	67	135
Solar Thermal (transformation *)	..	71	134	143	142	138	145	136
Solar Thermal (direct use **)	..	1 514	3 042	2 974	3 007	2 935	2 932	2 968
Tide/Wave/Ocean	..	52	52	49	49	49	47	49
Wind	..	631	2 453	2 976	4 150	5 013	6 596	8 046
Ambient Heat (Heat Pumps)	..	339	378	395	406	336	450	497
Municipal Waste (Renewable)	..	6 535	8 912	8 677	9 290	9 385	9 651	10 114
Solid Biomass	..	123 778	127 986	120 096	119 669	125 916	130 974	133 853
Biogasoline	..	2 676	3 147	3 211	4 124	5 845	7 317	8 412
Biodiesel	..	185	657	733	958	1 258	1 761	2 817
Other Liquid Biomass	..	11	17	23	149	296	429	1 015
Biogas	..	2 429	5 705	6 606	7 669	7 633	8 259	8 928
Non-Renewable Wastes	..	**12 236**	**16 348**	**16 239**	**16 863**	**17 486**	**16 757**	**15 714**
% contribution	-	0.3	0.3	0.3	0.3	0.3	0.3	0.3
Industrial Waste	..	5 951	7 907	8 064	8 123	8 522	7 512	6 007
Municipal Waste (Non-Renewable)	..	6 285	8 442	8 175	8 740	8 964	9 246	9 708
Not separately identified ***	..	-	-	-	-	-	-	-
% contribution	-	-	-	-	-	-	-	-
*Memo: Total Wastes *****	..	*18 770*	*25 261*	*24 916*	*26 153*	*26 871*	*26 408*	*25 828*
ELECTRICITY / ELECTRICITE (GWh)								
TOTAL ELECTRICITY GENERATED	**7 281 090**	**8 145 394**	**9 205 751**	**9 068 202**	**9 363 733**	**9 458 022**	**9 707 889**	**9 962 211**
% contribution of Renewables and Wastes	-	17.3	16.0	15.2	15.6	15.4	15.6	15.5
Renewables	..	**1 388 817**	**1 442 125**	**1 344 337**	**1 424 129**	**1 422 504**	**1 475 499**	**1 507 094**
% contribution	-	17.1	15.7	14.8	15.2	15.0	15.2	15.1
Hydro (excl. pumped storage)	..	1 263 939	1 272 131	1 172 775	1 225 425	1 206 627	1 228 466	1 228 907
Geothermal	..	23 850	25 751	25 218	26 045	26 646	27 231	28 347
Solar Photovoltaic	..	55	157	237	333	520	780	1 570
Solar Thermal Electric	..	824	526	565	569	548	587	596
Tide/Wave/Ocean	..	601	605	575	568	572	549	565
Wind	..	7 341	28 527	34 600	48 253	58 293	76 696	93 556
Municipal Waste (Renewable)	..	13 178	18 903	19 561	20 588	21 774	22 378	24 520
Solid Biomass	..	72 889	82 555	76 605	85 084	88 599	98 159	104 445
Biogas/Liquid Biomass	..	6 140	12 970	14 201	17 264	18 925	20 653	24 588
Non-Renewable Wastes	..	**21 941**	**31 362**	**34 901**	**36 695**	**37 173**	**38 084**	**34 099**
% contribution	-	0.3	0.3	0.4	0.4	0.4	0.4	0.3
Industrial Waste	..	9 102	13 384	16 222	17 049	16 326	16 248	10 343
Municipal Waste (Non-Renewable)	..	12 839	17 978	18 679	19 646	20 847	21 836	23 756
Not separately identified ***	..	-	-	-	-	-	-	-
% contribution	-	-	-	-	-	-	-	-
*Memo: Total Wastes *****	..	*35 119*	*50 265*	*54 462*	*57 283*	*58 947*	*60 462*	*58 619*

* Primary energy used in the production of electricity and heat by main activity producers or autoproducers in electricity plants, CHP plants and heat plants (e.g. solar thermal power plants, geothermal power plants, etc.).
Energie primaire utilisée pour la production d'électricité, de cogénération et de chaleur par des producteurs dont c'est l'activité principale ou des autoproducteurs (installations héliothermiques, géothermiques, etc.).

** Primary energy used elsewhere than in transformation as described above (e.g. remote photovoltaic electricity production for households, heating of buildings/greenhouses by geothermal, etc.).
Energie primaire utilisée ailleurs que dans la transformation décrite ci-dessus (ex : production isolée d'électricité photovoltaïque, chauffage des bâtiments/serres à partir d'énergie géothermique, etc.).

*** Includes non-specified combustible renewables and waste.
Comprend les énergies renouvelables combustibles et les déchets non spécifiés.

**** Includes municipal waste and industrial waste.
Comprend les déchets municipaux et les déchets industriels.

Australia / Australie

Contribution from Renewable Energies and Energy from Wastes

Part des énergies renouvables et de l'énergie tirée des déchets

	1990	1995	2000	2001	2002	2003	2004	2005
			TPES / ATEP (ktoe / ktep)					
TOTAL PRIMARY ENERGY SUPPLY	**87 546**	**94 386**	**110 487**	**108 345**	**111 957**	**113 046**	**113 538**	**121 956**
% contribution of Renewables and Wastes	6.0	6.1	5.9	6.1	6.2	5.9	6.0	5.5
Renewables	**5 074**	**5 529**	**6 386**	**6 461**	**6 749**	**6 526**	**6 615**	**6 621**
% contribution	5.8	5.9	5.8	6.0	6.0	5.8	5.8	5.4
Hydro	1 217	1 366	1 443	1 412	1 364	1 380	1 348	1 349
Geothermal (transformation *)	-	-	-	-	-	-	-	-
Geothermal (direct use **)	-	-	-	-	-	-	-	-
Solar Photovoltaic (transformation *)	-	-	-	-	-	1	1	1
Solar Thermal (transformation *)	-	-	-	-	-	-	-	-
Solar Thermal (direct use **)	81	80	82	86	88	89	62	63
Tide/Wave/Ocean	-	-	-	-	-	-	-	-
Wind	-	1	5	18	31	60	60	76
Ambient Heat (Heat Pumps)	-	-	-	-	-	-	-	-
Municipal Waste (Renewable)	-	-	-	-	-	-	-	-
Solid Biomass	3 776	4 067	4 718	4 722	5 003	4 752	4 869	4 818
Biogasoline	-	-	-	-	-	-	-	11
Biodiesel	-	-	-	-	-	-	-	-
Other Liquid Biomass	-	-	-	-	-	-	-	-
Biogas	-	16	138	223	263	244	274	304
Non-Renewable Wastes	**185**	**187**	**179**	**140**	**148**	**148**	**154**	**102**
% contribution	0.2	0.2	0.2	0.1	0.1	0.1	0.1	0.1
Industrial Waste	185	187	179	140	148	148	154	102
Municipal Waste (Non-Renewable)	-	-	-	-	-	-	-	-
Not separately identified ***	-	-	-	-	-	-	-	-
% contribution	-	-	-	-	-	-	-	-
*Memo: Total Wastes *****	*185*	*187*	*179*	*140*	*148*	*148*	*154*	*102*
			ELECTRICITY / ELECTRICITE (GWh)					
TOTAL ELECTRICITY GENERATED	**154 345**	**173 007**	**207 397**	**216 475**	**226 182**	**227 918**	**238 842**	**250 920**
% contribution of Renewables and Wastes	9.6	9.6	8.6	8.1	7.9	8.0	7.6	7.4
Renewables	**14 748**	**16 585**	**17 900**	**17 622**	**17 804**	**18 213**	**18 214**	**18 608**
% contribution	9.6	9.6	8.6	8.1	7.9	8.0	7.6	7.4
Hydro (excl. pumped storage)	14 148	15 885	16 777	16 416	15 855	16 048	15 680	15 686
Geothermal	-	-	-	-	-	-	-	-
Solar Photovoltaic	-	-	3	4	5	7	9	11
Solar Thermal Electric	-	-	-	-	-	-	-	-
Tide/Wave/Ocean	-	-	-	-	-	-	-	-
Wind	-	7	56	207	361	699	700	881
Municipal Waste (Renewable)	-	-	-	-	-	-	-	-
Solid Biomass	600	670	685	633	729	796	1 070	1 100
Biogas/Liquid Biomass	-	23	379	362	854	663	755	930
Non-Renewable Wastes	-	-	-	-	-	-	-	-
% contribution	-	-	-	-	-	-	-	-
Industrial Waste	-	-	-	-	-	-	-	-
Municipal Waste (Non-Renewable)	-	-	-	-	-	-	-	-
Not separately identified ***	-	-	-	-	-	-	-	-
% contribution	-	-	-	-	-	-	-	-
*Memo: Total Wastes *****	-	-	-	-	-	-	-	-

* Primary energy used in the production of electricity and heat by main activity producers or autoproducers in electricity plants, CHP plants and heat plants (e.g. solar thermal power plants, geothermal power plants, etc.).
Energie primaire utilisée pour la production d'électricité, de cogénération et de chaleur par des producteurs dont c'est l'activité principale ou des autoproducteurs (installations héliothermiques, géothermiques, etc.).

** Primary energy used elsewhere than in transformation as described above (e.g. remote photovoltaic electricity production for households, heating of buildings/greenhouses by geothermal, etc.).
Energie primaire utilisée ailleurs que dans la transformation décrite ci-dessus (ex : production isolée d'électricité photovoltaïque, chauffage des bâtiments/serres à partir d'énergie géothermique, etc.).

*** Includes non-specified combustible renewables and waste.
Comprend les énergies renouvelables combustibles et les déchets non spécifiés.

**** Includes municipal waste and industrial waste.
Comprend les déchets municipaux et les déchets industriels.

Austria / Autriche

Contribution from Renewable Energies and Energy from Wastes

Part des énergies renouvables et de l'énergie tirée des déchets

	1990	1995	2000	2001	2002	2003	2004	2005
				TPES / ATEP (ktoe / ktep)				
TOTAL PRIMARY ENERGY SUPPLY	**25 071**	**27 155**	**29 036**	**30 861**	**31 366**	**32 988**	**33 254**	**34 363**
% contribution of Renewables and Wastes	20.7	22.3	23.4	22.9	22.5	20.0	21.6	21.3
Renewables	**5 004**	**5 840**	**6 558**	**6 754**	**6 716**	**6 229**	**6 696**	**6 867**
% contribution	20.0	21.5	22.6	21.9	21.4	18.9	20.1	20.0
Hydro	2 710	3 188	3 598	3 456	3 434	2 828	3 132	3 085
Geothermal (transformation *)	-	2 e	18 e	18 e	21 e	27 e	28 e	29
Geothermal (direct use **)	4	3 e	5 e	5 e	8 e	6 e	6 e	6
Solar Photovoltaic (transformation *)	-	-	-	-	1	1	1	1
Solar Thermal (transformation *)	-	-	-	-	-	-	-	-
Solar Thermal (direct use **)	15	36	64	68	73	79	85	91
Tide/Wave/Ocean	-	-	-	-	-	-	-	-
Wind	-	-	6	15	17	31	79	114
Ambient Heat (Heat Pumps)	-	-	-	-	-	-	4	4
Municipal Waste (Renewable)	22 e	35 e	42 e	43 e	45 e	53 e	59 e	57 e
Solid Biomass	2 247	2 544	2 786	3 100	3 079	3 161	3 232	3 368
Biogasoline	-	-	-	-	-	-	-	-
Biodiesel	-	-	-	-	-	-	-	29
Other Liquid Biomass	6	11	17	19	20	20	40	52
Biogas	-	20	22	29	18	22	28	31
Non-Renewable Wastes	**193**	**225**	**226**	**301**	**349**	**383**	**484**	**444**
% contribution	0.8	0.8	0.8	1.0	1.1	1.2	1.5	1.3
Industrial Waste	157	167	160	234	276	298	362	331
Municipal Waste (Non-Renewable)	36 e	58 e	66 e	67 e	73 e	85 e	122 e	114
Not separately identified * **	-	-	-	-	-	-	-	-
% contribution	-	-	-	-	-	-	-	-
*Memo: Total Wastes *** **	*215*	*261*	*268*	*344*	*393*	*436*	*543*	*502*
				ELECTRICITY / ELECTRICITE (GWh)				
TOTAL ELECTRICITY GENERATED	**49 296**	**55 179**	**60 161**	**60 688**	**60 416**	**57 683**	**61 601**	**62 980**
% contribution of Renewables and Wastes	66.3	70.6	72.7	69.7	69.5	61.2	64.4	63.2
Renewables	**32 635**	**38 904**	**43 590**	**42 075**	**41 794**	**35 027**	**39 237**	**39 357**
% contribution	66.2	70.5	72.5	69.3	69.2	60.7	63.7	62.5
Hydro (excl. pumped storage)	31 509	37 067	41 840	40 187	39 931	32 878	36 423	35 874
Geothermal	-	-	-	-	3	3	2	2
Solar Photovoltaic	-	1	3	4	7	11	14	14
Solar Thermal Electric	-	-	-	-	-	-	-	-
Tide/Wave/Ocean	-	-	-	-	-	-	-	-
Wind	-	1	67	172	203	366	924	1 328
Municipal Waste (Renewable)	10 e	15 e	29 e	25 e	30 e	118 e	101 e	100 e
Solid Biomass	1 116	1 766	1 583	1 579	1 580	1 602	1 694	1 930
Biogas/Liquid Biomass	-	54	68	108	40	49	79	109
Non-Renewable Wastes	**54**	**72**	**133**	**237**	**210**	**254**	**454**	**446**
% contribution	0.1	0.1	0.2	0.4	0.3	0.4	0.7	0.7
Industrial Waste	38	48	80	175	161	186	218	221
Municipal Waste (Non-Renewable)	16 e	24 e	53 e	62 e	49 e	68 e	236 e	225 e
Not separately identified * **	-	-	-	-	-	-	-	-
% contribution	-	-	-	-	-	-	-	-
*Memo: Total Wastes *** **	*64*	*87*	*162*	*262*	*240*	*372*	*555*	*546*

* Primary energy used in the production of electricity and heat by main activity producers or autoproducers in electricity plants, CHP plants and heat plants (e.g. solar thermal power plants, geothermal power plants, etc.).
Energie primaire utilisée pour la production d'électricité, de cogénération et de chaleur par des producteurs dont c'est l'activité principale ou des autoproducteurs (installations héliothermiques, géothermiques, etc.).

** Primary energy used elsewhere than in transformation as described above (e.g. remote photovoltaic electricity production for households, heating of buildings/greenhouses by geothermal, etc.).
Energie primaire utilisée ailleurs que dans la transformation décrite ci-dessus (ex : production isolée d'électricité photovoltaïque, chauffage des bâtiments/serres à partir d'énergie géothermique, etc.).

*** Includes non-specified combustible renewables and waste.
Comprend les énergies renouvelables combustibles et les déchets non spécifiés.

**** Includes municipal waste and industrial waste.
Comprend les déchets municipaux et les déchets industriels.

Belgium / Belgique

Contribution from Renewable Energies and Energy from Wastes

Part des énergies renouvables et de l'énergie tirée des déchets

	1990	1995	2000	2001	2002	2003	2004	2005
TPES / ATEP (ktoe / ktep)								
TOTAL PRIMARY ENERGY SUPPLY	**49 161**	**52 377**	**59 085**	**58 844**	**56 793**	**59 439**	**58 099**	**56 653**
% contribution of Renewables and Wastes	1.6	1.8	1.8	2.1	2.1	2.4	2.6	3.0
Renewables	**480**	**527**	**637**	**702**	**710**	**866**	**965**	**1 212**
% contribution	1.0	1.0	1.1	1.2	1.3	1.5	1.7	2.1
Hydro	23	29	40	38	31	21	27	25
Geothermal (transformation *)	-	-	-	-	-	-	-	-
Geothermal (direct use **)	1	1	2	2	2	2	2	2
Solar Photovoltaic (transformation *)	-	-	-	-	-	-	-	-
Solar Thermal (transformation *)	-	-	-	-	-	-	-	-
Solar Thermal (direct use **)	1	1	1	1	2	2	3	3
Tide/Wave/Ocean	-	-	-	-	-	-	-	-
Wind	1	1	1	3	5	8	12	20
Ambient Heat (Heat Pumps)	-	-	-	-	-	-	-	69
Municipal Waste (Renewable)	112 e	129 e	141 e	143 e	135 e	182 e	172 e	187 e
Solid Biomass	336	354	423	470	490	599	677	808
Biogasoline	-	-	-	-	-	-	-	-
Biodiesel	-	-	-	-	-	-	-	-
Other Liquid Biomass	-	-	-	-	-	-	-	18
Biogas	6	11	29	44	46	52	72	81
Non-Renewable Wastes	**300**	**409**	**443**	**529**	**488**	**574**	**569**	**508**
% contribution	0.6	0.8	0.7	0.9	0.9	1.0	1.0	0.9
Industrial Waste	131	215	261	317	295	289	287	205
Municipal Waste (Non-Renewable)	169 e	194 e	182 e	212 e	193 e	285 e	282 e	302
Not separately identified ***	-	-	-	-	-	-	-	-
% contribution	-	-	-	-	-	-	-	-
*Memo: Total Wastes *****	*412*	*538*	*584*	*672*	*624*	*756*	*741*	*695*
ELECTRICITY / ELECTRICITE (GWh)								
TOTAL ELECTRICITY GENERATED	**70 292**	**73 516**	**82 773**	**78 618**	**80 939**	**83 561**	**84 353**	**85 709**
% contribution of Renewables and Wastes	1.4	1.9	2.2	2.6	2.6	2.3	2.9	3.2
Renewables	**555**	**668**	**1 044**	**1 075**	**1 138**	**1 192**	**1 497**	**2 106**
% contribution	0.8	0.9	1.3	1.4	1.4	1.4	1.8	2.5
Hydro (excl. pumped storage)	266	338	460	441	360	247	317	288
Geothermal	-	-	-	-	-	-	-	-
Solar Photovoltaic	-	-	-	-	-	-	1	1
Solar Thermal Electric	-	-	-	-	-	-	-	-
Tide/Wave/Ocean	-	-	-	-	-	-	-	-
Wind	7	9	16	37	57	88	142	227
Municipal Waste (Renewable)	140 e	187 e	306 e	297 e	313 e	306 e	292 e	326 e
Solid Biomass	135	121	164	173	271	377	512	960
Biogas/Liquid Biomass	7	13	98	127	137	174	233	304
Non-Renewable Wastes	**441**	**721**	**768**	**986**	**941**	**766**	**910**	**660**
% contribution	0.6	1.0	0.9	1.3	1.2	0.9	1.1	0.8
Industrial Waste	231	441	385	527	493	284	413	136
Municipal Waste (Non-Renewable)	210 e	280 e	383 e	459 e	448 e	482 e	497 e	524 e
Not separately identified ***	-	-	-	-	-	-	-	-
% contribution	-	-	-	-	-	-	-	-
*Memo: Total Wastes *****	*581*	*908*	*1 074*	*1 283*	*1 254*	*1 072*	*1 202*	*986*

* Primary energy used in the production of electricity and heat by main activity producers or autoproducers in electricity plants, CHP plants and heat plants (e.g. solar thermal power plants, geothermal power plants, etc.).
Energie primaire utilisée pour la production d'électricité, de cogénération et de chaleur par des producteurs dont c'est l'activité principale ou des autoproducteurs (installations héliothermiques, géothermiques, etc.).

** Primary energy used elsewhere than in transformation as described above (e.g. remote photovoltaic electricity production for households, heating of buildings/greenhouses by geothermal, etc.).
Energie primaire utilisée ailleurs que dans la transformation décrite ci-dessus (ex : production isolée d'électricité photovoltaïque, chauffage des bâtiments/serres à partir d'énergie géothermique, etc.).

*** Includes non-specified combustible renewables and waste.
Comprend les énergies renouvelables combustibles et les déchets non spécifiés.

**** Includes municipal waste and industrial waste.
Comprend les déchets municipaux et les déchets industriels.

Canada

Contribution from Renewable Energies and Energy from Wastes

Part des énergies renouvables et de l'énergie tirée des déchets

	1990	1995	2000	2001	2002	2003	2004	2005
TPES / ATEP (ktoe / ktep)								
TOTAL PRIMARY ENERGY SUPPLY	**209 412**	**231 439**	**249 178**	**246 070**	**250 142**	**262 365**	**268 701**	**271 955**
% contribution of Renewables and Wastes	16.1	16.7	17.0	16.1	16.8	15.6	15.5	16.2
Renewables	**33 668**	**38 661**	**42 349**	**39 482**	**41 833**	**40 778**	**41 573**	**43 927**
% contribution	16.1	16.7	17.0	16.0	16.7	15.5	15.5	16.2
Hydro	25 519	28 889	30 832	28 665	30 148	29 020	29 312	31 262
Geothermal (transformation *)	-	-	-	-	-	-	-	-
Geothermal (direct use **)	-	-	-	-	-	-	-	-
Solar Photovoltaic (transformation *)	-	-	1 e	2 e	2 e	2 e	1	1
Solar Thermal (transformation *)	-	-	-	-	-	-	-	-
Solar Thermal (direct use **)	-	-	-	-	-	-	-	-
Tide/Wave/Ocean	2	3	3	3	3 e	3 e	3	3
Wind	-	5	23	29	35	71	82	127
Ambient Heat (Heat Pumps)	-	-	-	-	-	-	-	-
Municipal Waste (Renewable)	4 e	4 e	4 e	4 e	4 e	4 e	4 e	4 e
Solid Biomass	8 136	9 747	11 167	10 460	11 317	11 343	11 835	12 168
Biogasoline	-	-	133	133	133	143	143	170
Biodiesel	-	-	-	-	-	-	-	-
Other Liquid Biomass	-	-	-	-	-	-	-	-
Biogas	7	12	186	186	191	191	192	192
Non-Renewable Wastes	**42**	**91**	**80**	**76**	**114**	**109**	**109**	**109**
% contribution	0.0	0.0	0.0	0.0	0.0	0.0	0.0	0.0
Industrial Waste	37	86	76	72	110	105	105	105
Municipal Waste (Non-Renewable)	4 e	4 e	4 e	4 e	4 e	4 e	4 e	4
Not separately identified ***	-	-	-	-	-	-	-	-
% contribution	-	-	-	-	-	-	-	-
Memo: Total Wastes ****	*46*	*95*	*84*	*80*	*119*	*113*	*113*	*113*
ELECTRICITY / ELECTRICITE (GWh)								
TOTAL ELECTRICITY GENERATED	**481 943**	**559 871**	**605 462**	**589 646**	**601 024**	**589 856**	**600 128**	**628 083**
% contribution of Renewables and Wastes	62.4	61.0	60.6	58.0	59.9	58.9	58.4	59.6
Renewables	**300 625**	**341 537**	**366 904**	**342 176**	**359 923**	**347 243**	**350 510**	**374 080**
% contribution	62.4	61.0	60.6	58.0	59.9	58.9	58.4	59.6
Hydro (excl. pumped storage)	296 737	335 923	358 509	333 319	350 554	337 445	340 835	363 515
Geothermal	-	-	-	-	-	-	-	-
Solar Photovoltaic	-	4	16 e	19 e	22 e	23 e	13	17
Solar Thermal Electric	-	-	-	-	-	-	-	-
Tide/Wave/Ocean	26	33	32	32	32	33	31	31
Wind	-	59	264	337	408	826	954	1 471
Municipal Waste (Renewable)	10 e	10 e	10 e	10 e	10 e	10 e	10 e	10 e
Solid Biomass	3 829	5 465	7 365	7 751	8 169	8 178	7 936	8 305
Biogas/Liquid Biomass	23	43	708	708	728	728	731	731
Non-Renewable Wastes	**9**	**9**	**9**	**9**	**9**	**9**	**9**	**9**
% contribution	0.0	0.0	0.0	0.0	0.0	0.0	0.0	0.0
Industrial Waste	-	-	-	-	-	-	-	-
Municipal Waste (Non-Renewable)	9 e	9 e	9 e	9 e	9 e	9 e	9 e	9 e
Not separately identified ***	-	-	-	-	-	-	-	-
% contribution	-	-	-	-	-	-	-	-
Memo: Total Wastes ****	*19*	*19*	*19*	*19*	*19*	*19*	*19*	*19*

* Primary energy used in the production of electricity and heat by main activity producers or autoproducers in electricity plants, CHP plants and heat plants (e.g. solar thermal power plants, geothermal power plants, etc.).
Energie primaire utilisée pour la production d'électricité, de cogénération et de chaleur par des producteurs dont c'est l'activité principale ou des autoproducteurs (installations héliothermiques, géothermiques, etc.).

** Primary energy used elsewhere than in transformation as described above (e.g. remote photovoltaic electricity production for households, heating of buildings/greenhouses by geothermal, etc.).
Energie primaire utilisée ailleurs que dans la transformation décrite ci-dessus (ex : production isolée d'électricité photovoltaïque, chauffage des bâtiments/serres à partir d'énergie géothermique, etc.).

*** Includes non-specified combustible renewables and waste.
Comprend les énergies renouvelables combustibles et les déchets non spécifiés.

**** Includes municipal waste and industrial waste.
Comprend les déchets municipaux et les déchets industriels.

Czech Republic / République tchèque

Contribution from Renewable Energies and Energy from Wastes

Part des énergies renouvables et de l'énergie tirée des déchets

	1990	1995	2000	2001	2002	2003	2004	2005
			TPES / ATEP (ktoe / ktep)					
TOTAL PRIMARY ENERGY SUPPLY	**48 993**	**41 111**	**40 392**	**41 392**	**41 961**	**44 576**	**45 770**	**45 205**
% contribution of Renewables and Wastes	0.2	1.5	2.0	2.1	2.5	3.7	4.1	4.3
Renewables	**100**	**604**	**614**	**680**	**863**	**1 527**	**1 740**	**1 786**
% contribution	0.2	1.5	1.5	1.6	2.1	3.4	3.8	4.0
Hydro	100	172	151	177	214	119	174	205
Geothermal (transformation *)	-	-	-	-	-	-	-	-
Geothermal (direct use **)	-	-	-	-	-	-	-	-
Solar Photovoltaic (transformation *)	-	-	-	-	-	-	-	-
Solar Thermal (transformation *)	-	-	-	-	-	-	-	-
Solar Thermal (direct use **)	-	-	-	-	-	-	2	2
Tide/Wave/Ocean	-	-	-	-	-	-	-	-
Wind	-	-	-	-	-	-	1	2
Ambient Heat (Heat Pumps)	-	-	-	-	-	-	-	-
Municipal Waste (Renewable)	-	-	44 e	53 e	54 e	50 e	63 e	58 e
Solid Biomass	..	382	319	368	493	1 253	1 417	1 460
Biogasoline	-	-	-	-	-	-	-	-
Biodiesel	-	16	64	46	66	64	33	3
Other Liquid Biomass	-	-	-	-	-	-	-	-
Biogas	-	34	36	37	36	41	50	56
Non-Renewable Wastes	**..**	**28**	**176**	**186**	**187**	**119**	**141**	**170**
% contribution	-	0.1	0.4	0.4	0.4	0.3	0.3	0.4
Industrial Waste	..	28	132	134	133	69	99	131
Municipal Waste (Non-Renewable)	-	-	44 e	53 e	54 e	50 e	42 e	39
Not separately identified ***	-	-	-	-	-	-	-	-
% contribution	-	-	-	-	-	-	-	-
*Memo: Total Wastes *****	..	*28*	*220*	*239*	*241*	*170*	*204*	*228*
			ELECTRICITY / ELECTRICITE (GWh)					
TOTAL ELECTRICITY GENERATED	**62 271**	**60 575**	**72 911**	**74 234**	**75 995**	**82 816**	**83 790**	**81 931**
% contribution of Renewables and Wastes	1.9	4.0	3.4	3.7	4.2	2.3	3.3	3.8
Renewables	**1 161**	**2 407**	**2 277**	**2 570**	**2 990**	**1 876**	**2 741**	**3 133**
% contribution	1.9	4.0	3.1	3.5	3.9	2.3	3.3	3.8
Hydro (excl. pumped storage)	1 161	2 002	1 758	2 054	2 492	1 383	2 019	2 380
Geothermal	-	-	-	-	-	-	-	-
Solar Photovoltaic	-	-	-	-	-	-	-	-
Solar Thermal Electric	-	-	-	-	-	-	-	-
Tide/Wave/Ocean	-	-	-	-	-	-	-	-
Wind	-	-	-	-	2	4	10	22
Municipal Waste (Renewable)	-	-	2 e	2 e	2 e	8 e	10 e	11 e
Solid Biomass	..	302	382	381	367	373	564	560
Biogas/Liquid Biomass	..	103	135	133	127	108	138	160
Non-Renewable Wastes	**..**	**16**	**204**	**197**	**193**	**8**	**8**	**7**
% contribution	-	0.0	0.3	0.3	0.3	0.0	0.0	0.0
Industrial Waste	..	16	201	195	191	-	1	-
Municipal Waste (Non-Renewable)	-	-	3 e	2 e	2 e	8 e	7 e	7 e
Not separately identified ***	-	-	-	-	-	-	-	-
% contribution	-	-	-	-	-	-	-	-
*Memo: Total Wastes *****	..	*16*	*206*	*199*	*195*	*16*	*18*	*18*

* Primary energy used in the production of electricity and heat by main activity producers or autoproducers in electricity plants, CHP plants and heat plants (e.g. solar thermal power plants, geothermal power plants, etc.).
Energie primaire utilisée pour la production d'électricité, de cogénération et de chaleur par des producteurs dont c'est l'activité principale ou des autoproducteurs (installations héliothermiques, géothermiques, etc.).

** Primary energy used elsewhere than in transformation as described above (e.g. remote photovoltaic electricity production for households, heating of buildings/greenhouses by geothermal, etc.).
Energie primaire utilisée ailleurs que dans la transformation décrite ci-dessus (ex : production isolée d'électricité photovoltaïque, chauffage des bâtiments/serres à partir d'énergie géothermique, etc.).

*** Includes non-specified combustible renewables and waste.
Comprend les énergies renouvelables combustibles et les déchets non spécifiés.

**** Includes municipal waste and industrial waste.
Comprend les déchets municipaux et les déchets industriels.

Denmark / Danemark

Contribution from Renewable Energies and Energy from Wastes

Part des énergies renouvables et de l'énergie tirée des déchets

	1990	1995	2000	2001	2002	2003	2004	2005
			TPES / ATEP (ktoe / ktep)					
TOTAL PRIMARY ENERGY SUPPLY	**17 895**	**20 003**	**19 361**	**19 941**	**19 642**	**20 784**	**20 199**	**19 610**
% contribution of Renewables and Wastes	6.7	7.7	11.0	11.5	12.5	13.5	15.1	16.2
Renewables	**1 094**	**1 413**	**1 961**	**2 124**	**2 275**	**2 602**	**2 850**	**2 971**
% contribution	6.1	7.1	10.1	10.7	11.6	12.5	14.1	15.1
Hydro	2	3	3	2	3	2	2	2
Geothermal (transformation *)	2 e	2 e	3 e	3	4	4	4 e	3
Geothermal (direct use **)	-	-	-	-	-	-	-	-
Solar Photovoltaic (transformation *)	-	-	-	-	-	-	-	-
Solar Thermal (transformation *)	-	-	1	1	1	1	1	1
Solar Thermal (direct use **)	2	5	7	7	8	8	8	9
Tide/Wave/Ocean	-	-	-	-	-	-	-	-
Wind	52	101	365	370	419	478	566	569
Ambient Heat (Heat Pumps)	-	2	-	-	-	-	-	-
Municipal Waste (Renewable)	264 e	419 e	564 e	598 e	628 e	679 e	686 e	685 e
Solid Biomass	752	839	950	1 069	1 132	1 345	1 493	1 610
Biogasoline	-	-	-	-	-	-	-	-
Biodiesel	-	-	-	-	-	-	-	-
Other Liquid Biomass	-	-	-	-	-	-	-	-
Biogas	18	42	70	73	80	85	89	91
Non-Renewable Wastes	**106**	**128**	**162**	**172**	**181**	**195**	**197**	**197**
% contribution	0.6	0.6	0.8	0.9	0.9	0.9	1.0	1.0
Industrial Waste	-	-	-	-	-	-	-	-
Municipal Waste (Non-Renewable)	106 e	128 e	162 e	172 e	181 e	195 e	197 e	197
Not separately identified * **	-	-	-	-	-	-	-	-
% contribution	-	-	-	-	-	-	-	-
*Memo: Total Wastes *** **	*370*	*547*	*726*	*770*	*809*	*874*	*883*	*882*
			ELECTRICITY / ELECTRICITE (GWh)					
TOTAL ELECTRICITY GENERATED	**25 977**	**36 653**	**36 049**	**37 726**	**39 283**	**46 181**	**40 432**	**36 275**
% contribution of Renewables and Wastes	3.3	5.8	17.0	17.1	18.9	18.9	25.2	29.3
Renewables	**830**	**1 978**	**5 851**	**6 145**	**7 103**	**8 414**	**9 848**	**10 216**
% contribution	3.2	5.4	16.2	16.3	18.1	18.2	24.4	28.2
Hydro (excl. pumped storage)	28	30	30	28	32	21	27	23
Geothermal	-	-	-	-	-	-	-	-
Solar Photovoltaic	-	-	1	1	1	2	2	2
Solar Thermal Electric	-	-	-	-	-	-	-	-
Tide/Wave/Ocean	-	-	-	-	-	-	-	-
Wind	610	1 177	4 241	4 306	4 877	5 561	6 583	6 614
Municipal Waste (Renewable)	44 e	455 e	959 e	1 021 e	1 075 e	1 153 e	1 123 e	1 405 e
Solid Biomass	108	208	411	568	878	1 401	1 834	1 898
Biogas/Liquid Biomass	40	108	209	221	240	276	279	274
Non-Renewable Wastes	**18**	**139**	**276**	**293**	**309**	**332**	**323**	**404**
% contribution	0.1	0.4	0.8	0.8	0.8	0.7	0.8	1.1
Industrial Waste	-	-	-	-	-	-	-	-
Municipal Waste (Non-Renewable)	18 e	139 e	276 e	293 e	309 e	332 e	323 e	404 e
Not separately identified * **	-	-	-	-	-	-	-	-
% contribution	-	-	-	-	-	-	-	-
*Memo: Total Wastes *** **	*62*	*594*	*1 235*	*1 314*	*1 384*	*1 485*	*1 446*	*1 809*

* Primary energy used in the production of electricity and heat by main activity producers or autoproducers in electricity plants, CHP plants and heat plants (e.g. solar thermal power plants, geothermal power plants, etc.).
Energie primaire utilisée pour la production d'électricité, de cogénération et de chaleur par des producteurs dont c'est l'activité principale ou des autoproducteurs (installations héliothermiques, géothermiques, etc.).

** Primary energy used elsewhere than in transformation as described above (e.g. remote photovoltaic electricity production for households, heating of buildings/greenhouses by geothermal, etc.).
Energie primaire utilisée ailleurs que dans la transformation décrite ci-dessus (ex : production isolée d'électricité photovoltaïque, chauffage des bâtiments/serres à partir d'énergie géothermique, etc.).

*** Includes non-specified combustible renewables and waste.
Comprend les énergies renouvelables combustibles et les déchets non spécifiés.

**** Includes municipal waste and industrial waste.
Comprend les déchets municipaux et les déchets industriels.

Finland / Finlande

Contribution from Renewable Energies and Energy from Wastes

Part des énergies renouvables et de l'énergie tirée des déchets

	1990	1995	2000	2001	2002	2003	2004	2005
			TPES / ATEP (ktoe / ktep)					
TOTAL PRIMARY ENERGY SUPPLY	**29 171**	**29 632**	**32 980**	**33 667**	**35 425**	**37 551**	**37 854**	**34 961**
% contribution of Renewables and Wastes	18.8	20.7	24.1	22.7	22.3	21.4	23.1	23.2
Renewables	**5 489**	**6 127**	**7 733**	**7 393**	**7 659**	**7 729**	**8 621**	**8 017**
% contribution	18.8	20.7	23.4	22.0	21.6	20.6	22.8	22.9
Hydro	934	1 112	1 261	1 136	927	825	1 296	1 185
Geothermal (transformation *)	-	-	-	-	-	-	-	-
Geothermal (direct use **)	-	-	-	-	-	-	-	-
Solar Photovoltaic (transformation *)	-	-	-	-	-	-	-	-
Solar Thermal (transformation *)	-	-	-	-	-	-	-	-
Solar Thermal (direct use **)	-	-	-	-	-	-	-	-
Tide/Wave/Ocean	-	-	-	-	-	-	-	-
Wind	-	1	7	6	6	8	10	15
Ambient Heat (Heat Pumps)	-	-	-	-	-	-	73	73
Municipal Waste (Renewable)	11 e	7 e	27 e	46 e	44 e	78 e	96 e	108 e
Solid Biomass	4 544	5 007	6 420	6 187	6 664	6 794	7 115	6 593
Biogasoline	-	-	-	-	1	4	5	-
Biodiesel	-	-	-	-	-	-	-	-
Other Liquid Biomass	-	-	-	-	-	-	-	-
Biogas	-	-	18	17	17	20	26	42
Non-Renewable Wastes	**7**	**5**	**225**	**244**	**245**	**324**	**112**	**101**
% contribution	0.0	0.0	0.7	0.7	0.7	0.9	0.3	0.3
Industrial Waste	-	-	207	214	215	284	59	52
Municipal Waste (Non-Renewable)	7 e	5 e	18 e	31 e	30 e	40 e	53 e	49
Not separately identified * **	-	-	-	-	-	-	-	-
% contribution	-	-	-	-	-	-	-	-
*Memo: Total Wastes **** *	*19*	*12*	*252*	*291*	*290*	*402*	*208*	*210*
			ELECTRICITY / ELECTRICITE (GWh)					
TOTAL ELECTRICITY GENERATED	**54 377**	**64 035**	**69 991**	**74 453**	**74 901**	**84 230**	**85 847**	**70 550**
% contribution of Renewables and Wastes	20.0	30.5	33.7	29.5	28.0	23.6	30.1	33.5
Renewables	**10 859**	**19 545**	**23 273**	**21 608**	**20 597**	**19 270**	**25 601**	**23 448**
% contribution	20.0	30.5	33.3	29.0	27.5	22.9	29.8	33.2
Hydro (excl. pumped storage)	10 859	12 925	14 660	13 205	10 776	9 591	15 070	13 784
Geothermal	-	-	-	-	-	-	-	-
Solar Photovoltaic	-	1	2	2	2	2	2	3
Solar Thermal Electric	-	-	-	-	-	-	-	-
Tide/Wave/Ocean	-	-	-	-	-	-	-	-
Wind	-	11	78	70	64	93	120	170
Municipal Waste (Renewable)	-	-	35 e	120 e	129 e	175 e	191 e	230 e
Solid Biomass	..	6 608	8 476	8 189	9 596	9 385	10 196	9 239
Biogas/Liquid Biomass	-	-	22	22	30	24	22	22
Non-Renewable Wastes	-	-	**348**	**356**	**375**	**588**	**220**	**173**
% contribution	-	-	0.5	0.5	0.5	0.7	0.3	0.2
Industrial Waste	-	-	324	276	289	472	109	56
Municipal Waste (Non-Renewable)	-	-	24 e	80 e	86 e	116 e	111 e	117 e
Not separately identified * **	-	-	-	-	-	-	-	-
% contribution	-	-	-	-	-	-	-	-
*Memo: Total Wastes **** *	-	-	*383*	*476*	*504*	*763*	*411*	*403*

* Primary energy used in the production of electricity and heat by main activity producers or autoproducers in electricity plants, CHP plants and heat plants (e.g. solar thermal power plants, geothermal power plants, etc.).
Energie primaire utilisée pour la production d'électricité, de cogénération et de chaleur par des producteurs dont c'est l'activité principale ou des autoproducteurs (installations héliothermiques, géothermiques, etc.).

** Primary energy used elsewhere than in transformation as described above (e.g. remote photovoltaic electricity production for households, heating of buildings/greenhouses by geothermal, etc.).
Energie primaire utilisée ailleurs que dans la transformation décrite ci-dessus (ex : production isolée d'électricité photovoltaïque, chauffage des bâtiments/serres à partir d'énergie géothermique, etc.).

*** Includes non-specified combustible renewables and waste.
Comprend les énergies renouvelables combustibles et les déchets non spécifiés.

**** Includes municipal waste and industrial waste.
Comprend les déchets municipaux et les déchets industriels.

France

Contribution from Renewable Energies and Energy from Wastes

Part des énergies renouvables et de l'énergie tirée des déchets

	1990	1995	2000	2001	2002	2003	2004	2005
				TPES / ATEP (ktoe / ktep)				
TOTAL PRIMARY ENERGY SUPPLY	**227 816**	**241 373**	**258 356**	**266 896**	**266 682**	**271 335**	**274 929**	**275 970**
% contribution of Renewables and Wastes	7.2	7.6	7.0	7.1	6.4	6.4	6.3	6.0
Renewables	**15 783**	**17 712**	**17 164**	**18 027**	**16 156**	**16 329**	**16 327**	**15 718**
% contribution	6.9	7.3	6.6	6.8	6.1	6.0	5.9	5.7
Hydro	4 627	6 272	5 774	6 419	5 211	5 088	5 144	4 446
Geothermal (transformation *)	-	-	-	-	-	-	-	-
Geothermal (direct use **)	110	132	126	128	128	129	130	130
Solar Photovoltaic (transformation *)	-	-	-	1	1	1	1	1
Solar Thermal (transformation *)	-	-	-	-	-	-	-	-
Solar Thermal (direct use **)	19	20	17	16	16	17	19	22
Tide/Wave/Ocean	49	49	49	47	46	46	45	46
Wind	-	-	7	11	23	34	51	82
Ambient Heat (Heat Pumps)	-	-	-	-	-	-	-	-
Municipal Waste (Renewable)	573 e	721 e	928 e	966 e	1 021 e	972 e	931 e	920 e
Solid Biomass	10 332	10 266	9 759	9 922	9 152	9 481	9 436	9 429
Biogasoline	-	33	80	78	78	66	69	100
Biodiesel	-	138	279	280	279	292	293	333
Other Liquid Biomass	-	-	-	-	-	-	-	-
Biogas	72	82	145	160	199	203	207	209
Non-Renewable Wastes	**573**	**721**	**928**	**966**	**1 021**	**972**	**931**	**920**
% contribution	0.3	0.3	0.4	0.4	0.4	0.4	0.3	0.3
Industrial Waste	-	-	-	-	-	-	-	-
Municipal Waste (Non-Renewable)	573 e	721 e	928 e	966 e	1 021 e	972 e	931 e	920
Not separately identified ***	-	-	-	-	-	-	-	-
% contribution	-	-	-	-	-	-	-	-
*Memo: Total Wastes *****	*1 146*	*1 442*	*1 857*	*1 931*	*2 043*	*1 943*	*1 862*	*1 839*
				ELECTRICITY / ELECTRICITE (GWh)				
TOTAL ELECTRICITY GENERATED	**417 206**	**491 068**	**536 100**	**545 715**	**553 875**	**561 774**	**568 584**	**570 646**
% contribution of Renewables and Wastes	13.4	15.4	13.3	14.5	11.9	11.6	11.6	10.2
Renewables	**55 786**	**75 321**	**70 506**	**78 145**	**64 564**	**63 423**	**64 344**	**56 658**
% contribution	13.4	15.3	13.2	14.3	11.7	11.3	11.3	9.9
Hydro (excl. pumped storage)	53 804	72 925	67 137	74 634	60 598	59 159	59 819	51 699
Geothermal	-	-	-	-	-	-	-	-
Solar Photovoltaic	-	1	5	7	8	10	12	15
Solar Thermal Electric	-	-	-	-	-	-	-	-
Tide/Wave/Ocean	571	568	573	543	536	539	518	534
Wind	-	5	77	131	269	391	596	959
Municipal Waste (Renewable)	222 e	371 e	1 021 e	1 195 e	1 451 e	1 556 e	1 621 e	1 630 e
Solid Biomass	1 116	1 368	1 398	1 312	1 324	1 344	1 332	1 359
Biogas/Liquid Biomass	73	83	295	323	378	424	446	462
Non-Renewable Wastes	**221**	**371**	**1 021**	**1 195**	**1 451**	**1 556**	**1 621**	**1 630**
% contribution	0.1	0.1	0.2	0.2	0.3	0.3	0.3	0.3
Industrial Waste	-	-	-	-	-	-	-	-
Municipal Waste (Non-Renewable)	221 e	371 e	1 021 e	1 195 e	1 451 e	1 556 e	1 621 e	1 630 e
Not separately identified ***	-	-	-	-	-	-	-	-
% contribution	-	-	-	-	-	-	-	-
*Memo: Total Wastes *****	*443*	*742*	*2 042*	*2 390*	*2 902*	*3 112*	*3 242*	*3 260*

* Primary energy used in the production of electricity and heat by main activity producers or autoproducers in electricity plants, CHP plants and heat plants (e.g. solar thermal power plants, geothermal power plants, etc.).
Energie primaire utilisée pour la production d'électricité, de cogénération et de chaleur par des producteurs dont c'est l'activité principale ou des autoproducteurs (installations héliothermiques, géothermiques, etc.).

** Primary energy used elsewhere than in transformation as described above (e.g. remote photovoltaic electricity production for households, heating of buildings/greenhouses by geothermal, etc.).
Energie primaire utilisée ailleurs que dans la transformation décrite ci-dessus (ex : production isolée d'électricité photovoltaïque, chauffage des bâtiments/serres à partir d'énergie géothermique, etc.).

*** Includes non-specified combustible renewables and waste.
Comprend les énergies renouvelables combustibles et les déchets non spécifiés.

**** Includes municipal waste and industrial waste.
Comprend les déchets municipaux et les déchets industriels.

Germany / Allemagne

Contribution from Renewable Energies and Energy from Wastes

Part des énergies renouvables et de l'énergie tirée des déchets

	1990	1995	2000	2001	2002	2003	2004	2005
				TPES / ATEP (ktoe / ktep)				
TOTAL PRIMARY ENERGY SUPPLY	**356 221**	**342 398**	**343 622**	**353 519**	**345 252**	**347 183**	**348 222**	**344 746**
% contribution of Renewables and Wastes	1.8	2.2	3.1	3.4	3.8	3.9	4.4	4.9
Renewables	**5 320**	**6 095**	**9 091**	**9 743**	**10 893**	**11 750**	**13 359**	**15 891**
% contribution	1.5	1.8	2.6	2.8	3.2	3.4	3.8	4.6
Hydro	1 499	1 873	1 869	1 955	1 989	1 657	1 813	1 684
Geothermal (transformation *)	-	-	-	-	-	20 e	20 e	22 e
Geothermal (direct use **)	7	123	123	124	127	122 e	124 e	127 e
Solar Photovoltaic (transformation *)	-	1	5	10	16	29	48	110
Solar Thermal (transformation *)	-	-	-	-	-	-	-	-
Solar Thermal (direct use **)	11	38	110	140	168	212	221	254
Tide/Wave/Ocean	-	-	-	-	-	-	-	-
Wind	6	147 e	804	899	1 364	1 622	2 194	2 342
Ambient Heat (Heat Pumps)	-	-	-	-	-	-	-	-
Municipal Waste (Renewable)	561 e	588 e	709 e	748 e	763 e	629 e	624 e	831 e
Solid Biomass	2 943	2 961	4 691	4 709	4 701	5 806	6 317	6 905
Biogasoline	-	-	-	-	-	-	42	166
Biodiesel	-	31	222	311	489	712	934	1 775
Other Liquid Biomass	-	-	-	4	5	20	20	242
Biogas	292	333	557	842	1 270	924	1 004	1 433
Non-Renewable Wastes	**999**	**1 436**	**1 681**	**2 246**	**2 070**	**1 817**	**1 812**	**835**
% contribution	0.3	0.4	0.5	0.6	0.6	0.5	0.5	0.2
Industrial Waste	490	901	1 028	1 561	1 370	1 188	1 188	5
Municipal Waste (Non-Renewable)	509 e	536 e	653 e	685 e	700 e	629 e	624 e	831
Not separately identified ***	-	-	-	-	-	-	-	-
% contribution	-	-	-	-	-	-	-	-
*Memo: Total Wastes *****	*1 561*	*2 024*	*2 390*	*2 994*	*2 833*	*2 446*	*2 436*	*1 666*
				ELECTRICITY / ELECTRICITE (GWh)				
TOTAL ELECTRICITY GENERATED	**547 650**	**532 814**	**567 122**	**581 820**	**566 905**	**595 646**	**609 988**	**613 164**
% contribution of Renewables and Wastes	4.1	5.9	7.3	7.9	9.1	8.9	10.4	10.5
Renewables	**19 093**	**25 932**	**35 475**	**37 895**	**44 477**	**46 438**	**56 500**	**61 625**
% contribution	3.5	4.9	6.3	6.5	7.8	7.8	9.3	10.1
Hydro (excl. pumped storage)	17 426	21 780	21 732	22 733	23 124	19 264	21 077	19 581
Geothermal	-	-	-	-	-	-	-	-
Solar Photovoltaic	1	7	60	116	188	333	557	1 282
Solar Thermal Electric	-	-	-	-	-	-	-	-
Tide/Wave/Ocean	-	-	-	-	-	-	-	-
Wind	71	1 712	9 352	10 456	15 856	18 859	25 509	27 229
Municipal Waste (Renewable)	1 219 e	1 348 e	1 844 e	1 859 e	1 949 e	2 162 e	2 116 e	3 038 e
Solid Biomass	129	496	804	639	543	2 775	3 900	4 647
Biogas/Liquid Biomass	247	589	1 683	2 092	2 817	3 045	3 341	5 848
Non-Renewable Wastes	**3 591**	**5 263**	**5 790**	**7 851**	**7 209**	**6 722**	**6 676**	**3 056**
% contribution	0.7	1.0	1.0	1.3	1.3	1.1	1.1	0.5
Industrial Waste	2 373	3 915	3 946	5 992	5 260	4 560	4 560	18
Municipal Waste (Non-Renewable)	1 218 e	1 348 e	1 844 e	1 859 e	1 949 e	2 162 e	2 116 e	3 038 e
Not separately identified ***	-	-	-	-	-	-	-	-
% contribution	-	-	-	-	-	-	-	-
*Memo: Total Wastes *****	*4 810*	*6 611*	*7 634*	*9 710*	*9 158*	*8 884*	*8 792*	*6 094*

* Primary energy used in the production of electricity and heat by main activity producers or autoproducers in electricity plants, CHP plants and heat plants (e.g. solar thermal power plants, geothermal power plants, etc.).
Energie primaire utilisée pour la production d'électricité, de cogénération et de chaleur par des producteurs dont c'est l'activité principale ou des autoproducteurs (installations héliothermiques, géothermiques, etc.).

** Primary energy used elsewhere than in transformation as described above (e.g. remote photovoltaic electricity production for households, heating of buildings/greenhouses by geothermal, etc.).
Energie primaire utilisée ailleurs que dans la transformation décrite ci-dessus (ex : production isolée d'électricité photovoltaïque, chauffage des bâtiments/serres à partir d'énergie géothermique, etc.).

*** Includes non-specified combustible renewables and waste.
Comprend les énergies renouvelables combustibles et les déchets non spécifiés.

**** Includes municipal waste and industrial waste.
Comprend les déchets municipaux et les déchets industriels.

Greece / Grèce

Contribution from Renewable Energies and Energy from Wastes

Part des énergies renouvables et de l'énergie tirée des déchets

	1990	1995	2000	2001	2002	2003	2004	2005
				TPES / ATEP (ktoe / ktep)				
TOTAL PRIMARY ENERGY SUPPLY	**22 181**	**23 482**	**27 821**	**28 704**	**29 030**	**29 877**	**30 471**	**30 977**
% contribution of Renewables and Wastes	5.0	5.6	5.3	4.7	4.9	5.3	5.2	5.3
Renewables	**1 104**	**1 289**	**1 402**	**1 318**	**1 393**	**1 538**	**1 559**	**1 632**
% contribution	5.0	5.5	5.0	4.6	4.8	5.1	5.1	5.3
Hydro	152	303	318	180	241	410	402	431
Geothermal (transformation *)	-	-	-	-	-	-	-	-
Geothermal (direct use **)	3	3	2	2	1	1	1	1
Solar Photovoltaic (transformation *)	-	-	-	-	-	-	-	-
Solar Thermal (transformation *)	-	-	-	-	-	-	-	-
Solar Thermal (direct use **)	56	82	99	100	99	99	107	101
Tide/Wave/Ocean	-	-	-	-	-	-	-	-
Wind	-	3	39	65	56	88	96	109
Ambient Heat (Heat Pumps)	-	-	-	-	-	-	-	-
Municipal Waste (Renewable)	-	-	-	-	-	-	-	-
Solid Biomass	893	897	944	937	947	909	917	957
Biogasoline	-	-	-	-	-	-	-	-
Biodiesel	-	-	-	-	-	-	-	-
Other Liquid Biomass	-	-	-	-	-	-	-	-
Biogas	-	1	1	33	48	31	36	33
Non-Renewable Wastes	**..**	**37**	**64**	**38**	**37**	**33**	**35**	**25**
% contribution	-	0.2	0.2	0.1	0.1	0.1	0.1	0.1
Industrial Waste	..	37	64	38	37	33	35	25
Municipal Waste (Non-Renewable)	-	-	-	-	-	-	-	-
Not separately identified * **	**-**	**-**	**-**	**-**	**-**	**-**	**-**	**-**
% contribution	-	-	-	-	-	-	-	-
*Memo: Total Wastes *** **	*..*	*37*	*64*	*38*	*37*	*33*	*35*	*25*
				ELECTRICITY / ELECTRICITE (GWh)				
TOTAL ELECTRICITY GENERATED	**34 775**	**41 299**	**53 425**	**53 076**	**53 945**	**57 905**	**58 813**	**59 427**
% contribution of Renewables and Wastes	5.1	8.9	8.1	5.7	6.8	10.4	10.3	10.9
Renewables	**1 771**	**3 564**	**4 144**	**2 932**	**3 577**	**5 892**	**5 918**	**6 406**
% contribution	5.1	8.6	7.8	5.5	6.6	10.2	10.1	10.8
Hydro (excl. pumped storage)	1 769	3 529	3 693	2 097	2 800	4 766	4 672	5 017
Geothermal	-	-	-	-	-	-	-	-
Solar Photovoltaic	-	-	-	-	-	-	1	1
Solar Thermal Electric	-	-	-	-	-	-	-	-
Tide/Wave/Ocean	-	-	-	-	-	-	-	-
Wind	2	34	451	756	651	1 021	1 121	1 266
Municipal Waste (Renewable)	-	-	-	-	-	-	-	-
Solid Biomass	-	1	-	-	-	-	-	-
Biogas/Liquid Biomass	-	-	-	79	126	105	124	122
Non-Renewable Wastes	**..**	**103**	**163**	**103**	**108**	**141**	**139**	**100**
% contribution	-	0.2	0.3	0.2	0.2	0.2	0.2	0.2
Industrial Waste	..	103	163	103	108	141	139	100
Municipal Waste (Non-Renewable)	-	-	-	-	-	-	-	-
Not separately identified * **	**-**	**-**	**-**	**-**	**-**	**-**	**-**	**-**
% contribution	-	-	-	-	-	-	-	-
*Memo: Total Wastes *** **	*..*	*103*	*163*	*103*	*108*	*141*	*139*	*100*

* Primary energy used in the production of electricity and heat by main activity producers or autoproducers in electricity plants, CHP plants and heat plants (e.g. solar thermal power plants, geothermal power plants, etc.).
Energie primaire utilisée pour la production d'électricité, de cogénération et de chaleur par des producteurs dont c'est l'activité principale ou des autoproducteurs (installations héliothermiques, géothermiques, etc.).

** Primary energy used elsewhere than in transformation as described above (e.g. remote photovoltaic electricity production for households, heating of buildings/greenhouses by geothermal, etc.).
Energie primaire utilisée ailleurs que dans la transformation décrite ci-dessus (ex : production isolée d'électricité photovoltaïque, chauffage des bâtiments/serres à partir d'énergie géothermique, etc.).

*** Includes non-specified combustible renewables and waste.
Comprend les énergies renouvelables combustibles et les déchets non spécifiés.

**** Includes municipal waste and industrial waste.
Comprend les déchets municipaux et les déchets industriels.

Hungary / Hongrie

Contribution from Renewable Energies and Energy from Wastes

Part des énergies renouvables et de l'énergie tirée des déchets

	1990	1995	2000	2001	2002	2003	2004	2005
			TPES / ATEP (ktoe / ktep)					
TOTAL PRIMARY ENERGY SUPPLY	**28 558**	**25 696**	**25 014**	**25 421**	**25 813**	**26 341**	**26 358**	**27 762**
% contribution of Renewables and Wastes	1.7	2.4	2.1	2.0	3.5	3.5	3.7	4.4
Renewables	**467**	**600**	**487**	**470**	**877**	**906**	**949**	**1 155**
% contribution	1.6	2.3	1.9	1.9	3.4	3.4	3.6	4.2
Hydro	15	14	15	16	17	15	18	17
Geothermal (transformation *)	-	7	6	7	7	7	6	6
Geothermal (direct use **)	86	79	80	79	79	79	80	80
Solar Photovoltaic (transformation *)	-	-	-	-	-	-	-	-
Solar Thermal (transformation *)	-	-	-	-	-	-	-	-
Solar Thermal (direct use **)	-	-	-	1	2	2	2	2
Tide/Wave/Ocean	-	-	-	-	-	-	-	-
Wind	-	-	-	-	-	-	1	1
Ambient Heat (Heat Pumps)	-	-	-	-	-	-	-	-
Municipal Waste (Renewable)	12 e	26 e	29 e	31 e	24 e	18 e	16 e	33 e
Solid Biomass	354	474	356	334	746	780	820	1 003
Biogasoline	-	-	-	-	-	-	-	5
Biodiesel	-	-	-	-	-	-	-	-
Other Liquid Biomass	-	-	-	-	-	-	-	-
Biogas	-	-	-	2	3	5	7	7
Non-Renewable Wastes	**12**	**26**	**29**	**31**	**24**	**19**	**27**	**62**
% contribution	0.0	0.1	0.1	0.1	0.1	0.1	0.1	0.2
Industrial Waste	-	-	-	-	-	1	11	29
Municipal Waste (Non-Renewable)	12 e	26 e	29 e	31 e	24 e	18 e	16 e	33
Not separately identified * **	**-**	**-**	**-**	**-**	**-**	**-**	**-**	**-**
% contribution	-	-	-	-	-	-	-	-
*Memo: Total Wastes *** **	*24*	*52*	*58*	*62*	*48*	*37*	*44*	*95*
			ELECTRICITY / ELECTRICITE (GWh)					
TOTAL ELECTRICITY GENERATED	**28 436**	**34 018**	**35 191**	**36 415**	**36 157**	**34 145**	**33 708**	**35 756**
% contribution of Renewables and Wastes	0.7	0.8	0.8	0.9	0.7	1.1	2.9	5.4
Renewables	**195**	**219**	**243**	**257**	**237**	**336**	**936**	**1 870**
% contribution	0.7	0.6	0.7	0.7	0.7	1.0	2.8	5.2
Hydro (excl. pumped storage)	178	163	178	186	194	171	205	202
Geothermal	-	-	-	-	-	-	-	-
Solar Photovoltaic	-	-	-	-	-	-	-	-
Solar Thermal Electric	-	-	-	-	-	-	-	-
Tide/Wave/Ocean	-	-	-	-	-	-	-	-
Wind	-	-	-	1	1	4	6	10
Municipal Waste (Renewable)	17 e	48 e	55 e	56 e	30 e	34 e	26 e	59 e
Solid Biomass	-	8	10	7	6	109	678	1 574
Biogas/Liquid Biomass	-	-	-	7	6	18	21	25
Non-Renewable Wastes	**17**	**47**	**55**	**56**	**29**	**33**	**26**	**72**
% contribution	0.1	0.1	0.2	0.2	0.1	0.1	0.1	0.2
Industrial Waste	-	-	-	-	-	-	-	13
Municipal Waste (Non-Renewable)	17 e	47 e	55 e	56 e	29 e	33 e	26 e	59 e
Not separately identified * **	**-**	**-**	**-**	**-**	**-**	**-**	**-**	**-**
% contribution	-	-	-	-	-	-	-	-
*Memo: Total Wastes *** **	*34*	*95*	*110*	*112*	*59*	*67*	*52*	*131*

* Primary energy used in the production of electricity and heat by main activity producers or autoproducers in electricity plants, CHP plants and heat plants (e.g. solar thermal power plants, geothermal power plants, etc.).
Energie primaire utilisée pour la production d'électricité, de cogénération et de chaleur par des producteurs dont c'est l'activité principale ou des autoproducteurs (installations héliothermiques, géothermiques, etc.).

** Primary energy used elsewhere than in transformation as described above (e.g. remote photovoltaic electricity production for households, heating of buildings/greenhouses by geothermal, etc.).
Energie primaire utilisée ailleurs que dans la transformation décrite ci-dessus (ex : production isolée d'électricité photovoltaïque, chauffage des bâtiments/serres à partir d'énergie géothermique, etc.).

*** Includes non-specified combustible renewables and waste.
Comprend les énergies renouvelables combustibles et les déchets non spécifiés.

**** Includes municipal waste and industrial waste.
Comprend les déchets municipaux et les déchets industriels.

Iceland / Islande

Contribution from Renewable Energies and Energy from Wastes

Part des énergies renouvables et de l'énergie tirée des déchets

	1990	1995	2000	2001	2002	2003	2004	2005
				TPES / ATEP (ktoe / ktep)				
TOTAL PRIMARY ENERGY SUPPLY	**2 172**	**2 329**	**3 244**	**3 363**	**3 395**	**3 386**	**3 498**	**3 626**
% contribution of Renewables and Wastes	64.5	67.2	71.1	72.9	72.5	72.6	72.0	72.7
Renewables	**1 400**	**1 565**	**2 305**	**2 451**	**2 461**	**2 456**	**2 518**	**2 635**
% contribution	64.5	67.2	71.0	72.9	72.5	72.5	72.0	72.7
Hydro	362	403	547	566	600	610	614	604
Geothermal (transformation *)	448	612	1 129	1 266	1 268	1 219	1 259	1 444
Geothermal (direct use **)	591	549	629	618	592	627	644	586
Solar Photovoltaic (transformation *)	-	-	-	-	-	-	-	-
Solar Thermal (transformation *)	-	-	-	-	-	-	-	-
Solar Thermal (direct use **)	-	-	-	-	-	-	-	-
Tide/Wave/Ocean	-	-	-	-	-	-	-	-
Wind	-	-	-	-	-	-	-	-
Ambient Heat (Heat Pumps)	-	-	-	-	-	-	-	-
Municipal Waste (Renewable)	-	1 e	1 e	1 e	1 e	1 e	1 e	1 e
Solid Biomass	-	-	-	-	-	-	-	-
Biogasoline	-	-	-	-	-	-	-	-
Biodiesel	-	-	-	-	-	-	-	-
Other Liquid Biomass	-	-	-	-	-	-	-	-
Biogas	-	-	-	-	-	-	1	1
Non-Renewable Wastes	**-**	**1**	**1**	**1**	**1**	**1**	**1**	**1**
% contribution	-	0.0	0.0	0.0	0.0	0.0	0.0	0.0
Industrial Waste	-	-	-	-	-	-	-	-
Municipal Waste (Non-Renewable)	-	1 e	1 e	1 e	1 e	1 e	1 e	1
Not separately identified ***	**-**	**-**	**-**	**-**	**-**	**-**	**-**	**-**
% contribution	-	-	-	-	-	-	-	-
*Memo: Total Wastes *****	-	*1*	*1*	*1*	*2*	*2*	*2*	*2*
				ELECTRICITY / ELECTRICITE (GWh)				
TOTAL ELECTRICITY GENERATED	**4 510**	**4 981**	**7 684**	**8 033**	**8 416**	**8 500**	**8 623**	**8 686**
% contribution of Renewables and Wastes	99.9	99.8	99.9	100.0	99.9	99.9	100.0	99.9
Renewables	**4 504**	**4 972**	**7 679**	**8 029**	**8 410**	**8 494**	**8 619**	**8 681**
% contribution	99.9	99.8	99.9	100.0	99.9	99.9	100.0	99.9
Hydro (excl. pumped storage)	4 204	4 682	6 356	6 578	6 977	7 088	7 134	7 019
Geothermal	300	290	1 323	1 451	1 433	1 406	1 483	1 658
Solar Photovoltaic	-	-	-	-	-	-	-	-
Solar Thermal Electric	-	-	-	-	-	-	-	-
Tide/Wave/Ocean	-	-	-	-	-	-	-	-
Wind	-	-	-	-	-	-	-	-
Municipal Waste (Renewable)	-	-	-	-	-	-	-	-
Solid Biomass	-	-	-	-	-	-	-	-
Biogas/Liquid Biomass	-	-	-	-	-	-	2	4
Non-Renewable Wastes	**-**	**-**	**-**	**-**	**-**	**-**	**-**	**-**
% contribution	-	-	-	-	-	-	-	-
Industrial Waste	-	-	-	-	-	-	-	-
Municipal Waste (Non-Renewable)	-	-	-	-	-	-	-	-
Not separately identified ***	**-**	**-**	**-**	**-**	**-**	**-**	**-**	**-**
% contribution	-	-	-	-	-	-	-	-
*Memo: Total Wastes *****	-	-	-	-	-	-	-	-

* Primary energy used in the production of electricity and heat by main activity producers or autoproducers in electricity plants, CHP plants and heat plants (e.g. solar thermal power plants, geothermal power plants, etc.).
Energie primaire utilisée pour la production d'électricité, de cogénération et de chaleur par des producteurs dont c'est l'activité principale ou des autoproducteurs (installations héliothermiques, géothermiques, etc.).

** Primary energy used elsewhere than in transformation as described above (e.g. remote photovoltaic electricity production for households, heating of buildings/greenhouses by geothermal, etc.).
Energie primaire utilisée ailleurs que dans la transformation décrite ci-dessus (ex : production isolée d'électricité photovoltaïque, chauffage des bâtiments/serres à partir d'énergie géothermique, etc.).

*** Includes non-specified combustible renewables and waste.
Comprend les énergies renouvelables combustibles et les déchets non spécifiés.

**** Includes municipal waste and industrial waste.
Comprend les déchets municipaux et les déchets industriels.

Ireland / Irlande

Contribution from Renewable Energies and Energy from Wastes

Part des énergies renouvables et de l'énergie tirée des déchets

	1990	1995	2000	2001	2002	2003	2004	2005
TPES / ATEP (ktoe / ktep)								
TOTAL PRIMARY ENERGY SUPPLY	**10 365**	**10 804**	**14 282**	**15 262**	**15 550**	**14 997**	**15 151**	**15 289**
% contribution of Renewables and Wastes	1.6	1.5	1.8	1.7	1.9	1.8	2.0	2.6
Renewables	**168**	**165**	**258**	**261**	**288**	**263**	**310**	**391**
% contribution	1.6	1.5	1.8	1.7	1.9	1.8	2.0	2.6
Hydro	60	61	73	51	78	51	54	54
Geothermal (transformation *)	-	-	-	-	-	-	-	-
Geothermal (direct use **)	-	-	-	-	-	-	-	-
Solar Photovoltaic (transformation *)	-	-	-	-	-	-	-	-
Solar Thermal (transformation *)	-	-	-	-	-	-	-	-
Solar Thermal (direct use **)	-	-	-	-	-	-	-	-
Tide/Wave/Ocean	-	-	-	-	-	-	-	-
Wind	-	1	21	29	33	39	56	96
Ambient Heat (Heat Pumps)	-	-	-	-	-	-	-	-
Municipal Waste (Renewable)	-	-	-	-	-	-	-	-
Solid Biomass	105	99	136	152	152	147	170	206
Biogasoline	-	-	-	-	-	-	-	-
Biodiesel	-	-	-	-	-	-	-	1
Other Liquid Biomass	-	-	-	-	-	-	-	-
Biogas	2	3	28	28	24	25	30	34
Non-Renewable Wastes	**-**	**-**	**-**	**-**	**-**	**-**	**-**	**-**
% contribution	-	-	-	-	-	-	-	-
Industrial Waste	-	-	-	-	-	-	-	-
Municipal Waste (Non-Renewable)	-	-	-	-	-	-	-	-
Not separately identified * **	**-**	**-**	**-**	**-**	**-**	**-**	**-**	**-**
% contribution	-	-	-	-	-	-	-	-
*Memo: Total Wastes *** **	-	-	-	-	-	-	-	-
ELECTRICITY / ELECTRICITE (GWh)								
TOTAL ELECTRICITY GENERATED	**14 229**	**17 604**	**23 673**	**24 632**	**24 843**	**24 861**	**25 215**	**25 626**
% contribution of Renewables and Wastes	4.9	4.1	5.0	4.2	5.6	4.6	5.5	7.3
Renewables	**697**	**729**	**1 185**	**1 027**	**1 382**	**1 138**	**1 394**	**1 873**
% contribution	4.9	4.1	5.0	4.2	5.6	4.6	5.5	7.3
Hydro (excl. pumped storage)	697	713	846	596	912	598	630	631
Geothermal	-	-	-	-	-	-	-	-
Solar Photovoltaic	-	-	-	-	-	-	-	-
Solar Thermal Electric	-	-	-	-	-	-	-	-
Tide/Wave/Ocean	-	-	-	-	-	-	-	-
Wind	-	16	244	334	388	454	655	1 112
Municipal Waste (Renewable)	-	-	-	-	-	-	-	-
Solid Biomass	-	-	-	-	-	-	8	8
Biogas/Liquid Biomass	-	-	95	97	82	86	101	122
Non-Renewable Wastes	**-**	**-**	**-**	**-**	**-**	**-**	**-**	**-**
% contribution	-	-	-	-	-	-	-	-
Industrial Waste	-	-	-	-	-	-	-	-
Municipal Waste (Non-Renewable)	-	-	-	-	-	-	-	-
Not separately identified * **	**-**	**-**	**-**	**-**	**-**	**-**	**-**	**-**
% contribution	-	-	-	-	-	-	-	-
*Memo: Total Wastes *** **	-	-	-	-	-	-	-	-

* Primary energy used in the production of electricity and heat by main activity producers or autoproducers in electricity plants, CHP plants and heat plants (e.g. solar thermal power plants, geothermal power plants, etc.).
Energie primaire utilisée pour la production d'électricité, de cogénération et de chaleur par des producteurs dont c'est l'activité principale ou des autoproducteurs (installations héliothermiques, géothermiques, etc.).

** Primary energy used elsewhere than in transformation as described above (e.g. remote photovoltaic electricity production for households, heating of buildings/greenhouses by geothermal, etc.).
Energie primaire utilisée ailleurs que dans la transformation décrite ci-dessus (ex : production isolée d'électricité photovoltaïque, chauffage des bâtiments/serres à partir d'énergie géothermique, etc.).

*** Includes non-specified combustible renewables and waste.
Comprend les énergies renouvelables combustibles et les déchets non spécifiés.

**** Includes municipal waste and industrial waste.
Comprend les déchets municipaux et les déchets industriels.

Italy / Italie

Contribution from Renewable Energies and Energy from Wastes

Part des énergies renouvelables et de l'énergie tirée des déchets

	1990	1995	2000	2001	2002	2003	2004	2005
				TPES / ATEP (ktoe / ktep)				
TOTAL PRIMARY ENERGY SUPPLY	**147 967**	**161 047**	**173 123**	**173 487**	**173 678**	**180 680**	**182 798**	**185 185**
% contribution of Renewables and Wastes	4.5	4.9	6.0	6.1	5.9	6.0	6.8	6.5
Renewables	**6 472**	**7 719**	**10 032**	**10 291**	**9 754**	**10 092**	**11 822**	**11 371**
% contribution	4.4	4.8	5.8	5.9	5.6	5.6	6.5	6.1
Hydro	2 720	3 249	3 802	4 026	3 399	2 906	3 406	2 890
Geothermal (transformation *)	2 770	2 954	4 045 e	3 875 e	4 008 e	4 592	4 674	4 577
Geothermal (direct use **)	201	213	213 e	217 e	217 e	217	213	213
Solar Photovoltaic (transformation *)	-	1	2 e	2 e	2 e	2 e	2 e	3
Solar Thermal (transformation *)	-	-	-	-	-	-	-	-
Solar Thermal (direct use **)	5	7	11	11	11	11	18	20
Tide/Wave/Ocean	-	-	-	-	-	-	-	-
Wind	-	1	48	101	121	125	159	202
Ambient Heat (Heat Pumps)	-	-	-	-	-	-	-	-
Municipal Waste (Renewable)	11 e	62 e	167 e	199 e	213 e	346 e	493 e	555 e
Solid Biomass	764	1 209	1 614	1 704	1 568	1 638	2 285	2 411
Biogasoline	-	-	-	-	-	-	-	-
Biodiesel	-	-	-	-	-	-	252	176
Other Liquid Biomass	-	-	-	-	-	-	-	-
Biogas	1	23	131	157	216	255	319	324
Non-Renewable Wastes	**164**	**162**	**310**	**356**	**489**	**828**	**656**	**673**
% contribution	0.1	0.1	0.2	0.2	0.3	0.5	0.4	0.4
Industrial Waste	153	100	143	157	276	483	163	117
Municipal Waste (Non-Renewable)	11 e	62 e	167 e	199 e	213 e	346 e	493 e	555
Not separately identified ***	-	-	-	-	-	-	-	-
% contribution	-	-	-	-	-	-	-	-
*Memo: Total Wastes *****	*175*	*224*	*477*	*554*	*702*	*1 174*	*1 149*	*1 228*
				ELECTRICITY / ELECTRICITE (GWh)				
TOTAL ELECTRICITY GENERATED	**213 147**	**237 364**	**269 947**	**271 894**	**277 534**	**283 392**	**293 047**	**294 380**
% contribution of Renewables and Wastes	16.4	17.5	19.0	20.3	17.7	15.9	17.9	16.1
Renewables	**34 905**	**41 458**	**50 681**	**54 101**	**47 540**	**42 894**	**51 141**	**45 979**
% contribution	16.4	17.5	18.8	19.9	17.1	15.1	17.5	15.6
Hydro (excl. pumped storage)	31 626	37 782	44 205	46 811	39 520	33 785	39 608	33 608
Geothermal	3 222	3 436	4 705	4 507	4 662	5 341	5 437	5 324
Solar Photovoltaic	4	13	18 e	19 e	21 e	24 e	29 e	31
Solar Thermal Electric	-	-	-	-	-	-	-	-
Tide/Wave/Ocean	-	-	-	-	-	-	-	-
Wind	2	9	563	1 179	1 404	1 458	1 847	2 344
Municipal Waste (Renewable)	37 e	85 e	402 e	629 e	714 e	907 e	1 138 e	1 309 e
Solid Biomass	12	30	221	272	276	347	1 912	2 166
Biogas/Liquid Biomass	2	103	567	684	943	1 032	1 170	1 197
Non-Renewable Wastes	**52**	**171**	**718**	**1 001**	**1 579**	**2 206**	**1 416**	**1 480**
% contribution	0.0	0.1	0.3	0.4	0.6	0.8	0.5	0.5
Industrial Waste	16	87	316	372	865	1 301	278	170
Municipal Waste (Non-Renewable)	36 e	84 e	402 e	629 e	714 e	905 e	1 138 e	1 310 e
Not separately identified ***	-	-	-	-	-	-	-	-
% contribution	-	-	-	-	-	-	-	-
*Memo: Total Wastes *****	*89*	*256*	*1 120*	*1 630*	*2 293*	*3 113*	*2 554*	*2 789*

* Primary energy used in the production of electricity and heat by main activity producers or autoproducers in electricity plants, CHP plants and heat plants (e.g. solar thermal power plants, geothermal power plants, etc.).
Energie primaire utilisée pour la production d'électricité, de cogénération et de chaleur par des producteurs dont c'est l'activité principale ou des autoproducteurs (installations héliothermiques, géothermiques, etc.).

** Primary energy used elsewhere than in transformation as described above (e.g. remote photovoltaic electricity production for households, heating of buildings/greenhouses by geothermal, etc.).
Energie primaire utilisée ailleurs que dans la transformation décrite ci-dessus (ex : production isolée d'électricité photovoltaïque, chauffage des bâtiments/serres à partir d'énergie géothermique, etc.).

*** Includes non-specified combustible renewables and waste.
Comprend les énergies renouvelables combustibles et les déchets non spécifiés.

**** Includes municipal waste and industrial waste.
Comprend les déchets municipaux et les déchets industriels.

Japan / Japon

Contribution from Renewable Energies and Energy from Wastes

Part des énergies renouvables et de l'énergie tirée des déchets

	1990	1995	2000	2001	2002	2003	2004	2005
				TPES / ATEP (ktoe / ktep)				
TOTAL PRIMARY ENERGY SUPPLY	**444 471**	**499 099**	**527 562**	**519 453**	**519 877**	**515 323**	**532 260**	**530 463**
% contribution of Renewables and Wastes	3.5	3.2	3.3	3.2	3.2	3.5	3.4	3.2
Renewables	**15 199**	**15 877**	**16 600**	**16 029**	**16 066**	**17 328**	**17 158**	**15 881**
% contribution	3.4	3.2	3.1	3.1	3.1	3.4	3.2	3.0
Hydro	7 680	7 062	7 504	7 238	7 085	8 136	8 089	6 726
Geothermal (transformation *)	1 497	2 728	2 878	2 950	2 901	2 995	2 900	2 773
Geothermal (direct use **)	79	208	221	225	228	229	222	214
Solar Photovoltaic (transformation *)	-	-	-	-	-	-	-	-
Solar Thermal (transformation *)	-	-	-	-	-	-	-	-
Solar Thermal (direct use **)	1 168	1 006	808	747	740	636	579	579
Tide/Wave/Ocean	-	-	-	-	-	-	-	-
Wind	-	-	9	22	36	72	113	151
Ambient Heat (Heat Pumps)	-	-	-	-	-	-	-	-
Municipal Waste (Renewable)	196 e	303 e	489 e	551 e	620 e	705 e	707 e	708 e
Solid Biomass	4 537	4 476	4 560	4 163	4 333	4 426	4 399	4 588
Biogasoline	-	-	-	-	-	-	-	-
Biodiesel	-	-	-	-	-	-	-	-
Other Liquid Biomass	-	-	-	-	-	-	-	-
Biogas	42	96	131	133	125	130	148	142
Non-Renewable Wastes	**198**	**305**	**665**	**704**	**757**	**838**	**845**	**857**
% contribution	0.0	0.1	0.1	0.1	0.1	0.2	0.2	0.2
Industrial Waste	2	3	176	152	137	133	138	149
Municipal Waste (Non-Renewable)	196 e	303 e	489 e	551 e	620 e	705 e	707 e	708
Not separately identified * **	-	-	-	-	-	-	-	-
% contribution	-	-	-	-	-	-	-	-
*Memo: Total Wastes *** **	*394*	*608*	*1 154*	*1 255*	*1 377*	*1 543*	*1 553*	*1 564*
				ELECTRICITY / ELECTRICITE (GWh)				
TOTAL ELECTRICITY GENERATED	**836 742**	**961 984**	**1 051 282**	**1 032 999**	**1 052 107**	**1 041 680**	**1 071 249**	**1 094 191**
% contribution of Renewables and Wastes	12.2	10.2	10.1	10.0	9.8	11.3	11.0	9.4
Renewables	**100 806**	**96 665**	**103 733**	**100 736**	**99 995**	**113 718**	**113 919**	**99 146**
% contribution	12.0	10.0	9.9	9.8	9.5	10.9	10.6	9.1
Hydro (excl. pumped storage)	89 305	82 118	87 253	84 166	82 378	94 607	94 063	78 211
Geothermal	1 741	3 173	3 348	3 432	3 374	3 484	3 374	3 226
Solar Photovoltaic	1	-	2	2	2	2	2	2
Solar Thermal Electric	-	-	-	-	-	-	-	-
Tide/Wave/Ocean	-	-	-	-	-	-	-	-
Wind	-	1	109	252	415	833	1 310	1 754
Municipal Waste (Renewable)	903 e	1 401 e	2 352 e	2 668 e	3 031 e	3 446 e	3 446 e	3 446 e
Solid Biomass	8 856	9 972	10 669	10 216	10 795	11 346	11 724	12 507
Biogas/Liquid Biomass	-	-	-	-	-	-	-	-
Non-Renewable Wastes	**904**	**1 402**	**2 454**	**2 709**	**3 069**	**3 498**	**3 538**	**3 587**
% contribution	0.1	0.1	0.2	0.3	0.3	0.3	0.3	0.3
Industrial Waste	-	-	100	39	38	50	90	139
Municipal Waste (Non-Renewable)	904 e	1 402 e	2 354 e	2 670 e	3 031 e	3 448 e	3 448 e	3 448 e
Not separately identified * **	-	-	-	-	-	-	-	-
% contribution	-	-	-	-	-	-	-	-
*Memo: Total Wastes *** **	*1 807*	*2 803*	*4 806*	*5 377*	*6 100*	*6 944*	*6 984*	*7 033*

* Primary energy used in the production of electricity and heat by main activity producers or autoproducers in electricity plants, CHP plants and heat plants (e.g. solar thermal power plants, geothermal power plants, etc.).
Energie primaire utilisée pour la production d'électricité, de cogénération et de chaleur par des producteurs dont c'est l'activité principale ou des autoproducteurs (installations héliothermiques, géothermiques, etc.).

** Primary energy used elsewhere than in transformation as described above (e.g. remote photovoltaic electricity production for households, heating of buildings/greenhouses by geothermal, etc.).
Energie primaire utilisée ailleurs que dans la transformation décrite ci-dessus (ex : production isolée d'électricité photovoltaïque, chauffage des bâtiments/serres à partir d'énergie géothermique, etc.).

*** Includes non-specified combustible renewables and waste.
Comprend les énergies renouvelables combustibles et les déchets non spécifiés.

**** Includes municipal waste and industrial waste.
Comprend les déchets municipaux et les déchets industriels.

Korea / Corée

Contribution from Renewable Energies and Energy from Wastes

Part des énergies renouvables et de l'énergie tirée des déchets

	1990	1995	2000	2001	2002	2003	2004	2005
				TPES / ATEP (ktoe / ktep)				
TOTAL PRIMARY ENERGY SUPPLY	**93 388**	**147 935**	**190 148**	**192 838**	**202 900**	**207 439**	**213 281**	**213 771**
% contribution of Renewables and Wastes	1.4	0.8	0.9	0.9	0.9	1.1	1.1	1.2
Renewables	**1 007**	**430**	**755**	**783**	**815**	**1 007**	**960**	**1 091**
% contribution	1.1	0.3	0.4	0.4	0.4	0.5	0.5	0.5
Hydro	547	237	345	357	278	422	372	316
Geothermal (transformation *)	-	-	-	-	-	-	-	-
Geothermal (direct use **)	-	-	-	-	-	-	1	3
Solar Photovoltaic (transformation *)	-	-	-	1	1	1	1	1
Solar Thermal (transformation *)	-	-	-	-	-	-	-	-
Solar Thermal (direct use **)	10	22	42	37	35	33	36	35
Tide/Wave/Ocean	-	-	-	-	-	-	-	-
Wind	-	-	1 e	1 e	1 e	2 e	4 e	11
Ambient Heat (Heat Pumps)	-	-	-	-	-	-	-	12
Municipal Waste (Renewable)	4 e	18 e	109 e	180 e	244 e	259 e	282 e	303 e
Solid Biomass	428	120	225	170	191	205	166	318
Biogasoline	-	-	-	-	-	-	-	-
Biodiesel	-	-	-	-	1	2	4	11
Other Liquid Biomass	-	-	-	-	-	-	-	-
Biogas	18	33	33	36	65	83	92	81
Non-Renewable Wastes	**281**	**798**	**1 010**	**1 037**	**1 068**	**1 255**	**1 463**	**1 430**
% contribution	0.3	0.5	0.5	0.5	0.5	0.6	0.7	0.7
Industrial Waste	279	786	937	917	906	1 082	1 275	1 228
Municipal Waste (Non-Renewable)	3 e	12 e	73 e	120 e	162 e	173 e	188 e	202
Not separately identified * **	**-**	**-**	**-**	**-**	**-**	**-**	**-**	**-**
% contribution	-	-	-	-	-	-	-	-
*Memo: Total Wastes *****	*285*	*817*	*1 119*	*1 217*	*1 312*	*1 514*	*1 745*	*1 733*
				ELECTRICITY / ELECTRICITE (GWh)				
TOTAL ELECTRICITY GENERATED	**105 371**	**181 139**	**263 386**	**281 202**	**329 804**	**343 191**	**366 612**	**387 874**
% contribution of Renewables and Wastes	6.0	1.7	1.6	1.5	1.1	1.5	1.3	1.1
Renewables	**6 362**	**3 012**	**4 124**	**4 258**	**3 434**	**5 123**	**4 631**	**4 052**
% contribution	6.0	1.7	1.6	1.5	1.0	1.5	1.3	1.0
Hydro (excl. pumped storage)	6 361	2 760	4 010	4 151	3 233	4 902	4 330	3 673
Geothermal	-	-	-	-	-	-	-	-
Solar Photovoltaic	1	2	5	6	7	8	10	15
Solar Thermal Electric	-	-	-	-	-	-	-	-
Tide/Wave/Ocean	-	-	-	-	-	-	-	-
Wind	-	-	17	13	15	25	47	130
Municipal Waste (Renewable)	..	-	22 e	27 e	57 e	60 e	69 e	71 e
Solid Biomass	-	250	70	55	51	28	24	33
Biogas/Liquid Biomass	-	-	-	6	71	100	151	130
Non-Renewable Wastes	**-**	**-**	**14**	**18**	**52**	**59**	**124**	**60**
% contribution	-	-	0.0	0.0	0.0	0.0	0.0	0.0
Industrial Waste	-	-	-	-	13	20	78	12
Municipal Waste (Non-Renewable)	-	-	14 e	18 e	39 e	39 e	46 e	48 e
Not separately identified * **	**-**	**-**	**-**	**-**	**-**	**-**	**-**	**-**
% contribution	-	-	-	-	-	-	-	-
*Memo: Total Wastes *****	*..*	*-*	*36*	*45*	*109*	*119*	*193*	*131*

* Primary energy used in the production of electricity and heat by main activity producers or autoproducers in electricity plants, CHP plants and heat plants (e.g. solar thermal power plants, geothermal power plants, etc.).
Energie primaire utilisée pour la production d'électricité, de cogénération et de chaleur par des producteurs dont c'est l'activité principale ou des autoproducteurs (installations héliothermiques, géothermiques, etc.).

** Primary energy used elsewhere than in transformation as described above (e.g. remote photovoltaic electricity production for households, heating of buildings/greenhouses by geothermal, etc.).
Energie primaire utilisée ailleurs que dans la transformation décrite ci-dessus (ex : production isolée d'électricité photovoltaïque, chauffage des bâtiments/serres à partir d'énergie géothermique, etc.).

*** Includes non-specified combustible renewables and waste.
Comprend les énergies renouvelables combustibles et les déchets non spécifiés.

**** Includes municipal waste and industrial waste.
Comprend les déchets municipaux et les déchets industriels.

Luxembourg

Contribution from Renewable Energies and Energy from Wastes

Part des énergies renouvables et de l'énergie tirée des déchets

	1990	1995	2000	2001	2002	2003	2004	2005
			TPES / ATEP (ktoe / ktep)					
TOTAL PRIMARY ENERGY SUPPLY	**3 571**	**3 376**	**3 683**	**3 834**	**4 041**	**4 262**	**4 680**	**4 776**
% contribution of Renewables and Wastes	0.9	1.4	1.5	1.6	1.4	1.4	1.6	1.6
Renewables	**15**	**32**	**39**	**42**	**40**	**40**	**49**	**52**
% contribution	0.4	0.9	1.1	1.1	1.0	0.9	1.0	1.1
Hydro	6	8	10	11	10	7	9	9
Geothermal (transformation *)	-	-	-	-	-	-	-	-
Geothermal (direct use **)	-	-	-	-	-	-	-	-
Solar Photovoltaic (transformation *)	-	-	-	-	-	-	1	2
Solar Thermal (transformation *)	-	-	-	-	-	-	-	-
Solar Thermal (direct use **)	-	-	-	-	-	-	-	-
Tide/Wave/Ocean	-	-	-	-	-	-	-	-
Wind	-	-	2	2	2	2	3	4
Ambient Heat (Heat Pumps)	-	-	-	-	-	-	-	-
Municipal Waste (Renewable)	9 e	9 e	10 e	10 e	10 e	12 e	14 e	13 e
Solid Biomass	-	15	16	16	15	15	15	15
Biogasoline	-	-	-	-	-	-	-	-
Biodiesel	-	-	-	-	-	-	1	1
Other Liquid Biomass	-	-	-	-	-	-	-	-
Biogas	-	-	1	2	2	4	5	7
Non-Renewable Wastes	**16**	**15**	**17**	**18**	**17**	**20**	**24**	**23**
% contribution	0.4	0.4	0.5	0.5	0.4	0.5	0.5	0.5
Industrial Waste	-	-	-	-	-	-	-	-
Municipal Waste (Non-Renewable)	16 e	15 e	17 e	18 e	17 e	20 e	24 e	23
Not separately identified * **	**-**	**-**	**-**	**-**	**-**	**-**	**-**	**-**
% contribution	-	-	-	-	-	-	-	-
*Memo: Total Wastes *** **	*25*	*23*	*27*	*28*	*27*	*31*	*38*	*36*

	1990	1995	2000	2001	2002	2003	2004	2005
			ELECTRICITY / ELECTRICITE (GWh)					
TOTAL ELECTRICITY GENERATED	**624**	**487**	**433**	**498**	**2 794**	**2 780**	**3 368**	**3 351**
% contribution of Renewables and Wastes	16.7	29.0	46.9	44.0	7.2	6.1	6.8	7.3
Renewables	**83**	**107**	**170**	**187**	**167**	**139**	**195**	**214**
% contribution	13.3	22.0	39.3	37.6	6.0	5.0	5.8	6.4
Hydro (excl. pumped storage)	70	88	120	133	113	77	106	99
Geothermal	-	-	-	-	-	-	-	-
Solar Photovoltaic	-	-	-	1	1	1	9	18
Solar Thermal Electric	-	-	-	-	-	-	-	-
Tide/Wave/Ocean	-	-	-	-	-	-	-	-
Wind	-	-	27	26	25	26	39	52
Municipal Waste (Renewable)	13 e	19 e	19 e	19 e	19 e	18 e	21 e	18 e
Solid Biomass	-	-	-	-	-	-	-	-
Biogas/Liquid Biomass	-	-	4	8	9	17	20	27
Non-Renewable Wastes	**21**	**34**	**33**	**32**	**33**	**30**	**35**	**30**
% contribution	3.4	7.0	7.6	6.4	1.2	1.1	1.0	0.9
Industrial Waste	-	-	-	-	-	-	-	-
Municipal Waste (Non-Renewable)	21 e	34 e	33 e	32 e	33 e	30 e	35 e	30 e
Not separately identified * **	**-**	**-**	**-**	**-**	**-**	**-**	**-**	**-**
% contribution	-	-	-	-	-	-	-	-
*Memo: Total Wastes *** **	*34*	*53*	*52*	*51*	*52*	*48*	*56*	*48*

* Primary energy used in the production of electricity and heat by main activity producers or autoproducers in electricity plants, CHP plants and heat plants (e.g. solar thermal power plants, geothermal power plants, etc.).
Energie primaire utilisée pour la production d'électricité, de cogénération et de chaleur par des producteurs dont c'est l'activité principale ou des autoproducteurs (installations héliothermiques, géothermiques, etc.).

** Primary energy used elsewhere than in transformation as described above (e.g. remote photovoltaic electricity production for households, heating of buildings/greenhouses by geothermal, etc.).
Energie primaire utilisée ailleurs que dans la transformation décrite ci-dessus (ex : production isolée d'électricité photovoltaïque, chauffage des bâtiments/serres à partir d'énergie géothermique, etc.).

*** Includes non-specified combustible renewables and waste.
Comprend les énergies renouvelables combustibles et les déchets non spécifiés.

**** Includes municipal waste and industrial waste.
Comprend les déchets municipaux et les déchets industriels.

Mexico / Mexique

Contribution from Renewable Energies and Energy from Wastes

Part des énergies renouvables et de l'énergie tirée des déchets

	1990	1995	2000	2001	2002	2003	2004	2005
				TPES / ATEP (ktoe / ktep)				
TOTAL PRIMARY ENERGY SUPPLY	**124 341**	**132 654**	**150 323**	**152 090**	**155 457**	**159 764**	**165 220**	**176 534**
% contribution of Renewables and Wastes	11.1	11.4	10.6	10.1	9.5	9.5	9.7	9.7
Renewables	**13 768**	**15 071**	**15 915**	**15 337**	**14 810**	**15 194**	**15 951**	**17 047**
% contribution	11.1	11.4	10.6	10.1	9.5	9.5	9.7	9.7
Hydro	2 019	2 367	2 849	2 451	2 146	1 710	2 168	2 385
Geothermal (transformation *)	4 405	4 874	5 073	4 786	4 641	5 401	5 654	6 275
Geothermal (direct use **)	-	-	-	-	-	-	-	-
Solar Photovoltaic (transformation *)	-	-	2	3	3	3	3	3
Solar Thermal (transformation *)	-	-	-	-	-	-	-	-
Solar Thermal (direct use **)	-	-	43	51	57	66	73	73
Tide/Wave/Ocean	-	-	-	-	-	-	-	-
Wind	-	1	1	2	1	1	1	1
Ambient Heat (Heat Pumps)	-	-	-	-	-	-	-	-
Municipal Waste (Renewable)	-	-	-	-	-	-	-	-
Solid Biomass	7 344	7 830	7 940	8 038	7 955	8 004	8 041	8 300
Biogasoline	-	-	-	-	-	-	-	-
Biodiesel	-	-	-	-	-	-	-	-
Other Liquid Biomass	-	-	-	-	-	-	-	-
Biogas	-	-	6	6	7	10	11	10
Non-Renewable Wastes	-	-	-	-	-	-	-	-
% contribution	-	-	-	-	-	-	-	-
Industrial Waste	-	-	-	-	-	-	-	-
Municipal Waste (Non-Renewable)	-	-	-	-	-	-	-	-
Not separately identified ***	-	-	-	-	-	-	-	-
% contribution	-	-	-	-	-	-	-	-
*Memo: Total Wastes *****	-	-	-	-	-	-	-	-
				ELECTRICITY / ELECTRICITE (GWh)				
TOTAL ELECTRICITY GENERATED	**124 127**	**157 493**	**203 645**	**209 159**	**214 628**	**217 867**	**224 077**	**234 895**
% contribution of Renewables and Wastes	23.0	21.1	19.4	16.6	14.4	13.2	15.3	16.0
Renewables	**28 602**	**33 203**	**39 518**	**34 619**	**30 867**	**28 663**	**34 348**	**37 675**
% contribution	23.0	21.1	19.4	16.6	14.4	13.2	15.3	16.0
Hydro (excl. pumped storage)	23 478	27 528	33 133	28 502	24 951	19 880	25 206	27 732
Geothermal	5 124	5 669	5 901	5 567	5 398	6 282	6 577	7 299
Solar Photovoltaic	-	-	29	31	32	33	35	35
Solar Thermal Electric	-	-	-	-	-	-	-	-
Tide/Wave/Ocean	-	-	-	-	-	-	-	-
Wind	-	6	13	18	16	14	15	14
Municipal Waste (Renewable)	-	-	-	-	-	-	-	-
Solid Biomass	-	-	433	492	458	2 434	2 494	2 574
Biogas/Liquid Biomass	-	-	9	9	12	20	21	21
Non-Renewable Wastes	-	-	-	-	-	-	-	-
% contribution	-	-	-	-	-	-	-	-
Industrial Waste	-	-	-	-	-	-	-	-
Municipal Waste (Non-Renewable)	-	-	-	-	-	-	-	-
Not separately identified ***	-	-	-	-	-	-	-	-
% contribution	-	-	-	-	-	-	-	-
*Memo: Total Wastes *****	-	-	-	-	-	-	-	-

* Primary energy used in the production of electricity and heat by main activity producers or autoproducers in electricity plants, CHP plants and heat plants (e.g. solar thermal power plants, geothermal power plants, etc.).
Energie primaire utilisée pour la production d'électricité, de cogénération et de chaleur par des producteurs dont c'est l'activité principale ou des autoproducteurs (installations héliothermiques, géothermiques, etc.).

** Primary energy used elsewhere than in transformation as described above (e.g. remote photovoltaic electricity production for households, heating of buildings/greenhouses by geothermal, etc.).
Energie primaire utilisée ailleurs que dans la transformation décrite ci-dessus (ex : production isolée d'électricité photovoltaïque, chauffage des bâtiments/serres à partir d'énergie géothermique, etc.).

*** Includes non-specified combustible renewables and waste.
Comprend les énergies renouvelables combustibles et les déchets non spécifiés.

**** Includes municipal waste and industrial waste.
Comprend les déchets municipaux et les déchets industriels.

Netherlands / Pays-Bas

Contribution from Renewable Energies and Energy from Wastes

Part des énergies renouvables et de l'énergie tirée des déchets

	1990	1995	2000	2001	2002	2003	2004	2005
			TPES / ATEP (ktoe / ktep)					
TOTAL PRIMARY ENERGY SUPPLY	**66 751**	**72 488**	**75 861**	**77 985**	**78 684**	**80 967**	**82 173**	**81 849**
% contribution of Renewables and Wastes	1.4	1.6	2.4	2.4	2.6	2.6	2.9	3.5
Renewables	**733**	**840**	**1 257**	**1 325**	**1 460**	**1 411**	**1 671**	**2 107**
% contribution	1.1	1.2	1.7	1.7	1.9	1.7	2.0	2.6
Hydro	7	8	12	10	9	6	8	8
Geothermal (transformation *)	-	-	-	-	-	-	-	-
Geothermal (direct use **)	-	-	-	-	-	-	-	-
Solar Photovoltaic (transformation *)	-	-	1	1	1	3	3	3
Solar Thermal (transformation *)	-	-	-	-	-	-	-	-
Solar Thermal (direct use **)	2	5	11	13	14	16	18	19
Tide/Wave/Ocean	-	-	-	-	-	-	-	-
Wind	5	27	71	71	81	113	161	178
Ambient Heat (Heat Pumps)	-	-	-	-	-	-	-	-
Municipal Waste (Renewable)	315 e	369 e	609 e	588 e	609 e	598 e	622 e	637 e
Solid Biomass	343	315	428	514	594	545	648	814
Biogasoline	-	-	-	-	-	-	-	-
Biodiesel	-	-	-	-	-	-	-	-
Other Liquid Biomass	-	-	-	-	18	1	86	328
Biogas	61	117	124	128	133	129	126	122
Non-Renewable Wastes	**230**	**315**	**579**	**584**	**622**	**675**	**702**	**718**
% contribution	0.3	0.4	0.8	0.7	0.8	0.8	0.9	0.9
Industrial Waste	-	-	-	-	-	-	-	-
Municipal Waste (Non-Renewable)	230 e	315 e	579 e	584 e	622 e	675 e	702 e	718
Not separately identified * **	-	-	-	-	-	-	-	-
% contribution	-	-	-	-	-	-	-	-
*Memo: Total Wastes *** **	*545*	*684*	*1 188*	*1 172*	*1 232*	*1 273*	*1 324*	*1 355*
			ELECTRICITY / ELECTRICITE (GWh)					
TOTAL ELECTRICITY GENERATED	**71 938**	**80 977**	**89 652**	**93 781**	**96 065**	**96 763**	**100 770**	**100 219**
% contribution of Renewables and Wastes	1.7	2.5	4.7	4.8	5.4	5.5	6.6	8.9
Renewables	**801**	**1 400**	**2 994**	**3 313**	**3 978**	**3 969**	**5 320**	**7 465**
% contribution	1.1	1.7	3.3	3.5	4.1	4.1	5.3	7.4
Hydro (excl. pumped storage)	85	88	142	117	110	72	95	88
Geothermal	-	-	-	-	-	-	-	-
Solar Photovoltaic	-	1	8	13	17	31	33	34
Solar Thermal Electric	-	-	-	-	-	-	-	-
Tide/Wave/Ocean	-	-	-	-	-	-	-	-
Wind	56	317	829	825	946	1 318	1 867	2 067
Municipal Waste (Renewable)	539 e	705 e	1 292 e	1 235 e	1 220 e	1 225 e	1 199 e	1 287 e
Solid Biomass	34	41	435	823	1 278	1 007	1 458	2 246
Biogas/Liquid Biomass	87	248	288	300	407	316	668	1 743
Non-Renewable Wastes	**394**	**602**	**1 228**	**1 226**	**1 247**	**1 381**	**1 352**	**1 451**
% contribution	0.5	0.7	1.4	1.3	1.3	1.4	1.3	1.4
Industrial Waste	-	-	-	-	-	-	-	-
Municipal Waste (Non-Renewable)	394 e	602 e	1 228 e	1 226 e	1 247 e	1 381 e	1 352 e	1 451 e
Not separately identified * **	-	-	-	-	-	-	-	-
% contribution	-	-	-	-	-	-	-	-
*Memo: Total Wastes *** **	*933*	*1 307*	*2 520*	*2 461*	*2 467*	*2 606*	*2 551*	*2 738*

* Primary energy used in the production of electricity and heat by main activity producers or autoproducers in electricity plants, CHP plants and heat plants (e.g. solar thermal power plants, geothermal power plants, etc.).
Energie primaire utilisée pour la production d'électricité, de cogénération et de chaleur par des producteurs dont c'est l'activité principale ou des autoproducteurs (installations héliothermiques, géothermiques, etc.).

** Primary energy used elsewhere than in transformation as described above (e.g. remote photovoltaic electricity production for households, heating of buildings/greenhouses by geothermal, etc.).
Energie primaire utilisée ailleurs que dans la transformation décrite ci-dessus (ex : production isolée d'électricité photovoltaïque, chauffage des bâtiments/serres à partir d'énergie géothermique, etc.).

*** Includes non-specified combustible renewables and waste.
Comprend les énergies renouvelables combustibles et les déchets non spécifiés.

**** Includes municipal waste and industrial waste.
Comprend les déchets municipaux et les déchets industriels.

New Zealand / Nouvelle-Zélande

Contribution from Renewable Energies and Energy from Wastes

Part des énergies renouvables et de l'énergie tirée des déchets

	1990	1995	2000	2001	2002	2003	2004	2005
	TPES / ATEP (ktoe / ktep)							
TOTAL PRIMARY ENERGY SUPPLY	**13 758**	**15 826**	**17 954**	**18 074**	**17 604**	**17 131**	**17 428**	**16 909**
% contribution of Renewables and Wastes	34.6	32.7	30.9	28.8	27.9	27.6	29.5	28.9
Renewables	**4 767**	**5 169**	**5 549**	**5 213**	**4 909**	**4 722**	**5 133**	**4 893**
% contribution	34.6	32.7	30.9	28.8	27.9	27.6	29.5	28.9
Hydro	2 007	2 344	2 097	1 845	2 170	2 038	2 339	2 018
Geothermal (transformation *)	1 797	1 762	2 359	2 289	1 571	1 509	1 536	1 559
Geothermal (direct use **)	415	466	369	371	375	372	371	374
Solar Photovoltaic (transformation *)	-	-	-	-	-	-	-	-
Solar Thermal (transformation *)	-	-	-	-	-	-	-	-
Solar Thermal (direct use **)	-	-	-	-	4	5	5	5
Tide/Wave/Ocean	-	-	-	-	-	-	-	-
Wind	-	-	10	12	13	13	31	53
Ambient Heat (Heat Pumps)	-	-	-	-	-	-	24	12
Municipal Waste (Renewable)	-	-	-	-	-	-	-	-
Solid Biomass	524	534	683	663	737	745	792	836
Biogasoline	-	-	-	-	-	-	-	-
Biodiesel	-	-	-	-	-	-	-	-
Other Liquid Biomass	-	-	-	-	-	-	-	-
Biogas	23	62	30	33	39	42	36	34
Non-Renewable Wastes	-	-	-	-	-	-	-	-
% contribution	-	-	-	-	-	-	-	-
Industrial Waste	-	-	-	-	-	-	-	-
Municipal Waste (Non-Renewable)	-	-	-	-	-	-	-	-
Not separately identified * **	-	-	-	-	-	-	-	-
% contribution	-	-	-	-	-	-	-	-
*Memo: Total Wastes *** **	-	-	-	-	-	-	-	-
	ELECTRICITY / ELECTRICITE (GWh)							
TOTAL ELECTRICITY GENERATED	**32 272**	**35 316**	**39 223**	**39 434**	**41 108**	**41 249**	**42 794**	**42 956**
% contribution of Renewables and Wastes	80.5	84.9	71.4	63.0	70.1	65.8	72.1	64.3
Renewables	**25 966**	**29 979**	**28 016**	**24 825**	**28 810**	**27 144**	**30 866**	**27 619**
% contribution	80.5	84.9	71.4	63.0	70.1	65.8	72.1	64.3
Hydro (excl. pumped storage)	23 340	27 259	24 386	21 455	25 229	23 699	27 201	23 470
Geothermal	2 216	2 172	2 921	2 838	2 866	2 769	2 754	2 852
Solar Photovoltaic	-	-	-	-	-	-	-	-
Solar Thermal Electric	-	-	-	-	-	-	-	-
Tide/Wave/Ocean	-	-	-	-	-	-	-	-
Wind	-	1	120	137	156	148	358	616
Municipal Waste (Renewable)	-	-	-	-	-	-	-	-
Solid Biomass	330	336	478	289	431	387	431	565
Biogas/Liquid Biomass	80	211	111	106	128	141	122	116
Non-Renewable Wastes	-	-	-	-	-	-	-	-
% contribution	-	-	-	-	-	-	-	-
Industrial Waste	-	-	-	-	-	-	-	-
Municipal Waste (Non-Renewable)	-	-	-	-	-	-	-	-
Not separately identified * **	-	-	-	-	-	-	-	-
% contribution	-	-	-	-	-	-	-	-
*Memo: Total Wastes *** **	-	-	-	-	-	-	-	-

* Primary energy used in the production of electricity and heat by main activity producers or autoproducers in electricity plants, CHP plants and heat plants (e.g. solar thermal power plants, geothermal power plants, etc.).
Energie primaire utilisée pour la production d'électricité, de cogénération et de chaleur par des producteurs dont c'est l'activité principale ou des autoproducteurs (installations héliothermiques, géothermiques, etc.).

** Primary energy used elsewhere than in transformation as described above (e.g. remote photovoltaic electricity production for households, heating of buildings/greenhouses by geothermal, etc.).
Energie primaire utilisée ailleurs que dans la transformation décrite ci-dessus (ex : production isolée d'électricité photovoltaïque, chauffage des bâtiments/serres à partir d'énergie géothermique, etc.).

*** Includes non-specified combustible renewables and waste.
Comprend les énergies renouvelables combustibles et les déchets non spécifiés.

**** Includes municipal waste and industrial waste.
Comprend les déchets municipaux et les déchets industriels.

Norway / Norvège

Contribution from Renewable Energies and Energy from Wastes

Part des énergies renouvables et de l'énergie tirée des déchets

	1990	1995	2000	2001	2002	2003	2004	2005
TPES / ATEP (ktoe / ktep)								
TOTAL PRIMARY ENERGY SUPPLY	**21 511**	**23 882**	**25 809**	**26 476**	**25 100**	**27 144**	**28 268**	**32 125**
% contribution of Renewables and Wastes	53.3	48.6	51.6	44.3	50.2	38.6	37.9	40.7
Renewables	**11 415**	**11 536**	**13 257**	**11 644**	**12 509**	**10 358**	**10 599**	**12 956**
% contribution	53.1	48.3	51.4	44.0	49.8	38.2	37.5	40.3
Hydro	10 418	10 435	11 947	10 174	11 130	9 083	9 362	11 678
Geothermal (transformation *)	-	-	-	-	-	-	-	-
Geothermal (direct use **)	-	-	-	-	-	-	-	-
Solar Photovoltaic (transformation *)	-	-	-	-	-	-	-	-
Solar Thermal (transformation *)	-	-	-	-	-	-	-	-
Solar Thermal (direct use **)	-	-	-	-	-	-	-	-
Tide/Wave/Ocean	-	-	-	-	-	-	-	-
Wind	-	1	3	2	6	19	22	44
Ambient Heat (Heat Pumps)	19	20	21	29	28	18	26	32
Municipal Waste (Renewable)	54 e	57 e	62 e	67 e	67 e	97 e	91 e	93 e
Solid Biomass	923	1 006	1 199	1 350	1 251	1 116	1 074	1 084
Biogasoline	-	-	-	-	-	-	-	-
Biodiesel	-	-	-	-	-	-	-	-
Other Liquid Biomass	-	-	-	-	-	-	-	-
Biogas	-	16	26	23	26	26	24	25
Non-Renewable Wastes	**54**	**61**	**73**	**85**	**85**	**110**	**105**	**105**
% contribution	0.3	0.3	0.3	0.3	0.3	0.4	0.4	0.3
Industrial Waste	-	4	11	18	18	13	14	12
Municipal Waste (Non-Renewable)	54 e	57 e	62 e	67 e	67 e	97 e	91 e	93
Not separately identified ***	-	-	-	-	-	-	-	-
% contribution	-	-	-	-	-	-	-	-
Memo: Total Wastes ****	*108*	*118*	*135*	*152*	*152*	*207*	*196*	*198*
ELECTRICITY / ELECTRICITE (GWh)								
TOTAL ELECTRICITY GENERATED	**121 611**	**122 055**	**139 608**	**119 163**	**130 283**	**106 801**	**110 189**	**137 332**
% contribution of Renewables and Wastes	99.8	99.7	99.7	99.6	99.6	99.5	99.4	99.5
Renewables	**121 358**	**121 642**	**139 202**	**118 581**	**129 740**	**106 160**	**109 474**	**136 638**
% contribution	99.8	99.7	99.7	99.5	99.6	99.4	99.4	99.5
Hydro (excl. pumped storage)	121 145	121 343	138 915	118 299	129 415	105 612	108 863	135 796
Geothermal	-	-	-	-	-	-	-	-
Solar Photovoltaic	-	-	-	-	-	-	-	-
Solar Thermal Electric	-	-	-	-	-	-	-	-
Tide/Wave/Ocean	-	-	-	-	-	-	-	-
Wind	-	10	31	27	75	218	252	506
Municipal Waste (Renewable)	29 e	24 e	30 e	58 e	34 e	67 e	62 e	43 e
Solid Biomass	184	265	226	197	216	263	297	293
Biogas/Liquid Biomass	-	-	-	-	-	-	-	-
Non-Renewable Wastes	**29**	**24**	**30**	**77**	**66**	**97**	**90**	**49**
% contribution	0.0	0.0	0.0	0.1	0.1	0.1	0.1	0.0
Industrial Waste	-	-	-	19	32	29	28	6
Municipal Waste (Non-Renewable)	29 e	24 e	30 e	58 e	34 e	68 e	62 e	43 e
Not separately identified ***	-	-	-	-	-	-	-	-
% contribution	-	-	-	-	-	-	-	-
Memo: Total Wastes ****	*58*	*48*	*60*	*135*	*100*	*164*	*152*	*92*

* Primary energy used in the production of electricity and heat by main activity producers or autoproducers in electricity plants, CHP plants and heat plants (e.g. solar thermal power plants, geothermal power plants, etc.).
Energie primaire utilisée pour la production d'électricité, de cogénération et de chaleur par des producteurs dont c'est l'activité principale ou des autoproducteurs (installations héliothermiques, géothermiques, etc.).

** Primary energy used elsewhere than in transformation as described above (e.g. remote photovoltaic electricity production for households, heating of buildings/greenhouses by geothermal, etc.).
Energie primaire utilisée ailleurs que dans la transformation décrite ci-dessus (ex : production isolée d'électricité photovoltaïque, chauffage des bâtiments/serres à partir d'énergie géothermique, etc.).

*** Includes non-specified combustible renewables and waste.
Comprend les énergies renouvelables combustibles et les déchets non spécifiés.

**** Includes municipal waste and industrial waste.
Comprend les déchets municipaux et les déchets industriels.

Poland / Pologne

Contribution from Renewable Energies and Energy from Wastes

Part des énergies renouvables et de l'énergie tirée des déchets

	1990	1995	2000	2001	2002	2003	2004	2005
				TPES / ATEP (ktoe / ktep)				
TOTAL PRIMARY ENERGY SUPPLY	**99 880**	**99 743**	**89 427**	**90 039**	**89 167**	**91 451**	**91 786**	**92 969**
% contribution of Renewables and Wastes	2.4	4.8	4.8	5.0	5.2	5.1	5.2	5.3
Renewables	**1 579**	**3 923**	**3 801**	**4 070**	**4 141**	**4 147**	**4 320**	**4 485**
% contribution	1.6	3.9	4.3	4.5	4.6	4.5	4.7	4.8
Hydro	122	162	181	200	196	144	179	189
Geothermal (transformation *)	-	-	-	-	-	-	-	-
Geothermal (direct use **)	-	-	3	3	6	7	8	9
Solar Photovoltaic (transformation *)	-	-	-	-	-	-	-	-
Solar Thermal (transformation *)	-	-	-	-	-	-	-	-
Solar Thermal (direct use **)	-	-	-	-	-	-	-	-
Tide/Wave/Ocean	-	-	-	-	-	-	-	-
Wind	-	-	-	1	5	11	12	12
Ambient Heat (Heat Pumps)	-	-	-	-	-	-	-	-
Municipal Waste (Renewable)	-	-	1 e	-	-	-	-	8 e
Solid Biomass	1 448	3 748	3 587	3 830	3 901	3 918	4 061	4 165
Biogasoline	-	-	-	-	-	28	13	34
Biodiesel	-	-	-	-	-	-	-	14
Other Liquid Biomass	-	-	-	-	-	-	-	-
Biogas	9	13	29	35	32	39	46	54
Non-Renewable Wastes	**772**	**838**	**448**	**471**	**507**	**501**	**481**	**461**
% contribution	0.8	0.8	0.5	0.5	0.6	0.5	0.5	0.5
Industrial Waste	772	838	447	471	507	501	480	452
Municipal Waste (Non-Renewable)	-	-	1 e	-	-	-	-	8
Not separately identified ***	-	-	-	-	-	-	-	-
% contribution	-	-	-	-	-	-	-	-
*Memo: Total Wastes *****	*772*	*838*	*449*	*472*	*507*	*501*	*481*	*469*
				ELECTRICITY / ELECTRICITE (GWh)				
TOTAL ELECTRICITY GENERATED	**134 415**	**137 042**	**143 174**	**143 721**	**142 499**	**150 009**	**152 550**	**155 359**
% contribution of Renewables and Wastes	1.2	1.6	1.9	2.2	2.3	1.7	2.2	2.7
Renewables	**1 472**	**1 955**	**2 332**	**2 783**	**2 767**	**2 250**	**3 075**	**3 846**
% contribution	1.1	1.4	1.6	1.9	1.9	1.5	2.0	2.5
Hydro (excl. pumped storage)	1 417	1 887	2 106	2 325	2 279	1 671	2 082	2 201
Geothermal	-	-	-	-	-	-	-	-
Solar Photovoltaic	-	-	-	-	-	-	-	-
Solar Thermal Electric	-	-	-	-	-	-	-	-
Tide/Wave/Ocean	-	-	-	-	-	-	-	-
Wind	-	1	5	14	61	124	142	135
Municipal Waste (Renewable)	-	-	-	-	-	-	-	-
Solid Biomass	55	54	190	402	379	399	768	1 399
Biogas/Liquid Biomass	-	13	31	42	48	56	83	111
Non-Renewable Wastes	**203**	**297**	**331**	**322**	**464**	**286**	**330**	**393**
% contribution	0.2	0.2	0.2	0.2	0.3	0.2	0.2	0.3
Industrial Waste	203	297	331	322	464	286	330	393
Municipal Waste (Non-Renewable)	-	-	-	-	-	-	-	-
Not separately identified ***	-	-	-	-	-	-	-	-
% contribution	-	-	-	-	-	-	-	-
*Memo: Total Wastes *****	*203*	*297*	*331*	*322*	*464*	*286*	*330*	*393*

* Primary energy used in the production of electricity and heat by main activity producers or autoproducers in electricity plants, CHP plants and heat plants (e.g. solar thermal power plants, geothermal power plants, etc.).
Energie primaire utilisée pour la production d'électricité, de cogénération et de chaleur par des producteurs dont c'est l'activité principale ou des autoproducteurs (installations héliothermiques, géothermiques, etc.).

** Primary energy used elsewhere than in transformation as described above (e.g. remote photovoltaic electricity production for households, heating of buildings/greenhouses by geothermal, etc.).
Energie primaire utilisée ailleurs que dans la transformation décrite ci-dessus (ex : production isolée d'électricité photovoltaïque, chauffage des bâtiments/serres à partir d'énergie géothermique, etc.).

*** Includes non-specified combustible renewables and waste.
Comprend les énergies renouvelables combustibles et les déchets non spécifiés.

**** Includes municipal waste and industrial waste.
Comprend les déchets municipaux et les déchets industriels.

Portugal

Contribution from Renewable Energies and Energy from Wastes

Part des énergies renouvables et de l'énergie tirée des déchets

	1990	1995	2000	2001	2002	2003	2004	2005
TPES / ATEP (ktoe / ktep)								
TOTAL PRIMARY ENERGY SUPPLY	**17 746**	**20 706**	**25 290**	**25 432**	**26 457**	**25 778**	**26 549**	**27 166**
% contribution of Renewables and Wastes	18.5	16.0	15.2	16.1	13.8	16.8	14.7	13.2
Renewables	**3 278**	**3 318**	**3 759**	**4 009**	**3 551**	**4 241**	**3 799**	**3 474**
% contribution	18.5	16.0	14.9	15.8	13.4	16.5	14.3	12.8
Hydro	788	717	974	1 207	671	1 352	849	407
Geothermal (transformation *)	3	37	69	90	83	77	76	65
Geothermal (direct use **)	-	1	1	1	1	1	1	1
Solar Photovoltaic (transformation *)	-	-	-	-	-	-	-	-
Solar Thermal (transformation *)	-	-	-	-	-	-	-	-
Solar Thermal (direct use **)	11	15	18	19	20	20	21	22
Tide/Wave/Ocean	-	-	-	-	-	-	-	-
Wind	-	1	14	22	31	43	70	152
Ambient Heat (Heat Pumps)	-	-	-	-	-	-	-	-
Municipal Waste (Renewable)	-	-	87 e	87 e	91 e	95 e	95 e	103 e
Solid Biomass	2 476	2 546	2 594	2 582	2 654	2 652	2 682	2 713
Biogasoline	-	-	-	-	-	-	-	-
Biodiesel	-	-	-	-	-	-	-	-
Other Liquid Biomass	-	-	-	-	-	-	-	-
Biogas	-	1	1	1	1	1	4	10
Non-Renewable Wastes	**-**	**-**	**87**	**87**	**91**	**99**	**102**	**109**
% contribution	-	-	0.3	0.3	0.3	0.4	0.4	0.4
Industrial Waste	-	-	-	-	-	4	7	5
Municipal Waste (Non-Renewable)	-	-	87 e	87 e	91 e	95 e	95 e	103
Not separately identified * **	**-**	**-**	**-**	**-**	**-**	**-**	**-**	**-**
% contribution	-	-	-	-	-	-	-	-
*Memo: Total Wastes *** **	-	-	*174*	*175*	*182*	*193*	*197*	*212*
ELECTRICITY / ELECTRICITE (GWh)								
TOTAL ELECTRICITY GENERATED	**28 355**	**33 154**	**43 372**	**46 168**	**45 650**	**46 521**	**44 827**	**46 188**
% contribution of Renewables and Wastes	34.7	28.3	30.3	34.6	21.9	38.7	28.1	18.5
Renewables	**9 852**	**9 390**	**12 868**	**15 741**	**9 733**	**17 703**	**12 314**	**8 260**
% contribution	34.7	28.3	29.7	34.1	21.3	38.1	27.5	17.9
Hydro (excl. pumped storage)	9 157	8 343	11 323	14 034	7 800	15 723	9 869	4 731
Geothermal	4	42	80	105	96	90	84	71
Solar Photovoltaic	1	1	1	1	2	3	3	3
Solar Thermal Electric	-	-	-	-	-	-	-	-
Tide/Wave/Ocean	-	-	-	-	-	-	-	-
Wind	1	16	168	256	362	496	816	1 773
Municipal Waste (Renewable)	-	-	257 e	256 e	262 e	276 e	263 e	296 e
Solid Biomass	689	987	1 037	1 086	1 208	1 112	1 264	1 351
Biogas/Liquid Biomass	-	1	2	3	3	3	15	35
Non-Renewable Wastes	**-**	**-**	**257**	**255**	**261**	**278**	**268**	**305**
% contribution	-	-	0.6	0.6	0.6	0.6	0.6	0.7
Industrial Waste	-	-	-	-	-	3	6	9
Municipal Waste (Non-Renewable)	-	-	257 e	255 e	261 e	275 e	262 e	296 e
Not separately identified * **	**-**	**-**	**-**	**-**	**-**	**-**	**-**	**-**
% contribution	-	-	-	-	-	-	-	-
*Memo: Total Wastes *** **	-	-	*514*	*511*	*523*	*554*	*531*	*601*

* Primary energy used in the production of electricity and heat by main activity producers or autoproducers in electricity plants, CHP plants and heat plants (e.g. solar thermal power plants, geothermal power plants, etc.).
Energie primaire utilisée pour la production d'électricité, de cogénération et de chaleur par des producteurs dont c'est l'activité principale ou des autoproducteurs (installations héliothermiques, géothermiques, etc.).

** Primary energy used elsewhere than in transformation as described above (e.g. remote photovoltaic electricity production for households, heating of buildings/greenhouses by geothermal, etc.).
Energie primaire utilisée ailleurs que dans la transformation décrite ci-dessus (ex : production isolée d'électricité photovoltaïque, chauffage des bâtiments/serres à partir d'énergie géothermique, etc.).

*** Includes non-specified combustible renewables and waste.
Comprend les énergies renouvelables combustibles et les déchets non spécifiés.

**** Includes municipal waste and industrial waste.
Comprend les déchets municipaux et les déchets industriels.

Slovak Republic / République slovaque

Contribution from Renewable Energies and Energy from Wastes

Part des énergies renouvables et de l'énergie tirée des déchets

	1990	1995	2000	2001	2002	2003	2004	2005
				TPES / ATEP (ktoe / ktep)				
TOTAL PRIMARY ENERGY SUPPLY	**21 315**	**17 827**	**17 738**	**18 584**	**18 742**	**18 629**	**18 333**	**18 831**
% contribution of Renewables and Wastes	1.6	4.0	4.6	4.4	4.2	3.6	4.2	4.6
Renewables	**328**	**497**	**488**	**768**	**746**	**646**	**730**	**807**
% contribution	1.5	2.8	2.8	4.1	4.0	3.5	4.0	4.3
Hydro	162	420	397	424	453	299	353	399
Geothermal (transformation *)	-	-	-	8	8	7	7 e	7
Geothermal (direct use **)	-	-	-	1	2	1	1 e	1
Solar Photovoltaic (transformation *)	-	-	-	-	-	-	-	-
Solar Thermal (transformation *)	-	-	-	-	-	-	-	-
Solar Thermal (direct use **)	-	-	-	-	-	-	-	-
Tide/Wave/Ocean	-	-	-	-	-	-	-	-
Wind	-	-	-	-	-	-	1	1
Ambient Heat (Heat Pumps)	-	-	-	-	-	-	-	-
Municipal Waste (Renewable)	-	-	-	12 e	2 e	13 e	14 e	17 e
Solid Biomass	166	78	91	286	275	320	347	367
Biogasoline	-	-	-	-	-	-	-	-
Biodiesel	-	-	-	31	3	2	1	10
Other Liquid Biomass	-	-	-	-	-	-	-	-
Biogas	-	-	-	5	3	4	6	5
Non-Renewable Wastes	**8**	**210**	**322**	**47**	**50**	**29**	**38**	**50**
% contribution	0.0	1.2	1.8	0.3	0.3	0.2	0.2	0.3
Industrial Waste	8	210	322	35	48	17	24	33
Municipal Waste (Non-Renewable)	-	-	-	12 e	2 e	13 e	14 e	17
Not separately identified ***	-	-	-	-	-	-	-	-
% contribution	-	-	-	-	-	-	-	-
*Memo: Total Wastes *****	*8*	*210*	*322*	*59*	*52*	*42*	*53*	*68*
				ELECTRICITY / ELECTRICITE (GWh)				
TOTAL ELECTRICITY GENERATED	**25 497**	**26 428**	**30 798**	**31 856**	**32 212**	**30 986**	**30 460**	**31 352**
% contribution of Renewables and Wastes	7.4	18.5	15.1	16.0	16.8	11.6	13.6	15.0
Renewables	**1 880**	**4 880**	**4 615**	**5 081**	**5 420**	**3 581**	**4 126**	**4 676**
% contribution	7.4	18.5	15.0	15.9	16.8	11.6	13.5	14.9
Hydro (excl. pumped storage)	1 880	4 880	4 615	4 927	5 268	3 480	4 100	4 638
Geothermal	-	-	-	-	-	-	-	-
Solar Photovoltaic	-	-	-	-	-	-	-	-
Solar Thermal Electric	-	-	-	-	-	-	-	-
Tide/Wave/Ocean	-	-	-	-	-	-	-	-
Wind	-	-	-	-	-	2	6	6
Municipal Waste (Renewable)	-	-	-	-	-	13 e	15 e	23 e
Solid Biomass	-	-	-	153	150	84	3	4
Biogas/Liquid Biomass	-	-	-	1	2	2	2	5
Non-Renewable Wastes	-	-	**32**	**6**	**6**	**14**	**15**	**24**
% contribution	-	-	0.1	0.0	0.0	0.0	0.0	0.1
Industrial Waste	-	-	32	6	6	1	-	-
Municipal Waste (Non-Renewable)	-	-	-	-	-	13 e	15 e	24 e
Not separately identified ***	-	-	-	-	-	-	-	-
% contribution	-	-	-	-	-	-	-	-
*Memo: Total Wastes *****	-	-	*32*	*6*	*6*	*27*	*30*	*47*

* Primary energy used in the production of electricity and heat by main activity producers or autoproducers in electricity plants, CHP plants and heat plants (e.g. solar thermal power plants, geothermal power plants, etc.).
Energie primaire utilisée pour la production d'électricité, de cogénération et de chaleur par des producteurs dont c'est l'activité principale ou des autoproducteurs (installations héliothermiques, géothermiques, etc.).

** Primary energy used elsewhere than in transformation as described above (e.g. remote photovoltaic electricity production for households, heating of buildings/greenhouses by geothermal, etc.).
Energie primaire utilisée ailleurs que dans la transformation décrite ci-dessus (ex : production isolée d'électricité photovoltaïque, chauffage des bâtiments/serres à partir d'énergie géothermique, etc.).

*** Includes non-specified combustible renewables and waste.
Comprend les énergies renouvelables combustibles et les déchets non spécifiés.

**** Includes municipal waste and industrial waste.
Comprend les déchets municipaux et les déchets industriels.

Spain / Espagne

Contribution from Renewable Energies and Energy from Wastes

Part des énergies renouvables et de l'énergie tirée des déchets

	1990	1995	2000	2001	2002	2003	2004	2005
			TPES / ATEP (ktoe / ktep)					
TOTAL PRIMARY ENERGY SUPPLY	**91 073**	**102 818**	**124 695**	**127 857**	**131 622**	**136 094**	**142 340**	**145 196**
% contribution of Renewables and Wastes	6.9	5.6	5.7	6.5	5.4	6.9	6.4	6.0
Renewables	**6 193**	**5 509**	**6 930**	**8 171**	**7 042**	**9 248**	**8 929**	**8 523**
% contribution	6.8	5.4	5.6	6.4	5.4	6.8	6.3	5.9
Hydro	2 186	1 988	2 543 e	3 528	1 971	3 531	2 714	1 682
Geothermal (transformation *)	-	-	-	-	-	-	-	-
Geothermal (direct use **)	-	3	8	8	8	8	8	8
Solar Photovoltaic (transformation *)	1	1	2	2	3	4	5	7 e
Solar Thermal (transformation *)	-	-	-	-	-	-	-	-
Solar Thermal (direct use **)	-	25	31	36	40	45	53	61
Tide/Wave/Ocean	-	-	-	-	-	-	-	-
Wind	1	23	407	581	803	1 038	1 350	1 826
Ambient Heat (Heat Pumps)	-	-	-	-	-	-	-	-
Municipal Waste (Renewable)	41 e	94 e	115 e	139 e	97 e	114 e	140 e	188 e
Solid Biomass	3 955	3 300	3 623	3 670	3 811	4 061	4 137	4 175
Biogasoline	-	-	-	-	72	99	115	113
Biodiesel	-	-	72	72	68	93	113	146
Other Liquid Biomass	-	-	-	-	-	-	-	-
Biogas	10	75	131	134	170	257	295	317
Non-Renewable Wastes	**61**	**214**	**190**	**139**	**97**	**114**	**140**	**188**
% contribution	0.1	0.2	0.2	0.1	0.1	0.1	0.1	0.1
Industrial Waste	20	120	75	-	-	-	-	-
Municipal Waste (Non-Renewable)	41 e	94 e	115 e	139 e	97 e	114 e	140 e	188
Not separately identified * **	**-**	**-**	**-**	**-**	**-**	**-**	**-**	**-**
% contribution	-	-	-	-	-	-	-	-
*Memo: Total Wastes *******	*101*	*308*	*304*	*279*	*195*	*227*	*281*	*377*
			ELECTRICITY / ELECTRICITE (GWh)					
TOTAL ELECTRICITY GENERATED	**151 150**	**165 628**	**222 235**	**233 206**	**241 613**	**257 884**	**277 122**	**290 607**
% contribution of Renewables and Wastes	17.3	14.9	16.4	21.3	14.6	22.0	18.4	15.1
Renewables	**25 976**	**24 408**	**35 808**	**49 441**	**34 878**	**56 354**	**50 684**	**43 490**
% contribution	17.2	14.7	16.1	21.2	14.4	21.9	18.3	15.0
Hydro (excl. pumped storage)	25 414	23 112	29 570 e	41 027	22 920	41 054	31 554	19 553
Geothermal	-	-	-	-	-	-	-	-
Solar Photovoltaic	6	15	18	24	30	41	56	78 e
Solar Thermal Electric	-	-	-	-	-	-	-	-
Tide/Wave/Ocean	-	-	-	-	-	-	-	-
Wind	14	270	4 727	6 759	9 342	12 075	15 700	21 233
Municipal Waste (Renewable)	80 e	196 e	334 e	334 e	283 e	331 e	335 e	449 e
Solid Biomass	462	668	841	969	1 831	2 095	2 214	1 595
Biogas/Liquid Biomass	-	147	318	328	472	758	825	582
Non-Renewable Wastes	**130**	**313**	**607**	**333**	**283**	**330**	**335**	**449**
% contribution	0.1	0.2	0.3	0.1	0.1	0.1	0.1	0.2
Industrial Waste	50	118	274	..	..	..	..	..
Municipal Waste (Non-Renewable)	80 e	195 e	333 e	333 e	283 e	330 e	335 e	449 e
Not separately identified * **	**-**	**-**	**-**	**-**	**-**	**-**	**-**	**-**
% contribution	-	-	-	-	-	-	-	-
*Memo: Total Wastes *******	*210*	*509*	*941*	*667*	*566*	*661*	*670*	*898*

* Primary energy used in the production of electricity and heat by main activity producers or autoproducers in electricity plants, CHP plants and heat plants (e.g. solar thermal power plants, geothermal power plants, etc.).
Energie primaire utilisée pour la production d'électricité, de cogénération et de chaleur par des producteurs dont c'est l'activité principale ou des autoproducteurs (installations héliothermiques, géothermiques, etc.).

** Primary energy used elsewhere than in transformation as described above (e.g. remote photovoltaic electricity production for households, heating of buildings/greenhouses by geothermal, etc.).
Energie primaire utilisée ailleurs que dans la transformation décrite ci-dessus (ex : production isolée d'électricité photovoltaïque, chauffage des bâtiments/serres à partir d'énergie géothermique, etc.).

*** Includes non-specified combustible renewables and waste.
Comprend les énergies renouvelables combustibles et les déchets non spécifiés.

**** Includes municipal waste and industrial waste.
Comprend les déchets municipaux et les déchets industriels.

Sweden / Suède

Contribution from Renewable Energies and Energy from Wastes

Part des énergies renouvables et de l'énergie tirée des déchets

	1990	1995	2000	2001	2002	2003	2004	2005
TPES / ATEP (ktoe / ktep)								
TOTAL PRIMARY ENERGY SUPPLY	**47 566**	**50 923**	**48 213**	**51 206**	**52 304**	**51 105**	**53 180**	**52 174**
% contribution of Renewables and Wastes	24.7	26.3	32.0	29.1	26.5	25.7	26.1	29.9
Renewables	**11 530**	**13 153**	**15 098**	**14 597**	**13 503**	**12 713**	**13 484**	**15 135**
% contribution	24.2	25.8	31.3	28.5	25.8	24.9	25.4	29.0
Hydro	6 235	5 857	6 758	6 799	5 707	4 604	5 171	6 261
Geothermal (transformation *)	-	-	-	-	-	-	-	-
Geothermal (direct use **)	-	-	-	-	-	-	-	-
Solar Photovoltaic (transformation *)	-	-	-	-	-	-	-	-
Solar Thermal (transformation *)	-	-	-	-	-	-	-	-
Solar Thermal (direct use **)	3	5	5	4	4	5	5	6
Tide/Wave/Ocean	-	-	-	-	-	-	-	-
Wind	1	9	39	41	52	58	73	80
Ambient Heat (Heat Pumps)	..	317	357	365	377	317	323	294
Municipal Waste (Renewable)	140 e	158 e	199 e	198 e	192 e	241 e	254 e	294 e
Solid Biomass	5 152	6 782	7 706	7 139	7 103	7 378	7 465	7 935
Biogasoline	-	-	-	14	33	71	135	144
Biodiesel	-	-	-	2	2	3	6	6
Other Liquid Biomass	-	-	-	-	-	-	18	84
Biogas	-	25	32	34	31	36	35	30
Non-Renewable Wastes	**215**	**239**	**324**	**325**	**339**	**409**	**404**	**482**
% contribution	0.5	0.5	0.7	0.6	0.6	0.8	0.8	0.9
Industrial Waste	5	2	25	28	51	48	23	41
Municipal Waste (Non-Renewable)	210 e	237 e	299 e	297 e	288 e	361 e	381 e	441
Not separately identified * **	-	-	-	-	-	-	-	-
% contribution	-	-	-	-	-	-	-	-
*Memo: Total Wastes *** **	*355*	*397*	*524*	*523*	*531*	*650*	*658*	*777*
ELECTRICITY / ELECTRICITE (GWh)								
TOTAL ELECTRICITY GENERATED	**145 984**	**148 292**	**145 230**	**161 593**	**146 698**	**135 377**	**151 671**	**158 363**
% contribution of Renewables and Wastes	51.0	47.6	57.4	51.7	48.7	43.6	45.5	51.8
Renewables	**74 452**	**70 555**	**83 139**	**83 319**	**71 143**	**58 729**	**68 174**	**81 230**
% contribution	51.0	47.6	57.2	51.6	48.5	43.4	44.9	51.3
Hydro (excl. pumped storage)	72 503	68 102	78 584	79 060	66 360	53 540	60 123	72 803
Geothermal	-	-	-	-	-	-	-	-
Solar Photovoltaic	-	-	-	-	-	-	-	-
Solar Thermal Electric	-	-	-	-	-	-	-	-
Tide/Wave/Ocean	-	-	-	-	-	-	-	-
Wind	6	99	457	482	608	679	850	936
Municipal Waste (Renewable)	41 e	46 e	96 e	90 e	112 e	142 e	493 e	524 e
Solid Biomass	1 902	2 278	3 970	3 666	4 036	4 305	6 611	6 848
Biogas/Liquid Biomass	-	30	32	21	27	63	97	119
Non-Renewable Wastes	**62**	**70**	**244**	**244**	**264**	**326**	**798**	**866**
% contribution	0.0	0.0	0.2	0.2	0.2	0.2	0.5	0.5
Industrial Waste	-	-	101	109	97	113	58	81
Municipal Waste (Non-Renewable)	62 e	70 e	143 e	135 e	167 e	213 e	740 e	785 e
Not separately identified * **	-	-	-	-	-	-	-	-
% contribution	-	-	-	-	-	-	-	-
*Memo: Total Wastes *** **	*103*	*116*	*340*	*334*	*376*	*468*	*1 291*	*1 390*

* Primary energy used in the production of electricity and heat by main activity producers or autoproducers in electricity plants, CHP plants and heat plants (e.g. solar thermal power plants, geothermal power plants, etc.).
Energie primaire utilisée pour la production d'électricité, de cogénération et de chaleur par des producteurs dont c'est l'activité principale ou des autoproducteurs (installations héliothermiques, géothermiques, etc.).

** Primary energy used elsewhere than in transformation as described above (e.g. remote photovoltaic electricity production for households, heating of buildings/greenhouses by geothermal, etc.).
Energie primaire utilisée ailleurs que dans la transformation décrite ci-dessus (ex : production isolée d'électricité photovoltaïque, chauffage des bâtiments/serres à partir d'énergie géothermique, etc.).

*** Includes non-specified combustible renewables and waste.
Comprend les énergies renouvelables combustibles et les déchets non spécifiés.

**** Includes municipal waste and industrial waste.
Comprend les déchets municipaux et les déchets industriels.

Switzerland / Suisse

Contribution from Renewable Energies and Energy from Wastes

Part des énergies renouvables et de l'énergie tirée des déchets

	1990	1995	2000	2001	2002	2003	2004	2005
TPES / ATEP (ktoe / ktep)								
TOTAL PRIMARY ENERGY SUPPLY	**24 992**	**24 989**	**26 159**	**27 676**	**26 774**	**26 870**	**27 134**	**27 153**
% contribution of Renewables and Wastes	14.2	17.1	17.4	18.1	16.6	17.1	17.6	17.6
Renewables	**3 245**	**3 886**	**4 062**	**4 509**	**3 976**	**4 027**	**4 090**	**4 066**
% contribution	13.0	15.6	15.5	16.3	14.8	15.0	15.1	15.0
Hydro	2 562	3 025	3 168	3 552	3 028	2 994	2 902	2 685
Geothermal (transformation *)	-	-	-	-	-	-	-	-
Geothermal (direct use **)	61	78	91	107	109	119	124	137
Solar Photovoltaic (transformation *)	-	-	1	1	1	1	1	2
Solar Thermal (transformation *)	-	-	-	-	-	-	-	-
Solar Thermal (direct use **)	8	15	23	25	22	23	24	25
Tide/Wave/Ocean	-	-	-	-	-	-	-	-
Wind	-	-	-	-	-	-	1	1
Ambient Heat (Heat Pumps)	-	-	-	-	-	-	-	-
Municipal Waste (Renewable)	140 e	173 e	218 e	229 e	215 e	291 e	391 e	419 e
Solid Biomass	436	543	502	533	540	539	587	732
Biogasoline	-	-	-	-	-	-	-	1
Biodiesel	-	-	-	-	-	-	2	5
Other Liquid Biomass	-	-	-	-	-	-	-	-
Biogas	38	52	59	61	59	59	58	58
Non-Renewable Wastes	**301**	**375**	**489**	**500**	**481**	**576**	**676**	**707**
% contribution	1.2	1.5	1.9	1.8	1.8	2.1	2.5	2.6
Industrial Waste	160	202	271	271	266	285	285	288
Municipal Waste (Non-Renewable)	140 e	173 e	218 e	229 e	215 e	291 e	391 e	419
Not separately identified * **	-	-	-	-	-	-	-	-
% contribution	-	-	-	-	-	-	-	-
*Memo: Total Wastes **** *	*441*	*549*	*706*	*729*	*696*	*868*	*1 067*	*1 126*
ELECTRICITY / ELECTRICITE (GWh)								
TOTAL ELECTRICITY GENERATED	**54 988**	**62 249**	**66 126**	**71 060**	**65 475**	**65 403**	**63 876**	**57 752**
% contribution of Renewables and Wastes	55.6	58.3	58.4	60.7	56.7	56.2	56.0	57.7
Renewables	**30 234**	**35 749**	**37 690**	**42 203**	**36 151**	**35 788**	**34 754**	**32 276**
% contribution	55.0	57.4	57.0	59.4	55.2	54.7	54.4	55.9
Hydro (excl. pumped storage)	29 795	35 169	36 834	41 308	35 214	34 819	33 748	31 226
Geothermal	-	-	-	-	-	-	-	-
Solar Photovoltaic	1	5	11	12	14	17	17	19
Solar Thermal Electric	-	-	-	-	-	-	-	-
Tide/Wave/Ocean	-	-	-	-	-	-	-	-
Wind	-	-	3	4	5	5	6	8
Municipal Waste (Renewable)	318 e	411 e	634 e	678 e	707 e	722 e	763 e	797 e
Solid Biomass	40	41	58	43	57	72	73	77
Biogas/Liquid Biomass	80	123	150	158	154	153	147	149
Non-Renewable Wastes	**362**	**517**	**904**	**948**	**966**	**953**	**1 009**	**1 075**
% contribution	0.7	0.8	1.4	1.3	1.5	1.5	1.6	1.9
Industrial Waste	44	106	270	270	259	231	246	278
Municipal Waste (Non-Renewable)	318 e	411 e	634 e	678 e	707 e	722 e	763 e	797 e
Not separately identified * **	-	-	-	-	-	-	-	-
% contribution	-	-	-	-	-	-	-	-
*Memo: Total Wastes **** *	*680*	*928*	*1 538*	*1 626*	*1 673*	*1 675*	*1 772*	*1 872*

* Primary energy used in the production of electricity and heat by main activity producers or autoproducers in electricity plants, CHP plants and heat plants (e.g. solar thermal power plants, geothermal power plants, etc.).
Energie primaire utilisée pour la production d'électricité, de cogénération et de chaleur par des producteurs dont c'est l'activité principale ou des autoproducteurs (installations héliothermiques, géothermiques, etc.).

** Primary energy used elsewhere than in transformation as described above (e.g. remote photovoltaic electricity production for households, heating of buildings/greenhouses by geothermal, etc.).
Energie primaire utilisée ailleurs que dans la transformation décrite ci-dessus (ex : production isolée d'électricité photovoltaïque, chauffage des bâtiments/serres à partir d'énergie géothermique, etc.).

*** Includes non-specified combustible renewables and waste.
Comprend les énergies renouvelables combustibles et les déchets non spécifiés.

**** Includes municipal waste and industrial waste.
Comprend les déchets municipaux et les déchets industriels.

Turkey / Turquie

Contribution from Renewable Energies and Energy from Wastes

Part des énergies renouvables et de l'énergie tirée des déchets

	1990	1995	2000	2001	2002	2003	2004	2005
TPES / ATEP (ktoe / ktep)								
TOTAL PRIMARY ENERGY SUPPLY	**52 968**	**61 860**	**77 027**	**71 009**	**75 200**	**78 793**	**81 905**	**85 205**
% contribution of Renewables and Wastes	18.2	17.4	13.1	13.2	13.4	12.7	13.2	11.9
Renewables	**9 657**	**10 775**	**10 101**	**9 376**	**10 042**	**10 020**	**10 782**	**10 130**
% contribution	18.2	17.4	13.1	13.2	13.4	12.7	13.2	11.9
Hydro	1 991	3 057	2 656	2 065	2 897	3 038	3 963	3 402
Geothermal (transformation *)	69	74	65	77	90	76	80	81
Geothermal (direct use **)	364	437	618	687	730	784	811	926
Solar Photovoltaic (transformation *)	-	-	-	-	-	-	-	-
Solar Thermal (transformation *)	-	-	-	-	-	-	-	-
Solar Thermal (direct use **)	28	143	262	287	318	350	375	385
Tide/Wave/Ocean	-	-	-	-	-	-	-	-
Wind	-	-	3	5	4	5	5	5
Ambient Heat (Heat Pumps)	-	-	-	-	-	-	-	-
Municipal Waste (Renewable)	-	-	-	-	-	-	-	-
Solid Biomass	7 205	7 065	6 492	6 250	5 997	5 759	5 541	5 324
Biogasoline	-	-	-	-	-	-	-	-
Biodiesel	-	-	-	-	-	-	-	-
Other Liquid Biomass	-	-	-	-	-	-	-	-
Biogas	-	-	5	5	6	7	7	7
Non-Renewable Wastes	**-**	**-**	**15**	**13**	**13**	**11**	**8**	**25**
% contribution	-	-	0.0	0.0	0.0	0.0	0.0	0.0
Industrial Waste	-	-	15	13	13	11	8	25
Municipal Waste (Non-Renewable)	-	-	-	-	-	-	-	-
Not separately identified ***	**-**	**-**	**-**	**-**	**-**	**-**	**-**	**-**
% contribution	-	-	-	-	-	-	-	-
*Memo: Total Wastes *****	-	-	*15*	*13*	*13*	*11*	*8*	*25*
ELECTRICITY / ELECTRICITE (GWh)								
TOTAL ELECTRICITY GENERATED	**57 543**	**86 247**	**124 922**	**122 725**	**129 400**	**140 581**	**150 698**	**161 956**
% contribution of Renewables and Wastes	40.4	41.6	25.0	19.9	26.3	25.3	30.7	24.6
Renewables	**23 228**	**35 849**	**31 154**	**24 346**	**33 966**	**35 559**	**46 311**	**39 748**
% contribution	40.4	41.6	24.9	19.8	26.2	25.3	30.7	24.5
Hydro (excl. pumped storage)	23 148	35 541	30 879	24 010	33 683	35 330	46 084	39 561
Geothermal	80	86	76	90	105	89	93	94
Solar Photovoltaic	-	-	-	-	-	-	-	-
Solar Thermal Electric	-	-	-	-	-	-	-	-
Tide/Wave/Ocean	-	-	-	-	-	-	-	-
Wind	-	-	33	62	48	61	58	59
Municipal Waste (Renewable)	-	-	-	-	-	-	-	-
Solid Biomass	-	222	145	160	104	48	46	5
Biogas/Liquid Biomass	-	-	21	24	26	31	30	29
Non-Renewable Wastes	**-**	**-**	**54**	**46**	**44**	**37**	**28**	**88**
% contribution	-	-	0.0	0.0	0.0	0.0	0.0	0.1
Industrial Waste	-	-	54	46	44	37	28	88
Municipal Waste (Non-Renewable)	-	-	-	-	-	-	-	-
Not separately identified ***	**-**	**-**	**-**	**-**	**-**	**-**	**-**	**-**
% contribution	-	-	-	-	-	-	-	-
*Memo: Total Wastes *****	-	-	*54*	*46*	*44*	*37*	*28*	*88*

* Primary energy used in the production of electricity and heat by main activity producers or autoproducers in electricity plants, CHP plants and heat plants (e.g. solar thermal power plants, geothermal power plants, etc.).
Energie primaire utilisée pour la production d'électricité, de cogénération et de chaleur par des producteurs dont c'est l'activité principale ou des autoproducteurs (installations héliothermiques, géothermiques, etc.).

** Primary energy used elsewhere than in transformation as described above (e.g. remote photovoltaic electricity production for households, heating of buildings/greenhouses by geothermal, etc.).
Energie primaire utilisée ailleurs que dans la transformation décrite ci-dessus (ex : production isolée d'électricité photovoltaïque, chauffage des bâtiments/serres à partir d'énergie géothermique, etc.).

*** Includes non-specified combustible renewables and waste.
Comprend les énergies renouvelables combustibles et les déchets non spécifiés.

**** Includes municipal waste and industrial waste.
Comprend les déchets municipaux et les déchets industriels.

United Kingdom / Royaume-Uni

Contribution from Renewable Energies and Energy from Wastes

Part des énergies renouvables et de l'énergie tirée des déchets

	1990	1995	2000	2001	2002	2003	2004	2005
				TPES / ATEP (ktoe / ktep)				
TOTAL PRIMARY ENERGY SUPPLY	**212 176**	**223 443**	**233 863**	**234 583**	**228 620**	**232 328**	**233 461**	**233 931**
% contribution of Renewables and Wastes	0.5	0.9	1.0	1.2	1.4	1.5	1.7	2.0
Renewables	**1 029**	**1 836**	**2 264**	**2 316**	**2 568**	**2 748**	**3 284**	**3 834**
% contribution	0.5	0.8	1.0	1.0	1.1	1.2	1.4	1.6
Hydro	448	416	437	349	412	278	424	427
Geothermal (transformation *)	-	-	-	-	-	-	-	-
Geothermal (direct use **)	1	1	1	1	1	1	1	1
Solar Photovoltaic (transformation *)	-	-	-	-	-	-	-	1
Solar Thermal (transformation *)	-	-	-	-	-	-	-	-
Solar Thermal (direct use **)	10	10	11	13	16	20	25	29
Tide/Wave/Ocean	-	-	-	-	-	-	-	-
Wind	1	34	81	83	108	111	166	250
Ambient Heat (Heat Pumps)	-	-	-	-	-	-	-	-
Municipal Waste (Renewable)	70 e	136 e	264 e	333 e	364 e	382 e	371 e	368 e
Solid Biomass	303	886	659	633	705	815	928	1 237
Biogasoline	-	-	-	-	-	-	-	45
Biodiesel	-	-	-	-	3	14	16	35
Other Liquid Biomass	-	-	-	-	-	-	-	-
Biogas	196	354	810	904	960	1 128	1 353	1 440
Non-Renewable Wastes	**58**	**164**	**189**	**545**	**679**	**707**	**768**	**870**
% contribution	0.0	0.1	0.1	0.2	0.3	0.3	0.3	0.4
Industrial Waste	16	46	35	346	461	478	546	649
Municipal Waste (Non-Renewable)	42 e	119 e	154 e	200 e	218 e	229 e	222 e	221
Not separately identified * **	-	-	-	-	-	-	-	-
% contribution	-	-	-	-	-	-	-	-
*Memo: Total Wastes *** **	*128*	*300*	*453*	*878*	*1 043*	*1 089*	*1 139*	*1 238*
				ELECTRICITY / ELECTRICITE (GWh)				
TOTAL ELECTRICITY GENERATED	**317 755**	**332 489**	**374 375**	**382 367**	**384 596**	**395 473**	**392 657**	**397 594**
% contribution of Renewables and Wastes	1.9	2.2	2.8	3.2	3.6	3.4	4.4	5.2
Renewables	**5 811**	**6 871**	**9 970**	**9 550**	**11 129**	**10 627**	**14 172**	**16 919**
% contribution	1.8	2.1	2.7	2.5	2.9	2.7	3.6	4.3
Hydro (excl. pumped storage)	5 207	4 838	5 086	4 056	4 788	3 227	4 930	4 961
Geothermal	-	-	-	-	-	-	-	-
Solar Photovoltaic	-	-	1	3	3	3	4	8
Solar Thermal Electric	-	-	-	-	-	-	-	-
Tide/Wave/Ocean	-	-	-	-	-	-	-	-
Wind	9	391	947	965	1 256	1 285	1 935	2 908
Municipal Waste (Renewable)	140 e	471 e	840 e	880 e	908 e	965 e	971 e	964 e
Solid Biomass	-	199	541	776	1 128	1 538	1 949	3 388
Biogas/Liquid Biomass	455	972	2 555	2 870	3 046	3 609	4 383	4 690
Non-Renewable Wastes	**83**	**412**	**519**	**2 519**	**2 863**	**2 843**	**2 980**	**3 847**
% contribution	0.0	0.1	0.1	0.7	0.7	0.7	0.8	1.0
Industrial Waste	-	-	-	1 991	2 318	2 264	2 397	3 268
Municipal Waste (Non-Renewable)	83 e	412 e	519 e	528 e	545 e	579 e	583 e	579 e
Not separately identified * **	-	-	-	-	-	-	-	-
% contribution	-	-	-	-	-	-	-	-
*Memo: Total Wastes *** **	*223*	*883*	*1 359*	*3 399*	*3 771*	*3 808*	*3 951*	*4 811*

* Primary energy used in the production of electricity and heat by main activity producers or autoproducers in electricity plants, CHP plants and heat plants (e.g. solar thermal power plants, geothermal power plants, etc.).
Energie primaire utilisée pour la production d'électricité, de cogénération et de chaleur par des producteurs dont c'est l'activité principale ou des autoproducteurs (installations héliothermiques, géothermiques, etc.).

** Primary energy used elsewhere than in transformation as described above (e.g. remote photovoltaic electricity production for households, heating of buildings/greenhouses by geothermal, etc.).
Energie primaire utilisée ailleurs que dans la transformation décrite ci-dessus (ex : production isolée d'électricité photovoltaïque, chauffage des bâtiments/serres à partir d'énergie géothermique, etc.).

*** Includes non-specified combustible renewables and waste.
Comprend les énergies renouvelables combustibles et les déchets non spécifiés.

**** Includes municipal waste and industrial waste.
Comprend les déchets municipaux et les déchets industriels.

United States / États-Unis

Contribution from Renewable Energies and Energy from Wastes

Part des énergies renouvables et de l'énergie tirée des déchets

	1990	1995	2000	2001	2002	2003	2004	2005
TPES / ATEP (ktoe / ktep)								
TOTAL PRIMARY ENERGY SUPPLY	**1 927 457**	**2 090 003**	**2 306 637**	**2 259 706**	**2 289 803**	**2 282 777**	**2 328 555**	**2 340 286**
% contribution of Renewables and Wastes	5.2	5.3	4.8	4.3	4.3	4.6	4.6	4.7
Renewables	**96 165**	**104 844**	**101 948**	**89 195**	**91 351**	**97 386**	**100 963**	**102 923**
% contribution	5.0	5.0	4.4	3.9	4.0	4.3	4.3	4.4
Hydro	23 491	27 014	21 776	16 190	22 965	23 960	23 316	23 430
Geothermal (transformation *)	13 765	12 844	12 569	12 317	7 674	7 638	7 843	7 780
Geothermal (direct use **)	336	406	519	569	600	751	751	852
Solar Photovoltaic (transformation *)	-	-	-	-	-	-	1	1
Solar Thermal (transformation *)	57	71	133	143	141	137	144	135
Solar Thermal (direct use **)	-	-	1 440	1 361	1 328	1 264	1 264	1 233
Tide/Wave/Ocean	-	-	-	-	-	-	-	-
Wind	264	275	486	585	899	972	1 229	1 538
Ambient Heat (Heat Pumps)	-	-	-	-	-	-	-	-
Municipal Waste (Renewable)	2 076 e	3 227 e	4 095 e	3 463 e	3 849 e	3 581 e	3 539 e	3 547 e
Solid Biomass	55 444	57 342	55 015	48 279	46 292	49 652	51 956	52 347
Biogasoline	..	2 644	2 934	2 986	3 807	5 462	6 808	7 655
Biodiesel	..	-	21	21	50	79	108	296
Other Liquid Biomass	..	-	-	-	106	255	265	291
Biogas	732	1 022	2 960	3 280	3 640	3 634	3 739	3 817
Non-Renewable Wastes	**4 003**	**6 294**	**8 207**	**6 916**	**7 259**	**7 150**	**6 292**	**6 054**
% contribution	0.2	0.3	0.4	0.3	0.3	0.3	0.3	0.3
Industrial Waste	1 928	3 067	4 112	3 452	3 411	3 569	2 753	2 508
Municipal Waste (Non-Renewable)	2 076 e	3 227 e	4 095 e	3 463 e	3 849 e	3 581 e	3 539 e	3 547
Not separately identified ***	-	-	-	-	-	-	-	-
% contribution	-	-	-	-	-	-	-	-
*Memo: Total Wastes *****	*6 079*	*9 520*	*12 302*	*10 379*	*11 108*	*10 731*	*9 831*	*9 601*
ELECTRICITY / ELECTRICITE (GWh)								
TOTAL ELECTRICITY GENERATED	**3 202 813**	**3 558 374**	**4 025 705**	**3 838 614**	**4 026 141**	**4 054 351**	**4 147 708**	**4 268 381**
% contribution of Renewables and Wastes	11.8	11.1	8.6	7.1	9.0	9.2	9.0	8.9
Renewables	**369 241**	**384 343**	**330 184**	**260 209**	**347 879**	**360 135**	**356 804**	**364 678**
% contribution	11.5	10.8	8.2	6.8	8.6	8.9	8.6	8.5
Hydro (excl. pumped storage)	273 152	314 116	253 204	188 252	267 034	278 609	271 118	272 447
Geothermal	16 012	14 941	14 621	14 246	14 939	14 870	15 487	16 778
Solar Photovoltaic	3	4	3	3	3	2	6	16
Solar Thermal Electric	663	824	526	565	569	548	587	596
Tide/Wave/Ocean	-	-	-	-	-	-	-	-
Wind	3 066	3 196	5 650	6 806	10 459	11 300	14 291	17 881
Municipal Waste (Renewable)	5 306 e	7 386 e	8 364 e	8 102 e	8 252 e	8 093 e	8 128 e	8 507 e
Solid Biomass	68 545	40 587	42 586	36 821	40 210	39 711	40 432	41 791
Biogas/Liquid Biomass	2 494	3 289	5 230	5 414	6 413	7 002	6 755	6 662
Non-Renewable Wastes	**10 017**	**11 655**	**15 533**	**14 210**	**15 134**	**14 726**	**15 725**	**14 255**
% contribution	0.3	0.3	0.4	0.4	0.4	0.4	0.4	0.3
Industrial Waste	4 710	4 268	7 170	6 108	6 881	6 635	7 599	5 748
Municipal Waste (Non-Renewable)	5 307 e	7 387 e	8 363 e	8 102 e	8 253 e	8 091 e	8 126 e	8 507 e
Not separately identified ***	-	-	-	-	-	-	-	-
% contribution	-	-	-	-	-	-	-	-
*Memo: Total Wastes *****	*15 323*	*19 041*	*23 897*	*22 312*	*23 386*	*22 819*	*23 853*	*22 762*

* Primary energy used in the production of electricity and heat by main activity producers or autoproducers in electricity plants, CHP plants and heat plants (e.g. solar thermal power plants, geothermal power plants, etc.).
Energie primaire utilisée pour la production d'électricité, de cogénération et de chaleur par des producteurs dont c'est l'activité principale ou des autoproducteurs (installations héliothermiques, géothermiques, etc.).

** Primary energy used elsewhere than in transformation as described above (e.g. remote photovoltaic electricity production for households, heating of buildings/greenhouses by geothermal, etc.).
Energie primaire utilisée ailleurs que dans la transformation décrite ci-dessus (ex : production isolée d'électricité photovoltaïque, chauffage des bâtiments/serres à partir d'énergie géothermique, etc.).

*** Includes non-specified combustible renewables and waste.
Comprend les énergies renouvelables combustibles et les déchets non spécifiés.

**** Includes municipal waste and industrial waste.
Comprend les déchets municipaux et les déchets industriels.

MULTILINGUAL GLOSSARIES

English	Français	Deutsch
coal	charbon	Kohle
crude oil and NGL	pétrole brut et LGN	Rohöl und Kondensate
petroleum products	produits pétroliers	Ölprodukte
natural gas	gaz naturel	Erdgas
nuclear energy	énergie nucléaire	Kernenergie
hydro energy	énergie hydraulique	Wasserkraft
geothermal energy	énergie géothermique	Geothermischer Energie
solar energy	énergie d'origine solaire	Sonnenenergie
wind energy	énergie d'origine éolienne	Windenergie
tide energy	énergie des marées	Gezeitenenergie
combustible renewables and waste	énergies renouvelables combustibles et déchets	Erneuerbare Brennstoffe und Abfälle
electricity	électricité	Elektrizität
heat	chaleur	Wärme
total energy	énergie totale	Total Energie

	Français	Deutsch
1	Production	Produktion
2	Importations	Importe
3	Exportations	Exporte
4	Soutes maritimes internationales	Bunker
5	Variation des stocks	Bestandsveränderungen
6	**APPROV. TOTAUX EN ENERGIE PRIMAIRE**	**GESAMTENERGIEAUFKOMMEN**
7	Transferts	Transfer
8	Ecarts statistiques	Stat. Differenzen
9	Centrales électriques	Elektrizitätswerke
10	Centrales de cogénération	Elektrizitäts- und Heizkraftwerke
11	Centrales calogènes	Heizkraftwerke
12	Usines à gaz	Ortsgas
13	Raffineries de pétrole	Raffinerien
14	Transformation du charbon	Kohleumwandlung
15	Unités de liquéfaction	Verflüssigung
16	Autres transformations	Sonst. Umwandlungsbereich
17	Consommation propre	Eigenverbrauch
18	Pertes de distribution et de transport	Verteilungsverluste
19	**CONSOMMATION FINALE TOTALE**	**ENDENERGIEVERBRAUCH**
20	**SECTEUR INDUSTRIE**	**INDUSTRIE**
21	Sidérurgie	Eisen- und Stahlindustrie
22	Industrie chimique et pétrochimique	Chemische Industrie
23	Métaux non ferreux	Ne-Metallerzeugung
24	Produits minéraux non métalliques	Glas- und Keramikindustrie
25	Matériel de transport	Fahrzeugbau
26	Construction mécanique	Maschinenbau
27	Industries extractives	Bergbau- und Steinbrüche
28	Produits alimentaires, boissons et tabacs	Nahrungs- und Genußmittel
29	Pâtes à papier, papier et imprimerie	Zellstoff, Papier, Pappeerzeugung
30	Bois et produits dérivés	Holz und Holzprodukte
31	Construction	Baugewerbe
32	Textiles et cuir	Textil- und Lederindustrie
33	Non spécifiés	Sonstige
34	**SECTEUR TRANSPORTS**	**VERKEHRSSEKTOR**
35	Aviation internationale	Internationaler Luftverkehr
36	Aviation intérieure	Inland Luftverkehr
37	Transport routier	Straßenverkehr
38	Transport ferroviaire	Schienenverkehr
39	Transport par conduits	Rohrleitungen
40	Navigation intérieure	Binnenschiffahrt
41	Non spécifiés	Sonstige
42	**AUTRES SECTEURS**	**ANDERE SEKTOREN**
43	Résidentiel	Wohungssektor
44	Commerce et services publics	Handel- und öffentliche Einrichtungen
45	Agriculture / Sylviculture	Landwirtschaft / Forstwirtschaft
46	Pêche	Fischfang
47	Non spécifiés	Sonstige
48	**UTILISATIONS NON ENERGETIQUES**	**NICHTENERGETISCHER VERBRAUCH**
49	Dans l'industrie/transformation/énergie	In Industrie/Umwandlung/Energiesektor
50	*Dont : produits d'alimentation*	*Davon: Feedstocks*
51	Dans les transports	In Verkehr
52	Dans les autres secteurs	In anderen Sektoren
53	***Electricité produite - TWh***	***Elektrizitätsproduktion - TWh***
54	*Centrales électriques*	*Elektrizitätswerke*
55	*Centrales de cogénération*	*Elektrizitäts- und Heizkraftwerke*
56	***Chaleur produite - PJ***	***Wärmeerzeugung - PJ***
57	*Centrales de cogénération*	*Elektrizitäts- und Heizkraftwerke*
58	*Centrales calogènes*	*Heizkraftwerke*

English	Italiano	Japanese
coal	carbone	石炭
crude oil and NGL	petrolio grezzo e LGN	原油 及び NGL
petroleum products	prodotti petroliferi	石油製品
natural gas	gas naturale	天然ガス
nuclear energy	energia nucleare	原子力
hydro energy	energia idroelettrica	水力
geothermal energy	energia geotermica	地熱
solar energy	energia solare	太陽光
wind energy	energia eolica	風力
tide energy	energia maremotrice	潮力
combustible renewables and waste	combustibili rinnovabili e da rifiuti	可燃性再生可能エネルギー 及び廃棄物
electricity	energia elettrica	電力
heat	calore	熱
total energy	energia totale	総エネルギー

	Italiano	**Japanese**
1	Produzione	国内生産
2	Importazioni	輸入
3	Esportazioni	輸出
4	Bunkeraggi	バンカー
5	Variazioni di stock	在庫変動
6	**TOTALE RISORSE PRIMARIE**	**国内供給計**
7	Ritorni e trasferimenti	変換
8	Differenza statistica	統計誤差
9	Centrali elettriche	電気事業者・自家発
10	Impianti di cogenerazione	コージェネレーション
11	Impianti di produzione di calore	熱供給事業者
12	Officine del gas	ガス業
13	Raffinerie di petrolio	石油精製
14	Trasformazione del carbone	石炭変換
15	Liquefazione	液化
16	Altri settori di trasformazione	その他転換
17	Autoconsumo	自家消費
18	Perdite di distribuzione	送配電ロス
19	**CONSUMI FINALI**	**最終エネルギー消費計**
20	**SETTORE INDUSTRIALE**	**産業部門**
21	Siderurgico	鉄鋼業
22	Chimico	化学工業
23	Metalli non ferrosi	非鉄金属
24	Minerali non metalllici	窯業土石
25	Equipaggiamento per trasporti	輸送用機械
26	Meccanico	金属機械
27	Estrattivo	鉱業
28	Alimentare e del tabacco	食料品・たばこ
29	Cartario e grafico	紙・パルプ
30	Legno e prodotti del legno	木製品
31	Costruzioni	建設業
32	Tessile e pelli	繊維工業
33	Non specificato	その他製造業
34	**SETTORE DEI TRASPORTI**	**運輸部門**
35	Aviazione internazionale	国際航空輸送
36	Aviazione nazionale	国内航空輸送
37	Trasporti stradali	道路運送業
38	Trasporti ferroviari	鉄道業
39	Trasporti per condotti	パイプライン輸送
40	Trasporti fluviali interni	国内水運
41	Non specificato	その他
42	**ALTRI SETTORI**	**他の部門**
43	Domestico	民生・家庭用
44	Commercio e servizi pubblici	民生・業務用
45	Agricoltura / Selvicoltura	農林業
46	Pesca	漁業
47	Non specificato	その他
48	**USI NON ENERGETICI**	**非エネルギー**
49	Dell'industria	産業・変換・エネルギー部門
50	*Di cui: prodotti intermedi*	*(含原料油・半製品)*
51	Dei trasporti	運輸部門
52	Degli altri settori	他の部門
53	***Elettricità Prodotta - TWh***	***発電実績— TWh***
54	*Centrali elettriche*	*電気事業者・自家発*
55	*Impianti di cogenerazione*	*コージェネレーション*
56	***Calore Prodotto - PJ***	***発熱実績— PJ***
57	*Impianti di cogenerazione*	*コージェネレーション*
58	*Impianti di produzione di calore*	*熱供給事業者*

English	Español	русский язык
coal	carbón	Уголь
crude oil and NGL	petróleo crudo y LGN	Сырая нефть/ Газ. конденсаты
petroleum products	productos petrolíferos	Нефтепродукты
natural gas	gas natural	Природный газ
nuclear energy	energía nuclear	Атомная энергия
hydro energy	energía hidráulica	Гидроэнергия
geothermal energy	energía geotérmica	Геотермальная энергия
solar energy	energía solar	Солнечная энергия
wind energy	energía eólica	Энергия ветра
tide energy	energía maremotriz	Энергия приливов
combustible renewables and waste	combustibles renovables y desechos	Горючие возобнов. Вид. топ./ отход.
electricity	electricidad	Электричество
heat	calor	Тепло
total energy	energía total	Всего источников энергии

	Español	**русский язык**
1	Producción	Собственное производство
2	Importaciones	Импорт
3	Exportaciones	Экспорт
4	Bunkers	Международная морская бункеровка
5	Cambio de stocks	Изменение остатков
6	**SUMINISTRO AL CONSUMO**	ОБЩАЯ ПЕРВИЧНАЯ ПОСТАВКА ТОПЛИВА И ЭНЕРГИИ
7	Transferencias	Передачи
8	Diferencias estadísticas	Статистическое расхождение
9	Central eléctrica	Электростанции
10	Central combinada de calor y electricidad	Тепло-электроцентрали
11	Central de calor	Теплоцентрали
12	Gas ciudad	Газовые заводы
13	Refinerías de petróleo	Нефтепереработка
14	Transformación de carbón	Переработка угля
15	Licuefacción	Ожижение
16	Otros Sect. de transformación	Др. отрасли преобразования и переработки топлива
17	Consumos propios	Собственное использование в ТЭК
18	Pérdidas de distribución	Потери при распределении
19	**CONSUMO FINAL**	КОНЕЧНОЕ ПОТРЕБЛЕНИЕ
20	**SECTOR INDUSTRIA**	СЕКТОР ПРОМЫШЛЕННОСТИ
21	Siderurgia	Черная металлургия
22	Químico	Химия и нефтехимия
23	Metales no férreos	Цветная металлургия
24	Minerales no metálicos	Неметалл. минералы
25	Equipos de transporte	Транспортное оборудование
26	Maquinaria	Машиностроение
27	Extracción y minas	Горнодобывающая промышленность
28	Alimentación y tabaco	Пищевая и табачная промышленность
29	Papel, pasta e impresión	Бум.-целл. и полиграф. пр-сть
30	Madera	Пр-во древесины и деревообработка
31	Construcción	Строительство
32	Textil y piel	Текст.-кожевенная пр-сть
33	No especificado	Др. отрасли промышленности
34	**SECTOR TRANSPORTE**	СЕКТОР ТРАНСПОРТА
35	Transporte aéreo internacional	Международный воздушный транспорт
36	Transporte aéreo interno	Внутренний воздушный транспорт
37	Transporte por carretera	Автодорожный транспорт
38	Ferrocarril	Железнодорожный транспорт
39	Oleoducto	Транспортировка по трубопроводам
40	Navegación interna	Внутренний водный транспорт
41	No especificado	Неспецифицированный транспорт
42	**OTROS SECTORES**	ДРУГИЕ СЕКТОРЫ
43	Residencial	Бытовой сектор
44	Comercio y serv. públicos	Торговля и услуги
45	Agricultura / Selvicultura	Сельское хозяйство / Лесное хозяйство
46	Pesca	Рыболовство
47	No especificado	Неспецифицированные другие секторы
48	**USOS NO ENERGETICOS**	НЕЭНЕРГЕТИЧЕСКОЕ ИСПОЛЬЗОВАНИЕ
49	En la industria/tranf./energia	В промышленности/преобраз.-переработке/топл.-энергетике
50	*Incl.: prod. de aliment.*	*в т.ч. П/фабрикаты нефтепереработки*
51	En el transporte	В транспорте
52	En otros sectores	В других секторах
53	***Electr. Producida - TWh***	*Производство электроэнергии - Твт.ч*
54	*Central Eléctrica*	*Электростанции*
55	*Central combinada de calor y electricidad*	*Тепло-электроцентрали*
56	***Calor producido - PJ***	*Производство тепла - ПДж*
57	*Central combinada de calor y electricidad*	*Тепло-электроцентрали*
58	*Central de calor*	*Теплоцентрали*

English	Chinese
Coal	煤
crude oil and NGL	原油和液态天然气
petroleum products	石油产品
natural gas	天然气
nuclear energy	核能
hydro energy	水能
geothermal energy	地热能
solar energy	太阳能
wind energy	风能
tide energy	潮汐能
combustible renewables and waste	可燃烧生物质能和垃圾
electricity	电力
heat	热能
total energy	能源合计

Chinese

1	本国产量
2	进口
3	出口
4	国际海运加油
5	库存变化
6	**一次能源供应量（TPES）**
7	转换
8	统计差额
9	发电厂
10	热电联产厂
11	热力厂
12	制气厂
13	炼油厂
14	煤煤转化
15	液化
16	其它转化
17	自用
18	分配损耗
19	**最终消费合计（TFC）**
20	**工业部门**
21	钢铁
22	化学和石化
23	有色金属
24	非金属矿物
25	交通设备
26	机械工业
27	采矿和挖掘
28	食品和烟草
29	纸，纸浆和印刷
30	木材和木材制品
31	建筑业
32	纺织和皮革
33	其它
34	**交通运输部门**
35	国际航空
36	国内航空
37	公路运输
38	铁路运输
39	管道运输
40	国内海运
41	其它
42	**其它部门**
43	居民消费
44	商业和公共事业
45	农业林业
46	捕鱼业
47	其它
48	**非能源使用**
49	工业 / 转化 / 能源
50	*其中：用做原料*
51	交通
52	其它部门
53	***发电（10^9千瓦时）***
54	*发电厂*
55	*热电联产厂*
56	***供热（10^{15}焦）***
57	*热电联产厂*
58	*热力厂*

INTERNATIONAL ENERGY AGENCY ENERGY STATISTICS DIVISION POSSIBLE STAFF VACANCIES

The Division is responsible for statistical support and advice to the policy and operational Divisions of the International Energy Agency. It also produces a wide range of annual and quarterly publications complemented by CD-ROMs and on-line data services. For these purposes, the Division maintains extensive international databases covering most aspects of energy supply and use.

Vacancies for statisticians occur from time to time. Typically their work includes:

- Gathering and vetting data from questionnaires and publications, discussions on data issues with respondents to questionnaires in national administrations and fuel companies.
- Managing energy databases in order to maintain accuracy and timeliness of output.
- Creating and maintaining computer procedures for the production of tables, reports and analyses.
- Preparing studies on an ad-hoc basis as required by other Divisions of the International Energy Agency.

Nationals of any OECD Member country are eligible for appointment. Basic salaries range from 2 800 to 3 800 Euros per month, depending on qualifications. The possibilities for advancement are good for candidates with appropriate qualifications and experience. Tentative enquiries about future vacancies are welcomed from men and women with relevant qualifications and experience. Applications in French or English, accompanied by a curriculum vitae, should be sent to:

Ms. Beth Hunter
Head of Administrative Unit
IEA, 9 rue de la Fédération
75739 Paris Cedex 15, FRANCE
beth.hunter@iea.org

AGENCE INTERNATIONALE DE L'ENERGIE
DIVISION DES STATISTIQUES DE L'ENERGIE
VACANCES D'EMPLOI EVENTUELLES

La Division est chargée de fournir une aide et des conseils dans le domaine statistique aux Divisions administratives et opérationnelles de l'Agence internationale de l'énergie. En outre, elle diffuse une large gamme de publications annuelles et trimestrielles complétées par CD-ROMs ainsi que des services de données sur internet. A cet effet, la Division tient à jour de vastes bases de données internationales portant sur la plupart des aspects de l'offre et de la consommation d'énergie.

Des postes de statisticien sont susceptibles de se libérer de temps à autre. Les fonctions dévolues aux titulaires de ces postes sont notamment les suivantes :

- Rassembler et valider les données tirées de questionnaires et de publications, ainsi que d'échanges de vues sur les données avec les personnes des Administrations nationales ou des entreprises du secteur de l'énergie qui répondent aux questionnaires.
- Gérer des bases de données relatives à l'énergie en vue de s'assurer de l'exactitude et de l'actualisation des données de sortie.
- Gérer et maintenir des procédures informatiques pour la réalisation de tableaux, rapports et analyses.
- Effectuer des études en fonction des besoins des autres Divisions de l'Agence internationale de l'énergie.

Ces postes sont ouverts aux ressortissants des pays Membres de l'OCDE. Les traitements de base sont compris entre 2 800 et 3 800 euros par mois, suivant les qualifications. Les candidats possédant les qualifications et l'expérience appropriées se verront offrir des perspectives de promotion. Les demandes de renseignements sur les postes susceptibles de se libérer qui émanent de personnes dotées des qualifications et de l'expérience voulues seront les bienvenues. Les candidatures, rédigées en français ou en anglais et accompagnées d'un curriculum vitae, doivent être envoyées à l'adresse suivante :

Ms. Beth Hunter
Head of Administrative Unit
IEA, 9 rue de la Fédération
75739 Paris Cedex 15, FRANCE
beth.hunter@iea.org

On-Line Data Services

Users can instantly access not only all the data published in this book, but also all the time series used for preparing this publication and all the other statistics publications of the IEA. The data are available on-line, either through annual subscription or pay-per-view access. More information on this service can be found on our website: http://data.iea.org

Ten Annual Publications

Energy Statistics of OECD Countries

No other publication offers such in-depth statistical coverage. It is intended for anyone involved in analytical or policy work related to energy issues. It contains data on energy supply and consumption in original units for coal, oil, natural gas, combustible renewables/wastes and products derived from these primary fuels, as well as for electricity and heat. Data are presented for the two most recent years available in detailed supply and consumption tables. Historical tables summarise data on production, trade and final consumption. Each issue includes definitions of products and flows and explanatory notes on the individual country data.

Published June 2007 - Price €110

Energy Balances of OECD Countries

A companion volume to *Energy Statistics of OECD Countries*, this publication presents standardised energy balances expressed in million tonnes of oil equivalent. Energy supply and consumption data are divided by main fuel: coal, oil, gas, nuclear, hydro, geothermal/solar, combustible renewables/wastes, electricity and heat. This allows for easy comparison of the contributions each fuel makes to the economy and their interrelationships through the conversion of one fuel to another. All of this is essential for estimating total energy supply, forecasting, energy conservation, and analysing the potential for interfuel substitution. Complete energy balances are presented for the two most recent years available. Historical tables summarise key energy and economic indicators as well as data on production, trade and final consumption. Each issue includes definitions of products and flows and explanatory notes on the individual country data as well as conversion factors from original units to tonnes of oil equivalent.

Published June 2007 - Price €110

Energy Statistics of Non-OECD Countries

This publication offers the same in-depth statistical coverage as the homonymous publication covering OECD countries. It includes data in original units for more than 100 individual countries and nine main regions. The consistency of OECD and non-OECD countries' detailed statistics provides an accurate picture of the global energy situation. For a description of the content, please see *Energy Statistics of OECD Countries* above.

Published August 2007 - Price €110

Energy Balances of Non-OECD Countries

A companion volume to the publication *Energy Statistics of Non-OECD Countries*, this publication presents energy balances in million tonnes of oil equivalent and key economic and energy indicators for more than 100 individual countries and nine main regions. It offers the same statistical coverage as the homonymous publication covering OECD countries, and thus provides an accurate picture of the global energy situation. For a description of the content, please see *Energy Balances of OECD Countries* above.

Published August 2007 - Price €110

Electricity Information

This reference document provides essential statistics on electricity and heat for each OECD member countries by bringing together information on production, installed capacity, input energy mix to electricity and heat production, input fuel prices, consumption, end-user electricity prices and electricity trades. The document also presents selected non-OECD country statistics on the main electricity and heat flows. It is an essential document for electricity and heat market and policy analysts.

Published August 2007 - Price €130

Coal Information

This well-established publication provides detailed information on past and current evolution of the world coal market. It presents country specific statistics for OECD member countries and selected non-OECD countries on coal production, demand, trade and prices. This publication represents a key reference tool for all those involved in the coal supply or consumption stream, as well as institutions and governments involved in market and policy analysis of the world coal market.

Published August 2007 - Price €150

Natural Gas Information

A detailed reference work on gas supply and demand, covering not only the OECD countries but also the rest of the world. Contains essential information on LNG and pipeline trade, gas reserves, storage capacity and prices. The main part of the book, however, concentrates on OECD countries, showing a detailed gas supply and demand balance for each individual country and for the three OECD regions: North America, Europe and Asia-Pacific, as well as a breakdown of gas consumption by end-user. Import and export data are reported by source and destination.

Published August 2007 - Price €150

Oil Information

A comprehensive reference book on current developments in oil supply and demand. The first part of this publication contains key data on world production, trade, prices and consumption of major oil product groups, with time series back to the early 1970s. The second part gives a more detailed and comprehensive picture of oil supply, demand, trade, production and consumption by end-user for each OECD country individually and for the OECD regions. Trade data are reported extensively by origin and destination.

Published August 2007 - Price €150

Renewables Information

This reference document brings together in one volume essential statistics on renewables and waste energy sources. It presents a detailed and comprehensive picture of developments for renewable and waste energy sources for each of the OECD member countries, encompassing energy indicators, generating capacity, electricity and heat production from renewable and waste sources, as well as production and consumption of renewable and waste products. It also includes a selection of indicators for non-OECD countries. This report provides a strong foundation for renewables energy policy and market analysis to assess progress towards domestic and international objectives.

Published August 2007 - Price €80

CO_2 Emissions from Fuel Combustion

In order for nations to tackle the problem of climate change, they need accurate greenhouse gas emissions data. This publication provides a basis for comparative analysis of CO_2 emissions from fossil fuel combustion, a major source of anthropogenic emissions. The data in this book are designed to assist in understanding the evolution of the emissions of CO_2 from 1971 to 2005 for more than 140 countries and regions by sector and by fuel. Emissions were calculated using IEA energy databases and the default methods and emissions factors from the *Revised 1996 IPCC Guidelines for National Greenhouse Gas Inventories.*

Published November 2007 - Price €150

Two Quarterlies

Oil, Gas, Coal and Electricity, Quarterly Statistics

This publication provides up-to-date, detailed quarterly statistics on oil, coal, natural gas and electricity for the OECD countries. Oil statistics cover production, trade, refinery intake and output, stock changes and consumption for crude oil, NGL and nine selected oil product groups. Statistics for electricity, natural gas and coal show supply and trade. Import and export data are reported by origin and destination. Moreover, oil as well as hard coal and brown coal production are reported on a worldwide basis.

Published Quarterly - Price €110, annual subscription €350

Energy Prices and Taxes

This publication responds to the needs of the energy industry and OECD governments for up-to-date information on prices and taxes in national and international energy markets. It contains prices at all market levels for OECD countries and certain non-OECD countries: import prices, industry prices and consumer prices. The statistics cover the main petroleum products, gas, coal and electricity, giving for imported products an average price both for importing country and country of origin. Every issue includes full notes on sources and methods and a description of price mechanisms in each country.

Published Quarterly - Price €110, annual subscription €350

Electronic Editions

CD-ROMs and Online Data Services

To complement its publications, the Energy Statistics Division produces CD-ROMs containing the complete databases which are used for preparing the statistics publications. State-of-the-art software allows you to access and manipulate all these data in a very user-friendly manner and includes graphic facilities. These databases are also available on the internet from our online data service.

Annual CD-ROMS / Online Databases

- Energy Statistics of OECD Countries, 1960-2005 — Price: €500 (single user)
- Energy Balances of OECD Countries, 1960-2005 — Price: €500 (single user)
- Energy Statistics of Non-OECD Countries, 1971-2005 — Price: €500 (single user)
- Energy Balances of Non-OECD Countries, 1971-2005 — Price: €500 (single user)
- *Combined subscription of the above four series* — *Price: € 1 200 (single user)*

- Electricity Information 2007 — Price: €500 (single user)
- Coal Information 2007 — Price: €500 (single user)
- Natural Gas Information 2007 — Price: €500 (single user)
- Oil Information 2007 — Price: €500 (single user)
- Renewables Information 2007 — Price: €300 (single user)
- CO_2 Emissions from Fuel Combustion, 1971-2005 — Price: €500 (single user)

Quarterly CD-ROMs / Online Databases

- Energy Prices and Taxes — Price: (four quarters) €800 (single user)

A description of these services are available on our website: **http://data.iea.org**

Other Online Services

The Monthly Oil Data Service

The IEA Monthly Oil Data Service provides the detailed databases of historical and projected information which is used in preparing the IEA's monthly *Oil Market Report* (OMR). The IEA Monthly Oil Data Service comprises three packages available separately or combined as a subscriber service on the Internet. The data are available at the same time as the official release of the Oil Market Report.

The packages include:

- Supply, Demand, Balances and Stocks — Price: €5 500 (single user)
- Trade — Price: €1 650 (single user)
- Field-by-Field Supply — Price: €2 750 (single user)
- *Complete Service* — *Price: €8 250 (single user)*

A description of this service is available on our website: **http://modsinfo.iea.org**

The Monthly Gas Data Service

The Monthly Gas Data Service provides for OECD countries historical and current data on natural gas supply and demand, as well as detailed information on trade origins and destinations.

The packages include:

- Natural Gas Balances & Trade
  Historical plus 12 monthly updates Price: €440 (single user)
- Natural Gas Balances & Trade
  Historical Price: €330 (single user)

A description of this service is available on our website: **http://data.iea.org**

Moreover, the IEA statistics website contains key energy indicators by country, graphs on the world and OECD's energy situation evolution from 1971 to the most recent year available, as well as selected databases for demonstration.

The IEA statistics website can be accessed at: http://www.iea.org/statistics/

The Online Bookshop

International Energy Agency

All IEA publications may be bought online on the IEA website:

www.iea.org/books

You may also obtain PDFs of all IEA books at 20% discount.

Books published before January 2006 - with the exception of the statistics publications - can be downloaded in PDF, free of charge, from the IEA website.

IEA BOOKS

Tel: +33 (0)1 40 57 66 90
Fax: +33 (0)1 40 57 67 75
E-mail: books@iea.org

International Energy Agency
9, rue de la Fédération
75739 Paris Cedex 15, France

CUSTOMERS IN NORTH AMERICA

Turpin Distribution
The Bleachery
143 West Street, New Milford
Connecticut 06776, USA
Toll free: +1 (800) 456 6323
Fax: +1 (860) 350 0039
oecdna@turpin-distribution.com
www.turpin-distribution.com

You may also send your order to your nearest OECD sales point or use the OECD online services: www.oecdbookshop.org

CUSTOMERS IN THE REST OF THE WORLD

Turpin Distribution Services Ltd
Stratton Business Park,
Pegasus Drive, Biggleswade,
Bedfordshire SG18 8QB, UK
Tel.: +44 (0) 1767 604960
Fax: +44 (0) 1767 604640
oecdrow@turpin-distribution.com
www.turpin-distribution.com

Notes

Notes

Notes

Notes

Notes